Modern Concepts in

BIOCHEMISTRY

ROBERT C. BOHINSKI

Associate Professor of Biochemistry
Department of Chemistry
John Carroll University

Allyn and Bacon, Inc.   Boston

To   My Wife, Glorianne
     My Children, Susan, Robert John, and Martin,
        and
     My Parents

Contents

Preface

This book is intended for use in a one-semester or two-quarter upper-division course designed to introduce the modern principles of biochemistry. Because of its intermediate size, however, some may find it sufficient for two-semester courses by using it in conjunction with supplementary lectures and selected materials. Although the level of material is appropriate for students majoring in chemistry or biology, it is also suitable for those enrolled in medical technology and nursing programs. Formal training in physical chemistry—while obviously helpful in any study of biochemistry—is not a prerequisite. If deficiencies exist in the student's background, the necessary prerequisites—physicochemical principles of ionization equilibria, kinetics, thermodynamics, and the nature of electromagnetic radiation—are developed in separate chapters at an introductory level.

All major areas of biochemistry are covered first by treating the structures of the main classes of biomolecules and then by treating their metabolism. The material emphasizes (1) the relationship between structure and function at the cellular, subcellular, and molecular levels, (2) the function of metabolic pathways, and (3) the efficiency of the regulation and integration of metabolic pathways. It is certain that my selection (and omission) of topics and the depth of discussion given them will not have universal agreement. Of course, these characteristics reflect my own attitudes and classroom experiences as well as my objective to limit the scope of the book to something less than encyclopedic. It is anticipated, however, that individual professors—guided by their own attitudes—will satisfy whatever shortcomings may exist.

One unique feature is an early and unified discussion (in Chapter 2) of the strategy and methods of biochemical studies. In terms of basic theory and general application, the techniques discussed are chromatography, ultracentrifugation, electrophoresis, spectroscopy, radioisotopes, electron microscopy, and x-ray diffraction. Generally, early exposure to biochemical techniques, particularly in nonlaboratory courses, is well received by students: It catalyzes their interest for more descriptive material and results in better comprehension. The usual approach of introducing methods as parts of primary topics often dilutes the effectiveness of the presentation. In addition, Chapter 2, together with Chapter 1, gives a prospective of the remainder of the book. Because biochemistry is both vast and complex, the importance of achieving such a prospective should not be underestimated. It is possible, however, to use Chapter 2 out of sequence and in segments.

Chapter 3 deals with ionization equilibria and the nature and role of buffers in biological systems. Chapters 4 through 8 discuss proteins, enzymes, nucleic acids, carbohydrates, and lipids, with emphasis on the relationship between molecular structure and biological function. Particular attention is given to the relationship of amino acid sequence to the conformation and function of polypeptides (proteins). Thorough descriptions of the Michaelis-Menten theory and allosterism are included in the chapter on enzymes. The many drawings and photographs of space-filling molecular models provide meaningful images of the three-dimensional structure of individual molecules.

The examination in Chapter 9 of the ultrastructure of living cells and the major subcellular organelles is supplemented by electron micrographs. (Superb transparencies of actual electron micrographs for use with a standard overhead classroom projector may be purchased at a modest price from General Biological Supply House, Inc., 8200 South Hayne Avenue, Chicago, Illinois, 60620.)

Principles of bioenergetics are analyzed in Chapter 10 by presenting a basic but thorough development of the meaning of the free energy change and its utility in describing the flow of energy in metabolism. Chapters 11 through 18 are devoted entirely to metabolism—the core of biochemistry—and although each area of metabolism is discussed separately, the theme of metabolic integration is stressed. Several examples of the regulation of metabolism at the level of the enzyme-catalyzed reaction are also provided. Three main areas discussed from this standpoint are the glycolytic pathway, the citric acid cycle, and the biosynthesis of nucleotides. Metabolic control according to the theory of induction and repression of gene activity is discussed in Chapter 18.

Discussion of such topics as muscle contraction, metabolic diseases, alcohol addiction, the chemistry of vision, the manipulation of genes, nutrition, and some new discoveries in cancer research illustrate the significance of basic biochemical principles.

References cited at the end of each chapter include annual serial publications, monographs, review articles, original research papers, and articles from *Scientific American*. A listing of the articles available as offprints may be obtained from W. H. Freeman, Inc., San Francisco, California.

With the exception of Chapters 1 and 9, all chapters contain exercises of various types and degrees of difficulty, thereby giving students opportunity to challenge their understanding of the subject as they progress. These exercises should be a welcomed complement to the text.

There are many people who deserve much more than a written acknowledgment of their help to me in writing this book. They are my students, who have been, and I hope will be, a powerful catalytic force in my life. Of the group associated with me during this project, individual acknowledgment is due James Grendell, who read and criticized several chapters. Some colleagues who reviewed parts of the manuscript and offered valuable suggestions for its improvement include J. Kúc, M. Konrad, G. Toralballa, P. Heyman, C. Vestling, A. Rule, and

P. Khairallah. I am also grateful to Robert Nook and Charles Blumle for affording me their time and photographic talent, Trudy Bumm her excellent typing services, and my colleagues in the Chemistry Department at John Carroll University their encouragement.

I also thank the following individuals for photographs and permissions to reproduce their work: Y. Anraku, H. Buc, R. C. Clowes, R. E. Dickerson, D. W. Fawcett, J. C. Gerhart, N. E. Good, P. B. Hamilton, W. A. Jensen, J. C. Kendrew, H. H. Mollenhauer, A. B. Pardee, L. Pauling, E. Racker, J. D. Robertson, L. K. Shumway, H. Slayter, A. S. Szegedy, and R. Traut. The cooperation of the editorial, production, and managing offices of Academic Press, Carl Zeiss, Inc., Cold Spring Harbor Laboratory, Columbia University Press, Cornell University Press, the Ealing Corporation, Federation of European Biochemical Societies, W. B. Saunders Co., *Biochemistry, Journal of Bacteriology, Journal of Biological Chemistry, Nature,* and *Science* is also appreciated. I am also grateful to the editors of Allyn and Bacon for the expert and professional attention they devoted to this book. Individual acknowledgment is extended to W. M. Roberts, A. Prudente, B. Johnson, and New England Illustrators, Inc.

No one contributed more than Glorianne, my wife, and Susan, Bobby John, and Martin, my children. Their contribution, especially Glorianne's, was special and critical because it was one not only of encouragement and understanding but also of sacrifice. I am blessed to have them.

My goal was to write a book that would contribute to a student's understanding of biochemistry and perhaps provide a stimulation toward further study of it. I sincerely hope that it accomplishes that goal. If it does not, I invite both professor and student to advise me as to any constructive changes that will make this a better book.

University Heights, Ohio   ROBERT C. BOHINSKI

1

The Scope of Biochemistry

What is biochemistry? This question is currently being asked with great frequency by individuals who are beginning to sense the impact of biochemistry in the scientific community and in the world at large. The question is simple and straightforward; unfortunately, however, it is difficult to answer it in the same manner. This is not because biochemistry is so mysterious, but rather because it is so heterogeneous and complex. Consequently, when I am asked this question by students, I respond by asking how much time they have. This normally is received with a grin and that in turn generates a small exchange of humorous dialogue. Having challenged his interest, I then quickly point out that my initial reaction to his inquiry was meant to be serious and was, in a very indirect way, providing him with an answer. Our discussion then proceeds with a more systematic and penetrating analysis of the subject. At this time, however, I do not intend to embark on a lengthy narration of such a discussion. Having generated your interest as a reader, I don't want to lose it with an overwhelming avalanche of printed words. On the other hand, brevity is not appropriate either, since it would not enhance your interest. As a compromise I present to you the following synopsis. After completing this course, hopefully you will be able to extend and embellish upon these general characteristics when you yourself are asked what biochemistry is.

Although it is difficult to give a precise definition of biochemistry, let us begin our discussion with an attempt at so doing and then continue with an analysis of the statement. *Biochemistry is a scientific discipline dealing with physicobiochemical analyses of all types of cellular activities.* This statement says many things and at the same time does not say enough. We can arrive at an understanding of its substance by recognizing that it consists of three elements.

The *first* and most positive *element of the definition* is that it specifically states that *biochemistry is indeed a science*. The most important consequence of this is that biochemical investigation, like any other scientific pursuit, is characterized by and subject to the scientific method. By way of review, the tenets of the scientific method are as follows. Phenomena are observed and measured; a hypothesis is formulated based on these observations; the hypothesis is tested by additional observations and measurements; if necessary, the original hypothesis is modified and the system under study is re-examined; the cycle is repeated until an acceptable theory is developed; and finally the theory is tested for general application. This brief outline of the scientific method is, for many, a recapitulation of what was learned in high school science courses or freshman chemistry. The purpose of the reiteration is to focus your attention on the fact that biochemistry is concerned with making observations and measurements in the laboratory. Indeed, biochemistry is absolutely dependent on such an approach. Data are collected, analyzed, and formulated into workable theories. Thus, the first element of the definition can and should be modified and strengthened to read: *Biochemistry is an experimental science.* It will become apparent that this fundamental characteristic has guided my approach in developing a large portion of this book.

The *second element of the definition* is that *the nature of biochemical studies is multidisciplinary,* as indicated by the inclusion of the word "physicobiochemical." This characteristic should not be dismissed without reflecting on its implication. Furthermore, it is not merely a characteristic of biochemistry in particular, but is common to biological science in general. Basically, it means that a complete analysis and subsequent understanding of living systems is predicated on a multipronged approach which employs physical, biological, and chemical principles. A striking example of this is evident in considering the basic phenomena of energy production and energy utilization in a living cell. On the physical level, one must first recognize the basic concept of energy, the various forms of same, and the reality of their interconversions. On the biological level, the cellular processes are studied in an attempt to identify and characterize those that require energy, those that yield energy, and the intricate balance and relationship between both types. On the chemical level, we are interested in defining the flow of energy through the chemical compounds which participate in and thus distinguish all of these processes. Notice the trend here. The analysis began with the physical concept of energy, a general application was made to living systems, and this finally was reduced to the molecular level.

As a student of biochemistry, you will clearly discern this interdisciplinary character as you proceed into future chapters. This approach is not adopted because I desire to author a sophisticated and difficult textbook. On the contrary, such an approach is demanded by the reality of modern biological science, which is not merely a systematic collection of superficial and unexplainable observations of the living world. Although this type of activity was true of biology until the beginning of the twentieth century, it is no longer valid. Before proceeding with a further analysis of the definition of biochemistry, let us expand on this aspect in a historical context.

Until the 1860s *vitalism* was the popular biological theory. The proponents of this theory claimed that the generation of life, and to some extent the maintenance of the essential life processes, were controlled by an unexplainable and unmeasurable vital force. In the latter part of the nineteenth century the vitalistic attitude was finally refuted by the notable efforts of Louis Pasteur, and an alternative explanation for the living process was demanded. The demise of vitalism created a climate in the scientific community that resulted in changing attitudes between the biologists on one side and the physicists and chemists on the other. They started to talk and listen to each other. The biologists finally began to realize that the phenomena of life were not necessarily so mysterious that they demanded explanations equally mysterious and even mystical. Those in the then more exact sciences of physics and chemistry had been saying this for years and were somewhat miffed by the reluctance of the vitalists to listen. The basic premise of the physical scientists was simple. They argued that natural (living) phenomena could be reduced to a physical explanation. Difficult as it must have been—human nature being what it is—the limits of professional polarization began to shrink, and ultimately the marriage of the exact physical sciences of physics and chemistry and the then non-exact natural sciences occurred. The early years were not completely harmonious, and scientific history reveals that heated debate was commonplace. The important part, however, is that these sciences began to share a common scientific philosophy and common methods. Through it all biology matured as an exact science, and only then did it advance. This interdisciplinary exchange is manifested today—more so than ever—by the emergence of hybrid specializations such as biochemistry, biophysics, molecular biology, biotechnology, bioengineering, theoretical biology, biosystematics, and so on. This hybridization has caused a problem in communication, but it does not represent a fragmentation in modern biology based on a true scission of a common philosophy. Each represents a specialized division with a specialized strategy and specialized tactics. An excellent summary of these thoughts is provided by the words of Samuel Devons (see suggested readings at the end of the chapter):

"... The victorious advances of physics and chemistry in the present century, their penetration into much of what was erstwhile biological territory, and their culmination in the spectacular discoveries of the past decade or two, have completely changed the whole character of the debate. [The debate between natural and physical scientists.] The power of its physical science, its concepts, methods, and techniques, are firmly established. There is no longer any feature of living matter which presents a clearly demarked frontier beyond which physics or chemistry cannot pass. Science may not be fully unified, but the boundaries are not the fixed, impenetrable ones that some imagined and even hoped for a century ago."

The *third element of the definition* refers to the subject of this scientific analysis, namely, *the living cell*. Notice that there is no particular reference to any specific type of cellular activity or biological phenomenon as the sole domain of biochemistry. On the contrary, biochemical investigations encompass a wide spectrum of topics, ranging from multicellular organisms to unicellular organisms; from whole cellular systems to compartmentalized subcellular systems; and from subcellular molecular aggregates to molecules themselves. In short, it can be said that modern biochemistry, which serves as the basis for all modern biology, is concerned with any phenomenon associated with any organism, be it animal, plant, bacterial, or viral.

To elaborate on these general statements, a listing of the major areas of contemporary biochemical research is given below. The numerical sequence is not to be interpreted as implying any hierarchy of importance or relevance to the various areas. Each area is accompanied by a brief description of the experimental objectives common to it. Although the descriptions are general, the reader is advised not to dismiss them with little or no consideration. Study the outline carefully and reflect on the principles that are enumerated. You can accept this survey of research areas as a useful guide to what you can expect from this course, since the majority of these topics will be analyzed in subsequent chapters. The scope of biochemical research is also evidenced by the extensive and varied listing of literature sources that provide the basis for scientific communication between those working in different areas (see Appendix I).

MAIN RESEARCH AREAS OF BIOCHEMISTRY

1. Intermediary metabolism. The term *intermediary metabolism* refers to *the totality. of reactions that occur in an organism—any organism*. Research in this area basically attempts to identify: (a) the reactant(s) and the product(s) in each reaction; (b) the catalyst required for each reaction (virtually every reaction in a living cell involves the participation of a catalyst, called an *enzyme*, which allows the reaction to proceed at a very high rate); (c) any special requirements of each reaction; and (d) the possible interrelationships that exist among a set or sets of reactions. Within this investigative structure one can identify several specialized divisions, each claiming large numbers of researchers. Three such areas of current importance are listed below.

A. *Bioenergetics.* Investigations in this area are designed to study the flow of energy in a living cell. Particular attention is given to those processes involving the formation and utilization of *adenosine triphosphate* (ATP), a compound selected by nature to fulfill the central function of bridging the gap between the energy supplied to the cell from the environment and the utilization of that energy by the cell. Since ATP must be formed within the cell before it can be used in energy-requiring processes, it is logical that most of the research in the field of bioenergetics should be aimed at defining the molecular mechanics of ATP formation, and so it is. The bulk of ATP production in most non-photosynthetic, oxygen-dependent organisms occurs within a highly organized subcellular organelle called the *mitochondrion*. Consequently, a sizeable portion of the research effort deals with the molecular architecture of this specialized particulate.

B. *Biosynthesis of proteins and nucleic acids.* Studies in this area are designed to unravel the intricate details of how a cell synthesizes these two important classes of compounds. The biosynthesis of nucleic acids is of prime importance in the living process. During cell division a new set of identical *chromosomes* is produced; that is, the original set of chromosomes is replicated. Since the chromosomes contain the *genes* which determine the individuality of the cell, the fact that the process is replicative insures perpetuation of the species in a relatively unvarying manner. In chemical terms, however, a chromosome is a molecule of *deoxyribonucleic acid* (DNA), and the individual genes are segments of the intact DNA molecule. Accordingly then, a discussion of chromosome production (replication) is reduced to the events of nucleic acid biosynthesis, particularly the biosynthesis of DNA. Furthermore, the phenomenon of *mutation,* which results in the formation of a modified gene or contingent of genes, can be described through alterations in this process. The expression of genetic information in DNA involves both nucleic acid and protein biosynthesis, occurring in that order. First, *ribonucleic acid* (RNA) is synthesized from the information in the genes of DNA. The information in RNA is then used to direct the assembly of proteins.

Protein biosynthesis is equally crucial, since the proteins are the molecular instruments selected by nature that are directly responsible for virtually all of the dynamic processes occurring in a cell. This role is fulfilled most notably by those proteins which function as reaction catalysts (the *enzymes*). At this point the reader should take note that every known enzyme is a protein. Because of the great reaction specificity manifested by enzymes, one can state that *the biochemical essence of a cell is due to a specific set of proteins which are synthesized by the cell according to the specific information that is ultimately localized in the chromosomes (genes).*

C. *Cellular control mechanisms.* This area has had an extremely short history, with many of the substantial discoveries having been made within the past ten to fifteen years. Basically, studies are designed to unravel the intricate network of checks and balances within a living cell which allows for *regulated control of cellular reactions rather than random activity.* The existence and nature of these regulatory mechanisms will constitute one of the main themes of the text.

2. Nature of enzyme-catalyzed reactions. Research in this field is devoted to determining the characteristics which define the conversion of a reactant (generally called the substrate) to a product, catalyzed by an enzyme. This type of investigation is an extension of area 1. The general objectives are to determine (a) how the enzyme participates in the reaction, and (b) what factors may enhance (activate) or reduce (inhibit) the activity of the enzyme.

3. Chemical structure of biopolymers. The objective here is to define the complete structure of the complex polymers found in nature, especially the proteins and nucleic acids. This involves the determination of the position of every monomeric unit—indeed, every atom—in the polymeric molecule, so that ultimately a visual, three-dimensional model can be formulated. The obvious question is why, and if you fail to recall a basic tenet learned in general chemistry, the rationale may not be clear at this time. This tenet is the fundamental principle of explaining a set of properties for any material or group of materials in terms of chemical structure. The principle can be paraphrased in more direct and forceful language as follows: *The chemical and physical properties of a substance are a direct consequence of the number, the type, and the arrangement of its constituent parts.*

This relationship between function (properties) and structure is very evident in biologically occurring compounds, especially the biopolymers. Accordingly then, this principle will be referred to repeatedly throughout this text. It will become clear, for example, that our current understanding of the chemical basis for life is largely based on our understanding of how proteins and nucleic acids fulfill their specialized functions in relationship to their structure. We are not concerned merely with knowing what the functions are, but also want to explain how they are realized. This is the justification of the efforts of those who seek to unravel the structural details of participating compounds. Although this field is still in its infancy, many achievements have been made. Two of the historic landmarks were: (a) the report of a model for the three-dimensional structure of deoxyribonucleic acid (DNA) by J. D. Watson, F. H. C. Crick, and M. H. F. Wilkins in 1953, and (b) the achievement of the first three-dimensional structural analysis of the protein myoglobin by J. C. Kendrew and coworkers in 1960. Discoveries like these have contributed greatly to our advanced state of knowledge concerning biological processes. Further discussion and additional examples, however, will be deferred to subsequent chapters. At this point it is important only that you grasp the general meaning of the structure–function relationship. It is vital to your appreciation of biochemistry.

4. Cellular and subcellular anatomy. Investigations here attempt to establish the ultrastructural details of both the whole cell and the subcellular particulates called *organelles*. Special attention is given to the latter, since they generally exhibit a greater degree of specialization and are in fact responsible for many of the specialized functions of the whole cell. Work in this area is not, however, concerned merely with superficial structural characteristics such as size and shape. Analysis of ultrastructural details means much more, namely, determination of what types of materials are found in the organelle and the manner in which they are arranged or compartmentalized. Coupled to this is the objective to establish the relationship that may exist between the ultrastructure of any organelle and its particular functions. This is another example of the theme of structure and function, dealing with multicomponent systems rather than individual molecules.

5. Molecular basis of biological phenomena. This is an extension of area 3. The objective is to define the molecular basis for the phenomenon in question. To paraphrase, the ultimate goal is to determine how the participating molecules participate and then to explain how this participation manifests itself in a unique way. Evident once again is this theme of structure and function. Included here are investigations into the nature of gene expression and gene control, and of various physiological phenomena such as muscle contraction, vision, nerve transmission, hormonal control, and mental and physical disease.

6. Development of analytical procedures. This is an indispensable phase of modern research. In fact, the fantastic growth rate of biochemistry during the past twenty-five years is directly due to the refinement of established procedures and the development of new analytical techniques. Research in biochemistry and the biological sciences in general will continue to become more versatile, more sensitive, more accurate, and simpler as methodologies improve. Remember, biochemistry is basically an experimental science, and to a large extent then the observation and measurement of a system are limited both quantitatively and

qualitatively by the limitations of the experimental tools that are available. This principle is so vital that specific attention will be given in the next chapter to some of the more important biochemical methods.

From the preceding material it should now be apparent to you what was meant by earlier remarks that it is difficult, if not impossible, to give a clear and concise definition of biochemistry. Reflecting on the content of these pages, you should be impressed with two things. First, the scientific discipline of biochemistry includes as a subject of study any biological phenomenon on a cellular, subcellular, or molecular level. Its scope is vast. Secondly, biochemistry does serve as the fundamental language of all modern biology, which continues to seek the many answers to the nagging question that has haunted mankind throughout his existence, namely, "What is life?"

With regard to the latter point, I do not mean to imply that the discoveries that are presently being made and those that will come in the future will provide a metaphysical answer to this question. Heaven forbid! If this were to happen, it would mean that a man might cease to wonder about himself and his own existence, and things could get pretty dull. However, the discoveries of modern biochemical science will certainly provide mankind with a more complete knowledge of his own material existence as well as of his surroundings. As individuals you will have to determine for yourself what this type of knowledge would mean in terms of the same question asked in a metaphysical context.

POSTSCRIPT

This first chapter has done more than consider the nature of biochemistry. Although this was certainly the primary goal, a number of other ends have been accomplished in fulfilling that objective. Most notable were: (a) a brief description of two central themes of modern biological chemistry and of this textbook, namely, the principles of cellular control mechanisms and the relationship of structure to function; (b) a preliminary exposure to the biological importance of proteins and nucleic acids, with a particular definition of those proteins which function as reaction catalysts, i.e., the enzymes; and (c) reference to the important contemporary relationship between biology and the physical sciences.

Before closing this chapter, I wish to offer some advice to you, the student. It is imperative that you accept and identify with the importance of the last point, which reinforces previous remarks that our current knowledge of the living process is largely due to the extensive penetration of the principles and methods of the physical sciences. Therefore, it is inevitable that our analysis of the subject will reflect this penetration by assuming a physicochemical nature. Indeed, it would be absurd to even attempt such an analysis without doing so. Consequently, your comprehension of biochemistry will depend to a large degree on your willingness to commit yourself to an intellectual confrontation with a few physicochemical principles. As a student of biochemistry then, don't dilute your effort and, more important, your understanding of the material by developing an aversion to discussions dealing with topics such as ionization, charged particles, chemical structure, dipole-dipole interactions, thermodynamics, oxidation-reduction potentials, reaction kinetics, and methodology. While some prior knowledge of physical chemistry would certainly be helpful, it is not an indispensable prerequisite to using this book. Accordingly, wherever appropriate, an effort has been made to develop in meaningful and straightforward language the essentials of those physicochemical principles pertinent to the study of biochemistry. Enjoy yourself. I hope that you will ultimately discover that biochemistry is both fascinating and exciting.

LITERATURE

DEVONS, S., ed., *Biology and the Physical Sciences*. New York, London: Columbia University Press, 1969. A collection of technical essays covering diverse subjects delivered by authorities in each field at a symposium on the relationship between biology and physical science. The brief Foreword and Postscript written by S. Devons focus attention on the interdisciplinary nature of modern biology.

GREEN, D. E., and R. F. GOLDBERGER, *Molecular Insights Into the Living Process*. New York, London: Academic Press, Inc., 1967. This book presents a unified picture of biochemistry from the standpoint of universal principles that apply to all living organisms. Chapter 17 is devoted to an incisive discussion of the strategic aspects of biochemical research.

WHITE, A., P. HANDLER, and E. L. SMITH, *Principles of Biochemistry,* Fourth Edition. New York: McGraw-Hill Book Company, 1968. A highly regarded biochemistry text. Chapter 1 provides a brief and skillful analysis of the scope of biochemistry.

2

Methods of Biochemistry

In the preceding chapter it was emphasized that biochemistry is an experimental science and that, as such, the limits of investigation are greatly restricted by the limitations and availability of analytical techniques. This was especially true in the early part of the twentieth century when relatively few analytical techniques existed and those that were available usually lacked a high level of specificity and sensitivity. In addition, the procedures were generally not automated and the collection of data was slow and tedious. In the past thirty years, however, the advancements in technology have been fantastic. Coupled with this rapid technological revolution were the development of many new analytical techniques and the refinement of existing techniques, which tremendously benefited the exact sciences. As previously pointed out, advancements in this area contributed greatly to the acceleration of the growth of biochemistry.

This chapter is therefore devoted to a descriptive analysis of methodology. In addition, it is my firm conviction, based on experience as both a student and a teacher of biochemistry, that the digestion and assimilation of biochemical principles are made easier and more interesting by first acquiring an appreciation of how the data, which then serve as the basis for the formulation of principles, are collected. The validity of this premise may not be immediately apparent at this time, nor will it necessarily be so after you complete this chapter. Rather, it will emerge gradually as you read subsequent chapters and research papers.

The inclusion of an early chapter devoted exclusively to experimental techniques pertinent to biochemical investigations represents a heretofore unused approach in writing a biochemistry textbook. Traditionally, methods are introduced only when they first become necessary. This usually means that the development of analytical principles is joined to a discussion of another primary topic. The main disadvantage of this latter approach is that the attention of the student is diverted. Rather than focusing all of his attention on the primary subject—for example, amino acids and proteins—he has to pause and learn the principles of chromatography, electrophoresis, ultracentrifugation, and other methods. The tactic employed in this book is to divorce the initial analysis of analytical techniques from such primary topics. Consequently, attention is not diverted from either aspect—methodology or biochemical principle.

In this chapter, then, we will explore the distinguishing *principles* of those primary techniques which are central to contemporary biochemical research. *This can be done without any prior knowledge of the nature of biologically occurring compounds or systems. It is anticipated, however, that you will refer to these pages again and again, and you should.* Only by repeated cross-reference will you achieve the maximum value of this chapter. For some students much of this material may be a review, whereas others may have studied only a few areas. In either case the purpose and merit of this chapter should not be minimized.

OBJECTIVES OF BIOCHEMICAL ANALYSIS

The objectives of biochemical analysis are a logical extension of the nature of biochemistry as outlined in the previous chapter. It would obviously be redundant to reiterate the scope of biochemistry, but we can and should recapitulate the theme that permeates all of biochemical research. That theme is simply to study in detail any or all substances that participate in a biological phenomenon. In this regard, biochemical investigations can be classified as *in vivo* or *in vitro* studies. *In vivo* studies utilize *intact* cellular systems whereas *in vitro* investigations deal with *cell-free* systems. Additional discussion is given in Chapter 10 (page 231). With *in vitro* studies, attention may be directed to an intact subcellular organelle, to any component of same, or to any specific soluble compound released when the cell is broken. The *in vitro* approach is used more frequently, and thus, in the discussion to follow, it is to be presumed that the methods in question find most application in the *in vitro* type of analysis. Of those to be considered, the only methods that have a basic application to whole-cell studies are electron microscopy and the utilization of radioisotopes as metabolic tracers.

With this introduction we can now identify the following basic objectives of biochemical analysis. Collectively they describe the analytical philosophy of biochemistry.

1. *Separation and isolation.* This is the first and fundamental step in any program designed to identify and investigate any substance that participates in some aspect of the living process. The substance must be separated from other substances and then isolated in as pure a state as possible. Normally the isolation is not difficult and usually is an outgrowth of the separation process. Problems are encountered, however, in the separation of one particular substance from a mixture which may contain several different substances.

The difficulties are compounded when the mixture is homogeneous and contains a number of substances that are very similar to each other. The two extremes are the separation of only one substance from all of the others and the resolution of the complete mixture into all of its component parts. Both extremes, as well as intermediate situations, are frequently encountered and methods are available to deal with them successfully.

2. *Determination of purity.* After separation and isolation, the immediate objective is to determine the purity of the sample. This is usually a negative procedure in that it is normally accomplished by demonstrating that no large amount of any other contaminating substance is present. The optimal situation is, of course, to isolate a substance in absolutely pure form with no contaminants of any kind. The demonstration of purity is normally accomplished by the same procedures that are used to characterize the substance.

3. *Characterization.* This phase of analysis is where most biochemists expend the bulk of their efforts and creativity. Note, however, that phases 1 and 2 are prerequisite to characterization. *By characterization is meant the determination of the physicochemical and biological properties that distinguish the substance under study.* Depending on the nature of the substance being investigated, this can mean a variety of things. To illustrate the point, however, consider that the substance in question is a protein and that it functions as an *antibody.* (Antibodies, found in the blood of all vertebrates, are substances that serve as a natural defense mechanism against invasion of the body by foreign materials called *antigens.*) We are interested in learning as much as possible about the physicochemical structure of this protein. What is its molecular weight? What types of monomeric units (amino acids) are present? What is the amount of each amino acid present? What is the sequence of the amino acids? What are the ionic properties of the protein? What is the structural basis for its activity? With an antibody, we inquire as follows. Is it specific for a certain type of antigen? If so, what is the antigen? Is the antibody produced only in the presence of the antigen? Is it produced by all members of the same species and by other species as well? Does it have any clinical value in treating disease? In what way is it similar to and/or distinct from other antibodies? Again the questions and problems are numerous and varied, but methods do exist that afford a basis for their solution. Notice the theme of structure and function which permeates the inquiries listed above.

4. *Structure determination.* At this point an explanation of the goals associated with this aspect would be superfluous. They have been enunciated before. A variety of laboratory and instrumental methods are currently available for the determination of various aspects of cellular, subcellular, and molecular structure. The ultimate technique currently available for the complete three-dimensional analysis of a *molecule* is *X-ray diffraction. Electron microscopy* is utilized to study the ultrastructural architecture of *whole cells* and *subcellular particulates.*

5. *Maintenance of structural and functional integrity.* This is perhaps the most important consideration common to biochemical investigation. In addition, it is not something that constitutes a singular phase of analytical work requiring attention only once. Rather, it permeates all of the aforementioned operations, especially during procedures of separation and isolation. In the simplest terms, maintenance of biochemical integrity means taking precautions to

insure that the substance is not exposed to harsh procedures which might damage its structure and hence probably also its biological properties. The problem is especially acute when working with biopolymers such as the proteins and nucleic acids, which are sensitive and delicate materials easily subject to structural changes.

To fulfill these objectives, the biochemist has at his disposal many and varied techniques. Those widely used which will be discussed in this chapter are *chromatography, electrophoresis, ultracentrifugation, spectroscopy, electron microscopy, radioisotopes,* and *X-ray diffraction.*

CHROMATOGRAPHY

Undoubtedly the most widely used separation technique is chromatography. Its popularity is due to a combination of four factors. First, chromatographic techniques do not require expensive apparatus; secondly, most methods require a minimun of technical skill; thirdly, most methods possess a very high resolving power for mixtures containing a large population of similar compounds; and fourthly, there is now available a large selection of different chromatographic procedures which permit the resolution of all classes of biological compounds.

Before discussing different techniques, it is necessary to first establish the general principle of chromatography. Consider the following definition. *Chromatography is a process characterized by the uniform percolation of a fluid mixture (gas or liquid) through a region of another relatively immobilized substance (liquid or solid) which, through various means, allows for the differential migration of the components of the mixture.* While this definition may appear very nonspecific, it does refer to two common characteristics of all chromatographic techniques.

1. They are *dynamic* and *cascade processes* involving the continual movement of one phase (moving phase), which originally contained the mixture, relative to an immobile phase (stationary phase).
2. Separation is accomplished by the *differential movement* of the respective components of the mixture due to their selective interaction with the stationary phase.

The feature that distinguishes one chromatographic procedure from another is the basis for the interaction with the stationary phase. This interaction is based almost exclusively on the principle of *adsorption,* of *partition based on solubility,* or of *ion exchange.* Several methods employ a combination of these principles. Further explanation can best be accomplished by considering specific procedures.

PAPER CHROMATOGRAPHY

Classical paper chromatography is based primarily on *the partition of the components in a mixture between two liquid phases due to differences in the solubility of the components in each phase.* Recall that this is the same principle that governs the removal of substances dissolved in one liquid phase by extraction in a separatory funnel with another liquid that is relatively immiscible in the first. The paper itself, if not chemically modified during manufacturing and processing, consists primarily of cellulose fibers and as such is relatively inert. The primary function of the paper is to serve as an immobile support for water, which serves as the stationary phase. The moving phase is a homogeneous liquid mixture, termed a *chromatographic developing solution,* consisting of an organic solvent saturated with water.

To gain a deeper insight into the principles of paper chromatography and of chromatography in general, let us briefly examine the mechanics of this process. A small aliquot of the sample mixture is applied to a localized region near one end of a sheet of chromatographic paper. This paper is specially prepared for chromatography; several production grades are available, varying in porosity which controls the rate of solvent migration. The point of application—termed the origin— is then dried, leaving the solutes of the mixture embedded in the cellulose fibers. The spotted paper is then exposed to vapors of the developing solvent by suspending it in a container saturated with same. After this equilibration, the origin end of the paper is folded (for descending migration) or suspended (for ascending migration) in a reservoir of the chromatographic developing solvent. Note that the origin itself does not come in direct contact with the developing solvent when the unit is first assembled. Refer to panel A of Figure 2–1. As soon as contact is made, the developing solvent will begin to move along the paper by capillary action, with the non-absorbed organic mixture constituting the more non-polar, moving phase. This process will continue until the chamber is opened.

When the solvent front reaches the origin, the material spotted there will be dissolved to different extents between the two phases. That is to say, there will be an initial distribution of all solutes at the origin between the polar, aqueous, stationary phase supported on the paper and the non-polar, organic, moving phase. This distribution will be governed by the relative differences of the solubilities of each solute in the two phases.

With these introductory remarks, we can now focus on the basis for separation in this method and for chromatography in general. After an initial equilibrium distribution of each solute is achieved, solutes that are distributed to different degrees will undergo a differential zonal displacement from the origin as long as the migration of the moving phase is continuous and uninterrupted. For example, in paper chromatographic separation those materials which are more soluble in the moving organic phase will migrate further than those which are more soluble in the stationary water phase. The migration of any component relative to the total migration of the developing solvent is a reproducible chromatographic property of the component in the specified solvent as long as conditions are not varied. This property is termed the R_f value and is defined as

$$R_f = \frac{\text{distance traveled by compound}}{\text{total distance traveled by developing solvent}}$$

Theoretically then, we conclude that all materials which differ in their distribution (that is, have different R_f values) should be separated. Practically, we observe, however, that clear separation is controlled by

(A)

(B)

(C)

Figure 2–1 One-dimensional, descending paper chromatography of an amino acid mixture containing aspartic acid (ASP), methionine (MET), and alanine (ALA). *Panel A:* paper strip suspended in trough of developing solvent; no migration has occurred; rectangle designates origin. *Panel B:* solvent front has migrated nearly the length of the paper. *Panel C:* appearance of paper strip after removal and treatment with ninhydrin.

the capacity of the method to resolve small differences so that discrete zones can be detected. The resolving power in paper chromatography is good but is exceeded in other methods.

After the solvent has traveled nearly the length of the paper, the paper is removed and dried. The final phase of the operation is to detect the location of each member of the mixture. If the solutes are all pigments, there is obviously no problem, but this is usually not the situation. For non-colored substances, other detection procedures are available and generally fall into either of two categories. One approach is to treat the paper with a chemical reagent that will selectively interact with the resolved materials to produce a colored product. This procedure often destroys the compounds and thus prevents their isolation for further study. Panel C of Figure 2–1 depicts a paper chromatogram of a mixture of three amino acids which was developed in a phenol–water solvent, dried, and then sprayed with a *ninhydrin* reagent. Ninhydrin reacts with amino acids to produce a blue-violet color in most cases. This is one of the classical reactions of amino acids and will be discussed briefly in Chapter 4 (page 70). The second approach is physical in nature, for example exposing the paper to ultraviolet light. Here the materials can be detected if they interact with the incident radiation via absorption or fluorescence. This procedure seldom destroys the compounds, and hence the solute can be recovered for additional studies. The absorbing or fluorescing regions can be circled, the zones can then be cut out and the material extracted from the paper with an appropriate solvent.

The technique of paper chromatography is unbelievably simple, as should be evident from this discussion. Despite this simplicity, its development was not announced until 1944 by R. Consden, A. H. Gordon, and A. J. P. Martin. Although other chromatographic techniques were available at that time, the development of paper chromatography revolutionized the field because of its penetration into liquid–liquid partition. (*Aside:* Martin and R. L. M. Synge collaborated during the 1940's in developing various methods of partition chromatography including gas–liquid chromatography. As an indication of the fantastic impact of chromatography on the scientific community and of the distinctive contributions of Martin and Synge in that area, it should be noted that they were co-recipients of the Nobel Prize in Chemistry in 1952.) The versatility and good resolving power of paper chromatography are also noteworthy. To illustrate this point, consider the technique of two-dimensional paper chromatography. The discussion above limited migration of the developing solvent to only one direction, that is, a one-dimensional analysis. As is evident in panel C of Figure 2–1, this was sufficient to achieve separation of the components in the simple mixture of only three amino acids. When the mixture contains a greater number of similar components, however, complete separation of all materials by development in only one direction is often impossible with a single solvent. In this case the problem can normally be circumvented by developing the chromatogram in two different solvent systems in two different directions, with migration in the second direction being at a right angle to the path of the first solvent. Remarkable success can be achieved by judicious selection of the two solvent systems. In this instance a picture is worth a thousand words. The panels of Figure 2–2 show ninhydrin-treated chromatograms of a mixture of twelve amino acids. Panels A and B depict the results of a one-dimensional and a two-dimensional analysis, respectively. The increased resolving power of the two-dimensional analysis is clearly evident.

Although classical paper chromatography has been and continues to be widely used, it does have limitations. First, its resolving power is limited even with a two-dimensional run, and incomplete resolution of complex mixtures is frequently encountered. Secondly, it is not very useful for separating mixtures of nonpolar materials, since they would have limited solubility in the stationary phase and would tend to migrate as a unit. Other types of papers, formed by special processing procedures, are available and do counteract these two problems to an extent. A third disadvantage is that recovery of each resolved component is tedious and can be time consuming. The fourth and perhaps greatest drawback is that paper chromatography has no application whatsoever to resolving a mixture of biopolymers, for example a mixture of proteins.

This analysis was intended to provide you with more than a detailed explanation of the mechanics and principles of paper chromatography. It should also have strengthened your appreciation of the basic characteristics common to all chromatographic procedures as mentioned on page 12. If you are still uncomfortable about the *principles of a continuous selective distribution between a moving and a stationary phase, resulting in differential migration,* it is advised that you reread the last few pages before continuing with subsequent sections. Comprehension of this principle will be assumed, and emphasis will be placed on analyzing the basis of selective distribution.

ION EXCHANGE COLUMN CHROMATOGRAPHY

When the solutes to be separated are ionic in nature, this method is one of the most popular chromatographic techniques, primarily because of its very high resolving power. In contrast to paper chromatography, the stationary phase in this procedure is not an inert support. On the contrary, it has a direct and active function in the process, participating as an ion exchanger. Before considering the phenomenon of ion exchange, it would be advantageous to first describe the chemical nature of the stationary phase.

Physically speaking, the majority of ion exchangers appear as identical, minute, semi-solid spheres and are normally referred to as *ion exchange resins.* Chemically speaking, each type of resin particle is composed of a branched polymer containing ionizable groups which exchange reversibly with other ions in a surrounding fluid. For each type, a family of resins exist which possess various degrees of crosslinking. If the ionic group is acidic, the resin is termed a *cation exchanger.* In this case positive ions (cations) are exchanged between the resin and the surrounding medium. If the group is *basic,* the resin is termed an *anion exchanger.* In this case negative ions (anions) are exchanged between the resin and the surrounding medium. For reasons of simplicity and brevity, our discussion will emphasize cation exchangers.

A photograph of a typical resin in spherical bead form is shown in Figure 2–3. The representations to the right are an attempt to contribute some conceptual meaning to the photo. Depicted are the characteristic

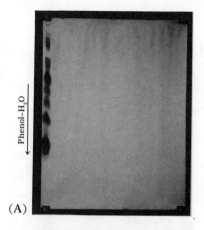

(A)

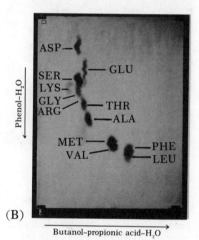

(B)

Figure 2–2 A comparison of the resolving power of one-dimensional (*panel A*) and two-dimensional (*panel B*) paper chromatography. A mixture of twelve amino acids was applied to each origin (rectangle), and the papers were developed under identical conditions and then sprayed with a ninhydrin solution. In each photograph the ninhydrin-positive spots appear as dark areas against the white background. The developing solvents used for each direction are indicated on the borders. In the two-dimensional analysis, the paper was developed first with the phenol solvent. (Amino acid abbreviations are identified in Table 4–1, page 61.)

Strong Cation Exchange Resin

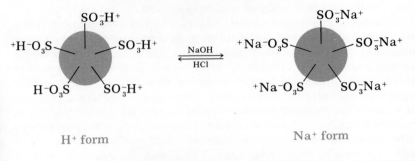

H⁺ form   Na⁺ form

Weak Cation Exchange Resin

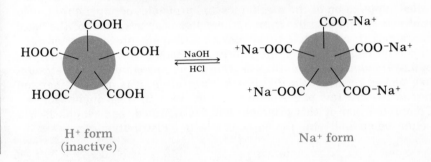

H⁺ form
(inactive)   Na⁺ form

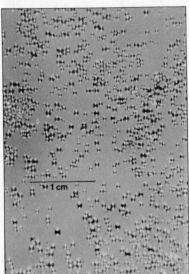

Figure 2–3 A photograph of typical ion exchange resin particles. *Right:* diagrammatic representations of the spherical particle, depicting the attachment of functional groups to the branched polymeric backbone symbolized by the spherical shaded area. Weak cation exchangers are useful only in the Na⁺ salt form.

structural features of a *strong* cation exchanger (containing strongly acidic sulfonic acid groupings, that is, —SO₃H) and a *weak* cation exchanger (containing weakly acidic carboxyl groups, that is, —COOH). Both would be used in the separation of positively charged solutes (X⁺), with the choice of strong versus weak being dictated by the exchange properties of the solutes. The acidic groups of the cation exchangers can be converted to salt forms by treatment with strong base as shown. In the case of the weak exchanger, this transformation is actually necessary for its use, since the carboxyl group is not appreciably ionized at lower pH, and hence the functional group would have a minimal exchange capacity. The sulfonic acid grouping is considerably ionized even in acid solution and thus can be used in either the acid form or the salt form.

After selecting and converting the exchanger into the desired form, a slurry is prepared and then poured into a cylindrical column to a height of several centimeters. A small volume of the mixture containing positively charged solutes (X⁺) is applied to the top of the resin bed. An aqueous solution of known pH is then continuously run through the column to constitute the moving phase. A typical system in full assembly is shown in Figure 2–4. As the ionic solutes come into contact with the ionic resin particles, a reversible exchange reaction can occur at any functional site in accordance with basic principles of electrostatic attraction.

$$R_p(SO_3^-H^+)_n + X^+ \rightleftarrows R_p(SO_3^-H^+)_{n-1}(SO_3^-X^+) + H^+$$

Because the resin particles are stationary, however, the effect of exchange is to retard the movement of ionic solutes through the column as dissolved materials in the moving phase. The extent of binding will be primarily controlled by the magnitude of the electrostatic force of attraction between X^+ and the resin particle. Consequently, if a mixture contains a number of solutes, each with a different net positive charge, they will exchange to different degrees with the ion exchange resin. Solutes with a greater net positive charge will interact with the resin particles to a greater degree and thus be retarded on the column for a longer time. This difference in exchange constitutes the basis of selective and differential migration through the column. The effluent emerging from the bottom of the column can by systematically collected as small-volume fractions, and the presence of a solute can be detected by a suitable procedure. A specific example of the resolving power of this technique is given in Chapter 4 (page 68). Generally speaking, the resolving power of ion exchange chromatography is very high, and consequently this technique has extensive application in biochemical analysis.

Anion exchangers consist of a polymeric matrix containing positively charged functional groupings, usually substituted aminoethyl groups in chloride salt form, that is

$$\text{polymer} \left(\text{CH}_2\text{CH}_2\overset{+}{\underset{\text{H}}{\text{N}}}\text{R}_2 \; \text{Cl}^- \right)_n$$

A popular anion exchanger is DEAE (diethylaminoethyl)-cellulose where $R = -\text{CH}_2\text{CH}_3$. It is particularly efficient in the chromatography of protein mixtures. With negatively charged solutes (X^-), the basic exchange reaction would be as follows.

$$X^- + \text{polymer} \left(\text{CH}_2\text{CH}_2\overset{+}{\underset{\text{H}}{\text{N}}}\text{R}_2 \; \text{Cl}^- \right)_n \rightleftarrows \text{polymer} \left(\text{CH}_2\text{CH}_2\overset{+}{\underset{\text{H}}{\text{N}}}\text{R}_2 \; \text{Cl}^- \right)_{n-1} \left(\text{CH}_2\text{CH}_2\overset{+}{\underset{\text{H}}{\text{N}}}\text{R}_2 \; X^- \right) + \text{Cl}^-$$

The principle of operation is, of course, the same as for cation exchangers.

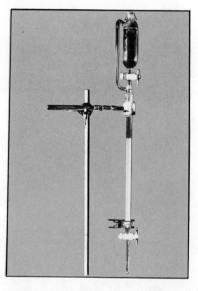

Figure 2–4 A photograph of a typical column assembly for chromatographic separations. The eluting solvent, contained in the top reservoir, flows through the column, which is usually packed with a solid phase that actively participates (ion exchange, adsorption, or gel permeation) to retard the migration of dissolved solutes originally applied to the top of the solid bed in a small volume. Fractions are collected dropwise from the bottom of the assembly.

GEL PERMEATION CHROMATOGRAPHY

Sometimes called molecular sieve or molecular exclusion chromatography, this technique has been extensively used in recent years, particularly in the separation and isolation of biopolymers. Differential migration is based on *variations in molecular size and shape.* However, molecular shape is usually not a significant variable and size differences constitute the controlling factor. For discussion purposes, we will assume a spherical molecular shape.

The stationary phase consists of small, spherical gel particles which can be regarded as *molecular sieves.* The gel is obtained by cross-linking polymeric chains of *dextran,* a carbohydrate. A large family of gel particles are available that differ in the extent of cross-linkage between the component chains. When the gel particles are placed in water,

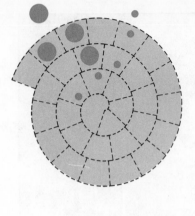

polymeric
backbone

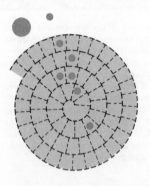

Given solutes ⬤ and ● : Both
would penetrate granule ⬤ top,
with ● exhibiting a greater degree of penetration; only ● would
penetrate granule at bottom, with
⬤ being excluded.

Figure 2–5 A schematic representation
of a highly cross-linked, spherical gel
granule with small pore size (*bottom*) and
a minimally cross-linked granule with
large pore size (*top*). Solid circles correspond to solutes with different molecular dimensions.

they swell and the cross-linked polymeric structure provides a three-
dimensional porous network, with the size of the pores determined by
the degree of cross-linking. Figure 2–5 shows a simplified representation
of a large-pore and a small-pore gel.

When a mixture is applied to the top of a column containing a
bed of swollen gel particles, the molecules in the mixture will penetrate
the gel particles if their molecular dimensions are smaller than the pores
of the swollen granules. This process is, of course, reversible and molecules can exit from the particles. The degree of penetration, and hence
the degree of retarded flow, will be a function of the difference between
pore size and molecular size, with smaller molecules being retained on
the column for a greater time. Solutes with molecular dimensions
greater than the largest pores of the swollen gel granules will not penetrate the stationary phase and will pass directly through the column
dissolved in the moving phase. Once again fractions of the effluent can
be systematically collected and analyzed for the presence of solute.

In addition to an obvious application for separation and isolation,
this technique can also be used for the measurement of the molecular
weight of a solute, since molecular weight is, in general, a function of
molecular size. It is a particularly good analytical tool in this regard for
biopolymers, especially for proteins. First a column of swollen gel is
calibrated by determining the specific volumes of eluting solvent required to displace several proteins of known molecular weight from the
column. Then the protein of unknown molecular weight is passed
through the column in the same solvent, and the volume required for
its displacement is determined. By comparison to the calibrated retention volumes of the control samples, a reasonable estimate of the molecular weight can be made.

To supplement the collection of cross-linked dextran gels differing
only in porosity, modified dextran materials have recently been introduced which have both improved the resolving power and extended
application. Most notable are those substances which can be used in
organic solvents and those which include ion exchange groups attached
to the cross-linked polymeric backbone.

GAS–LIQUID CHROMATOGRAPHY

The method of gas–liquid chromatography was first developed by A. T.
James and A. J. P. Martin in 1952 as a means of separating volatile
compounds. Resolution of solute mixtures and instrument sensitivity
are very high. The original objective of designing a technique to separate such compounds, which could not be efficiently resolved by other
procedures, has been exceeded many times over. Due to the development
of (a) a wider range of stationary phase materials and (b) chemical
methods to prepare volatile derivations of non-volatile materials, gas-
liquid chromatography can now be used to resolve nearly every class of
biologically occurring organic compounds with the notable exception
of the biopolymers.

The distinguishing feature of gas–liquid chromatography is the
use of an inert gas, such as helium or argon, as the mobile phase in a
column containing a high-boiling-liquid stationary phase. The complete column is normally maintained at a constant elevated temperature. After injection of a sample, the solutes in the mixture are vaporized

and transported through the column in the vapor state via the inert carrier gas. As the vapor comes in contact with the liquid stationary phase—the selection of which is governed by the nature of the solutes to be separated—the solutes are partitioned on the basis of different solubilities between the moving gas phase and the stationary liquid phase. A variety of special methods are available for the detection and quantitative analysis of the compounds as the moving phase emerges from the column. Some of the devices are extremely sensitive and capable of detecting quantities of material as low as 10^{-12} mole. For a material with a molecular weight of 100, this corresponds to 0.0000000001 gram. A simplified sketch of a gas-liquid partition system is shown in Figure 2-6.

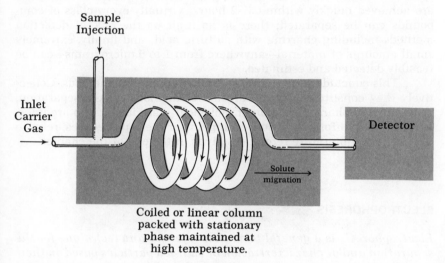

Figure 2-6 A schematic diagram of the essential components of a gas chromatograph.

ADSORPTION CHROMATOGRAPHY

The operational principle responsible for selective migration of solutes in any method of this type is the distribution between a mobile liquid phase and a solid stationary phase, controlled by the differential adsorption of the solutes on the surface of the stationary phase. Again this interaction between the solutes and the solid adsorbent is a reversible process counteracted by the solubility of the solute in the mobile phase. Unlike what occurs in ion exchange and gel permeation chromatography, the solutes do not penetrate the particles of the solid adsorbent phase. The interaction between dissolved solute and suspended solid particles is basically a surface phenomenon involving weak non-covalent associations such as hydrogen bonding, for example (see Chapter 3, page 55). It is important to specify the general nature of the linkage because, since it is non-covalent, the interaction between the solute and the adsorbent is a reversible process.

There are a variety of materials used as adsorbents such as powdered cellulose, silica gel, alumina, magnesium oxide, and others. Each has a peculiar set of advantages and disadvantages depending on the materials to be resolved. The design of the experimental apparatus also varies from the use of columns as described earlier to the utilization of very thin, horizontal layers of powdered adsorbents. The latter technique is referred to as *thin-layer chromatography.* Thin layers of any desired thickness can easily be prepared in the laboratory using glass plates as a supporting surface. Alternatively, commercially fabricated thin sheets of adsorbent can be purchased. In either case the mechanics of thin-layer chromatography are very similar to those of paper chromatography (page 13), including two-dimensional analysis. The thin-layer principle has recently been expanded to the use of stationary phases that operate on principles other than adsorption, for example, in thin-layer molecular sieve and thin-layer ion exchange chromatography.

The wide popularity of thin-layer chromatography is due to several advantages: solute resolution is good to excellent; most separations are achieved quickly within 0.5–2 hours; virtually every class of compounds can be separated; there is no limit on the type of detection methods including charring with sulfuric acid; and finally, extremely small amounts of material—anywhere from 1 to 5 micrograms—can be feasibly detected and estimated.

This concludes our analysis of chromatographic methods. Collectively they constitute a potent arsenal of methods for the separation, isolation, and characterization of biological materials. If you are interested in more information concerning any of these procedures, refer to the suggested literature references given at the end of the chapter.

ELECTROPHORESIS

Electrophoresis is a general term that refers to any technique for the separation and/or characterization of charged particles based on their specific migration rates in an electric field. Electrophoretic methods were first developed by A. Tiselius approximately 35 years ago. Advancements since then have resulted in the evolution of electrophoresis as one of the most effective methods of separation and characterization. The only requirements are that (a) the components of a mixture must be in or be convertible to an ionic form, and (b) each component must possess a different net charge. In biochemical studies, electrophoresis has been very valuable in the separation and isolation of proteins and in the direct determination of the number of proteins in a mixture. There are two primary reasons for this: (a) electrophoretic methods can be performed under very mild conditions, thus protecting the extremely labile proteins from any severe structural modifications, and (b) some of the methods have a high resolving power, resulting in the clear separation of similarly charged protein molecules.

An in-depth analysis of the theoretical aspects of electrophoresis is beyond the scope of this book. Instead, let us briefly examine some of the fundamentals. In physicochemical language, the degree of movement of a charged particle in an electrical field is termed the *electrophoretic mobility* (μ), and for a spherical charged particle not experiencing any strong electrostatic interaction from surrounding ions, it can be shown via a theoretical analysis that

$$\mu = \frac{Q}{6\pi\eta r}$$

where Q = the charge on the particle,
        r = the radius of the particle in cm,
        η = the viscosity of the solvent.

This fundamental equation reveals the essence of an electrophoretic analysis. On the assumption that the environment is constant (η has a fixed value), the equation states that the migration of a particle is controlled by the ratio of two variables, Q/r. As this ratio increases, the mobility increases. If we further assume that the components of a mixture do not differ appreciably in molecular size, the equation is reduced to a direct relationship of the form μ = (constant) Q. This is nothing more than a mathematical statement that the migration of ionic particles similar in size is directly dependent on their respective charges. The greater the charge, the greater the migration.

All methods of electrophoresis can be classified as *moving-boundary* or *zonal* methods. In moving-boundary methods, electrophoresis occurs in free solution. That is to say, the charged particles migrate freely through a vertical channel filled with a liquid, usually an aqueous salt solution. A natural consequence of this type of separation is that the solutes are never really separated from one another. The particles are displaced towards the electrode of opposite charge, and boundaries are formed which merely distinguish the presence of each component. A pure sample will be characterized by the presence of only one boundary between the migrating solute particles and the region of the channel containing free solution. Two boundaries will indicate the presence of two solutes, and so on. To test your comprehension of this principle, it is suggested that you perform Problem 2–4. The only practical application of moving-boundary methods is to check for purity of a sample and to estimate the relative concentrations of the solutes.

Zonal methods of electrophoresis have virtually displaced the practice of moving-boundary techniques. In addition to the application just mentioned for moving-boundary methods, zonal techniques are also effective for separation, since solutes are resolved as discrete zones. Zone electrophoresis does not occur in free solution, but requires a solid support and, depending on the apparatus, migration can occur either horizontally or vertically.

A variety of materials are now employed as solid supports since the original use of filter paper strips. A revolutionary advance in this area was reported in 1955 by O. Smithies, who developed the use of porous starch gel as a solid support. The resolving power of the starch gel method was far superior to that of any other technique. The increase in resolution is due to the fact that differential migration of the charged particles is mediated not only by charge differences but by size differences as well. Since the gel particles are porous, the solutes can reversibly diffuse into the granules. Thus, in gel methods the charge-to-size ratio (Q/r) is indeed a variable.

Variable results and difficulties in preparation of the solid support are, however, definite disadvantages in the use of starch gels. Both limitations are eliminated by the use of *polyacrylamide* gels developed in 1959 by L. Ornstein and B. J. Davis. In addition to a resolving power comparable to that of starch gel, polyacrylamide gels possess other desirable properties. They are thermostable, transparent, durable, relatively inert chemically, non-ionic, and easily prepared with a large

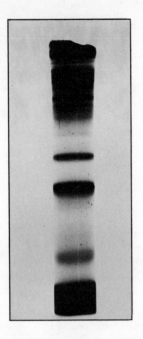

Figure 2–7 A photograph of an electrophoretic pattern of human serum proteins after staining of the gel. The stained proteins appear as dark bands of different intensities due to differences in the concentrations of the proteins. The stain used was Amido Schwarz.

range of average pore sizes. In addition, they can be used on a small scale for characterization or on a large scale for preparative work. The most popular apparatus employs cylindrical, vertical glass channels, and the technique is termed *polyacrylamide gel electrophoresis*. The interested reader is referred to the excellent paper of B. J. Davis for a description of the operational aspects of this technique. Alternatively, the application of the method can be appreciated by inspecting Figure 2–7, which depicts the electrophoretic analysis of 4 microliters of normal adult human serum on small polyacrylamide gel columns (2 inches in length; ¼ inch in diameter). After a running time of approximately 2.5 hours, the columns were removed from the apparatus (not shown) and the protein zones were located by a dye staining technique. The photographs of the stained gel reveal that approximately 18–20 individual zones can be recognized. Each corresponds to a separate protein.

ULTRACENTRIFUGATION

An ultracentrifuge is based on the fundamental principle common to any centrifuge, namely, that *substances of different densities can be separated from one another by subjecting them to a centrifugal force under high rotational speeds.* An *ultra*centrifuge is distinguished by the production of intense gravitational fields at extremely high speeds under vacuum. A variety of instruments and rotors are available capable of speeds in the range of 20,000–70,000 revolutions per minute and generating gravitational fields in the range of 50,000–500,000 × g. Two basic types are available—a *preparative* ultracentrifuge and an *analytical* ultracentrifuge. The former is used primarily in isolation procedures and the latter in purity analysis and molecular weight measurements. The greatest application of the ultracentrifuge is in the study of large biological macromolecules (biopolymers), particularly the proteins and nucleic acids.

All ultracentrifugal techniques can be classified as either *sedimentation* or *density gradient methods* (see Figure 2–8). In sedimentation methods, used primarily for characterization studies, solutes move in a medium (solvent) of *unchanging density*. In density gradient methods, used for separation and isolation, the movement of the solutes occurs in a medium with a *density that is gradually changing*. The events of each mode of operation are diagrammed in Figure 2–8. In sedimentation runs, the centrifuge tube or cell is initially filled with a homogeneous solution containing the solutes to be studied. As you might expect from the preceding discussion of moving-boundary electrophoresis, centrifugation in this case will result in the *formation of boundaries* between the solute and the solvent as the former moves toward the bottom of the tube. The principle of sedimentation is employed in the analytical ultracentrifuge, which analyzes the position of the boundary at any time during the course of the run. The purity of the sample can be judged by detecting the number of boundaries formed, with a pure sample exhibiting only one boundary. Measuring the rate at which the boundary moves provides a basis for calculating the molecular weight of the solute (see following page).

As shown in Figure 2–8, there are two types of density gradient runs. *Velocity density gradient centrifugation* utilizes a solvent medium having a *preformed gradient* with a linear change from low to high density going from the top to the bottom of the tube. A small volume of the sample to be studied is layered on top of the gradient. Then, as shown, the solutes move through the medium as *discrete zones*. Alternatively, in *equilibrium density gradient centrifugation*, the entire tube is initially filled with a homogeneous mixture containing the solute(s) under study dissolved in a solution of a very dense inorganic salt such as cesium chloride. During centrifugation a linear density gradient of the cesium chloride will be *self-generating*, and the solute will seek out a position in the tube with a density value equal to its own density. The latter technique has been extremely valuable in the laboratory study of nucleic acids—both RNA and DNA (see page 152, Chapter 6, and page 465, Chapter 17). In both the velocity and equilibrium density gradient methods, the solutes can be isolated by merely puncturing the tube bottom and collecting the tube contents dropwise, or by freezing and then slicing the tube in small sections.

As with any analytical procedure, ultracentrifugation continues to be subjected to a vigorous theoretical analysis. Although this again is beyond the scope of this book, we can consider the fundamental theory for *sedimentation* methods. First, we recognize that the sedimentation of any particle differing in density from the field in which it is moving (usually an aqueous solvent) is due to a centrifugal force. Secondly, we realize that the movement due to the centrifugal force is going to be retarded by opposing frictional forces of the solvent. Finally, we recognize that in an ultracentrifuge there is a very rapid establishment of equal forces, resulting in a constant rate of sedimentation. The equations expressing the physicochemical realities of these forces are given below, and from their equivalency it is indicated that one can ultimately derive an equation from which the molecular weight can be calculated. In equating the centrifugal and frictional forces, the minus sign is included to indicate that the forces are opposing each other.

$$\text{Centrifugal force} = \omega^2 x M (1 - \bar{V}\rho)$$

where
ω = angular velocity of centrifuge rotor in radians per second
x = distance in centimeters from the solute boundary to center of rotation
M = molecular weight of solute
$\bar{V}$ = *partial specific volume* (ml/g) of solute (volume resulting from the addition of 1 gram of solute to a large volume of solvent)
ρ = density (g/ml) of solvent

$$\text{Frictional force} = -fv = -\left(\frac{RT}{D}\right)\left(\frac{dx}{dt}\right)$$

where
f = *frictional coefficient* of solute and is equal to RT/D where R is molar gas constant, T is absolute temperature, and D is *diffusion constant* of solute
v = velocity (rate of movement, dx/dt, in cm/sec) of sedimenting solute

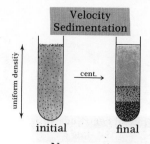

Velocity
Sedimentation

initial   final

No separation
1 solute = 1 boundary
2 solutes = 2 boundaries

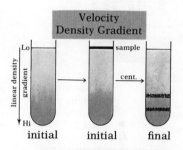

Velocity
Density Gradient

initial   initial   final

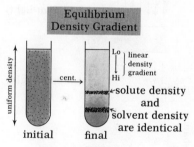

Equilibrium
Density Gradient

initial   final

solute density and solvent density are identical

Separation in both
1 solute = 1 zone
2 solute = 2 zones

solvent   solutes

Figure 2–8 A comparison of ultracentrifugation methods.

In the ultracentrifuge:

Centrifugal force = −Frictional force

$$\omega^2 x \mathrm{M}(1 - \bar{v}\rho) = \left(\frac{RT}{D}\right)\left(\frac{dx}{dt}\right)$$

For dilute solutions this equation reduces to

$$\mathrm{M} = \frac{RTs}{D(1 - \bar{V}\rho)}$$

where

$$s = \frac{(dx/dt)}{\omega^2 x}$$

The value measured in an ultracentifugal analysis is s, *the sedimentation coefficient*. If D, $\bar{V}$, and ρ were not available, they too would have to be determined. From the mathematical definition of s, it can be seen that the sedimentation coefficient is calculated by determining the displacement of the solute from the center of rotation and the velocity with which the displacement occurred. The analytical ultracentrifuge permits measurement of this displacement by detecting the position of the boundary at any time in the course of the run. (It is interesting to note here that the basic cost of the analytical instrument is approximately $30,000, ranging then to approximately $60,000 depending on accessories.) The angular rotation is known from the rotor speed. The sedimentation coefficient of most biopolymers is on the order of 10^{-13} sec. To eliminate the cumbersome exponent, the s value is normally multiplied by 10^{+13}, and the resulting number is designated as S and called the *Svedberg constant* in tribute to T. Svedberg, who pioneered the development of the ultracentrifuge. For example, a solute with a sedimentation coefficient of 2.5×10^{-13} sec would have a $2.5S$ value. As the particle becomes larger, the S value increases. A problem is provided at the end of the chapter for practice in applying this equation.

A variety of techniques are used in the analytical ultracentrifuge to detect the displacement of the boundary. Each device takes advantage of a property that distinguishes the solute from the solvent. For example, proteins can be detected by their ability to absorb ultraviolet radiation. Figure 2–9 diagrammatically depicts the essential events. After centrifugation for time t of a mixture containing two proteins (A and B), two boundaries would be produced. One would be between pure solvent and solvent containing the lighter of the two proteins (A). The second would be between regions in the tube containing only A (in solvent) and A and B (in solvent). At any time and without interrupting the centrifugation, the cell can be exposed to an incident beam (I_0) of UV light. Since proteins are capable of absorbing light energy in the ultraviolet region, the intensity of the transmitted light (I_T) will differ along the length of the cell according to the position and the amount of protein present. The analytical instrument contains a sophisticated optical system which in effect determines the rate at which the absorbance changes with respect to the length of the cell. This radiant image is allowed to strike a photographic plate. The film can then be developed to provide the information (dx/dt and x) necessary for calculating the sedimentation coefficient. Note that each peak corresponds to the position of one boundary in the analytical cell.

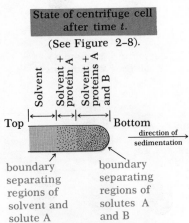

State of centrifuge cell after time t.
(See Figure 2–8).

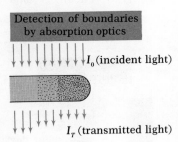

Detection of boundaries by absorption optics

I_0 (incident light)

I_T (transmitted light)

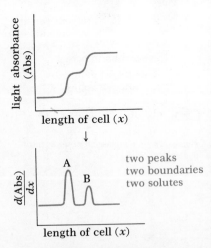

Figure 2–9 A schematic diagram depicting the detection of boundaries in a centrifuge cell by absorption optics. I_0 is the incident light intensity and I_T is the transmitted light intensity.

SPECTROSCOPY

Spectroscopic methods of analysis are all based on the interaction between matter and radiant energy. This interaction is quite specific for each substance and thus can be utilized as a distinguishing fingerprint in identifying a compound. In addition, the extent of interaction can serve as a quantitative measure of the concentration of the substance.

The three principles governing this interaction can be summarized as follows:

1. Any material is capable of undergoing transitions to excited states (higher energy levels) through the absorption of energy. The energy levels available, which are unique to every compound, are fixed by the structure of the compound (to be exact, the distribution of electrons contributed by the constituent atoms) and differentiated from each other by specific energy values called *quanta,* referring to small but finite amounts of energy.

2. Light has a dual nature exhibiting a wave and a particulate function. The particulate nature of light—as theorized by Einstein at the turn of the century—is a result of the fact that light is composed of discrete entities of energy, also called quanta. Einstein further theorized that the energy value of a quantum is dependent only on the wavelength of the light. Since the wavelength of electromagnetic radiation covers a broad continuous spectrum, Einstein's proposal means that any ray of light with a particular wavelength will differ in energy content from a ray of any other wavelength. A representation of this spectrum is shown in Figure 2–10 (see also page 365, Chapter 14).

3. When light interacts with matter, a transition to an excited state will occur only if the compound absorbs a whole quantum of energy from a light ray whose energy (quantum) value is identical to the energy required to raise the compound to one of the allowable energy levels specified by its structure. The distinctive pattern of energy absorption exhibited by a pure substance as the wavelength is varied is termed an *absorption spectrum.*

These principles have been exploited in the physical sciences to develop extremely sensitive spectrophotometric methods of analysis. The most widely used techniques are infrared (IR) and ultraviolet (UV) spectroscopy. The biochemist has derived most application from UV analysis, since many compounds of biological interest characteristically absorb in this region.

To illustrate these principles and their application, let us consider a specific set of compounds, namely, the oxidized and reduced forms of nicotinamide adenine dinucleotide, symbolized NAD⁺ and NADH, respectively. (The ⁺ indicates a net molecular charge of +1 in NAD due to a deficiency of one electron.) These are two compounds which participate in a large number of biological reactions to be discussed in subsequent chapters. The complete structures are shown on page 252 (Chapter 10), but for now all we need recognize is that the structural difference between them is very slight. The formula for NAD⁺ is $C_{21}H_{26}O_{14}N_7P_2$ and that for NADH is $C_{21}H_{27}O_{14}N_7P_2$. All atoms are arranged in the same way, but note that the reduced form has one more

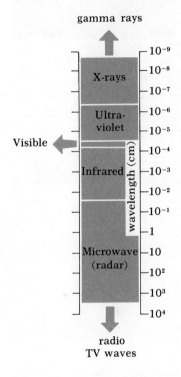

Figure 2–10 The regions of the electromagnetic spectrum.

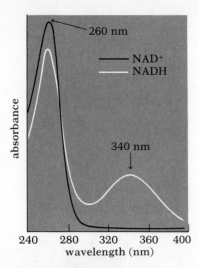

Figure 2–11 Ultraviolet absorption spectra of equimolar solutions of oxidized (NAD⁺) and reduced (NADH) nicotinamide adenine dinucleotide.

hydrogen atom (and one more electron) than the oxidized form. Because they possess nearly identical structures, they should possess—according to principle 1—a similar set of available energy levels. By the same principle, however, there should be some difference in available energy levels due to their structural difference, even if it is slight. This is clearly depicted in Figure 2–11, which illustrates the ultraviolet absorption spectrum of each compound (wavelength in nanometers, nm). Notice that the absorption of energy is—according to principles 2 and 3—dependent on the wavelength of energy. Both materials absorb maximally at 260nm, but the extent of absorption with the reduced form is somewhat less than with the oxidized form. More remarkable, however, is the appearance of a new absorption band with a maximum of 340nm in the reduced form which is totally absent in the spectrum of the oxidized form. Thus, the reduced absorption at 260nm and the unique absorption at 340nm are *spectrophotometric properties that, indeed, distinguish NADH from NAD⁺ and, under the conditions of the analysis, distinguish both from any other compound.*

Quantitative spectroscopic measurements are based on the *Beer-Lambert Law,* which states that the absorption of light energy at any wavelength is solely dependent on the concentration of the absorbing material and the length of the light path through the absorbing medium. A statement of this relationship is given below where the absorbance is defined as the logarithm of the ratio of incident light intensity (I_0) to transmitted light intensity (I_T).

$$\text{Absorbance} = \log_{10} \frac{I_0}{I_T} = \epsilon c l$$

The concentration is symbolized as c, l is the light path which usually is 1 centimeter, and ϵ is the *absorption extinction coefficient.* The latter is a constant corresponding to the light absorption of a known concentration of the compound at a specific wavelength. A brief but excellent analysis of the Beer-Lambert Law can be found in the laboratory manual by J. M. Clark.

RADIOISOTOPES

If one were to rate the value of the experimental tools available to the biochemist, radioisotopes would definitely be at the top of the list. They permit the *selective detection of the biochemical fate of a specific compound or specific atoms in a compound due to a specific set of reactions.* They are extremely useful if these reactions occur simultaneously in the presence of other reactions, although their use is not confined to *in vivo* studies. A second advantage is that extremely minute amounts of radioisotopes can be easily and accurately detected, permitting measurements of phenomena that would be difficult, if not impossible, by other means.

These advantages result from the nature of radioisotopes as *identical chemical forms* but *different unstable physical forms* of an element. The equivalence in chemical properties is due to an identical electron configuration in each isotope of the same element. Isotopes of any element differ due to a variance in the number of neutrons in the nucleus. Not all isotopes are unstable. Those that are can be considered as high-energy atoms which spontaneously tend to relieve the excessive interactions among subnuclear particles via a nuclear transformation. This type of phenomenon—sometimes termed *nuclear decay*—is generally associated with the emission of *alpha* (α), *beta* (β), or *gamma* (γ) radiation. Isotopes that behave in this fashion are called *radioisotopes* and the process is termed *radioactivity*. Alpha rays consist of positively charged particles identical to helium nuclei, He^{++}; beta rays are negatively charged particles consisting of high-speed electrons; gamma rays are nonparticulate, high-energy radiations similar to ordinary light waves.

Biochemical investigations have been immeasurably aided by the use of radioisotopes, especially C^{14}, H^3 (tritium), S^{35}, and P^{32}, all of which are β emitters. Although each is unstable, the decay rates (see Table 2–1) are not so great as to prohibit their practical use. For example, radioisotopic forms of oxygen (O^{19}) and nitrogen (N^{16}) are known, but they decay very rapidly. Stable isotopic forms of oxygen and nitrogen, O^{18} and N^{15}, are used instead, and measurement is based on their contribution through their larger atomic masses.

Table 2–1 A comparison of decay rates of radioisotopic forms of the primary biological elements.

Isotope	Radiation Emitted	Half-Life*
C^{14}	β	5770 years
H^3	β	12.26 years
S^{35}	β	86.7 days
P^{32}	β	14.3 days
O^{19}	β,γ	29 seconds
N^{16}	β,γ	7.35 seconds

* Time required for 50% of the material to decay.

The detection and quantitative measurement of radioactive isotopes—β emitters in particular—are generally accomplished in one of two ways. First we have the *ionization technique* using instruments dependent on Geiger-Muller tubes, which operate by measuring the number of negative ions produced when β particles collide with ionizable gas molecules within the compartment of the tube. These ions are collected at the anode of the tube, resulting in a small surge of current which is then amplified and finally registered as one electronic count. The level of radioactivity is then normally expressed as *counts per minute* (cpm). The second method is the *scintillation technique*. The phenomenon exploited here is the emission of light energy by materials called *scintillators* as they return to lower energy states, having been excited initially by absorbing energy from collisions with the high-speed electrons of β-radiation. The light energy is then converted to electrical energy via photomultipliers, and the small current surges are amplified and again electronically registered as one count. When the radioactive source and the scintillator coexist in a liquid solution, the technique is called *liquid scintillation*. Because of its high sensitivity, reproducibility, accuracy, and ability to discriminate between different isotopes, this is by far the most widely used method.

To briefly illustrate the application of radioisotopes, let us consider the following example. A biochemist wishes to verify (a) that an enzyme preparation he has isolated is capable of converting glucose-6-phosphate

(G6P) to ribulose-5-phosphate (R5P) and CO_2, and (b) that the CO_2 originates from the cleavage of the C^1—C^2 bond in glucose-6-phosphate as shown below.

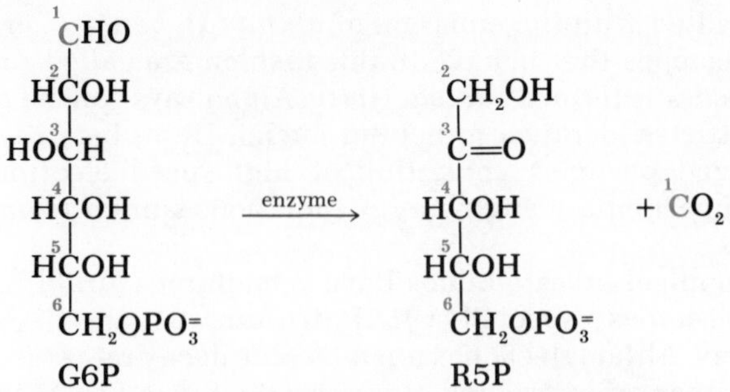

$$
\begin{array}{ccc}
\overset{1}{C}HO & & \\
| & & \\
H\overset{2}{C}OH & & \overset{2}{C}H_2OH \\
| & & | \\
HO\overset{3}{C}H & \xrightarrow{\text{enzyme}} & \overset{3}{C}{=}O \\
| & & | \\
H\overset{4}{C}OH & & H\overset{4}{C}OH \\
| & & | \\
H\overset{5}{C}OH & & H\overset{5}{C}OH \\
| & & | \\
\overset{6}{C}H_2OPO_3^= & & \overset{6}{C}H_2OPO_3^= \\
\text{G6P} & & \text{R5P}
\end{array}
\quad + \quad \overset{1}{C}O_2
$$

This can be accomplished by mixing the enzyme with G6P labeled specifically in the C^1 position with C^{14} and then demonstrating, after action of the enzyme, that the label is found in the carbon dioxide and not in the R5P. Experiments such as these are made possible by the commercial availability of hundreds of compounds labeled in specific positions; most of these materials are, however, rather expensive.

ELECTRON MICROSCOPY

A microscope permits the observation of objects that are not visible to the naked eye, by providing an increased resolving power and magnifying the image. However, the resolving power of microscopes is also limited. The ordinary light microscope, for example, cannot distinguish between objects that are closer than one-half the wavelength of illuminating light. Even with the most perfectly ground lenses, and with ordinary white light illumination having an average wavelength of 5500Å, the objective cannot resolve anything with a diameter less than 2750Å or 2.75×10^{-3} cm. Since many objects of interest to the biological scientist are much smaller than this, they would not be detected.

Increased resolving power is provided by electron microscopy. The basic principle of electron microscopy is the same as that of any microscope—an object is "illuminated" by radiation and an image of the interaction, which may then be magnified, is produced. In the electron microscope, however, the radiation does not consist of typical light waves, but rather is composed of rays of high-speed electrons. As these electrons pass through the specimen being viewed, a *differential absorption of electrons* will occur due to structural variations in the specimen, thus forming an image of the object which can be detected on an electron-sensitive photographic film. In the study of biological specimens, the resultant image is also related to the materials used in preparing the sample for observation. Staining the specimen prior to viewing is helpful in producing good images.

As with the ordinary light microscope, the resolving power of the electron microscope is still a function of the wavelength of incident radiation, which in this case is determined by the voltage used to produce the electron beam. For example, if the electron beam was produced under a potential of 50,000 volts, the approximate wavelength of a ray of high-speed electrons would be 0.05Å and the resolving power would be roughly 0.025Å. If the instrument were 100% efficient, this would mean that we would be able to see single hydrogen atoms. In reality, however, electron microscopes have an approximate efficiency of only 0.2–0.3%, due primarily to technical difficulties in construction. Despite the limitation, this is still sufficient to see objects of interest in great detail, even molecules of biopolymers.

Figure 2–12 contains five photographs which clearly depict the usefulness of electron microscopy. With the legend, the photographs speak for themselves. Several other examples will be given in subsequent chapters.

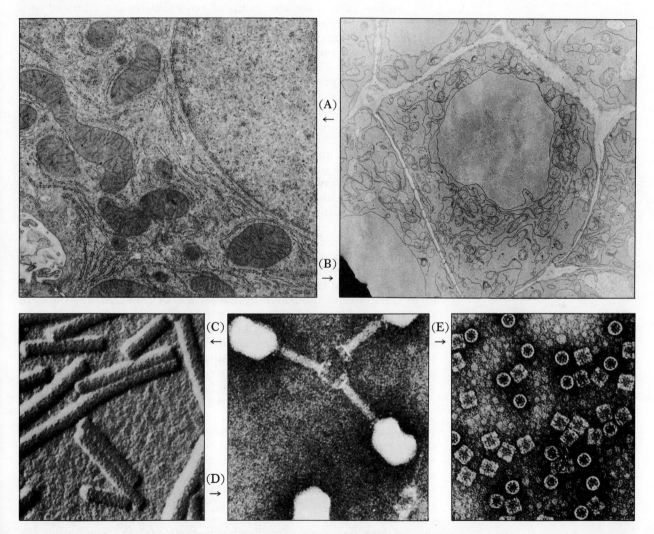

Figure 2–12 Electron micrographs of: *A*—a portion of the interior of a rat liver cell; magnification: 14,300×; *B*—an intact cell and pieces of neighboring cells of an onion bulb; magnification: 4,100×; *C*—several rod-shaped, tobacco mosaic virus particles; magnification: 222,000×; *D*—a few bacterial virus (bacteriophage) particles; magnification: 140,000×; *E*—molecules of hemocyanin (a copper-containing protein found in invertebrates and responsible for the transport of oxygen) obtained from snails; magnification: 140,000×. (Photos *A* and *B* were generously provided by Hilton H. Mollenhauer, Charles F. Kettering Research Laboratory, Yellow Springs, Ohio. Photos *C, D,* and *E* were generously provided by Carl Zeiss, Inc., New York.)

X–RAY DIFFRACTION

We are all familiar with the tremendous diagnostic utility of X-rays in the fields of medicine and dentistry wherein images of the human anatomy are produced and analyzed for structural defects. This technique is related to, but not identical with, a special type of spectroscopy called X-ray diffraction that measures the interaction of materials in the solid state with X-radiation. It is by far the most powerful tool available for the determination of fine structural details on the submicroscopic, *molecular level.*

In the solid state, the atoms of any material are arranged in a lattice configuration which consists of repeating units constituting an ordered, three-dimensional structural framework. X-rays are non-particulate, high-energy radiations of very short wavelength. Because of these properties, X-rays have a very high degree of penetrating power. We can further appreciate the penetration of a solid by X-rays by recognizing that the wavelength of X-radiation is approximately 10^{-8} cm, which is of the same order as the distances between neighboring points (atoms, ions, or molecules) in a crystalline lattice. Hence, a beam of X-rays will pass through a lattice-type structure until it strikes one of the lattice points and is *scattered* or *reflected* at various angles. If the material exposed to X-rays has an ordered structure with a point of symmetry, the X-rays will be reflected (diffracted) in an ordered fashion commensurate with the structure of the material. In addition, the intensity of the scattered radiation is dependent on the number and arrangement of electrons in the scattering atoms.

In X-ray spectroscopy, a solid sample is exposed to a beam of X-radiation of known wavelength and the scattered rays at any angle are detected photographically. The intensities of each scattered ray can then be measured from the film. Depending on the structural complexity of the material, thousands of images will be collected. The data are then fed to a programmed computer for analysis. In effect, the output of the computer analysis can be used to construct two-dimensional maps of the variance in electron density within any one of several planes in the crystal. By superimposing these two-dimensional contour maps of electron density for successive planes, a graphic three-dimensional representation of the solid can be constructed.

For reasons cited previously, we will not embark on an analysis of the theory or the mechanics of X-ray diffraction. The important point is that you appreciate that this method can be used effectively to reveal the structural aspects of a material in intimate detail. It can be envisioned as a form of molecular microscopy characterized by a high degree of resolving power. With modern instruments and with highly refined techniques, it is possible to attain a resolving power of 1.5×10^{-8} cm (1.5Å). *At this resolution, most of the atoms in a molecule may be unambiguously located by the images of X-ray diffraction.* Since 1960, the method has proven tremendously beneficial in deciphering the complete and partial structure of molecules of biopolymers, examples of which will be given in later chapters. A display of the uses of X-ray diffraction in the study of protein structure is given in Chapter 4 (page 92).

LITERATURE

ABBOTT, D., and R. S. ANDREWS. *An Introduction to Chromatography.* Boston: Houghton Mifflin Company, 1965. Theoretical and practical aspects of various chromatographic techniques are expertly covered in this paperback. The use of many diagrams makes the book very informative. Priced at less than two dollars.

CHASE, G. D., and J. L. RABINOWITZ, *Principles of Radioisotope Methodology,* Third Edition. Minneapolis: Burgess Publishing Co., 1967. An excellent book that combines both descriptive material and laboratory experiments in radioisotope methodology. Large number of references given to original literature.

CLARK, J. M., ed., *Experimental Biochemistry.* San Francisco–London: W. H. Freeman and Company, 1964. An excellent laboratory manual which contains a substantial amount of descriptive material. Noteworthy are Appendixes I, II, and III dealing with photometry, chromatography, and radioactive isotopes.

DAVIS, B. J., "Disc Electrophoresis-II: Method and Application to Human Serum Proteins," *Ann. N.Y. Acad. Sci.,* **121**:404–427 (1964). Original paper describing the technique of zone electrophoresis with polyacrylamide gels.

DYER, J. R., *Applications of Absorption Spectroscopy of Organic Compounds.* Englewood, N.J.: Prentice Hall, Inc., 1965. A short book, available in paperback, that provides a good introduction to the theory and use of absorption spectroscopic methods.

FINLAYSON, J. S., *Basic Biochemical Calculations.* Reading, Mass: Addison-Wesley Publishing Company, 1969. A book dealing with quantitative aspects of general biochemistry and designed to serve students with a minimum background in chemistry. Approximately one-fifth of the book is devoted to the basic theory, the techniques, and the biological applications of radioisotopic methods.

GAUCHER, G. M., "An Introduction to Chromatography," *J. Chem. Ed.,* **46**:729–733 (1969). A brief but informative article summarizing the important historical, practical, and theoretical aspects of chromatographic analysis.

KELLER, R. A., "Gas Chromatography," *Scientific American,* **205**:58–67 (1961). Clearly written article describing the principles of gas–liquid partition chromatography.

The Living Cell. San Francisco–London: W. H. Freeman and Company, 1965. Twenty-four articles selected from *Scientific American* devoted to various aspects of the cell. Several examples of the fantastic resolving power of electron microscopy are found throughout all articles.

MORRIS, C. J., O. R., and P. MORRIS, *Separation Methods in Biochemistry.* New York: Interscience Publishers—John Wiley & Sons, Inc., 1964. A complete coverage of the theories, techniques, and applications of a wide range of methods for the separation of biochemically important substances. Several references to important monographs and over 2000 references to the original literature are given.

SJÖSTRAND, F. S., *Electron Microscopy of Cells and Tissues.* New York: Academic Press, 1967. First volume of an intended two-volume work describing the instrumentation and techniques of electron microscopy. Excellent.

UMBREIT, W. W., R. H. BURRIS, and J. F. STAUFFER, *Manometric and Biochemical Techniques,* Fifth Edition. Minneapolis: Burgess Publishing Company, 1972. A revised and updated edition of a long-respected book. Although the major thrust is directed toward the theory and use of manometric techniques in the study of biological systems, this new edition covers most of the topics discussed in this chapter.

WILLIAMS, V. R., and H. B. WILLIAMS, *Basic Physical Chemistry for the Life Sciences.* San Francisco–London: W. H. Freeman and Company, 1967. An excellent text of physicochemical principles designed for students in life sciences. Chapter 7 deals with the principles of electrophoresis, ultracentrifugation, and other topics.

EXERCISES

2-1 Given the information below, determine which combination of developing solvents (Ph + BuAc or Ph + BuP) would provide optimum resolution of a mixture containing all seven of the amino acids listed by two-dimensional paper chromatography. Solve by making a sketch of the paper sheet as it would appear after ninhydrin treatment. (Represent the paper sheet as a 5-inch square and the ninhydrin zones as spheres with a diameter of ⅜ inch. You will find it convenient to use graph paper with ten squares to the inch.)

R_f values of amino acids on Whatman No. 1 paper

Amino Acid	Developing Solvent		
	Ph[1]	BuAc[2]	BuP[3]
glutamic acid	0.33	0.28	0.20
lysine	0.42	0.12	0.13
glycine	0.42	0.23	0.29
alanine	0.58	0.30	0.37
valine	0.78	0.51	0.48
serine	0.35	0.22	0.33
methionine	0.80	0.50	0.58

1. Phenol saturated with water.
2. n-Butanol-glacial acetic acid-water (12:3:5).
3. n-Butanol-pyridine-water (1:1:1).

2-2 The diagram below is a sketch of the ultraviolet absorption pattern from an analytical ultracentrifugal analysis of a protein solution after a 60-minute running time. Given this and the following data—partial specific volume of protein = 0.74 ml/g; diffusion constant of protein = 1 × 10⁻⁷ cm²/sec; density of solvent = 1.0 g/ml; angular rotation = 10,000 radians/sec; distance from center of rotation to meniscus of solution in centrifuge tube = 5 cm; and

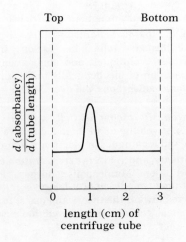

gas constant $= 8.3 \times 10^7$ ergs/deg/mole—calculate the Svedberg constant and the molecular weight of the protein. Assume that all measurements are expressed for 20°C. (In dimensional analysis, note that 1 erg = 1 dyne-cm and 1 dyne = 1 g-cm/sec² and radians are to be considered unitless.)

2-3 *Escherichia coli,* a bacterium, was allowed to grow in a medium which contained radioactive phosphorus in the form of $P^{32}O_4^{\equiv}$. These cells will incorporate the label into every phosphorus-containing compound. After a 45-minute incubation period, the cells were harvested and extracted with an organic solvent to remove the phospholipids—a class of P-containing lipids. A small aliquot of the extract was then chromatographed on a silica gel thin-layer plate. After the position of the radioactive regions was detected, they were scraped off, transferred to scintillation vials, and then counted by liquid scintillation. From the data below, determine the percent composition of the phospholipids in *E. coli* cells.

Component	R_f	Cpm in extract
phosphatidyl glycerol (PG)	0.3	96,695
phosphatidyl ethanolamine (PE)	0.5	421,402
cardiolipin (CL)	0.7	5,973

2-4 Moving-boundary electrophoresis is classically illustrated with a Tiselius electrophoretic cell. This is a U-shaped device containing two separate vertical compartments separated by a sliding gate. Initially, with the gate closed, one compartment is filled with a solution of solute(s) dissolved in a buffer solvent and the other compartment is filled with solvent. When a voltage potential is applied across the cell with the gate open, the ionic solutes begin to migrate from one compartment to the other. The migration is downward in the compartment that initially contained the solutes and upward in the solvent compartment. This, of course, assumes that all of the solutes are similarly charged and are moving toward an electrode of opposite charge. The diagram below illustrates the initial and final states of the Tiselius cell in this type of analysis on a mixture of three negatively charged proteins (*A*, *B*, and *C*). Given the fact that protein *A* and protein *C* have the greatest and smallest electrophoretic mobility, respectively, describe the composition of the three different regions (lined areas) that appear in each compartment after electrophoresis is complete. (Lined areas represent the presence of protein. One type of line—one protein; two types—two proteins; three types—three proteins.)

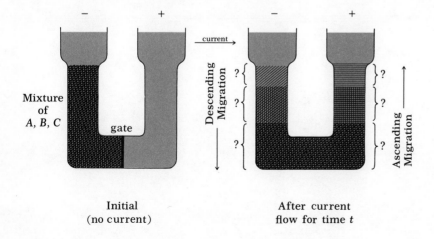

Initial	After current
(no current)	flow for time *t*

2-5 From the data below, construct the ultraviolet absorption spectrum of adenine—a nitrogen base found in all nucleic acids—and graphically estimate the wavelength at which maximum absorption occurs. Then, given that the extinction coefficient of a 1% solution is 890 at this wavelength, calculate the concentration of adenine in a solution which gives an absorbance of 0.15 at the same wavelength. (Assume a 1-cm light path.)

Spectral data for adenine	
Wavelength	Absorbance
235 mn	0.45
240	0.20
250	0.26
260	0.50
270	0.47
280	0.25
290	0.07

2-6 Assuming that a mixture of the three proteins from the previous problem is applied to the top (negative pole) of a column of polyacrylamide gel, draw a representative diagram of the gel after electrophoresis and staining.

3

The Ionic Environment and Buffers

One of the chief distinguishing chemical characteristics of cellular systems, often overlooked by students of the life sciences, is that the vast majority of compounds found in living organisms—inorganic and organic; small and large; those dissolved in the cytoplasm and those present in particulate bodies—are present as *ions*. Three types occur: negatively charged substances (*anions*), positively charged substances (*cations*), and substances possessing both negative and positive charges (*ampholytes*). This property of nature should not be treated simply as a statement of fact and dismissed without further analysis. On the contrary, because it is one of the fundamental and subtle properties responsible for virtually all cellular activity, further discussion is demanded.

Proof of this tenet can be very easily supplied by altering the surroundings of cellular systems such that the natural intracellular ionic population is modified. Excluded for the moment are changes in the ionic environment such as the presence of arsenate ion or cyanide ion, which in themselves are toxic and capable of causing extreme physiological damage including death of the organism. An example of an alternative but still rather direct method is to change the pH of the extracellular fluid to a very high or very low value. With few exceptions, one will observe that vital processes will operate at a reduced level, some will even cease, and ultimately the cell will stop functioning and die. Similar effects are observed when the concentration of ions other than hydrogen is changed appreciably. For example, considerable increases or decreases of potassium ion in blood plasma can cause serious physiological malfunctions in man, some of which can be fatal. Although these introductory remarks are in the nature of generalizations, let us not belittle the importance of the basic message, namely, the *totality of cellular activity is intimately dependent on the type and the concentration of ionic materials within the cell, both of which are subject to change by alterations in the extracellular environment.*

The twofold objective of this chapter is to explore (a) in general, the basic physicochemical principles underlying this dependency, and (b) in particular, the special control on the hydrogen ion concentration (pH) of intra- and extra-cellular fluids by buffer systems. The subject of buffers is given special consideration for two reasons. First, the potential for variations in pH of intracellular and extracellular fluids constantly exists in nature, but fortunately organisms possess the ability to resist *significant* changes through the action of buffer systems. For example, the pH of blood is closely maintained at 7.3–7.4 by the combined buffering action of a carbonic acid–bicarbonate (H_2CO_3–HCO_3^-) system and plasma proteins. Secondly, those engaged in biological research also attempt to minimize changes in the ionic composition of intracellular fluids by routinely including a buffer as part of the experimental system. In subsequent chapters we will encounter specific illustrations of how the chemical structure and the biological function of many molecules are dependent upon their specific ionic properties.

IONIC EQUILIBRIA

A knowledge of the chemistry of acids and bases, of ionization, and of ionization equilibria is basic to an understanding of the dynamics of pH regulation by buffer systems and of why, indeed, the latter is so important. Although most students are exposed to all of these areas in other courses, it is also true that many students—especially those in the life sciences—are deficient in their comprehension of the basic principles of these subjects. This situation is probably due to two factors (a) freshman chemistry courses have become more oriented toward theoretical and structural matters, and (b) previous exposure to these principles was in a purely physicochemical context and did not consider biological applications or implications. Consequently, we will begin by reviewing some of these points.

IONIZATION, ACIDS, AND BASES

The phenomenon of ionization was first introduced in the nineteenth century by Svante Arrhenius and served as the basis for his classification of acids and bases. This classification defined an *acid* as a substance which *yields hydrogen ions* (protons) *upon ionization* and a *base* as a substance which *yields hydroxide ions* (OH^-) *upon ionization*. Due to the production of ions, solutions of these materials are capable of conducting an electric current, and thus the substances were termed *electrolytes*. Arrhenius further distinguished between *strong* and *weak* electrolytes. A strong electrolyte is a material which undergoes complete ionization (essentially 100%), and a weak electrolyte is a material which undergoes partial ionization, that is, considerably less than 100%. These statements are summarized for some hypothetical acids and bases in equations 3–1a through 3–1d.

$$\text{Acids} \begin{cases} \text{HA(strong)} \xrightarrow{\text{H}_2\text{O}} \text{H}^+(\text{aq}) + \text{A}^-(\text{aq}) & \text{(3-1a)} \\ \text{HA(weak)} \xleftarrow{\text{H}_2\text{O}}\rightharpoonup \text{H}^+(\text{aq}) + \text{A}^-(\text{aq}) & \text{(3-1b)} \end{cases}$$

$$\text{Bases} \begin{cases} \text{MOH(strong)} \xrightarrow{\text{H}_2\text{O}} \text{M}^+(\text{aq}) + \text{OH}^-(\text{aq}) & \text{(3-1c)} \\ \text{MOH(weak)} \xleftarrow{\text{H}_2\text{O}}\rightharpoonup \text{M}^+(\text{aq}) + \text{OH}^-(\text{aq}) & \text{(3-1d)} \end{cases}$$

A single arrow corresponds to complete dissociation and represents the absence of any undissociated acid or base in solution. A set of arrows corresponds to a dynamic equilibrium between the forward and reverse processes and represents the coexistence of undissociated acid or base in solution with the corresponding ions. The longer arrow in the set indicates which process is favored and thus specifies which component or components will be in excess at equilibrium. The notation in parentheses designates an aqueous solution.

The majority of acids and bases found in biological systems are organic in nature and are weak electrolytes. Accordingly, emphasis will be given to these types of compounds. Before proceeding further, however, it would be beneficial to review an alternative and more useful theory of acids and bases, namely, the *Bronsted proposal* which classifies any material that *donates a proton* as an *acid*, and any material that *accepts a proton* as a *base*. To illustrate, equation 3–1b can be written to indicate the formation of the hydronium ion as follows:

$$\text{HA(aq)} + \text{H}_2\text{O} \rightleftharpoons \text{H}_3\text{O}^+(\text{aq}) + \text{A}^-(\text{aq}) \tag{3-2}$$

When the equation is written in this form, we can see that HA is donating a proton and thus functions as a Bronsted acid. H_2O is accepting the proton from HA and is functioning as a Bronsted base. Similarly, for the reverse process, H_3O^+ functions as a Bronsted acid and A^- as a Bronsted base. Because of the relationship between HA and A^-, they are referred to as a conjugate acid-base pair. That is to say, A^- is the conjugate base formed from the dissociation of the original Bronsted acid, HA. A similar relationship exists between H_2O and H_3O^+. The terminology of this classification will be employed throughout this chapter. (*Note:* Recall that the hydronium ion, H_3O^+, is the traditional representation of the hydrated proton, $\text{H}^+(\text{H}_2\text{O})$. For the usual reasons of simplification, this notation will not be routinely employed in the discussions to follow.)

Having exhausted the utility of hypothetical examples, we can now examine some specific examples that are given below. In each instance: BA = Bronsted acid; BB = Bronsted base; and CABP = the primary conjugate acid–base pair. The plus and minus signs in parentheses correspond to the charge of the different ionic forms of the same material. In these equations, arrows of equal length merely specify that the system has the potential to attain an equilibrium state and do not necessarily imply a 50–50 mixture of reactants and products. System A illustrates the ionization of a *carboxyl group of a weak, organic acid*. System B illustrates the ionization of a *protonated amine, which is likewise a weak acid*. The compound is tris(hydroxymethyl)aminomethane, symbolized TRIS, which is frequently used as a buffer in biological research. System C corresponds to the ionization of a *weak, inorganic acid*. Systems D and E illustrate the ionizations of glycine which, structurally speaking, is the simplest *amino acid*. The last two examples indicate that glycine can exist in either of two acidic forms wherein the proton is released from the ionization of a carboxyl group or a protonated amino group. This is true of all amino acids that occur in nature. In fact, some amino acids contain three ionizable groups. We will consider the amino acids in more detail in the next chapter.

System A:

$$CH_3COOH \rightleftharpoons CH_3COO^- + H^+$$

BA = acetic acid   BB = acetate ion (−)
CABP = CH_3COOH and CH_3COO^-

System B:

$$(HOCH_2)_3C\overset{+}{N}H_3 \rightleftharpoons (HOCH_2)_3CNH_2 + H^+$$

BA = TRIS(+)   BB = TRIS
(protonated form)   (free amine form)
CABP = TRIS(+) and TRIS

System C:

$$H_2PO_4^- \rightleftharpoons HPO_4^= + H^+$$

BA = dihydrogen   BB = monohydrogen
phosphate(−)   phosphate(=)
CABP = H_2PO_4 and $HPO_4^=$

System D:

$$H_3\overset{+}{N}CH_2COOH \rightleftharpoons H_3\overset{+}{N}CH_2COO^- + H^+$$

BA = glycine(+)   BB = glycine(∓)
CABP = glycine(+) and glycine(∓)

System E:

$$H_3\overset{+}{N}CH_2COO^- \rightleftharpoons H_2NCH_2COO^- + H^+$$

BA = glycine(∓)   BB = glycine(−)
CABP = glycine(∓) and glycine(−)

The very fact that all of the above acids are weak electrolytes dictates that in solution each system will be characterized by an *equilibrium of the conjugate acid–base pair.* Provided that no additions or removals of any participant are made and that the temperature remains constant, the extent of ionization and hence the equilibrium concentrations of the participants will be determined solely by the chemical nature of the original acid, that is, the unique structure which constitutes the chemical essence of each material. As previously implied, however, an equilibrium position is not permanent, but is subject to displacement. The direction of the displacement is predictable by *LeChatelier's principle,* which states that, if a stress is placed on a system at equilibrium, the system will respond by shifting to a new equilibrium position in such a way as to reduce the effect of the imposed stress. In subsequent discussions we will apply this principle constantly with attention confined to stresses involving the addition or removal of one or more of the products or reactants.

Let us now analyze this matter in greater depth for a specific system, namely, the ionization of the dihydrogen phosphate monoanion ($H_2PO_4^-$).

$$H_2PO_4^-(aq) \rightleftharpoons HPO_4^=(aq) + H^+(aq) \qquad (3\text{--}3)$$

This equation depicts the equilibrium of three ionic species, with the primary conjugate acid–base pair being $H_2PO_4^-$:$HPO_4^=$. If one now superimposes conditions of constant temperature and no additions or removals of any material, it can be shown that any change in the relative concentrations of the primary conjugate acid–base pair will be completely dependent upon the only remaining variable, which is the concentration of hydrogen ion. Since $-\log[H^+] \equiv pH$, the term "hydrogen ion concentration" will be interchanged with pH.

A clearer understanding of this point and proof of its validity are possible by developing a more quantitative argument. In this regard, we can apply the *Law of Mass Action* and describe the equilibrium state with a simple mathematical expression. For equation 3–3—assuming dilute conditions and constant temperature—this expression has the form

$$K_{eq} = \frac{[HPO_4^=(aq)][H^+(aq)]}{[H_2PO_4^-(aq)]} = K_a \qquad (3\text{--}4)$$

where K_{eq} corresponds to the *equilibrium constant* and the brackets refer to *molar equilibrium concentrations*. The most accurate expression of the equilibrium constant would employ *activities* instead of molar concentrations, but in dilute solutions the difference between activity and molarity is negligible. (A molar concentration expresses the *actual* concentration of dissolved solute as moles of solute per liter of solution, whereas the activity expresses the *effective* concentration of dissolved solute. The activity is directly proportional to the actual molar concentration, but it is unitless. The difference between the actual and effective concentration is attributed to the presence of interactions among dissolved solutes. For extremely dilute solutions with very little solute–solute interaction, the difference is negligible and the activity and molarity are the same. Increasing the concentration of solute, which will increase the extent of solute–solute interactions, causes a greater difference. When these interactions do occur, they tend to reduce the actual concentration of individual solute molecules and hence the activity will always be less than the molarity. The exact difference is based on the nature of the solute, its concentration, and the solvent.) Whenever the chemical system corresponds to the dissociation of a weak acid, an alternative notation—K_a—is used, where the subscript *a* specifically designates that the equilibrium constant is for the ionization of a weak acid. Characteristically then, K_a is simply referred to as an *ionization constant*. Using equation 3–4 as a guide, we can make a generalization about the form of the ionization constant for *any weak acid* by using the terminology of the Bronsted classification as follows.

$$K_a = \frac{[\text{conjugate base(aq)}][H^+(aq)]}{[\text{conjugate acid(aq)}]} \qquad (3\text{--}5)$$

This expression is valid for *any weak monoprotic acid* which undergoes dissociation to yield the corresponding conjugate base and a proton with the overall stoichiometry of $1 \rightarrow 1 + 1$.

Weak *diprotic* and *triprotic* acids, which have the potential on complete ionization to yield two and three protons respectively, would possess ionization constants for the *overall process* that contain a squared (diprotic) or cubed (triprotic) hydrogen ion term. In solution, however, these types of acids are considered to undergo a *stepwise dissociation* with two or three separate ionizations. In this case each individual ionization step can be expressed by a distinct ionization constant which would be *identical in form* to the above expression, with the only *difference being the chemical identity of the primary acid–base pair*. This is illustrated below for phosphoric acid, H_3PO_4, a triprotic acid containing three ionizable hydrogens.

Ionization	Ionization constant
Step 1: $\quad H_3PO_4 \rightleftarrows H_2PO_4^- + H^+$	$K_{a_1} = \dfrac{[H_2PO_4^-][H^+]}{[H_3PO_4]}$
Step 2: $\quad H_2PO_4^- \rightleftarrows HPO_4^= + H^+$	$K_{a_2} = \dfrac{[HPO_4^=][H^+]}{[H_2PO_4^-]}$
Step 3: $\quad HPO_4^= \rightleftarrows PO_4^\equiv + H^+$	$K_{a_3} = \dfrac{[PO_4^\equiv][H^+]}{[HPO_4^=]}$
Overall: $\quad H_3PO_4 \rightleftarrows PO_4^\equiv + 3H^+$	$K_{a_{net}} = \dfrac{[PO_4^\equiv][H^+]^3}{[H_3PO_4]}$

The subscripts attached to the K_a expressions correspond to the phases of the ionization, which occur in the order given. The sequence is based on acid strength, with the strongest Bronsted acid dissociating first and the weakest last. Thus, the three distinct monoprotic acids would be arranged as follows according to their relative acid strength:

$$H_3PO_4 > H_2PO_4^- > HPO_4^=$$

Having completed this brief digression concerning polyprotic acids, let us return to the analysis of the generalized mass action expression for a weak monoprotic acid (equation 3–5). The importance of this relationship becomes readily apparent by multiplying both sides of the equation by $1/[H^+(aq)]$, which gives

$$\frac{[\text{conjugate base(aq)}]}{[\text{conjugate acid(aq)}]} = \frac{K_a}{[H_2PO_4^-]}$$

and since K_a is a constant,

$$\frac{[\text{conjugate base(aq)}]}{[\text{conjugate acid(aq)}]} \propto \frac{1}{[H^+(aq)]}$$

This proportionality expresses the tenet that we deduced earlier with a qualitative analysis, namely, that at any given temperature the *ratio of the equilibrium concentrations of the conjugate acid–base pair is solely dependent on the hydrogen ion concentration or pH of the solution*. A *corollary* of this statement is that the *pH of a solution consisting of a conjugate acid–base pair is solely dependent on the ratio of their equilibrium concentrations*. Since a living cell is an equilibrium mixture consisting of an abundance of weak acids and their conjugate bases, it is clear that any alteration in the physiological pH can cause a significant change in the ionic composition of the cell. This point will be reiterated later in the chapter and a specific example will be given. Having established these general principles of ionization equilibria, we are now in a position to consider the nature of buffer systems.

BUFFER SYSTEMS

A buffer solution can be defined as an equilibrium mixture of a conjugate acid–base pair which is capable of resisting substantial changes in pH upon the addition of small amounts of acidic or basic substances. With some exceptions, either the acid or the base of the conjugate pair is a weak electrolyte. For this reason and to retain the pattern established in the previous section, all discussions will consider the dissociation of weak acids.

The basic intent of this section is to analyze the meaning of the definition given above. In fulfilling this objective, we will consider the titration of a weak acid with a strong base as a model system to develop and illustrate the distinguishing chemical characteristics of a buffer system. This strategy will also serve as a stimulus in the development of an analytical mental attitude that will enhance your comprehension and enjoyment of this and future subjects.

TITRATION OF WEAK MONOPROTIC ACIDS

From a pool of countless candidates, we will retain the system used earlier and specifically consider the titration of $H_2PO_4^-$ with NaOH. Although $H_2PO_4^-$ is a diprotic acid, we have seen previously that this type of material ionizes in a stepwise fashion and that each ionization corresponds to the dissociation of one ionizable hydrogen. Consequently, by limiting our attention for the moment to the titration of $H_2PO_4^-$ to $HPO_4^=$ and no further—that is, the neutralization of only one proton in the diprotic acid—the system will be essentially representative of the titration of a weak monoprotic acid. Furthermore, it should be pointed out that the general principles of the titration of this specific system are representative of *any* weak monoprotic acid.

To develop these principles, let us first consider briefly the mechanics of the titration and then inspect and interpret the data. We will assume the titration of 100 ml of an aqueous solution containing 0.01 mole of KH_2PO_4. The mechanics of the titration are simple. Small increments of a solution of sodium hydroxide are added to the acid-containing solution. After each addition, the pH of the solution is determined with a pH meter. In this case, since we are considering only the titration of one of the two ionizable protons in $H_2PO_4^-$, the experiment would be complete when 0.01 mole of base was added. The data collected in this type of experiment are graphically depicted in Figure 3–1.

Inspection of Figure 3–1 reveals that the pH does not change linearly between the start (point A) and the finish (point D) of the titration, but rather in three distinct phases. There is an initial (region AB) increase in pH relative to additions of base; then this rate of change is significantly reduced (region BC); finally, the terminal phase (region

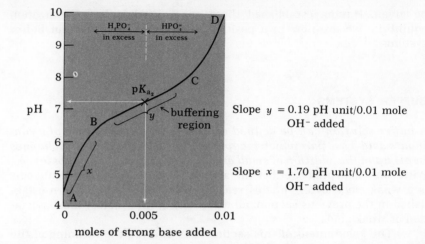

Figure 3-1 A titration curve of 100 ml of 0.1 M solution of KH_2PO_4 with strong base. The curve represents the complete titration of only one of the ionizable hydrogens in $H_2PO_4^-$: $H_2PO_4^- \rightarrow HPO_4^= + H^+$.

CD) is characterized by a return to the initial rate of change. The obvious question is: What is the significance of this?

This question can be resolved by first considering the nature of the initial state of the system. When KH_2PO_4, a crystalline salt and a strong electrolyte, is dissolved in water, it dissociates completely to yield an aqueous solution of K^+ and $H_2PO_4^-$:

$$KH_2PO_4(s) \quad + \quad H_2O(l) \xrightarrow{\text{complete}} K^+(aq) \quad + \quad H_2PO_4^-(aq)$$

0.01 mole   100 ml   0.01 mole   0.01 mole

However, $H_2PO_4^-$ is an acid and thus susceptible to further ionization in aqueous solution. But because it is a weak acid, only a small portion (approximately 0.00003 mole) will ionize. Although the dissociation is limited, the hydrogen ion concentration of the solution will be increased beyond that for water (0.0000001 M for pure water) and thus the salt solution will be acidic. This is reflected in the pH at the start of the titration before any base is added (pH = 4.5). The important point to realize is that, immediately upon dissolution of the salt, the resultant solution is an equilibrium mixture of the conjugate acid–base pair—$H_2PO_4^-$: $HPO_4^=$—with the monoanion in excess.

$$H_2PO_4^-(aq) \xleftrightarrow{\quad} HPO_4^=(aq) + H^+(aq)$$

When base is added, the hydroxide ion will act as a stress on this equilibrium due to its strong tendency to react with available hydrogen ion to form H_2O.

$$OH^-(aq) + H^+(aq) \xleftrightarrow{\quad} H_2O(aq)$$

This depletion of H^+ from the system is counteracted by a shift in the initial equilibrium favoring the formation of additional $HPO_4^=$ and H^+. The extent of this shift in equilibrium will be controlled by the amount of H^+ that is required to neutralize the added OH^-. The pH increases due to the combination of a continual depletion of the amount of hydrogen ion in solution and a continual increase in the concentration of OH^-

in solution. Thus, any point on the titration curve corresponds to a specific equilibrium state, with the equilibrium concentrations of the conjugate acid–base pair being determined by the pH or vice versa. Ultimately, at point D the equilibrium is strongly displaced to the right and essentially only the conjugate base, $HPO_4^=$, exists.

Our initial inspection of Figure 3–1 detailed three distinct regions in terms of the rate of pH change. In view of the discussion just completed, it should be apparent that each region can also be described in terms of the rate at which the equilibrium of the primary participants is being displaced. Without a prolonged analysis, suffice it to say that such is the case, with region BC characterized by a slower rate of displacement than either region AB or CD.

The titration curve is subject to further interpretation in terms of the buffer principle. If one were to employ a mixture of $H_2PO_4^-$ and $HPO_4^=$ as a buffer system, it should be apparent from the titration curve—by recalling that the function of a buffer solution is to resist significant changes in pH with added acid or base—that a mixture with a composition within the limits of region BC would be most suitable. As indicated in Figure 3–1, the amount of alkali required to produce a given pH change in region BC is roughly nine times that required for an identical change in regions AB and CD. Thus, we can conclude that the ability of an equilibrium mixture of a conjugate acid–base pair to act as a buffer system is restricted, due to its limited capacity to undergo a finite but minimal displacement from its original equilibrium state when acid or base is added. Non-buffering solutions would be subject to the same type of displacement but with smaller amounts of acid or base.

With the conclusion that the buffering capacity of a solution is confined to a pH region that is characterized by a changing composition of the acid–base pair, we can further deduce that the *buffering capacity* itself should also vary within this region. In this context, the term "buffering capacity" refers to the ability of a solution to resist large changes in pH upon the addition of either acid *or* base. This deduction is valid, and again without a detailed analysis, suffice it to say that the maximum buffering capacity is at the midpoint of the plateau region. In Figure 3–1 this point is designated X. The composition of the solution at X can be determined by translating the graphical point into ordinate and abscissa values. Accordingly, X corresponds to pH 7.2 and 0.005 mole alkali added. The significance of these values is clear by recognizing that this amount of base is one-half the amount required for complete titration to $HPO_4^=$. Thus, pH 7.2 corresponds to the midpoint of the titration where 50% of the phosphate-containing species exists as $H_2PO_4^-$ and 50% as $HPO_4^=$. A clearer understanding of this point is provided by manipulation of the mass action expression which defines the system in question. This, of course, is equation 3–4. Solving equation 3–4 for $[H^+(aq)]$ gives

$$[H^+(aq)] = K_a \frac{[H_2PO_4^-(aq)]}{[HPO_4^=(aq)]}$$

Taking the log of both sides of the equation and treating the right side of the equation as the product of two terms yields

$$\log[H^+(aq)] = \log K_a + \log \frac{[H_2PO_4^-(aq)]}{[HPO_4^=(aq)]}$$

which can be rewritten as

$$-\log[\mathrm{H^+(aq)}] = -\log K_a + \log \frac{[\mathrm{HPO_4^=(aq)}]}{[\mathrm{H_2PO_4^-(aq)}]}$$

The utility of this equation becomes apparent by first recognizing that $-\log[\mathrm{H^+(aq)}] \equiv \mathrm{pH}$. In a similar fashion, the p notation can be applied to the $-\log K_a$ term, and hence $-\log K_a \equiv pK_a$. When the appropriate substitutions are made, one obtains

$$\mathrm{pH} = pK_a + \log \frac{[\mathrm{HPO_4^=(aq)}]}{[\mathrm{H_2PO_4^-(aq)}]} \tag{3-6a}$$

or in a more general form

$$\mathrm{pH} = pK_a + \log \frac{[\text{conjugate Bronsted base}]}{[\text{Bronsted acid}]} \tag{3-6b}$$

The last expression—sometimes called the *Henderson-Hasselbalch* equation—is a mathematical statement which defines the pH of a solution of a conjugate acid–base pair in terms of the dissociation constant of the weak acid and the equilibrium concentrations of the acid and its conjugate base. In fact, the equation is a mathematical statement of the titration curve, defining the pH at any point in the course of the titration. It should be noted, however, that the equation is most valid in the region BC and suffers from limitations outside of the buffering region. It is not within the scope of this book to consider these limitations. Within region BC, however, the basis for designating point X as the pK_a value is quite clear from the Henderson-Hasselbalch equation. Recall that at X the concentrations are equal, which fixes the ratio of the acid–base pair at unity, and thus, at X:

$$\mathrm{pH} = pK_a + \log(1)$$

or

$$\mathrm{pH} = pK_a$$

Since the system under consideration corresponds to the second ionization of the triprotic acid $\mathrm{H_3PO_4}$, the complete designation of point X in Figure 3–1 is pK_{a_2}. Finally, note that on the acidic side of the pK_a value, the conjugate acid (the component with the greater positive charge) is always in excess, while on the basic side, the conjugate base (the component with the greater negative charge) is always in excess.

Essentially, this analysis has been a practical application of the descriptive statements given in the first section dealing with ionization equilibria. This repetition was deliberately designed to emphasize the point that the ionic composition of a mixture containing a weak electrolyte is subject to change by alterations in the pH of the solution. Furthermore, if the latter is controlled, the changes in composition will be regulated. The biological relevance of this is simply that nature utilizes buffer systems to prevent significant alterations in physiological pH (approximately 7) and thus maintains the majority of organic materials in certain ionic forms. One argument for the desirability of this situation is that it provides for an ion–ion interaction of biologically occurring materials. This interaction plays a role in the stabilization of structure, the transport of materials across membranes, the ordered interaction of reactants with specific reaction catalysts, and other phenomena.

For example, all of the phosphate esters of carbohydrates have pK_a values on the acid side of pH 7 and thus exist largely as anions in cellular fluids. At pH 7 the predominant form would be the dianion and the neutral species would not exist. This is shown below for glucose-6-phosphate.

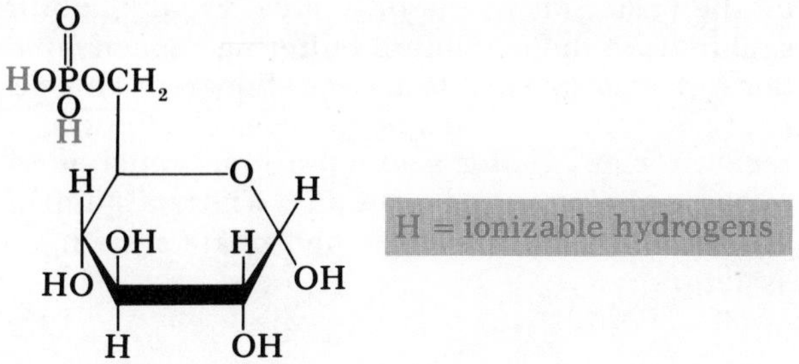

At pH 7:

glucose-6-OPO$_3$H$_2$ $\longrightarrow$ glucose-6-OPO$_3$H$^-$ $\rightleftharpoons$ glucose-6-OPO$_3^=$

    (none present)   (10%)   (90%)

MECHANISM OF BUFFER ACTION

In the preceding section we developed the concept of buffer solutions through an analysis of a titration. Although we briefly considered the subject of how a buffer operates, our major concern was to establish that buffer solutions are characterized by a capacity to resist significant changes in pH within a limited pH range characteristic of the buffer mixture. In this section we will focus specifically on the mechanism of buffer action. The foregoing discussions provide the necessary background for such an explanation and hence no new principles will be presented. In fact, by explaining how a buffer operates, we merely reiterate—in capsule form—much of the preceding material.

Suppose we have a 0.1 M phosphate buffer solution which contains 80% H$_2$PO$_4^-$ (0.08 mole/liter) and 20% HPO$_4^=$ (0.02 mole/liter). According to the Henderson-Hasselbalch equation, the pH of this solution will be approximately 6.52. When small increments of base are added, the effect will be to shift the initial equilibrium to the right to provide the amount of hydrogen ion required to react with the amount of hydroxide ion present. The capacity of this solution to buffer the added base will constantly decrease and ultimately reach a minimum when the solution pH approaches 8 (see Figure 3–1). At this point the composition of the solution will be approximately 10% H$_2$PO$_4^-$ and 90% HPO$_4^=$. As the solution becomes more enriched with HPO$_4^=$, it no longer has the capacity to effectively buffer the additions of hydroxide ion. When small increments of acid are added to the original solution, the pH will also change—it will decrease. Once again the initial shift in pH will not be directly proportional to the amount of acid added. In this case the bulk of the added H$^+$ will be scavenged by the Bronsted base in the system, HPO$_4^=$. This also causes a shift in the equilibrium, but here the formation of H$_2$PO$_4^-$ is favored. The acid-buffering capacity is likewise limited, with the minimum corresponding to a pH of approximately 6 and a composition of 90% H$_2$PO$_4^-$ and 10% HPO$_4^=$. As the concentration of the monoanion increases beyond this point (B in Figure 3–1), the solution is no longer an effective buffer. Notice that this specific buffer solution with a pH on the acid side of the pK_a value has a greater capacity to resist significant pH changes due to added base than those due to added acid. The reverse would be true if the pH of the original solution were on the basic side of the pK_a value. Finally, a buffer with a $pH = pK_a$ is said to have the maximum buffering capacity in that it can buffer additions of acid *or* base to an equal degree. This description of the phosphate buffer is generally applicable. The limits of the effective buffering region for any buffer solution are accepted as $pK_a + 1$ to $pK_a - 1$ with maximum efficiency at the pK_a. These arguments are summarized in the equations below for the phosphate system and for a general buffer system.

$$H_2PO_4^- \rightleftarrows HPO_4^= + H^+$$

Addition of H^+: $HPO_4^=$ reacts with H^+; equilibrium shifts to $\leftarrow$
Addition of OH^-: $H_2PO_4^-$ reacts with OH^-; equilibrium shifts to $\rightarrow$

$$\text{Bronsted acid} \rightleftarrows \text{Conjugate Bronsted base} + H^+$$

Addition of H^+:   Bronsted base reacts with H^+; equilibrium
               Shifts to $\leftarrow$
Addition of OH^-:   Bronsted acid reacts with OH^-; equilibrium
               Shifts to $\rightarrow$

Finally, it is to be noted that the effectiveness of a buffer will be dependent on still another factor, namely, the concentration of the buffer. For example, one can have two phosphate buffers, each containing a one-to-one ratio of the conjugate acid–base pair, and yet one may be a more effective buffer than the other. The reason is simply that the actual concentrations of the buffer components may be different. One liter of a 0.1 *M* phosphate buffer containing 0.05 mole of $H_2PO_4^-$ and 0.05 mole of $HPO_4^=$ will buffer a greater amount of H^+ or OH^- than one liter of a 0.01 *M* buffer containing 0.005 mole of $H_2PO_4^-$ and 0.005 mole of $HPO_4^=$.

REQUIREMENTS OF BIOLOGICAL BUFFERS

The natural importance of buffers in biological systems cannot be overemphasized. It has been stated on several occasions that there is a definite and very basic need to minimize significant variations in physiological pH in order to insure that any given material will be maintained in an ionic or molecular form suitable for its optimal participation in the life process. The primary natural buffer systems in cellular fluids are the *phosphate* system already discussed, dissolved *proteins,* and many *weak organic acids,* such as citric acid. Equally important is the practical significance of buffers in biochemical investigations. For the same reason cited above, it is fundamental to both *in vivo* and *in vitro* studies to first establish a physiological pH in the system and then to prevent significant changes in same. In addition, the investigator may also desire to study the effect of pH variations on a system which requires the establishment of any pH within a given range and maintenance of same.

The various factors to be considered in selecting a buffer for use in biological research were clearly stated by N. E. Good and co-workers in their report on the development of new buffers for laboratory use. Although the criteria assume research application, the specifications of optimum pK_a value, non-toxicity, stability, and water solubility are obvious requirements of *natural* buffer systems as well. These rules of merit are listed below.

1. The pK_a value should be between 6 and 8, since this is the buffering region of fewest buffers and the optimum range for most biological reactions.

2. The buffer should have a maximum solubility in water and a minimum solubility in organic solvents. A high water solubility is convenient in that it permits the use of concentrated stocks. Much more important, however, is the ratio of the solubility in water to the solubility in the relatively nonpolar solvents, since this determines the distribution of the buffer between the aqueous medium and the biological phase in the particulate systems. The latter phase has some nonpolar character due to the presence of lipid material in cellular membranes. Thus, for a given amount of buffering, the concentration of buffer *inside* the organelle is lower with the more polar buffers, since the buffer cannot readily pass through the membrane.

3. In the interest of simplicity, the buffers should not form complexes with any other ions in solution. If complexes do occur, they should be soluble in water and the extent of binding should be known and minimal.

4. The buffers should be stable. Specifically, they should resist chemical and biological degradation under the conditions of use. In addition to a loss of buffering value, the degradation products may be toxic to the system under study. The viable cell population may be reduced, or the activity of a purified organelle or enzyme may be inhibited.

5. Preferably, they should not absorb light in the visible or ultraviolet region of the electromagnetic spectrum. Since many biochemical assays employ spectrophotometric methods of analysis, the absorption by buffer components would interfere.

6. There should be a minimum influence of buffer concentration, temperature, and ionic composition of the medium on the dissociation of the buffer. The temperature effect is a specific criterion which is often ignored. As a consequence, a buffer is prepared at room temperature at a certain pH, but is then used in the cold room at temperatures of 2–4°C. The assumption is made that the pH of the buffer is the same regardless of the temperature. Such is not the case, and in some instances the pH at the lower temperatures is significantly different. This is true with Tris buffers, for example.

7. The buffers should be readily available and inexpensive.

The work of Good's group was designed to supplement the small number of available buffers—phosphate, Tris, and citrate being the most widely used—with additional materials which hopefully would be superior in one or more respects. They were successful in developing twelve new buffers that satisfied most of the above criteria. Table 3–1

Table 3–1 pK_a's for some conjugate acid–base pairs.

Acid	Base	pK_a
Acetic acid CH_3COOH	Acetate ion CH_3COO^-	4.74
Carbonic acid H_2CO_3	Bicarbonate ion HCO_3^-	6.35
Bicarbonate ion HCO_3^-	Carbonate ion $CO_3^=$	10.3
Citric acid H_2C—COOH HO—C—COOH H_2C—COOH	Citrate monoanion H_2C—COOH HO—C—COO$^-$ H_2C—COOH	3.09
Citrate monoanion H_2C—COOH HO—C—COO$^-$ H_2C—COOH	Citrate dianion H_2C—COO$^-$ HO—C—COO$^-$ H_2C—COOH	4.75
Citrate dianion H_2C—COO$^-$ HO—C—COO$^-$ H_2C—COOH	Citrate trianion H_2C—COO$^-$ HO—C—COO$^-$ H_2C—COO$^-$	5.41

N-Tris(hydroxymethyl)aminomethane

TRIS·H$^+$ (*protonated form*) $(HOCH_2)_3CNH_3^+$	TRIS (*free amine*) $(HOCH_2)_3CNH_2$	8.3

N-Tris(hydroxymethyl)methyl-2-aminoethane sulfonate [TES]

TES·H̄ $^+$ (*Zwitterionic form*) $(HOCH_2)_3C\overset{+}{N}H_2CH_2CH_2SO_3^-$	TĒS (*anionic form*) $(HOCH_2)_3CNHCH_2CH_2SO_3^-$	7.55

N-2-Hydroxyethylpiperazine-N'-2-ethane sulfonate [HEPES]

HEP̄ES·H̄ $^+$ (*Zwitterionic form*)	HEP̄ES (*anionic form*)	7.55

$HOCH_2CH_2\overset{+}{N}$⟨ ⟩$NCH_2CH_2SO_3^-$ $HOCH_2CH_2N$⟨ ⟩$NCH_2CH_2SO_3^-$

N-Tris(hydroxymethyl)methylglycine [TRICINE]

TRICĪNE·H̄ $^+$ (*Zwitterionic form*) $(HOCH_2)_3C\overset{+}{N}H_2CH_2COO^-$	TRICĪNE (*anionic form*) $(HOCH_2)_3CNHCOO^-$	8.15

illustrates the primary conjugate acid–base pair of three of these buffers, as well as others mentioned previously. All of Good's buffers were zwitterionic buffers. The term *zwitterionic* refers to the presence of a positive and a negative charge within the same molecular species. A general symbolic representation would be H^+A^-. Because of this dual electrostatic character, such ions are often referred to as *dipolar ions*. Zwitterions were introduced earlier in this chapter in illustrating the ionization equilibria of glycine (page 38). At this point we will focus attention on the *amphoteric* property of a zwitterion, that is, its capacity to function as an acid or base. This is illustrated in the reactions below for a general system and for one of Good's buffers. This principle will receive further discussion when we consider the amino acids in the next chapter.

$$H\overset{+}{A}H \underset{+H^+}{\overset{+OH^-}{\rightleftharpoons}} \overset{+}{H}\underset{-}{A} \underset{+H^+}{\overset{+OH^-}{\rightleftharpoons}} A^-$$

Zwitterionic species

$$HOCH_2CH_2\overset{+}{\underset{H}{N}}\hspace{-1em}\bigcirc\hspace{-1em}NCH_2CH_2SO_3^-$$

"HEPES"
N-2-*Hydroxyethylpiperazine-*
N'-2-*ethanesulfonate*

$$HOCH_2CH_2\overset{+}{\underset{H}{N}}\hspace{-1em}\bigcirc\hspace{-1em}NCH_2CH_2SO_3H$$

pK_{a_1} is very low; sulfonic group is strongly acidic

$$HOCH_2CH_2N\hspace{-1em}\bigcirc\hspace{-1em}NCH_2CH_2SO_3^-$$

p$K_{a_2} = 7.55$

An illustration of why buffer selection can be critical is also provided in their study. One of the *in vitro* biological assays that was used to test the effectiveness of the various buffer systems was the oxidation of succinate to fumarate by mitochondria, distinct subcellular particles found in all higher organisms. The oxidative metabolism of mitochondria will be discussed in greater detail in Chapter 13. At this point a brief summary will suffice. Initially, succinic acid dehydrogenase—an enzyme localized in mitochondria—removes the equivalent of two hydrogen atoms (2 protons and 2 electrons) from succinate (anion at pH 7). By a complex process involving several different participants in mitochondria, the protons and electrons are finally accepted by oxygen to produce water.

$$\underset{\text{succinate}}{{}^-OOCCH_2CH_2COO^-} \xrightarrow{\text{mitochondria}} \underset{\text{fumarate}}{{}^-OOCCH{=}CHCOO^-} + 2H^+ + 2e$$

Then

$$2H^+ + 2e + \tfrac{1}{2}O_2 \xrightarrow{\text{mitochondria}} H_2O$$

The basis of the assay was to determine the activity of the mitochondrial particles (isolated from beans) in the different buffer systems by monitoring the rate of oxygen consumption in the presence of succinate.

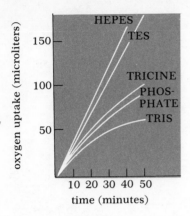

Figure 3–2 A study of the mitochondrial oxidation of succinate in the presence of different buffers (pH 7.4, 0.05 *M*, 20°C). Mitochondrial activity was assayed by measuring oxygen consumption. Data taken with permission from Good, N. E., G. D. Winget, W. Winter, T. N. Connolly, S. Izawa, and R. M. M. Singh, *Biochemistry,* **5:**467–477 (1966).

The system was buffered at pH 7.4 at a concentration of 0.05 *M*. The temperature was controlled at 20°C. The results of the experiment are summarized in Figure 3–2 for five different buffers.

Immediately obvious from Figure 3–2 is the fact that oxygen uptake (that is, mitochondrial activity) was observed to be different with each buffer that was assayed. It is also interesting to note that the traditional biological buffers, phosphate and Tris, were inferior to three of the newly described buffers. In fact, HEPES and TES were markedly superior, with as yet unexplained beneficial effects. Similar results were obtained with other types of assay systems, e.g., cell-free protein synthesis. Complete details can be found in the original paper. All of this points to the fact that the selection of buffers should not be routine. The presence of low biological activity or the complete absence of same in an *in vivo* or *in vitro* system should not be hastily concluded, since such results may be attributable to undesirable buffer effects. Although no buffer will completely satisfy all of the criteria stated above, it is most desirable to utilize a buffer that satisfies most of them.

PREPARATION OF BUFFER SOLUTIONS

In this day of sophistication, many biochemical suppliers make available—at a handsome cost—preweighed packets of buffer salts. All that is required to prepare the buffer is the skill to read instructions and dissolve the material in the specified volume of water. One cannot argue with this approach as a definite time-saving device, especially in busy clinical laboratories. However, it also perpetuates the inability of individuals to prepare buffer solutions from the raw materials on the laboratory shelf. With this in mind then, let us proceed to analyze the mechanics of preparing a buffer solution using the latter approach.

In general, the problem of buffer preparation is confined to two types of situations: (1) both components of the conjugate acid–base pair are weighed out separately to yield the desired ratio and then dissolved in water; or (2) both components are obtained from a prescribed amount of only one component, with the second being formed by the addition of a specified amount of strong acid or strong base. Although the solution to each is different, there are similarities. The tools needed to solve both types are a knowledge of the conjugate acid–base system involved, the pK_a for the system, and the Henderson-Hasselbalch equation. An example of each is given below.

Type 1. Both components weighed out separately.

EXAMPLE. It is desired to prepare 1 liter of a 0.5 *M* phosphate buffer at pH 7.5. Assume the availability of H_3PO_4, KH_2PO_4, K_2HPO_4, and K_3PO_4. How would the buffer be prepared?

Step 1. The first step is always to determine what the principal components of the buffer system will be. This is no problem with a monoprotic acid. With a diprotic or polyprotic system, however, the components can vary depending on the desired pH. In this instance pH 7.5 is specified. The equilibrium system will thus be determined by selecting the ionization which has the pK_a value closest to the desired pH. Reference to a compilation of ionization data for weak acids would show that the desired system in this case is $H_2PO_4^-$:

$HPO_4^=$ with a pK_{a_2} value of 7.21. The $H_3PO_4 : H_2PO_4^-$ system has a $pK_{a_1} = 2.12$ and the $HPO_4^= : PO_4^=$ system has a $pK_{a_3} = 12.3$. These are too low and too high, respectively, and neither would be an effective buffer at pH 7.5. Having established this, then write the equilibrium equation and identify the conjugate acid–base pair.

$$H_2PO_4^- \rightleftharpoons HPO_4^= + H^+ \qquad pK_{a_2} = 7.21$$

B. acid   B. base

Step 2. Calculate the desired ratio of the acid–base pair from the Henderson-Hasselbalch equation.

$$pH = pK_{a_2} + \log \frac{[HPO_4^=]}{[H_2PO_4^-]}$$

$$\log \frac{[HPO_4^=]}{[H_2PO_4^-]} = 7.5 - 7.21 = 0.29$$

$$\frac{[HPO_4^=]}{[H_2PO_4^-]} = \text{antilog } (0.29) = 1.95$$

Thus, the ratio desired is 1.95 parts of $HPO_4^=$ to 1 part of $H_2PO_4^-$. Since this represents a total of 2.95 parts, we can calculate directly the percentages of each component.

$$\% \, HPO_4^= = \frac{1.95}{2.95} \times 100 = 66.2$$

$$\% \, H_2PO_4^- = \frac{1.00}{2.95} \times 100 = 33.8$$

As a check on the solution to this point, determine whether the ratio is consistent with the desired pH. The pH in this case is on the alkaline side of the pK_a value, and thus there should be a larger concentration of the conjugate base than of the conjugate acid. This is verified by the ratio calculated.

Step 3. Determine the most feasible means of obtaining the desired components. In this instance, the obvious choice would be to weigh out the desired amount of the potassium salts of the acid–base pair—namely, K_2HPO_4 and KH_2PO_4—which upon dissolution will ionize completely to give both components of the conjugate pair.

Step 4. Calculate the amount of each material required. Since the total phosphate concentration was specified as 0.5 M and since 1 liter is desired,

number of moles of K_2HPO_4 required/liter = (0.662)(0.5) = 0.331

number of moles of KH_2PO_4 required/liter = (0.338)(0.5) = 0.169

Finally, the grams of each required is

(0.331 mole)(174.2 g/mole) = 57.7 grams for K_2HPO_4

and

(0.169 mole)(136.1 g/mole) = 23.0 grams for KH_2PO_4

Step 5. Prepare the buffer. Weigh out 23.0 grams of KH_2PO_4 and 57.7 grams of K_2HPO_4, and dissolve in about 750 ml of distilled water. Bring the total volume of the solution to 1 liter with distilled water, check the pH and adjust if necessary.

Type 2.   Both components obtained from the same source.

This situation generally presents some problems to students. However, the complexity of the problem is artificial and the key to the solution involves basic chemical principles.

EXAMPLE.   It is desired to prepare 1 liter of 0.1 M Tris buffer of pH 8.3. Assume the availability of crystalline Tris, 1 M HCl, and 1 M NaOH. How would you proceed? *Note:*   In the crystalline state, Tris exists primarily as the free amine.

Step 1.   The desired equilibrium is

$$(\text{HOCH}_2)_3\text{CNH}_2 + \text{H}^+ \rightleftarrows (\text{HOCH}_2)_3\text{CNH}_3^+ \qquad pK_a = 8.3$$
$$\text{B. base} \qquad\qquad\qquad \text{B. acid}$$

Step 2.   Calculate the base-to-acid ratio by use of the Henderson-Hasselbalch equation.

$$\text{pH} = pK_a + \log \frac{[\text{free amine}]}{[\text{protonated amine}]}$$

$$8.3 = 8.3 + \log \frac{[-\text{NH}_2]}{[-\text{NH}_3^+]}$$

$$\frac{[-\text{NH}_2]}{[-\text{NH}_3^+]} = \text{antilog} \ (0.0) = 1.0$$

Thus, the solution should contain 50% of the free amine and 50% of the protonated species. It should be apparent that this step was not really necessary. All one has to do is recognize that this will always be the situation when the pH of the buffer is equal to the pK_a.

Step 3.   Both of the buffer components will be formed from crystalline Tris. 0.1 mole of crystalline Tris would be required to yield 1 liter of buffer with a total Tris concentration of 0.1 M. The next problem is to determine the amount of strong acid that would be required to form the desired composition of the acid–base pair. Since the mixture must contain 50% of the protonated species, 0.05 mole of strong acid will be required. It will react with 0.1 mole of the free amine in a stoichiometric manner, giving the desired composition. 0.05 mole of H^+ would be provided by 50 ml of 1 M HCl.

Step 4.   Prepare the buffer. Weigh out 0.1 mole (12.1 grams) of crystalline Tris and dissolve it in approximately 500 ml of water. Add 50 ml of 1 M HCl and mix. Bring the total volume to 1 liter with distilled water, check the pH and adjust if necessary.

IONIC STRENGTH

Earlier in the chapter it was pointed out that the ionic concentration of cellular fluids is also critical for an organism to function normally. The optimal concentration is described in terms of the *ionic strength* (symbolized as μ) of the solution. The ionic strength is defined as follows.

$$\mu = \tfrac{1}{2} \sum_i c_i z_i^2$$

where $\quad c_i$ = molar concentration of the ith ionic species

$\quad\quad\quad z_i$ = electrostatic charge of the ith ionic species

$\quad\quad\quad \sum\limits_i$ = symbol for the summation of all cz^2 terms for each ionic species in solution

Inspection of this equation reveals that the ionic strength is a solution property which not only reflects the concentration of the ions in solution but also takes into account the ionic nature of the ions. Recall that the cellular activity is a function of both. Generally speaking, the ionic strength of solutions used for cellular studies is approximately 0.15. This value is commonly referred to then as the optimum physiological ionic strength. When whole cells are placed in a solution that does not contain an ionic concentration at least approximately equivalent to the ionic concentration of the intracellular fluid (protoplasm), one of two things (both undesirable) will occur. The cells will either take on water, swell, and ultimately burst, or they will lose water and shrink. Generally speaking, the former will occur when the ionic strength of the extracellular fluid is much less than that of the protoplasm. The latter effect is characteristic of extracellular fluids with an ionic strength much higher than 0.15. The type of study being performed, however, may require the use of solutions with a higher or lower ionic strength. For example, buffer solutions used in electrophoresis studies usually have an ionic strength between 0.01 and 0.2. Eluting solvents in column chromatographic separations frequently possess higher values as well.

The utilization of the equation is illustrated with the following examples.

EXAMPLE 1.   Calculate the ionic strength of physiological saline solution that is 0.154 M NaCl.

Solution:
$$\mu = \tfrac{1}{2} \sum_i c_i z_i^2$$

$$\text{NaCl} \;\rightarrow\; \text{Na}^+ \;+\; \text{Cl}^-$$
$$0.154\ M \quad\quad 0.154\ M \quad\quad 0.154\ M$$

Thus,

$$\mu = \tfrac{1}{2}[(c_{\text{Na}^+}\, z_{\text{Na}^+}^2) + (c_{\text{Cl}^-}\, z_{\text{Cl}^-}^2)]$$
$$\mu = \tfrac{1}{2}[(0.154)(1)^2 + (0.154)(1)^2]$$
$$\mu = 0.154\ M$$

EXAMPLE 2.   Calculate the ionic strength of the buffer prepared on page 51.

Solution: The buffer contains

$$\text{K}_2\text{HPO}_4 \;\rightarrow\; 2\text{K}^+ \;+\; \text{HPO}_4^=$$
$$0.331\ M \quad 2(0.331\ M) \quad 0.331\ M$$

$$\text{KH}_2\text{PO}_4 \;\rightarrow\; \text{K}^+ \;+\; \text{H}_2\text{PO}_4^-$$
$$0.169\ M \quad 0.169\ M \quad 0.169\ M$$

Therefore,

$$\mu = \tfrac{1}{2}[c_{\text{K}^+}\, z_{\text{K}^+}^2 + c_{\text{H}_2\text{PO}_4^-}\, z_{\text{H}_2\text{PO}_4^-}^2 + c_{\text{HPO}_4^=}\, z_{\text{HPO}_4^=}^2]$$
$$\mu = \tfrac{1}{2}[(0.831)(1)^2 + (0.169)(1)^2 + (0.331)(2)^2]$$

Note: Total $c_{\text{K}^+} = 2(0.331) + 0.169 = 0.831$

$$\mu = 1.16\ M$$

WATER—THE BIOLOGICAL SOLVENT

The existence of ions is dependent on the environment in which they are formed. The first statement of this relationship was put forth by Arrhenius as part of his theory on the ionization of electrolytes. One of the major objections to his theory was that positive and negative ions could not exist as individual particles in solution, since there would be a natural electrostatic force of attraction between them. Arrhenius countered this objection with the argument that the phenomenon of ionization is initiated and sustained by the physicochemical nature of the solvent which acts as the supporting medium. If the solvent molecules possess a polar character, the effect will be to minimize the force of attraction between oppositely charged particles. This capacity of a system to insulate oppositely charged particles from mutual interaction is reflected by the *dielectric constant,* **D**, of the medium. The relationship of the dielectric constant and the force of attraction (**F**) between two particles carrying a negative and positive charge (**Q**$^-$ and **Q**$^+$, respectively) separated by a distance r is evident from Coulomb's Law which states that

$$\mathbf{F} = \frac{\mathbf{Q^+Q^-}}{\mathbf{D}r^2}$$

Note that the force of attraction would be reduced in media with large dielectric constants. This, of course, is consistent with the statements above. Thus, we can see that the greater the polarity of the solvent (medium), the smaller the force of attraction between two oppositely charged particles (ions).

The dielectric constants of some common liquids are listed in Table 3–2. Observe that *water* has the highest value of those listed.

Table 3–2

Substance	Dielectric Constant (**D**)
Water	80.4
Methanol	33.6
Ethanol	24.3
Ammonia	17.3
Acetic acid	6.15
Chloroform	4.81
Ethyl ether	4.34
Benzene	2.28
Carbon tetrachloride	2.24

In fact, there are few materials that possess values greater than that for water. The significance of all this should not be too difficult to deduce. The biological system is ionic in nature, with the great majority of molecules found in cells being ions. Thus, nature has made a fortuitous selection of a physiological solvent that is compatible with supporting an ionic environment—water.

Additional properties of water that are related to its biological importance are (a) water has a high heat of vaporization (540 calories/

gram). The large amount of heat required to vaporize water is very useful in maintaining a constant bio-temperature. An organism can dissipate a large quantity of heat with the vaporization of small amounts of H_2O; (b) the amount of heat required to raise 1 gram of water 1 degree centigrade is 1 calorie. This, likewise, is a relatively large value for the heat capacity of a substance. The biological significance is that an organism can absorb significant amounts of heat without a correspondingly large change in bio-temperature: and (c) the density of liquid water has a maximum value at 4°C which is greater than that for ice. Consequently, ice floats and preserves an environment capable of supporting the existence of the countless aquatic organisms.

All of these properties are unique for water. That is to say, they are unexpected relative to the properties of other hydrides of Group VI elements in the periodic table, namely, H_2S, H_2Se, and H_2Te. They can all be explained, however, in terms of the highly polarized character of the water molecule. Because of the presence of oxygen, which is the second most *electronegative element,* the electrons of the two H—O covalent bonds are shared very unequally. Consequently, two *dipoles* are established in the molecule, which can be represented as follows:

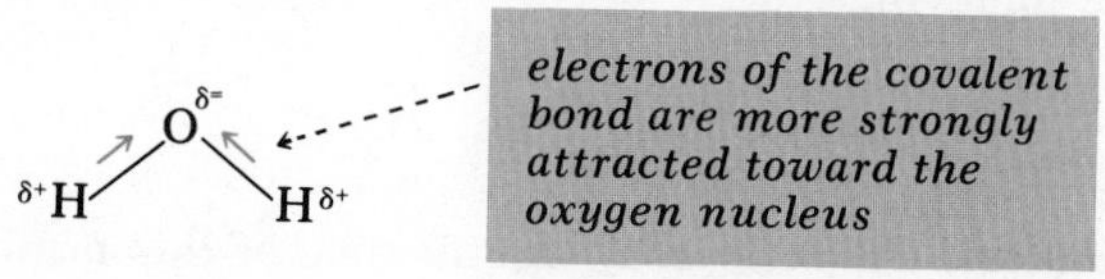

electrons of the covalent bond are more strongly attracted toward the oxygen nucleus

This strong dipolar character is responsible for the high dielectric constant of water. Positive and negative ions are shielded from mutual interaction by a sheath of water molecules which align themselves around the spherical ions according to electrostatic principles. This engulfment of ions stabilizes the ions in solution and maintains their existence. This phenomenon is specifically referred to as the *hydration* effect of solvent water molecules on dissolved solutes. This principle is diagrammed below in a two-dimensional representation for a positive and a negative ion.

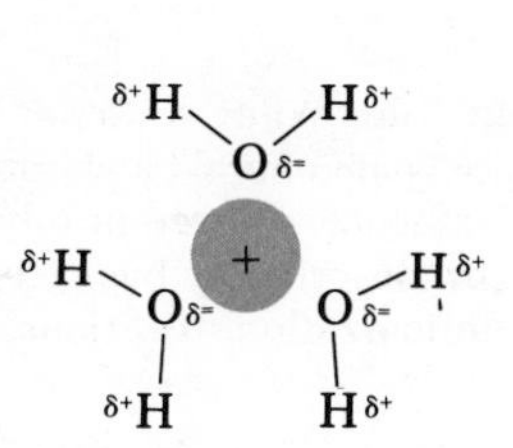

Hydration of ⊕ ion

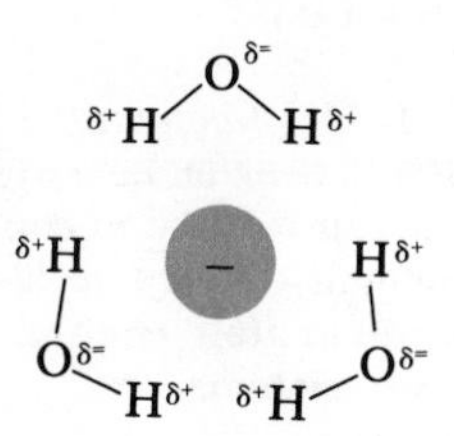

Hydration of ⊖ ion

The other properties of water can be explained on the basis of the mutual interaction of polar water molecules themselves through the phenomenon of *hydrogen bonding.* The presence of these *dipole-dipole interactions* is directly responsible for the high boiling point and the

$$\underset{\delta^+ \text{H}}{\overset{\overset{\delta^-}{\text{O}}\text{---}\overset{\delta^+}{\text{H}}}{}} \quad \overset{\text{hydrogen bond}}{||||||||||||||||||} \quad \underset{\delta^- \text{H}}{\overset{\overset{\delta^-}{\text{O}}\text{---}\overset{\delta^+}{\text{H}}}{}}$$

high heat of vaporization of water. The hydrogen bond itself is a weak bond, but the large population of such bonds must be taken into consideration when referring to a given volume of water. For example, it can be estimated that 1 milliliter of water contains approximately 3×10^{22} molecules. Now all of these molecules are not linked to one another to constitute one massive chain, but rather the majority of them are involved in hydrogen bond formation in small clusters with a constant exchange of participating molecules.

Hydrogen bonding is not exclusively confined to water. On the contrary, it is common to many systems, with the main requirement being the presence of two dipoles. It may occur intermolecularly (between different molecules) or intramolecularly (within the same molecule). Preferably, one dipole should contain a hydrogen atom with a partial positive charge, and the other dipole should contain an oxygen atom with a partial negative charge. For example, the giant protein and nucleic acid molecules are stabilized by hydrogen bonds between dipoles of the following type.

$$\overset{\delta^-}{\text{N}}\underset{\longleftarrow}{\text{---}}\overset{\delta^+}{\text{H}} \quad |||||||||||||||||||| \quad \overset{\delta^-}{\text{O}}\underset{\longleftarrow}{=\!=}\overset{\delta^+}{\text{C}}$$

In future chapters, the biological significance of this principle will be illustrated repeatedly. Indeed, we will be left with the inescapable conclusion that hydrogen bonding is not simply another chemical theory which can be dismissed lightly because it has little practical significance to the life sciences, but rather that it is a principle which plays a very relevant part in the astounding design of nature. In addition to serving as a stabilizing force in the structure of proteins and nucleic acids, hydrogen bonding is also involved in the biochemical expression of genes. An interesting transition—from hydrogen bonding to gene expression!

LITERATURE

SEGEL, I. H., *Biochemical Calculations*. New York: John Wiley & Sons, Inc., 1968. A book on how to solve mathematical problems in general biochemistry that can be used in conjunction with standard textbooks. A large number of problems—solved in detail—are accompanied by descriptive background. Approximately one-third of the book is devoted to ionization, titrations, and buffer systems.

SOBER, H. A., ed., *Handbook of Biochemistry: Selected Data for Molecular Biology*. Second Edition. Cleveland: The Chemical Rubber Company, 1970. A modern, in-depth compilation of evaluated data for those engaged in biochemical research. All of the main types of biologically occurring materials are treated. Highly recommended to those planning a career in biochemistry. Physicochemical data on ionization and buffers are tabulated in Section J.

WILLIAMS, V. R., and H. B. WILLIAMS, *Basic Physical Chemistry for the Life Sciences*. San Francisco-London: W. H. Freeman and Company, 1967. An excellent text of physicochemical principles designed for students in the life sciences. Acid–base equilibria and buffers are treated in Chapter 4.

EXERCISES

3–1 The structure and pertinent physicochemical data for 3-phosphoglyceralde-hyde—an intermediate in carbohydrate metabolism—are given below. Identify what ionic species would be present at physiological pH and cal-culate the approximate percentages of each.

$$\begin{array}{c} CHO \\ | \\ HCOH \\ | \\ CH_2OPO_3H_2 \end{array} \qquad pK_{a_1} = 2.10; \qquad pK_{a_2} = 6.80$$

3–2 Construct a reasonable facsimile of the titration curve for each of the following:
a) acetic acid with strong base
b) Tris (+ form) with strong base
c) glycine (± form) with strong base; pK_{a_2} for protonated amino group = 9.3
d) glycine (+ form) with strong base; pK_{a_1} for carboxyl group = 2.0
In each case identify the characteristic regions of the curve and give a description of the composition of the solution in same.

3–3 How would you prepare 1 liter of a 0.01 M citrate buffer at pH 4.65 from monosodium citrate (MW = 214 g/mole) and disodium citrate (MW = 236 g/mole)?

3–4 How would you prepare 1 liter of a 0.05 M HEPES buffer at pH 7.05? At room temperature HEPES is a crystalline solid existing largely in the zwitterionic state (MW = 238). Assume the availability of concentrated hydrochloric acid that is approximately 12 M and solid NaOH.

3–5 Calculate the ionic strength of the buffer prepared in problem 3–3.

3–6 Cells of *Escherichia coli* B were grown in two nutritionally complete growth media with the same composition except that one was buffered with phos-phate (P) salts and the other with Tris (T). Normal growth was observed in each medium as reflected by an identical generation time. After the cells were incubated in the complete media, they were harvested separately and transferred to similarly buffered media which contained no inorganic sul-fate. The intent of the experiment was to determine the response of the cells to a sulfur deficiency which represents the deprivation of an essential nutrient for normal growth. The population of viable cells in the sulfur-deficient media was determined at various times, and two sets of data are summarized below. Set A corresponds to the transfer of phosphate-grown

Viability of *E. coli* B in sulfur-deficient media				
Experiment A			Experiment B	
P-grown cells in P-buffered deficient medium	T-grown cells in T-buffered deficient medium	time (hours)	P-grown cells in T-buffered deficient medium	T-grown cells in P-buffered deficient medium
1.15*	1.31*	0	1.37*	1.45*
2.38	2.34	1	—	—
2.70	2.90	4	2.75	2.95
2.50	3.13	10	2.80	2.80
1.90	2.90	18	—	—
1.45	2.80	24	2.79	2.14
1.13	2.85	48	2.70	1.65

* (cells/ml) × 10⁻⁸; accuracy of figures is ±10%; different starting populations reflect vari-ations in handling and are not to be considered significant.

cells to a sulfur-deficient, phosphate-buffered medium and the transfer of Tris-grown cells to a Tris-buffered, sulfur-deficient medium. Set B corresponds to a hybridized transfer in that phosphate-grown cells were transferred to the Tris-buffered, sulfur-deficient medium and vice versa. Plot the data; determine the effects of the sulfur deficiency; compare the results of using different buffers; and finally, by comparing the data of sets A and B, determine whether the anomalous behavior is due to a pre-adaptation of the cells to the complete media or to a specific adaptation of identical cells to the different deficient media.

4

Amino Acids—Peptides—Proteins

In describing and analyzing the *dynamics* of the living process, considerable attention will be given to the biochemistry of proteins. This emphasis does not reflect any personal prejudice or bias which favors the proteins as an interesting class of compounds. Rather, it manifests the vital and transcendental functions of proteins in the activities of all living cells. This physiological importance is reflected in the word *protein* itself, which is derived from a Greek word meaning "first or primary."

Proteins are biopolymers ranging in molecular weight from 5,000 to several hundred thousand. The term *polymer* indicates that a protein is comprised of low-molecular-weight monomeric units that are linked together in a characteristic fashion. The *monomeric units* of proteins are the *amino acids,* which are covalently attached to one another by *peptide bonds.* Since several different types of amino acids are usually found in a protein, they can be viewed as heterogeneous polymers. A substance with several amino acids linked together via several peptide bonds is generally termed a *polypeptide.* Although a protein is a polypeptide, this term is customarily applied to a poly-amino acid material with a molecular weight less than the 5,000 minimum value stated above.

The physicobiochemical properties of proteins are a consequence of their size and shape. The shape—that is, the overall spatial conformation of the protein molecules—is most important. Indeed, it is the primary factor determining the biological function of a protein. In several cases, one or more specific properties is related to the presence of non-protein materials that may be complexed to the protein. Despite a large variety of biological functions and chemical structures, all proteins have a common denominator, namely, they are all synthesized from the same small group of amino acids. The factor which controls and indeed defines the conformational and functional individuality of each protein is the arrangement; that is, the *sequence* of the amino acids which comprise the polypeptide backbone. In addition, many of the properties of proteins are singularly or collectively related to the properties of constituent amino acids. Consequently, this chapter will begin with a discussion of the amino acids. We will then discuss some simple polypeptides and finally expand to the protein family. The principles and terminology to be developed in this systematic approach will be vital for a true appreciation of the complex structure and function of proteins. In addition, we will consider some specific physiological properties of a small number of individual amino acids and peptides.

Also in this chapter, initial use will be made of photographs of *space-filling molecular models* as a supplement to the traditional two-dimensional representations of chemical structure. It is not intended that they be memorized for examination purposes. Rather, they are included as visual aids for formulating a mental picture of the three-dimensional world of structure, which is crucial to developing an understanding of how the molecules of nature function.

AMINO ACIDS

OCCURRENCE AND STRUCTURE

At the present time there are approximately 200 different amino acids known to occur in nature. Many of these are found only in certain life species and some are found only in one organism. They occur either freely dissolved in protoplasm or covalently linked with other amino acids in peptides and proteins.

Although the individual identity of each is due to a specific chemical composition and structure, most of the natural amino acids possess the general structure

$$H_2N-\underset{\underset{R}{|}}{\overset{\overset{COOH}{|}}{C^\alpha}}-H$$

which represents an *alpha amino acid* wherein the functional amino (—NH$_2$) and carboxyl (—COOH) groups are both attached to the alpha (α) carbon. At physiological pH, both would exist almost exclusively in the ionic form (see section below). Other amino acids contain different acidic groups or have the amino group on a different carbon atom. Imino acids also occur with an imino group $\left(\diagdown N-H\right)$ instead of an amino group. The most common imino acids are proline and hydroxyproline (see Class VII in Table 4–1). The structural feature that distinguishes one alpha amino acid from another is the chemical nature of the R group. It can vary from a simple hydrogen atom in glycine to a more

complex structure such as $H_2N-\underset{\underset{NH}{\parallel}}{C}-NCH_2CH_2CH_2-$ in arginine. Table

(with H above the N) 4–1 gives the structure, names, shorthand abbreviations, and pertinent ionization data of some of the important amino acids. Others will be encountered in later chapters. The classification used in the tabulation is but one of many.

One of the remarkable unifying elements in nature is that, of the large number of amino acids that do exist, only the 24 listed in Table 4–1 are used by all organisms in the biosynthesis of proteins. Note, however, that thyroxine, hydroxylysine, and hydroxyproline have a limited occurrence, and thus the common pool is reduced to 21. If we consider cystine (containing a *disulfide bond*) as an oxidized form of cysteine (containing a *free sulfhydryl group*), the number is further reduced to 20. There are

Table 4–1 Amino and imino acids commonly found in proteins. (Classification of amino acids based on nature of side chain.)

Amino acid (standard abbreviation)	Structure (all ionizable groups shown in protonated form)	pK_a ($\alpha-COOH$)	pK_a ($\alpha-NH_3^+$)	pK_a (R)	Charge on R group ($pH \approx 7$)
Class I: Aliphatic amino acids with nonpolar R groups	$HOOC-\overset{\overset{NH_3^+}{\mid}}{\underset{\underset{H}{\mid}}{C^\alpha}}-R$				
1. Glycine (GLY) not optically active	$-\overset{\mid}{\underset{\mid}{C}}-H$	2.34	9.6	—	0
2. Alanine (ALA)	$-\overset{\mid}{\underset{\mid}{C}}-CH_3$	2.34	9.69	—	0
3. Valine (VAL)	$-\overset{\mid}{\underset{\mid}{C}}-\underset{CH_3}{CHCH_3}$	2.32	9.62	—	0
4. Leucine (LEU)	$-\overset{\mid}{\underset{\mid}{C}}-CH_2\underset{CH_3}{CHCH_3}$	2.36	9.60	—	0
5. Isoleucine (ILE)	$-\overset{\mid}{\underset{\mid}{C}}-\underset{CH_3}{CHCH_2CH_3}$	2.36	9.68	—	0
Class II: Hydroxyl amino acids					
6. Serine (SER)	$-\overset{\mid}{\underset{\mid}{C}}-CH_2OH$	2.21	9.15	—	0
7. Threonine (THR)	$-\overset{\mid}{\underset{\mid}{C}}-\underset{OH}{CHCH_3}$	2.63	10.43	—	0

Table 4-1 (continued)

Amino acid (standard abbreviation)	Structure (all ionizable groups shown in protonated form)	pK_a (α—COOH)	pK_a (α—NH$_3^+$)	pK_a (R)	Charge on R group (pH $\approx$ 7)
Class III: Sulfur amino acids					
8. Cysteine (CYSH or CYS)	—C—CH$_2$SH	1.71	10.78 pK_{a_3}	8.33 pK_{a_2}	0 $\longleftrightarrow$ —
9. Cystine (CYS$_2$)	—C—CH$_2$S / HOOC—CH—CH$_2$S, NH$_3^+$	1.65 / 2.26	7.85 / 9.85		
10. Methionine (MET)	—C—CH$_2$CH$_2$SCH$_3$	2.28	9.21	—	0
Class IV: Aromatic amino acids					
11. Phenylalanine (PHE) (could also be classified as nonpolar)	—C—CH$_2$—⬡	1.83	9.13	—	0
12. Tyrosine (TYR)	—C—CH$_2$—⬡—OH	2.20	10.07 pK_{a_3}	9.11 pK_{a_2}	0 $\longleftrightarrow$ —
13. Tryptophan (TRP) (could also be classified as nonpolar)	—C—CH$_2$— indole group	2.38	9.39	—	0
14. Thyroxine (found only in thyroglobulin)	—C—CH$_2$—(I,I ring)—O—(I,I ring)—OH				
Class V: Acidic amino acids and amide derivatives					
15. Aspartic acid (ASP)	—C—CH$_2$COOH	2.09	9.82 pK_{a_3}	3.86 pK_{a_2}	—
16. Asparagine (ASN)	—C—CH$_2$CONH$_2$	2.02	8.8	—	0

Table 4–1 (continued)

Amino acid $\left(\substack{\text{standard} \\ \text{abbreviation}}\right)$	Structure (all ionizable groups shown in protonated form)	pK_a $(\alpha-COOH)$	pK_a $(\alpha-NH_3^+)$	pK_a (R)	Charge on R group (pH $\approx$ 7)
17. Glutamic acid (GLU)	$-C\!\!-\!\!CH_2CH_2COOH$	2.19	9.67 pK_{a_3}	4.25 pK_{a_2}	–
18. Glutamine (GLN)	$-C\!\!-\!\!CH_2CH_2CONH_2$	2.17	9.13	—	0
Class VI: Basic amino acids					
19. Lysine (LYS)	*epsilon* amino group $-C\!\!-\!\!CH_2CH_2CH_2CH_2NH_3^+$	2.18	8.95	10.53	+
20. Hydroxylysine (found only in collagen and gelatin)	$-C\!\!-\!\!CH_2CH_2CHCH_2NH_3^+$ $\;\;\;\;\;\;\;\;OH$	2.13	8.62	9.67	+
21. Histidine (HIS)	$-C\!\!-\!\!CH_2$ $HN^+\!\!-\!\!NH$ imidazole group	1.82	9.17 pK_{a_3}	6.0 pK_{a_2}	0 $\longleftrightarrow$ +
22. Arginine (ARG)	$-C\!\!-\!\!CH_2CH_2CH_2\;\boxed{NHCNH_2\atop\|\;\;\;\;\;\;NH_2^+}$ guanidine group	2.17	9.04	12.48	+
Class VII: Imino acids	$\diagdown NH_2^+ \diagup$				
23. Proline (PRO)	—COOH $N^+\!H_2$ (pyrrolidine ring)	1.99	10.60	—	0
24. Hydroxyproline (found only in collagen and gelatin)	HO— —COOH $N^+\!H_2$ (pyrrolidine ring)	1.92	9.73	—	0

L Forms

CHO

HO—C̈—H

(A) CH₂OH

COO⁻

H₃N⁺—C̈—H

(B) R

(C)

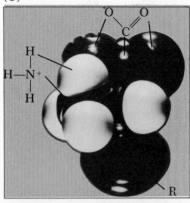

D Forms

CHO

H—C̈—OH

(D) CH₂OH

COO⁻

H—C̈—N⁺H₃

(E) R

(F)

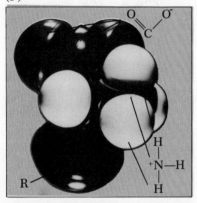

Figure 4–1 L and D forms. *Panel A:* a projection formula of L-glyceraldehyde. *Panel B:* a projection formula of an L-alpha amino acid (R ≠ H). *Panel C:* photograph of a space-filling model of an L-amino acid. (Large grouping at upper left is intended to represent the R group.) *Panel D:* a projection formula of D-glyceraldehyde. *Panel E:* a projection formula of a D-alpha amino acid. *Panel F:* photograph of a space-filling model of a D-alpha amino acid.

a small number of rare exceptions where an unusual derivative has been detected.

Although any given protein isolated from the same source will have a fixed amino acid composition, one of the basic differences among all proteins is the variation in the content of each amino acid. The frequency of occurrence of any one amino acid is also variable, covering a broad range. For example, salmine found in spermatazoa of salmon is a small protein (MW 8,000) containing 56 amino acid units in peptide linkage. 40 of these units are arginine, 7 are serine, 4 are proline, 3 are glycine, 2 are valine, and 1 is isoleucine. All others are absent. This type of situation is generally an exception; most proteins are composed of a greater variety of amino acids (Table 4–2).

With the notable exception of glycine, the alpha carbon atom of the amino acids is asymmetric, being tetrahedrally attached to four structurally distinct atoms or groups of atoms. Consequently, optically active stereoisomeric forms exist, distinguished only by the spatial orientation of the groups attached to the alpha carbon and by their ability to rotate a ray of polarized light. The two possible isomeric forms, designated as L and D, are distinguished relative to glyceraldehyde which is the accepted frame of reference. By convention the L form of glyceraldehyde designates the structure shown in Panel A of Figure 4–1 where the —OH group is spatially oriented to the left. The D form of glyceraldehyde (Panel D of Figure 4–1) corresponds to the structural isomer wherein the —OH group is oriented to the right. The L and D forms of the alpha amino acids are designated similarly in terms of the spatial orientation of the alpha amino group (Panels B, C, E, F in Figure 4–1). The importance of this is that *only* L-amino acids are known to occur in proteins. Once again we observe that the monomeric molecular language of proteins is limited. D-amino acids do exist in nature, however, as components of certain peptide antibiotics (Appendix 2) and the bacterial cell wall (page 188).

IONIC PROPERTIES

An application of the principles discussed in Chapter 3 is rather pertinent at this point. In the physiological environment or in any reproduction of same, the prevailing pH of approximately 7 will cause both of the functional groups attached to the alpha carbon to exist in the ionic form to yield a *zwitterion*. The zwitterionic structure also characterizes the amino acids in the crystalline solid state.

$$
\underset{\text{cationic form (low pH)}}{H_3\overset{+}{N}-\underset{\underset{COOH}{|}}{\overset{\overset{R}{|}}{C}}-H}
\quad\underset{+H^+}{\overset{+OH^-}{\rightleftharpoons}}\quad
\underset{\textit{zwitterion}}{H_3\overset{+}{N}-\underset{\underset{COO^-}{|}}{\overset{\overset{R}{|}}{C}}-H}
\quad\underset{+H^+}{\overset{+OH^-}{\rightleftharpoons}}\quad
\underset{\text{anionic form (high pH)}}{H_2N-\underset{\underset{COO^-}{|}}{\overset{\overset{R}{|}}{C}}-H}
$$

In addition to the alpha amino and alpha carboxyl groups, if the R group also contains an ionizable grouping, the charge on the molecule will reflect its presence. Of the compounds listed in Table 4–1, this is

Amino Acid—Class		Alpha chain —Human hemoglobin		Beta chain —Human hemoglobin		Cytochrome c — Human		Glyceraldehyde— Dehydrogenase		Coat protein —Tobacco mosaic virus		Lysozyme— Chicken		Human growth hormone	
Glycine		7		13		13		32		4		12		8	
Alanine		21		15		6		32		18		12		7	
Valine	Non-Polar	13	42%	18	44%	3	35%	34	41%	10	35%	6	34%	7	29%
Leucine		18		18		6		18		11		8		25	
Isoleucine		0		0		8		21		11		6		8	
Serine	Hydroxyl	11	14%	5	8%	2	9%	19	12%	13	17%	10	13%	18	15%
Threonine		9		7		7		22		13		7		10	
Cysteine	Sulfur	1	6%	2	2%	2	5%	4	4%	1	3%	8	8%	4	4%
Methionine		7		1		3		9		3		2		3	
Phenylalanine		7		8		3		14		6		3		13	
Tyrosine	Aromatic	3	8%	3	9%	5	9%	9	8%	7	10%	3	9%	8	12%
Tryptophan		1		2		1		3		2		6		1	
Aspartic	Acidic	8	9%	7	10%	3	11%	25	12%	5	8%	8	8%	14	18%
Glutamic		4		8		8		13		7		2		20	
Asparagine	Amides	4	3%	6	6%	5	7%	13	5%	12	17%	13	11%	6	6%
Glutamine		1		3		2		5		15		2		6	
Lysine		11		11		18		26		2		6		9	
Histidine	Basic	10	17%	9	16%	3	23%	11	14%	1	8%	1	14%	3	12%
Arginine		3		3		2		10		10		11		10	
Proline	Imino	7	5%	7	5%	4	4%	12	4%	8	5%	2	1%	8	4%
Total Residues		141		146		104		332		156		129		188	

Table 4–2 Amino acid composition of some proteins. (Values in each column specify number of residues present in each protein. Percentage of each amino acid class is also given.)

true of glutamic and aspartic acids (additional carboxyl group), histidine (additional imidazole group), tyrosine (additional phenolic hydroxyl group), arginine (additional guanidine group), cysteine (additional sulfhydryl group), lysine (additional amino group), and hydroxylysine (additional hydroxyl and amino groups). The physicochemical reality of each group is identified by a specific pK_a value. In the majority of cases, the alpha carboxyl group dissociates most easily and is designated as pK_{a_1} and the alpha amino group as pK_{a_2}. In the polyfunctional amino acids, the alpha amino group is designated pK_{a_3} if it is less acidic than the side chain function as in cysteine, glutamic acid, and aspartic acid (see Table 4–1). Due to the presence of the extra carboxyl group, glutamic acid and aspartic acid are termed *acidic* amino acids. The R groups of the two amides, glutamine and asparagine, are neutral. These two amino acids are generally classified with the acidic amino acids simply because they are derivatives. The presence of the weakly acidic (strongly basic) groupings in arginine, lysine, and histidine makes them *basic* amino acids. All of the other amino acids shown in Table 4–1 would be classified as *neutral*.

As with the functional groups attached to the alpha carbon, inspection of the pK_a values of the side chain groups indicates that they are considerably displaced on both the acidic and basic side of pH 7. The important point here is that under physiological conditions, the functional groups of the side chain will also exist largely in the ionic state.

The ionic nature of the amino acids, especially that conferred by the side chains, is a physicochemical fact that is particularly relevant to

Amino Acid Ionizations

Neutral amino acids (e.g., alanine)

$$H_3C—CH—COOH \xrightleftharpoons[2.34]{pK_{a_1}} H_3C—CH—COO^- \xrightleftharpoons[9.69]{pK_{a_2}} H_3C—CH—COO^-$$

with NH_3^+, NH_3^+, NH_2 respectively.

Net Charge = +1   N.C. = 0 (isoelectric)   N.C. = −1

Acidic amino acid (e.g., aspartic acid)

$$HOOCCH_2—CH—COOH \xrightleftharpoons[2.09]{pK_{a_1}} HOOCCH_2—CH—COO^- \xrightleftharpoons[3.86]{pK_{a_2}}$$

with NH_3^+, NH_3^+.

N.C. = +1   N.C. = 0 (isoelectric)

$$^-OOCCH_2—CH—COO^- \xrightleftharpoons[9.82]{pK_{a_3}} ^-OOCCH_2—CH—COO^-$$

with NH_3^+, NH_2.

N.C. = −1   N.C. = −2

Basic amino acid (e.g., lysine)

$$H_3\overset{+}{N}CH_2(CH_2)_3—CH—COOH \xrightleftharpoons[2.18]{pK_{a_1}} H_3\overset{+}{N}CH_2(CH_2)_3—CH—COO^- \xrightleftharpoons[8.95]{pK_{a_2}}$$

with NH_3^+, NH_3^+.

N.C. = +2   N.C. = +1

$$H_3\overset{+}{N}CH_2(CH_2)_3—CH—COO^- \xrightleftharpoons[10.53]{pK_{a_3}} H_2N—CH_2(CH_2)_3—CH—COO^-$$

with NH_2, NH_2.

N.C. = 0 (isoelectric)   N.C. = −1

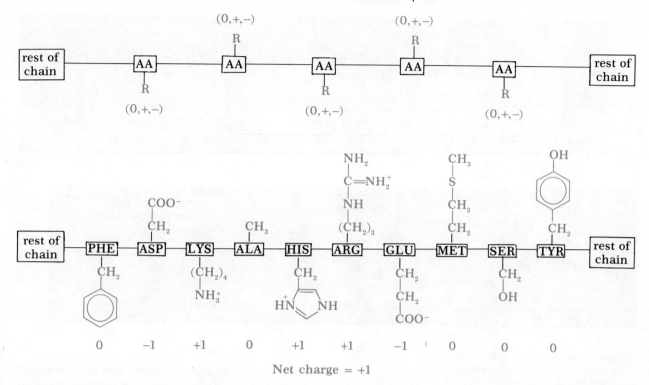

Figure 4–2 *Top:* A generalized representation of an abbreviated segment of an amino acid chain. Each rectangle designates an amino acid (AA) containing a neutral (0) or an ionic (+, −) side chain. The horizontal lines signify the peptide bonds involving the α-carboxyl and α-amino groups of adjacent amino acids. The bond itself is not shown in order to emphasize only the potential polyionic nature of the chain due to the abundant population of free side chains with functional groups. *Bottom:* A specific segment of a polypeptide chain illustrating the R groups of each amino acid type as they would exist at approximately pH 7.

the biochemistry of peptides and proteins. As previously described, the constituent amino acids are covalently linked to each other by a peptide bond which is formed—almost without exception—through the interaction of the alpha carboxyl and alpha amino groups. This results in the loss of their respective ionic charges. With the exception of the sulfhydryl group of cysteine, the side chains of the amino acids including the polyfunctional acids do not participate in any covalent bonding. Consequently, the ionic properties of a peptide or protein at physiological pH will be primarily due to the ionic nature of the side chains contributed by the polyfunctional amino acids. A negative and a positive charge will be contributed by acidic and basic amino acids, respectively, and the side chains of the neutral amino acids will be nonionic and uncharged. These principles are schematically summarized in Figure 4–2.

This *polyionic nature* of proteins and biologically active peptides plays a significant role in their overall structure, which in turn controls their biological function. This point will be exemplified later in this chapter.

ISOLATION AND SEPARATION

Since amino acids are present as ions in solution, one of the most useful techniques for their resolution in a mixture is ion exchange column chromatography (page 25, Chapter 2), coupled with a ninhydrin treatment for detection. With refined techniques and careful control of the pH of the eluting solvent, and by using an appropriate ion exchange resin,

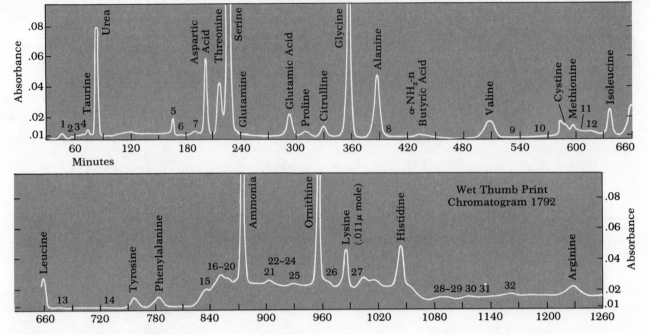

Figure 4-3 Amino acids found by ion exchange chromatography in a single thumb print made on a wet glass surface. For visual comparison of peaks, the amount of lysine (0.011 μmole) is indicated on the figure. On the abscissa, 1 minute is equivalent to 0.5 ml of column effluent volume. The high serine, high glycine, the presence of citrulline, and high ornithine, along with the virtual absence of cystine, seem to be characteristic of hand amino acids. Numbered peaks represent unidentified amino acids and other ninhydrin-sensitive materials also present. (Taken with permission from "Amino Acids on Hands," Hamilton, P. B., *Nature*, **205**, 284–285 (1965)).

a complex mixture can be readily analyzed. Amino acid analyzers are available which simultaneously permit automatic and continual elution through the column, treatment of the eluate with ninhydrin, measurement of the absorbancy of the colored products, and finally a printout of the absorbancy change on a strip recorder. A typical pattern is shown in Figure 4–3. The sample used was obtained by merely making a thumb print on a wetted glass surface. The choice of the example may seem insignificant, but this one was deliberately selected to illustrate the complex nature of biological systems, even from the most unexpected sources. The extreme of complexity is exemplified by systems such as human urine, which has been shown by the same method to contain 175 ninhydrin-sensitive materials.

An alternative technique gaining in popularity is gas chromatographic analysis. Before injection the mixture is first treated with an appropriate reagent to convert the amino acids into volatile forms such as the *N-trifluoroacetyl* derivatives (see Figure 4–4).

The ionic nature of peptides and proteins is also exploited by the biochemist in their separation, isolation, and characterization. The methods of both ion exchange chromatography and electrophoresis are frequently employed. An example of the latter in the separation of serum proteins was given in Chapter 2 on page 22. Electrophoresis also provides a direct method for the determination of the *isoelectric point* of a protein, the one pH at which the protein carries no net charge, due to the presence of an equal number of cationic and anionic groups. At this pH–*designated pI*–the electrophoretic mobility of the protein will be zero, that is, it will not be displaced from the origin. Knowledge of the isoelectric point can reveal some general information about amino acid composition. Thus, a protein with an appreciable amount of acidic amino acids will have a pI much less than 7, whereas one containing large amounts of the basic amino acids will have a pI much greater than 7. For example, pepsin, a digestive protein excreted by cells in the stomach and very rich in glutamic and aspartic acids, has a pI of about 1. On the other hand, proteins associated with nuclear material and very rich in arginine and lysine have a pI of approximately 12.

CHEMICAL PROPERTIES

The amino acids are capable of participating in a wide variety of chemical reactions. These include alkylation and arylation of the amino group, and ester and anhydride formation involving the carboxyl group. A large number of specific reactions of these types have been developed over the years by organic chemists in an effort to prepare useful amino acid derivatives for the chemical synthesis of peptides. The principal objectives in this type of work are the activation of either the alpha carboxyl or alpha amino group and the temporary blocking of same or of any other functional group not intended to participate in the formation of the peptide linkage. An example of the pertinent chemistry of each type is shown in Figure 4–4. Further discussion on this point is deferred to the section dealing with peptide synthesis.

Some of the amino acids undergo unique reactions with certain reagents due to the nature of the side chains. Many reactions of this type are characterized by the production of colored products. For example, tyrosine, because of its phenolic hydroxyl grouping, reacts with an alkaline copper-containing solution of phosphomolybdotungstic acid to yield a blue color. This reaction—originally termed the Folin-Ciocalteau reaction in view of their initial studies—has been developed by Lowry and co-workers into a very sensitive and hence widely used procedure for the quantitative estimation of the protein content of a sample. In the *Lowry method,* a sample is treated with a modified Folin-Ciocalteau reagent. If proteins are present, a blue color is produced due to the presence of the tyrosine residues in the proteins. The absorbancy (page 26, Chapter 2) is then measured and compared with that of similarly treated solutions containing known concentrations of reference protein. Due to variations in the content of tyrosine from one protein to another, however, equal amounts of different proteins will produce different color yields with the Lowry reagent. Consequently, measurements of *actual* protein concentration are not possible with this type of reaction. In many experimental situations, however, only a relative estimation is required for which this method is very satisfactory. A method more suitable for the measurement of actual protein concentration is the *Kjeldahl* procedure based on determining the organic nitrogen content of the sample. This is then converted to mass of protein by using the relationship that virtually all proteins contain approximately 16% nitrogen by weight.

Other reactions have been extremely useful in the qualitative and quantitative analysis of amino acids in general. The resultant derivatives may be solids with sharp melting points, may possess distinct and reproducible chromatographic properties, and/or may be colored and susceptible to quantitative photometric analysis. Three examples are (1) the reaction with *ninhydrin* mentioned frequently heretofore (2) the reaction with *2,4-dinitrofluorobenzene,* and (3) the reaction with *phenylisothiocyanate.* The pertinent chemistry of each is shown in Figure 4–4.

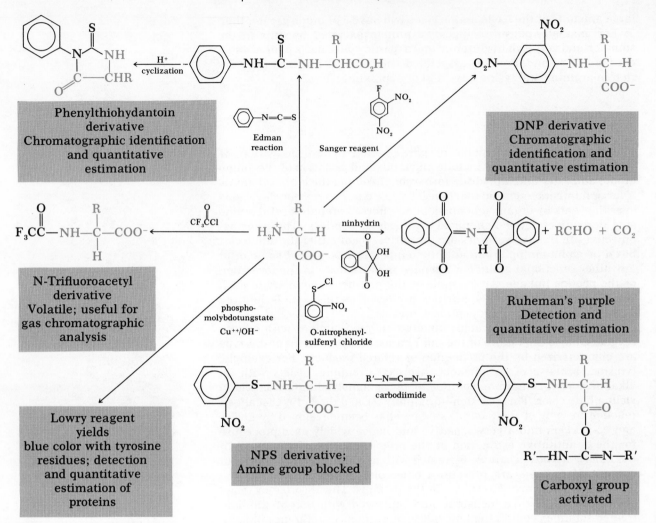

Figure 4–4 A summary of some important reactions of amino acids.

The reaction of amino acids with ninhydrin (triketohydrindene hydrate) was first reported by Ruheman in 1910. It has proven to be an indispensable biochemical tool. The reaction is general for any amino acid, resulting in the formation of a blue-violet color that has an absorption maximum at 540 nm. Exceptions are the imino acids, proline and hydroxyproline, which give yellow products absorbing maximally at 440 nm. The chromogenic products obey the Beer-Lambert relationship (see page 26, Chapter 2).

The reaction of amino acids with 2,4-dinitrofluorobenzene (DNFB) produces yellow derivatives that have distinct chromatographic and spectrophotometric properties. Accordingly, the reagent can be used for detection and quantitation. The DNFB reagent was originally developed by F. Sanger in 1945; he later used it as a major weapon in determining the complete amino acid sequence of the protein hormone, insulin (see page 84, this chapter).

The reaction of the amino group of amino acids with phenylisothiocyanate was originally developed by P. Edman in 1950. The reaction produces phenylthiohydantoin derivatives which are likewise easily characterized by chromatography, thus permitting the identification and quantitation of amino acids. This reaction also has an application similar to that of the Sanger reagent in determining the amino acid sequence of a polypeptide (see page 85, this chapter).

FORMATION OF PEPTIDES

Without question, the most important and biologically relevant chemical property of the amino acids is their ability to covalently interact with each other, via the alpha carboxyl group of one molecule and the alpha amino group of a second molecule, to form a *peptide* as shown below. The diagram also depicts that a growing peptide chain is elongated in a stepwise manner. As we will see, this is true of both the biological and

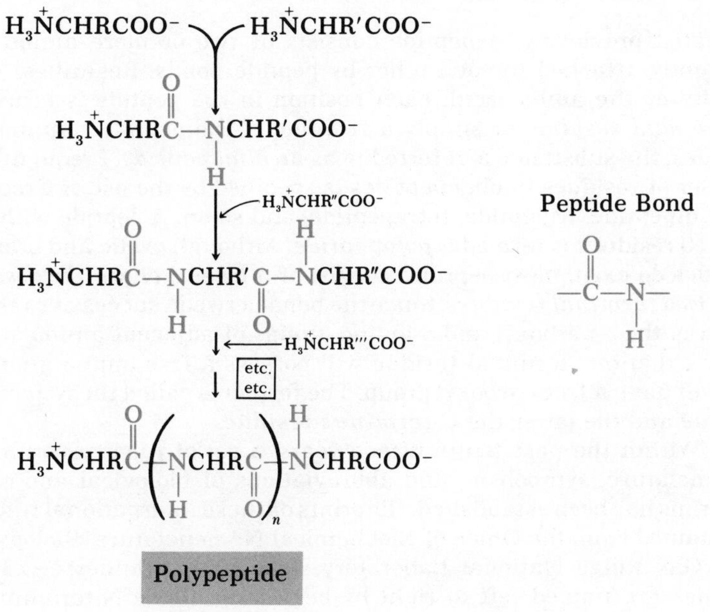

$$H_3\overset{+}{N}CHRCOO^- \quad H_3\overset{+}{N}CHR'COO^-$$

$$H_3\overset{+}{N}CHR\overset{O}{\overset{\|}{C}}-\underset{H}{N}CHR'COO^-$$

$$\text{Peptide Bond}$$

$$H_3\overset{+}{N}CHR\overset{O}{\overset{\|}{C}}-\underset{H}{N}CHR'\overset{H}{\underset{O}{\overset{\|}{C}}}-\underset{H}{N}CHR''COO^-$$

$$-\overset{O}{\overset{\|}{C}}-\underset{H}{N}-$$

$$\boxed{\text{etc.}} \; \boxed{\text{etc.}}$$

$$H_3\overset{+}{N}CHR\overset{O}{\overset{\|}{C}}\left(\underset{H}{N}CHR\underset{O}{\overset{\|}{C}}\right)_n\underset{H}{N}CHRCOO^-$$

Polypeptide

the chemical synthesis of peptides of any size. The nature of the peptide bond will shortly be discussed in greater depth. The primary message at this point is merely to indicate the general nature of this characteristic covalent linkage.

OTHER BIOLOGICAL PROPERTIES

To this point, emphasis has been given to the role of the amino acids in nature as the monomeric constituents of peptides and proteins. However, this is not their only biological property. As free materials dissolved in protoplasm, many have individual functions which can be enumerated only by considering the metabolism of each amino acid. For example, methionine functions as a donor of methyl groups; glutamic acid is a key intermediate in the detoxification of ammonia in mammals; glycine is one of the primary biosynthetic precursors of the heme group of hemoglobin; and the listing could go on and on. Some examples of this will be discussed in greater detail in Chapter 16. One specific and very interesting illustration is the therapeutic property of one amino acid in the treatment of Parkinson's disease, namely, *L-dihydroxyphenylalanine*–designated L-DOPA (see page 421, Chapter 16). Recently granted approval by the Food and Drug Administration in 1970, L-DOPA in daily doses can provide alleviation of the very discomforting and crippling symptoms for hundreds of thousands of individuals afflicted with this disease. The molecular mechanism of this therapeutic effect has not yet been determined.

PEPTIDES

TERMINOLOGY AND NOMENCLATURE

As stated previously, a peptide consists of two or more amino acids covalently attached to each other by peptide bonds. Regardless of the identity of the amino acid, each position in the peptide is termed an *amino acid residue,* or simply a *residue.* If the peptide contains 2-10 residues, the substance is referred to as an *oligopeptide.* Frequently, the number of residues in oligopeptides is specified by the use of Greek prefixes: dipeptide, tripeptide, tetrapeptide, and so on. A peptide with more than 10 residues is termed a *polypeptide.* Although cyclic and branched peptides do exist, most peptides consist of a *linear, chainlike assembly with two terminal residues.* Since the bond between successive residues involves the α-carboxyl and α-amino groups of adjacent amino acids, it follows that one terminal residue will possess a free amino group and one will have a free carboxyl group. The former is called the *N-terminus residue* and the latter the *C-terminus residue.*

Within the past ten to fifteen years, a set of rules governing the nomenclature, symbolism, and abbreviations of biological and related materials has been established. (Reprints of these international rules can be obtained from the Office of Biochemical Nomenclature, Biology Division, Oak Ridge National Laboratory, Oak Ridge, Tennessee.) Linear peptides are named left to right by beginning at the N-terminus and designating each residue as an acyl substituent of the α-amino group of the succeeding residue. The peptide bond is designated by a dash. If the exact sequence of the peptide or any part of it is unknown, the residues are enclosed by parentheses and the dash is replaced by a comma. An alternate, shorthand method of peptide nomenclature is to use abbreviations to. designate each residue. The abbreviations for the common amino acids are given in Table 4–1. These rules are applied below for the hypothetical peptide consisting of 2 arginine residues, 1 glutamic acid residue, 1 glycine residue, and 2 alanine residues.

If the sequence (hypothetical) is known:

residue number

$$\overset{1}{\text{arginyl}}-\overset{2}{\text{alanyl}}-\overset{3}{\text{glycyl}}-\overset{4}{\text{arginyl}}-\overset{5}{\text{glutamyl}}-\overset{6}{\text{alanine}}$$

(N-terminus) ———————————————→ (C-terminus)

or

ARG—ALA—GLY—ARG—GLU—ALA

or

$H_3\overset{+}{N}$—ARG—ALA—GLY—ARG—GLU—ALA—COO⁻

If only a partial sequence is known:

arginyl—(alanyl,arginyl,glycyl)—glutamyl—alanine
^{1} $^{(2,3,4)}$ ^{5} ^{6}

or

ARG—(ALA,ARG,GLY)—GLU—ALA

or

$H_3\overset{+}{N}$—ARG—(ALA,ARG,GLY)—GLU—ALA—COO$^-$

Individual residues are frequently designated numerically, with the N-terminal residue specified as the number 1 residue. Thus, in the example above, the glutamic acid residue linked to the C-terminus residue would be residue 5.

NATURALLY OCCURRING PEPTIDES

Nature contains a large number of peptides that perform many diverse functions. Structurally, they constitute a very heterogeneous group of materials characterized by cyclic chains, branched chains, the presence of D- and L-amino acids, and in some isolated cases a unique type of peptide bond. Some specific examples are briefly discussed below. Additional examples are given in Appendix 2.

GLUTATHIONE

γ-glutamyl-cysteinyl-glycine, commonly called glutathione and symbolized GSH, is universally distributed in animals, plants, and bacteria, and is probably the most abundant simple peptide. The distinguishing structural feature is of course the amino acid sequence. A second feature is that the reduced form of the tripeptide contains a functional sulfhydryl group (—SH) contributed by cysteine. With the exception of blood, over 90% of the non-protein thiol compounds in mammalian tissues is in the form of reduced glutathione. As shown below, GSH can be reversibly oxidized by the loss of two hydrogens, with the resultant formation of a

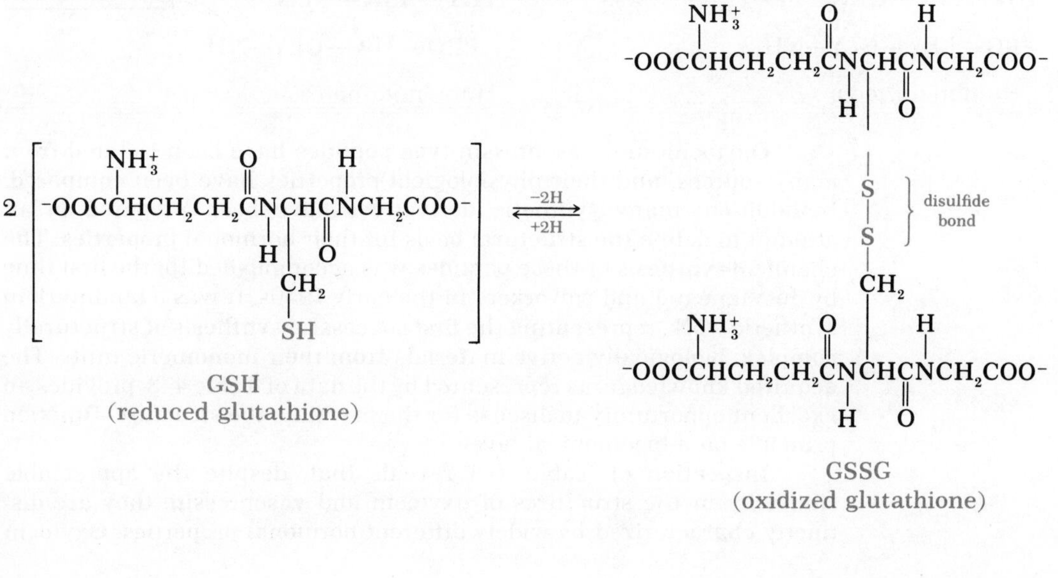

GSH
(reduced glutathione)

GSSG
(oxidized glutathione)

disulfide bond. (The disulfide linkage per se is an important type of bond in proteins.) Another interesting feature of glutathione structure is the participation of the γ-carboxyl group of glutamic acid, rather than the α-carboxyl group, in the peptide bond.

The functions of GSH are many and too diverse to enumerate here. Many have yet to be studied in detail, and indeed it is probable that many have yet to be discovered. Most glutathione-dependent processes, however, reflect the participation of the tripeptide as a *coenzyme* (see Chapter 5), a term applied to any low-molecular-weight material that acts in conjunction with an appropriate enzyme in providing an optimum system for the catalysis of cellular reactions. In this dependent partnership, glutathione frequently functions as a *hydrogen donor* in oxidation–reduction reactions because of its capacity for reversible oxidation.

$$A \quad + \quad 2(GSH) \xrightarrow{\text{enzyme}} AH_2 \quad + \quad 2(GSSG)$$

| oxidized | reduced | reduced | oxidized |
| reactant | glutathione | product | glutathione |

The reduced glutathione is then regenerated from its oxidized state in some other process. A specific illustration of the role of glutathione in normal metabolism is discussed on page 293 in Chapter 11.

Numerous other peptides exist that have more specific physiological functions. Two such examples are the partially cyclic nonapeptides, *oxytocin* and *vasopressin*. Both are produced by the neurohypophysis (posterior lobe of the pituitary gland) of mammals. Those found in the human and in the majority of other vertebrates have the structure shown below. *Note that the two peptides have an identical amino acid sequence with the exception of residues 3 and 8.*

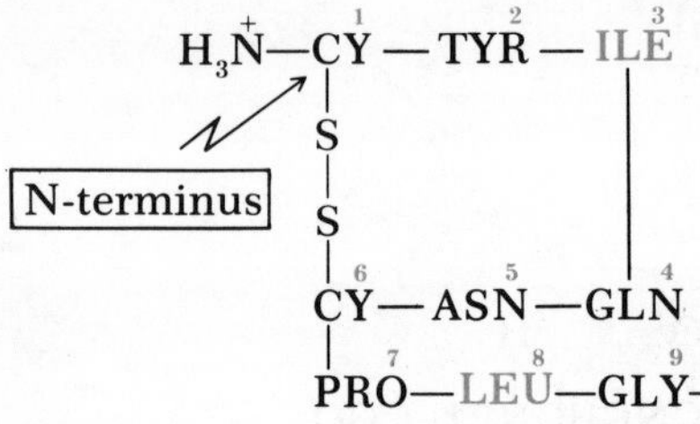

Human oxytocin

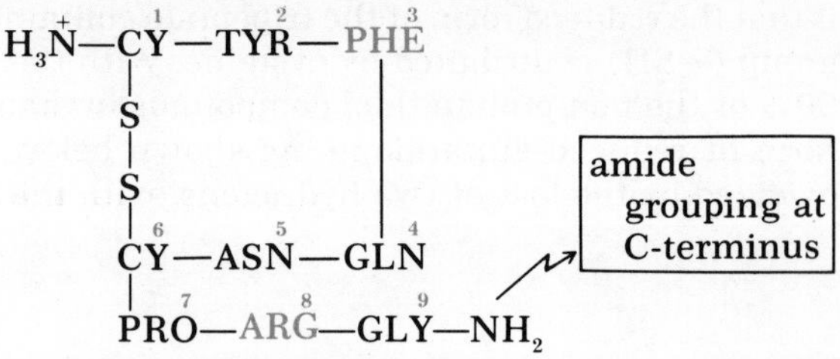

Human vasopressin

Oxytocin- and vasopressin-type peptides have been isolated from many sources, and their physiological properties have been compared. In addition, many synthetic derivatives have been prepared in an attempt to define the structural basis for their hormonal properties. The chemical synthesis of these peptides was accomplished for the first time by du Vigneaud and coworkers in the early 1950s. It was a landmark in synthetic work, representing the first successful synthesis of structurally complex, biologically active materials from their monomeric units. The acquired knowledge, as represented by the data of Table 4–3, provides an excellent opportunity to discuss for the first time the structure–function principle on a biochemical level.

Inspection of Table 4–3 reveals that, despite the appreciable similarity in the structures of oxytocin and vasopressin, they are distinctly characterized by widely different hormonal properties. Oxytocin

Property[a]	Human Peptides		Oxytocins Substituted in Residue 8 by:				
	Oxytocin	Vasopressin	D-LEU[8]	[b]ILE[8]	VAL[8]	[b]ARG[8]	LYS[8]
Lactation	450[c]	70	18	306	308	206	180
Uterine muscle contraction	450	20	18	288	198	200	76
Elevation of blood pressure	5	400	inhib.	7	8	220	115
Antidiuresis	5	400	0	1	1	225	22

Table 4–3 A comparison of the physiological effects of oxytocin and vasopressin nonapeptides.

a. All bioassays performed on adult rats.
b. Naturally occurring oxytocins.
c. All numbers are units of activity per milligram of peptide.

enhances the contraction of smooth muscle and the ejection of milk from the mammary glands in lactating females. Vasopressin, on the other hand, elicits the constriction of blood vessels, causing high blood pressure, and also has antidiuretic effects. By comparing their structure, one can draw the obvious conclusion that, if the sequence of amino acids is in any way related to this difference in properties, residues 3 and 8 are probably rather critical. Indeed, as stated earlier, the other seven amino acid residues are the same in both peptides. The remaining data of Table 4–3 support this deduction, with particular attention to position 8. All of the remaining peptides listed in Table 4–3 are specified as oxytocins substituted at position 8. Accordingly, the following analysis of the effects of the substitution will be given relative to the reference data given for human oxytocin.

The data are very interesting. Note first that every substitution at position 8 gives a peptide that assays differently from the human peptides. More specifically and in reference to human oxytocin, all of the residue 8-substituted peptides have a reduced ability to stimulate lactation and uterine contraction and increased pressor and antidiuretic effects. An exception is the D-LEU[8] peptide, which has little hormonal activity of any type. This clearly depicts the extreme of the structure–function relationship. Although the same amino acid is present in the synthetic and human oxytocin, the localized introduction of the D stereoisomer in place of the L probably results in a sufficiently extensive alteration of the overall three-dimensional conformation of the peptide to render it inactive as a hormone.

With regard to the other analogs, the partial loss of oxytocin properties with ILE[8] and VAL[8] substitutions argues for the importance of a highly non-polar amino acid in that position. However, neither is equivalent to LEU. The difference between the properties of ILE and LEU at position 8 is quite remarkable, however, when one considers that the only difference between these amino acids is the spatial position of a methyl($—CH_3$) group on the side chain. The enhancement of the pressor and antidiuretic properties in these two cases is not significant (at least in the rat), since the reference activity of human oxytocin is very small.

The insertion of a basic amino acid (LYS or ARG) at position 8 has the remarkable effect of rendering the nonapeptide more vasopressin-like, as exemplified by the 50-fold enhancement in those properties with ARG[8]-oxytocin. This certainly confirms that the pressor and antidiuretic effects of this type of nonapeptide are critically related to the presence of a basic amino acid in position 8, and indeed is consistent with the presence of ARG in position 8 in natural vasopressin. ARG[8]-oxytocin is an intriguing material in that it represents a true hybrid, with approximately equivalent hormonal effects of both human oxytocin and vasopressin. It may occur to you that this particular peptide may be present in nature in other species. Indeed it is, being widespread among fishes and amphibians.

In conclusion, the data illustrate the sensitive relationship between biological function and chemical structure. More precisely, this analysis depicts the importance of the amino acid sequence in a peptide. The same principle really applies to every residue in the nonapeptides, with ILE[3] being especially critical to the properties of oxytocin.

Several *antibiotics* are peptides. Examples are Bacitracin and Gramicidin S. Unusual are the presence of D and L forms in both, the presence of the amino acid *ornithine* (see page 424) in both, and the completely cyclic nature of the latter. The structures of these and other peptides can be found in Appendix 2.

As a final example of the biological role of peptides, let us consider the results of some recent research indicating that peptides may play an important biochemical function in the learning process of mammals. In 1970 a tetradecapeptide was isolated from the brain of rats which had been trained to develop a fear of the dark. The peptide was not present in brain extracts obtained from control groups of untrained rats. The purified peptide was then injected into a group of untrained rats. Another group received no injection. The result was a significant manifestation of the same trait in the injected rats. The investigators, headed by G. Ungar, propose that the peptide may be but one of a family of chemical *code words of memory* which serve for the coding of acquired information in the central nervous system. The sequence of this particular peptide—labeled *scotophobin,* meaning "dark fear"—is:

$$H_3\overset{+}{N}—SER—ASP—ASN—ASN—GLU—GLN—GLY—LYS—SER—GLN—GLY—GLY—GLN—TYR—COO^-$$

The implicit assumption underlying this proposal is that the overall structure of the peptide, which is synonomous with its amino acid sequence, is the molecular manifestation of the animal's learning to adapt to a stimulus. Once the information is acquired—that is, once the molecule has been synthesized—the appropriate message is translated by the brain through the central nervous system when the same stimulus is received. In other words, the assumption is that the learning process has a molecular basis. (A chemically synthesized peptide having the same amino acid sequence determined for scotophobin has given the same results when injected into untrained rats and fish.)

THE PEPTIDE BOND

In previous sections, the general nature of the peptide bond was described. At this point we will now examine the characteristics of this linkage in greater depth.

Our knowledge of the spatial arrangement of the atoms of the peptide bond and the resultant peptide chain is due primarily to the X-ray analyses of simple peptides reported by L. Pauling and R. B. Corey in the early 1950s. The results of their studies are shown in Figure 4–5, illustrating the features and dimensions of the peptide bond and a segment of a fully extended peptide chain of L-amino acids. The length of 7.23 Å corresponds to the *repeat distance* between two alpha carbons in the chain which immediately flank one complete amino acid residue. Based on unstrained bond angles and bond distances, the length of 7.23 Å represents the maximum allowable repeat distance. The significant features of the peptide bond are listed below, and all are represented by the drawings and photographs of Figure 4-5.

1. The C—N bond distance of 1.32 Å for the amide grouping (that is, the peptide bond) is intermediate in length between that of a double covalent bond (1.21 Å) and that of a single covalent bond (1.47 Å). Although the C—N bond is indeed a single covalent bond, we can deduce from this dimensional analysis that it does have an appreciable *double-bond character*. This can be explained in terms of a resonating structure.

The primary consequence of this closer attraction is that there is *restricted rotation around the C—N bond axis*. On the other hand, free rotation does occur in the $-\overset{|}{\underset{|}{C^\alpha}}-\overset{|}{\underset{H}{N}}-$ bond and the $-\overset{|}{\underset{|}{C^\alpha}}-\overset{O}{\overset{||}{C}}-$ bond, which are true sigma bonds not subject to resonance.

2. *The four atoms of the peptide bond and the two attached alpha carbons are all in the same spatial plane, that is to say, they are co-planar.* The H and R groups on the alpha carbons are projected in dimensions out of this common plane.

3. *The geometrical orientation of the O and H atoms in the peptide bond is* trans. In addition, the geometrical orientation of the two alpha carbon atoms, relative to the peptide bond to which they are attached, is also *trans*.

4. As a consequence of the spatial orientation in 3, and given the L configuration of each residue, the *R groups* on each of the alpha carbon atoms *are arranged in a repeating* trans *fashion*.

This subject has been discussed as a separate entity in order to direct attention to these basic structural characteristics of peptides and the peptide bond. For the moment this subject will not be diluted by an extended discussion of the biochemical significance of these properties. However, this analysis should not be interpreted as merely an academic exercise in chemical bonding. On the contrary, these principles provide the pertinent language for analyzing the three-dimensional orientation of protein molecules. Indeed, they are essential to a basic understanding of same. This point will be developed shortly.

CHEMICAL SYNTHESIS OF PEPTIDES

The synthesis of naturally occurring materials of all types has long attracted the attention of organic chemists and biochemists alike. If at

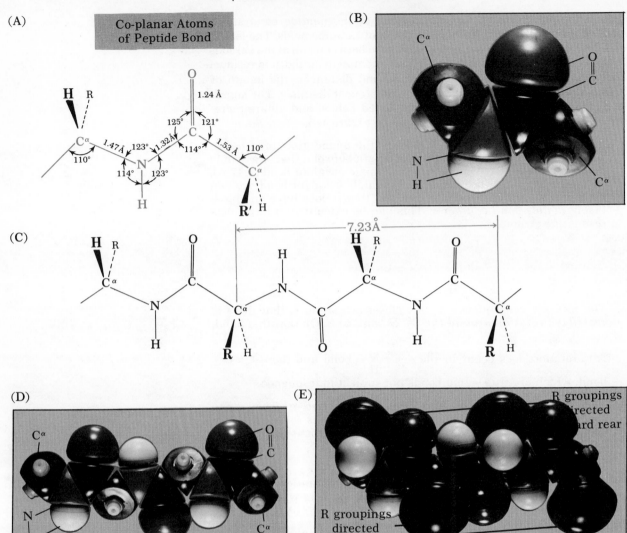

(A) Co-planar Atoms of Peptide Bond

Figure 4–5 *Panel A:* Dimensions and geometry of the peptide bond, illustrating the *trans* orientation of the R groups and of the imino hydrogen and carbonyl oxygen atoms. All atoms of the peptide bond are in the same spatial plane. *Panel B:* The symbolic diagram in Panel A shown as a space-filling model. *Panel C:* Drawing of a segment of a fully extended polypeptide chain of L-amino acids. *Panel D:* A space-filling model of the drawing in C. The studs correspond to bonds linking H and R groups to alpha carbons. *Panel E:* Repeat of panel D showing the H and R groups on the alpha carbons.

all possible, this approach is generally utilized as a final proof of the proposed structure of a natural material. More important, however, is the extra dimension given to biochemical investigations by the ability to synthesize the material under study. Such a capability generally means that defined structural modifications can be made at will in order to determine their effect on biological activity. This type of philosophy was just illustrated by our discussion of oxytocin peptides.

Peptides of known sequence were difficult to synthesize until recently. For example, du Vigneaud's original synthesis of oxytocin required many separate steps which had to be performed individually and took several months of effort. In 1963, however, Merrifield devised the *solid-state method* of peptide synthesis, which has had a revolutionary effect. Now automated, it is simpler and much shorter than the traditional methods developed by du Vigneaud and others and has essentially displaced them. In the Merrifield procedure, a column of an ion exchange resin is used to support the growing polypeptide chain.

Initially the ion exchange resin is treated with an amino acid suitably *activated* at the carboxyl group. The amino acid reacts with the resin particles, forming a *covalent linkage* through the carboxyl group. The resin with the attached C-terminal residue is then reacted with a second amino acid, likewise carboxyl group activated. Any reactive functional groups on the side chain are also *blocked* to prevent their participation in any reactions. They remain blocked until all residues are attached. The result is the formation of a dipeptide which remains attached to the resin. The process is then repeated until the desired number of residues are attached. Then any blocking groups on the side chains are removed, and finally the initial bond that was formed between the resin and the C-terminal residue is broken and the released peptide is recovered. Several peptides have been prepared since this procedure was developed. The most remarkable application occurred in 1969 when Merrifield and coworkers announced the successful synthesis of ribonuclease (see page 155), an enzyme that contains 124 amino acid residues. The automated process involved 369 different chemical reactions and 11,931 distinct steps, but with continuous operation the synthesis was completed within a few weeks—truly a milestone in synthetic biochemistry.

1. Attachment of C terminal residue to resin

$$B-NH-CHR_1-\overset{\overset{\displaystyle O}{\|}}{C}-A + Resin \rightarrow B-NH-CHR_1-\overset{\overset{\displaystyle O}{\|}}{C}-Resin + A$$

2. Removal of α-amino group blocking agent

$$B-NH-CHR_1-\overset{\overset{\displaystyle O}{\|}}{C}-Resin \rightarrow H_2N-CHR_1-\overset{\overset{\displaystyle O}{\|}}{C}-Resin + B$$

3. Formation of dipeptide

$$B-NH-CHR_2-\overset{\overset{\displaystyle O}{\|}}{C}-A + H_2N-CHR_1-\overset{\overset{\displaystyle O}{\|}}{C}-Resin \rightarrow$$

$$B-NH-CHR_2-\overset{\overset{\displaystyle O}{\|}}{C}-\underset{\underset{\displaystyle H}{|}}{N}-CHR_1-\overset{\overset{\displaystyle O}{\|}}{C}-Resin + A$$

4. Removal of α-amino group blocking agent

$$B-NH-CHR_2-\overset{\overset{\displaystyle O}{\|}}{C}-\underset{\underset{\displaystyle H}{|}}{N}-CHR_1-\overset{\overset{\displaystyle O}{\|}}{C}-Resin \rightarrow$$

$$H_2N-CHR_2-\overset{\overset{\displaystyle O}{\|}}{C}-\underset{\underset{\displaystyle H}{|}}{N}-CHR_1-\overset{\overset{\displaystyle O}{\|}}{C}-Resin$$

5. Repetition of steps 3 and 4 until desired polypeptide is assembled
6. Removal of any blocking agents in R groups
7. Release of peptide from resin and recovery of product

$$H_2N-CHR_n-\overset{\overset{\displaystyle H}{|}}{\underset{\underset{\displaystyle O}{\|}}{C}}-N-CHR_2-\overset{\overset{\displaystyle O}{\|}}{C}-\underset{\underset{\displaystyle H}{|}}{N}-CHR_1-COOH$$

More recently C. Li and coworkers, using the same technique, succeeded in synthesizing a polypeptide containing 188 amino acid residues (approximately 50% larger than ribonuclease) that possesses many chemical and biological properties of a substance termed the *human growth hormone* (HGH). One of several hormones produced by the pituitary gland, HGH is essential for normal body growth and metabolism and for the production of milk by the mammary glands. Physiological diseases associated with an inability to produce HGH can be treated by administration of the hormone obtained from other sources. However, the availability of natural HGH is quite limited. Thus, the chemical synthesis has obvious practical implications. Moreover, it may be that only a piece of the intact hormone is required for activity, and the synthesis of this would be even more feasible. The essential steps of the solid-state method are given below where B—NH— desig-

nates a *blocked* α-amino group and —$\overset{\overset{\displaystyle O}{\displaystyle \|}}{C}$—A designates an *activated* α-carboxyl group of an amino acid. Blocked R groups are not shown for reasons of simplicity.

PROTEINS

CLASSIFICATION

Proteins can be classified in different ways. The list in the margin distinguishes proteins on a *functional* basis. Since all the proteins in an organism are important to sustaining normal life processes, it is not appropriate to rank the various types in any specific hierarchy. However, as mentioned in previous chapters, proteins that function as *enzymes* do have a special importance. The enzymes are the molecular agents that catalyze all of the chemical reactions in a cell associated with the intake and utilization of matter and energy. The enzymes not only allow these reactions to occur at extremely fast rates but also function in modulating the extent to which they occur and thus provide the cell with an unequaled capacity of adapting to its changing needs in a most efficient and economical manner. This central role of enzymes does not, however, diminish the crucial biological significance of other individual proteins. For example, without insulin the disease of diabetes results; without antibodies our bodies would be defenseless against infection; without hemoglobin the supply of oxygen to cells would be nil; and the listing could go on and on.

On a *compositional basis* proteins can be broadly divided into two general classes: (1) the *simple proteins* which yield only α-amino acids on complete hydrolytic degradation; and (2) the *conjugated proteins* which on degradation yield, in addition to α-amino acids, a non-peptide, organic or inorganic grouping termed a *prosthetic group*. The simple proteins are further subclassified on the basis of solubility and amino acid composition. For example, *albumins* are rather soluble in water and dilute salt solutions; *globulins* are soluble in water, but are insoluble or minimally soluble in dilute salt solutions; *scleroproteins*, such as collagen, abundant in the connective tissue of animals, are insoluble in most solvents; *protamines* are distinguished by a high arginine content; *histones* also are rich in basic amino acids but not

Functions of Proteins:

Catalytic proteins: enzymes

Structural proteins: for example, collagen in the connective tissue of vertebrates (representing about 1/3 of the total protein in the body) and various proteins in cellular membranes

Contractile proteins: for example, myosin in muscle tissue

Natural-defense proteins: for example, the antibodies in the gamma globulin fraction of blood

Digestive proteins: various proteins present in gastro-intestinal secretions which convert dietary material to smaller substances

Transport proteins: for example, hemoglobin which transports oxygen in the blood

Blood proteins: for example, fibrinogen which participates in the clotting process

Hormonal proteins: proteins that regulate cellular activities such as insulin

Respiratory proteins: for example, the cytochromes which participate in the transport of electrons to suitable acceptors such as oxygen in aerobic organisms

Repressor proteins: proteins that regulate the expression of genes in chromosomes

exclusively arginine. The conjugated proteins are subclassified in terms of the nature of the prosthetic group. The common classes are: *lipoproteins,* which are distinguished by the conjugation of lipid material with the polypeptide chain; *mucoproteins* (glycoproteins), which contain a carbohydrate prosthetic group; *nucleoproteins,* which are a combination of protein and nucleic acid; *metalloproteins,* which contain a metal—generally as a cation—complexed to the protein; and finally *chromoproteins,* so designated because the prosthetic group is a pigment which confers a chromogenic character to the complete protein. There is no universal type of bond between the prosthetic group and the polypeptide chain. Although in most instances the linkage is non-covalent, in a few cases it is covalent.

A third classification is based on differences in three-dimensional *structure* and water *solubility.* The two divisions are the *fibrous proteins* and the *globular proteins.* Fibrous proteins are generally insoluble in water and are distinguished by stabilizing cross-linkages between linear polypeptide chains; this gives the molecule a distinct fibrillous character. Usually molecular weights are very high. Collagen is a classic example. On the other hand, globular proteins are generally water soluble and possess an ordered, highly folded three-dimensional structure resulting from intricate foldings of the polypeptide chain into a non-fibrillous elliptical or nearly spherical form. A greater variety and number of proteins are in the globular class. All enzymes are globular proteins.

fibrous

globular

STRUCTURE—AN INTRODUCTION

Protein molecules have a complex structure. The complexity is not due solely to the fact that they are large molecules but rather to the arrangement of all the atoms that constitute the molecule. This is particularly true of the globular proteins. To impose some organization to this subject, four levels of structure are generally identified: (1) the *primary level,* which specifically refers to the sequence of amino acid residues in the polypeptide chain; (2) the *secondary level,* which refers to the geometrical orientation of the polypeptide chain that serves as the backbone of the polymer; (3) the *tertiary level,* which refers to the complete, three-dimensional, spatial architecture of the protein including the orientation of any prosthetic group; and (4) the *quaternary level,* which considers an aspect of protein structure sometimes due to the non-covalent aggregation of two or more polypeptide chains. The remainder of the chapter will be devoted to a consideration of each level of structure in the order given.

PRIMARY STRUCTURE

The sequence of monomeric units is a fundamental structural property of any polymer. However, in contrast to the simplicity of this descriptive fact, the experimental determination of same is rather difficult and laborious. The fact that proteins generally contain varying amounts of 15–20 different amino acids and have an average chain length of 100–150 residues obviously compounds the difficulties with this type of polymer. Since the principle of amino acid sequence is so vital, let us briefly examine the experimental approach.

After a *purified* sample of the protein has been obtained certain preliminary measurements are performed. First, the molecular weight is found by ultracentrifugation and/or another method. Secondly, if the material is a conjugated protein, the type of the prosthetic group and its amount on a weight-weight basis are determined. Thirdly, the amino acid composition is determined. The latter is now a rather routine procedure. The protein is completely degraded to its monomeric units by treatment with dilute acid (6N HCl) or dilute alkali [2N NaOH] for 12–36 hours at 100–110°C. Alternatively, natural proteolytic agents can be used, such as *pronase,* an enzyme isolated from a microbe, which cleaves every peptide bond in the chain. Regardless of the method, the protein hydrolyzate (amino acid mixture) is then analyzed—qualitatively and quantitatively—generally by use of an amino acid analyzer. This is how the data of Table 4–2 were obtained, for example. Most of the commercial analyzers employ ion exchange column chromatography for separation (see page 25, Chapter 2). A known amount of the sample is applied to the top of column, and the flow of the eluting buffer (moving phase) into the column is begun. During operation the unit automatically monitors the chromatographic separation by continuously measuring the absorbance of the effluent from the column after it is first treated with ninhydrin. Finally the unit prints out on chart paper how the absorbance changes with the volume of effluent. The printout would be in the form of the pattern shown in Figure 4–3, with the area under each peak being directly proportional to the concentration of each amino acid. Depending on instrument design, the cost of the instrument can vary from about $12,000 to $30,000.

With these preliminaries completed, the next step is to determine whether the protein contains any *interchain* or *intrachain disulfide bonds* (—S—S—). This type of covalent linkage is not common to all proteins, but is usually critical to those that do possess it. One approach is to treat the native protein with a reagent which will selectively and oxidatively cleave disulfide bonds. The formation of sulfonic acid groupings will confer different ionic properties on the newly formed chain or chains; these properties can be detected and isolated by electrophoresis or ion exchange or gel permeation chromatography. If disulfide bonds are present, they are generally cleaved and the newly formed peptide(s) is then sequenced.

The actual sequencing generally begins with the determination of the terminal residues. A variety of methods are available, but limitations of time and space permit only a brief citation of selected examples.

The C-terminus can be easily determined by treating the intact polypeptide with hydrazine. The hydrazine will react hydrolytically at the carbonyl grouping of each peptide bond, resulting in the formation of acyl hydrazine derivatives of each residue—except the C-terminus. The C-terminus will not be modified, since its α-carboxyl group is not in peptide linkage, and thus it can be recovered and identified chromatographically. Another approach is to treat the polypeptide with sodium borohydride (NaBH₄), a strong reducing agent, which reduces the C-terminal carboxyl grouping to a hydroxymethyl grouping. After hydrolysis the α-amino alcohol can be detected in the hydrolyzate and identified. The corresponding acid is the C-terminal residue. A less reliable method is treatment of the polypeptide with *carboxypeptidase,* an enzyme obtained from the gastrointestinal secretions of mammals

Disulfide Bonds

Intrachain

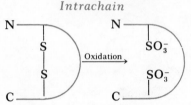

Result: One chain with a greater negative charge

Interchain

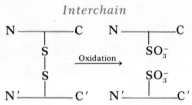

Result: Two chains with a greater negative charge

and relatively specific for removal of C-terminal residues from a polypeptide chain. Difficulties arise, however, because the enzyme does not stop after removing the initial C-terminal residue, but continues to attack new C-terminal residues every time the chain is shortened.

The N-terminus can be detected by treating the protein with phenyl isothiocyanate (Edman reagent), which will react with the alpha amino group of this residue. Subsequent hydrolysis of the treated peptide will yield a mixture of amino acids containing the N-terminal residue as a phenylthiohydantoin derivative. The latter can be easily recovered and identified against chromatographic standards. 2,4-Dinitrofluorobenzene can be used in a similar way, but it is less desirable because DNFB will react with any functional amino group, such as the ε-amino group of a lysine side chain, and thus confuse the issue. *Aminopeptidase,* another mammalian digestive enzyme with a specificity opposite to that of carboxypeptidase, can also be used, but it presents the same difficulties as carboxypeptidase.

Determining the sequence of amino acids sandwiched between the terminal residues is, of course, the real problem. Without a lengthy explanation, suffice it to say that the sequence of an average polypeptide chain of a protein cannot feasibly be determined by a systematic removal and identification of one residue at a time from either terminus. The limitation is primarily due to the size of the polypeptide. For example, with controlled and mild hydrolytic conditions, the Edman reagent can be used in this manner on small polypeptides containing 10–20 residues. Beyond that the efficiency of the technique is considerably reduced. Consequently, the experimental strategy is to degrade the large polypeptide into several smaller fragments which are then sequenced separately with the Edman reagent (see page 85). The main requirement, of course, is that the splitting of peptide bonds must occur with some degree of known specificity, so that after the sequence of each small peptide is determined, all of the fragments can ultimately be positioned in the proper order.

This requirement for specificity of action is best satisfied by the use of biological agents, namely, some of the other digestive proteolytic enzymes isolated from mammals. *Trypsin* and *chymotrypsin* (see page 104) are prominent examples and are widely used. Unlike aminopeptidase and carboxypeptidase, which tend to act at the ends of the polypeptide chain, trypsin and chymotrypsin act primarily within the chain. Neither is characterized by an absolute degree of specificity of peptide bond cleavage, but under carefully controlled conditions they do exhibit some degree of preferential action. Trypsin hydrolysis favors peptide bonds that contain a carbonyl group donated by one of the basic amino acids. Chymotrypsin prefers peptide bonds that contain a carbonyl or an amino group donated by one of the aromatic amino acids.

if either is donated by
an aromatic amino acid

$$\sim\!\!\sim\!\!COO^- + H_3\overset{+}{N}\!\!\sim\!\!\sim \quad \xleftarrow{\text{Chymotrypsin}} \quad \sim\!\!\sim\!\!\overset{\overset{\displaystyle O}{\|}}{C}\!\!-\!\!\underset{\underset{\displaystyle H}{|}}{N}\!\!\sim\!\!\sim \quad \xrightarrow{\text{Trypsin}} \quad \sim\!\!\sim\!\!COO^- + H_3\overset{+}{N}\!\!\sim\!\!\sim$$

if donated by a
basic amino acid

The isolation and sequencing of small peptides formed *only* by trypsinolysis, for example, does not solve the problem at all, since the fragments still need to be mapped in the proper order. Thus, the same procedure is repeated with chymotrypsin, with a combination of both enzymes, or with either enzyme under different conditions, in an attempt to obtain a *large collection of different peptide fragments formed by the cleavage of different peptide bonds within the same polypeptide.* Once all fragments from the different procedures are sequenced, the complete polypeptide chain can be mapped on the basis of positioning the fragments by searching for and aligning overlapping regions. This is more difficult than it appears. Recently a small number of chemical agents have been developed that are quite selective in their cleavage of peptide bonds. For example, cyanogen bromide selectively cleaves a bond containing a carbonyl group donated by methionine. In any event the task is arduous and generally requires several months, even years, depending on the size of the protein and the number of separate chains present in the molecule. The time and effort required have been significantly reduced by the development of automated peptide sequencers which employ the Edman degradation procedure to sequence the isolated peptide fragments. The essential events of the Edman procedure are shown on the following page.

The first protein to have its amino acid sequence detailed was insulin (51 residues) in 1955 by F. Sanger, who received the Nobel Prize for the techniques he developed in this heralded achievement. Sanger's use of the DNFB reagent to sequence small peptides produced by controlled enzymatic and acid hydrolysis of the insulin molecule has been replaced to a large degree by the Edman process. With the further exception of some specialized procedures and the availability of refined chromatographic techniques, the current *modus operandi* is basically the same as that developed by Sanger. Since 1955 the complete sequence of several proteins and smaller polypeptides has been determined. Among these proteins are the alpha (141 residues) and beta (146 residues) chains of human hemoglobin, myoglobin (153), ribonuclease (124), cytochrome *c* (104), lysozyme (129), the coat protein of tobacco mosaic virus (158), the coat protein of a bacterial virus (129), plant ferredoxin (97), bacterial ferredoxin (55), chymotrypsinogen (245), trypsinogen (229), papain (203), subtilisin (275), carboxypeptidase (307), the human growth hormone (188), and most remarkable of all, the recently published sequence of gamma globulin with 1320 residues.

The sequences of human insulin, whale myoglobin, and horse myoglobin are given in Figure 4-6. Insulin consists of two chains connected by two *interchain* disulfide bonds, with one chain also having an *intrachain* disulfide bond. On the other hand, myoglobin—a conjugated protein (see page 91 for discussion of the prosthetic group)—consists of a single polypeptide chain with no disulfide bonds. In fact, the only feature identical to both insulin and myoglobin is that they are composed of amino acids linked together by peptide bonds. Otherwise the two proteins are widely different. This, of course, is not a profound conclusion applicable only to insulin and myoglobin, but a basic generalization true of virtually all proteins that have a different function, regardless of natural source.

Alternatively, inspection of the sequences for horse and whale myoglobin shows that they are quite similar. Each is a single polypeptide

Edman Degradation and Sequencing of Small Peptides

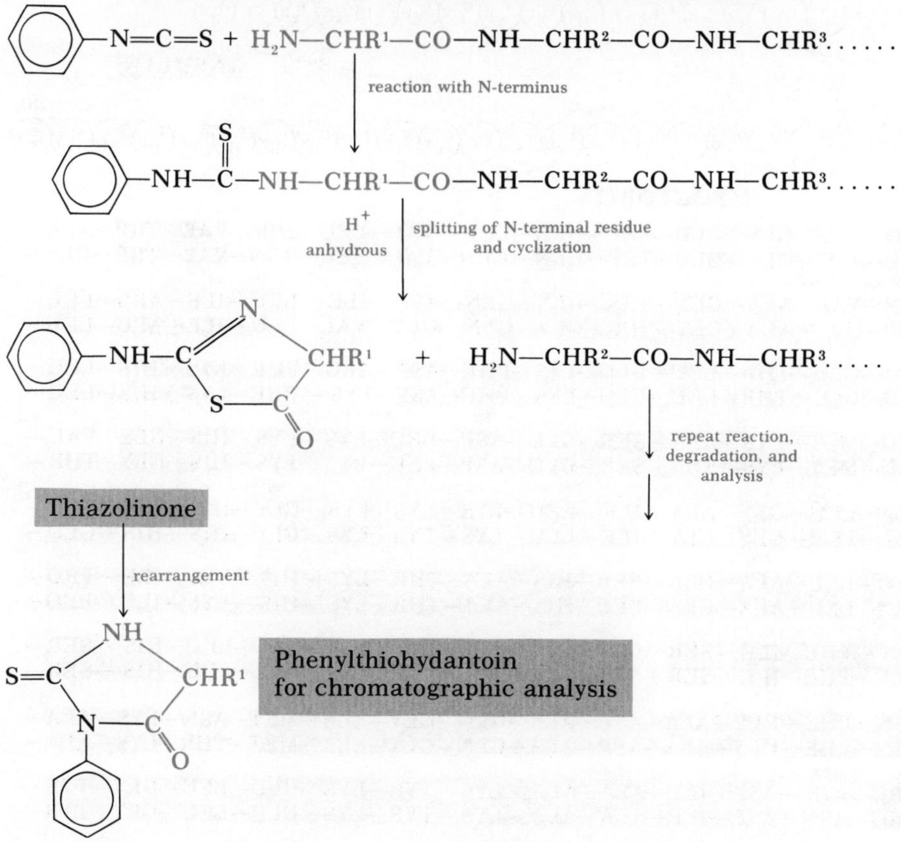

C₆H₅—N=C=S + H_2N—CHR¹—CO—NH—CHR²—CO—NH—CHR³......

reaction with N-terminus

C₆H₅—NH—C(=S)—NH—CHR¹—CO—NH—CHR²—CO—NH—CHR³......

H^+ anhydrous | splitting of N-terminal residue and cyclization

C₆H₅—NH—C(N)(S)(C=O)CHR¹ + H_2N—CHR²—CO—NH—CHR³....

repeat reaction, degradation, and analysis

Thiazolinone

rearrangement

S=C(NH)(N—C₆H₅)(C=O)CHR¹

Phenylthiohydantoin for chromatographic analysis

chain with the same number of residues, and in fact they differ in sequence in only 18 out of 153 positions. Closer study reveals that 11 of the 18 differences clearly involve the substitutions of structurally related amino acids, that is, an acidic amino acid replaces another (position 4, for example), a non-polar amino acid replaces another (position 21, for example), and so forth. Thus, only 7 distinct variations occur (position 132, for example). In contrast to the above generalizations of sequence dissimilarity among proteins of different function in the same organism or species, this pattern of sequence similarity is true of any two proteins of similar function that occur in different organisms. Extensive sequence studies on specific proteins that are found in nearly all organisms, such as cytochrome *c*, have shown rather convincingly that the extent of similarity is correlated with evolutionary relationships, with less sequence variation being common to the protein in organisms of the same phylogenetic class.

Having emphasized the element of sequence similarity in this type of situation, let us not neglect to recognize the fact that sequence variations do exist for the same protein occurring in different organisms, be they of the same or different species. More frequently than not, these variations are related to variations in biological function.

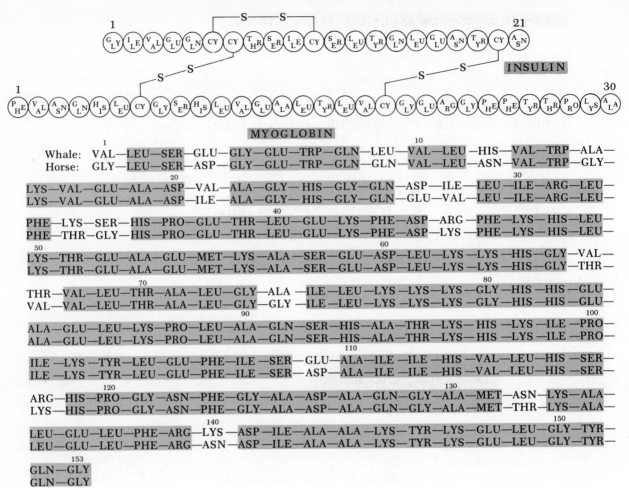

Figure 4–6 *Top:* amino acid sequence of the two polypeptide chains of human insulin. *Below:* amino acid sequence of the globin portion of myoglobin from the whale and horse. Solid lines shown in the globin sequences identify identical regions in the sequence of the two globin polypeptides. (Neither of these representations is intended to portray any three-dimensional character whatsoever. The three-dimensional structure of myoglobin can be found in Figure 4–8.)

BIOLOGICAL SIGNIFICANCE OF AMINO ACID SEQUENCE

The importance of amino acid sequence has been debated extensively. Currently, the school of thought with most support is one which proposes that the *higher orders of protein structure, in particular the overall conformation, and the biological activity of the protein are both intimately dependent upon and in fact controlled by the amino acid sequence.* A convincing argument favoring this principle was supplied by the chemical synthesis of the enzyme ribonuclease by Merrifield. After the polypeptide was assembled with a sequence identical to that known for native ribonuclease, the synthetic product was tested for biological activity with positive results. The ability of the synthetic material to function in a manner identical to that of natural enzyme suggests that the synthetic product did assume a three-dimensional conformation, which conferred on it the unique catalytic properties of ribonuclease. The only logical explanation is that the proper conformation was assumed as a result of the 124 amino acid residues being positioned in the order unique for ribonuclease. It is uncertain whether the conformation developed gradually during the assembly process or was formed after the product was liberated from the ion exchange column. Although there is no categorical evidence to verify that the conformations of the synthetic and natural enzymes are identical, it is quite probable that they are very similar. An X-ray analysis to demonstrate that such is indeed the case would appear to be a logical next step.

Another illustration of this tenet is provided from studies of *sickle cell anemia,* a hereditary disease of the red blood cells characterized by a low oxygen-binding capacity. The malfunction is attributable to the presence of abnormal hemoglobin molecules (HbS) in sickle cells—so named because of the characteristically abnormal shape they assume when the oxygen tension is low. Further investigation revealed that the malfunction of the hemoglobin molecule was associated with a single abnormal variation in the amino acid sequence of the β-chain. Specifically, valine is present in place of the normal glutamic acid residue in position 6. This is the *only* difference in sequence between HbS and normal adult hemoglobin (HbA) and is exemplary of the tenet stated previously. It would be incorrect, however, to conclude that every amino acid residue is similarly characterized as indispensable to the normal functioning of hemoglobin. Many other hemoglobin variants have been detected in *homo sapiens*; some of these are not associated with any respiratory deficiencies and, for all practical purposes, such hemoglobin molecules function normally.

In view of these and other studies, we can now formulate an important generalization concerning the molecular design in nature. Namely, *the structural and functional individuality of a protein is predicated on its unique amino acid sequence, with certain residues or small segments of adjacent residues playing crucial and indispensable roles.* Due to advances in biochemical genetics, we can extend the substance of this generalization even further by pointing out that the *amino acid sequence of a protein is genetically controlled.* Our current understanding of the molecular mechanics of this control will be discussed in other chapters, especially Chapter 18. Nevertheless, the profundity of the above statements can be appreciated at this time and should not be overlooked. In general terms, the statements mean that the genetic essence of any individual is manifested by the type of proteins found in the organism. In other words, any given function(s) is characteristic of an organism that possesses a gene(s) programmed for the synthesis of a specific protein(s) responsible for that function(s): No protein—no function! As a corollary, it should be noted that the explanation of certain physiological abnormalities can be reduced to malfunctional genes which contain a molecular program directing the assembly of malfunctional proteins (altered sequence of essential amino acids) or no protein at all. Finally, it should be recognized that this analysis also accounts for the fact that not every change in the genetic program of an organism—that is, a mutation—results in a modified individual with modified functions. On the contrary, because permissible replacements of amino acid residues can occur without any significant alteration in the structure or function of a protein, a certain amount of molecular flexibility does exist in nature. This latitude provides in part for the perpetuation of a normal species, even though minor changes may occur in the genetic program. Similar reasoning is consistent with the minor species variations that are common to the amino acid sequence in the same protein isolated from different sources, as previously illustrated with myoglobin.

SECONDARY STRUCTURE

The anatomy of a fully extended peptide chain of L-amino acids was discussed and diagrammed on page 78. In proteins, however, the polypeptide backbone does not normally possess this idealized type of conformation. Rather, it exists in an *ordered helical conformation,* an *ordered pleated-sheet conformation,* or a *disordered random-chain* conformation. The helical and sheet conformations are stabilized by hydrogen bonding (page 56, Chapter 3), whereas the random structure possesses no real stabilizing force except the covalent bonds that constitute the peptide chain itself. A random conformation is permissible because of the potential for free rotation ($\circlearrowleft$) that exists around the bonds, involving the alpha (α) carbons.

$$\sim\sim\text{RHC}^\alpha \circlearrowleft \text{N} \overset{\displaystyle\overset{O}{\|}}{\underset{\displaystyle\underset{H}{|}}{\text{—C—}}} \circlearrowleft \text{C}^\alpha\text{HR} \sim\sim$$

The helical conformation was first reported by L. Pauling and R. B. Corey in the early 1950's based on X-ray diffraction analyses (see page 30, Chapter 2) of synthetic polypeptides. A variety of helical arrangements are possible, but the one that predominates in nature is the *right-handed form of the α-helix.* The Greek letter designation refers to the number of residues that define one complete turn of the helix, with the α-helix having 3.6 residues per turn. An artist's sketch and a space-filling model of a segment of the alpha helix are shown in Figure 4-7.

The helical conformation represents a constrained chain and would not exist without the presence of stabilizing force. This role is fulfilled by hydrogen bonding that is prevalent along the chain. Note that the hydrogen bonding is *intrachain* in this case and involves the $\diagdown\text{C}=\text{O}$ and $\text{H}-\text{N}\diagup$ groupings of the peptide bonds, which are separated by roughly one turn in the helix. The optimum, nearly planar, alignment of all four atoms in the two dipoles is a consequence of the geometry of the peptide bond itself, which was discussed on page 77. The molecular fitness is remarkable. The right-handed helix is energetically favored over a left-handed helix due to the projection of the bulky amino acid side chains away from the main axis in the former, which minimizes steric hindrance.

The helical content of globular proteins varies from protein to protein, with none having 100% helicity. The majority contain a mixture of the random coil and helical conformation. The interested reader is referred to more advanced texts for information on the experimental methods for the measurement of the content of alpha helix in a polypeptide.

The second type of ordered conformation, the pleated-sheet structure, is also stabilized by hydrogen bonding. In this instance the hydrogen bonding still involves the $\diagdown\text{C}=\text{O}$ and $\text{H}-\text{N}\diagup$ groupings, but occurs on an *interchain* basis as shown on the following page.

The sheet structure is characteristic of many fibrous proteins as a

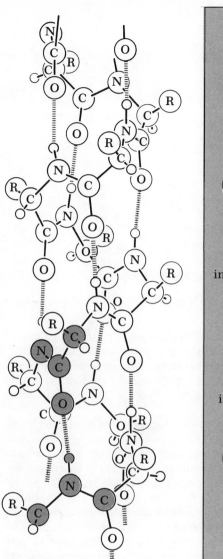

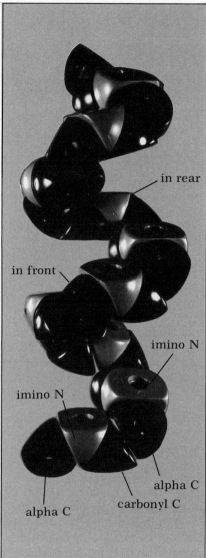

in rear

in front

imino N

imino N

alpha C

alpha C

carbonyl C

C=O

H

N

studs indicating positions of R groupings

Figure 4–7 The alpha helix conformation of a polypeptide chain. *Left:* A stick model. *Center:* A space-filling model of the backbone of the polypeptide chain. The model corresponds to the segment at the left. *Right:* Photo of the chain in the center panel with all carbonyl oxygens, imino hydrogens, and alpha carbon hydrogens inserted. The R groups of the alpha carbons are shown as studs so as not to obstruct the view of the hydrogen bonds that exist between different turns of the helix. (Drawing of the stick model reprinted from Pauling, L.: *The Nature of the Chemical Bond.* Copyright 1939 and 1940 by Cornell University. 3rd edition, 1960, by Cornell University. Used by permission of Cornell University Press.)

stabilizing force in the fibril alignment of separate chains. It does not appear to be prevalent in the globular proteins. Since we will be concerned primarily with the latter, the pleated-sheet conformation will not be discussed further.

TERTIARY STRUCTURE

The complete three-dimensional orientation of the polypeptide backbone and every atom or group of atoms attached to it constitutes the ultimate reality of protein structure. In this context it should be noted that, even though gross similarities do occur among the globular proteins, *every protein possesses a unique spatial conformation conferred on it by the* sheet conformation

all atoms in face of pleat are coplanar

amino acid sequence which uniquely defines each protein. An extension of this principle which has paramount importance is that the functional specificity of a protein is directly based on its specific conformation. That is to say, a protein has a specific biochemical function due to its specific conformation, which in turn is based on its specific amino acid sequence.

Knowledge of molecular structure in this detail is gained by X-ray diffraction studies of a protein crystal or a powdered sample. It is definitely not a weekend experiment. Even under the direction of specialized investigators with skilled technicians, the task is enormous. Frequently, a complete analysis requires years of study. Through the brilliant efforts of J. C. Kendrew, M. F. Perutz, and coworkers, initial success was reached in 1960 in unraveling the structural details of myoglobin, the oxygen-carrying protein of mammalian muscle consisting of a single polypeptide chain containing 153 amino acid residues and one prosthetic group, namely, an iron-containing tetrapyrrole group called *heme*. At about the same time, Perutz and coworkers began work on hemoglobin, the oxygen-carrying protein in blood, consisting of four polypeptide chains with a total of 574 amino acid residues and 4 heme groups (see next page). The study was successful, but for obvious reasons required a much greater effort, with the final solution being reported only recently. For their pioneering studies of protein structure by X-ray diffraction analysis, Kendrew and Perutz jointly received the Nobel Prize in 1962.

The heme grouping is a bulky planar ring system composed of four *pyrrole* units connected by methenyl (=CH—) bridges. The iron atom, with a coordination number of 6, is located in the core of the tetrapyrrole ring and is complexed to each of the four pyrrole nitrogens. In both myoglobin and hemoglobin, the iron is generally in the ferrous state (+2). There is strong evidence that the heme grouping is complexed to the polypeptide chain (globin) through a specific histidine residue (HIS) which occupies the fifth coordination site of iron. In hemoglobin, four such heme-polypeptide complexes exist (see page 95). When the proteins are oxygenated, the oxygen is transported as a ligand complexed to the sixth coordination site of iron. Various hemes are differentiated by the side chains of each pyrrole unit. The groups shown below are characteristic of myoglobin and hemoglobin.

Pyrrole

(Imidazole group of HIS)

Heme

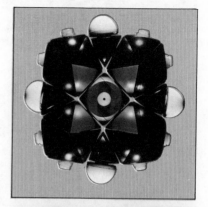

The similarity in function between hemoglobin and myoglobin is not coincidental. Furthermore, it argues for a similarity in structure between the two. In fact, such is the case, with the complete myoglobin molecule representative of each of the four heme-containing polypeptide chains in the tetrameric hemoglobin molecule. These structural and functional similarities suggest an evolutionary relationship among the oxygen-carrying proteins. This has been clearly established, and myoglobin is generally regarded as a molecular cousin of hemoglobin, with both evolving from a common ancestral polypeptide. This is probably a general phenomenon and is a twentieth century extension and refinement of Darwinian evolution. That is to say, *the higher life forms are physiological manifestations of a progressive evolution and natural selection of molecules.*

The structure of myoglobin was constructed by a sophisticated analysis of X-ray diffraction patterns as shown in Figure 4–8 (Panel A). Several such patterns were obtained from the same sample studied at different angles. With the indispensable aid of a computer, the intensity of diffraction at each point can be calculated, as well as the spacings between each point. The final studies of Kendrew and coworkers involved the determination of approximately 25,000 reflections, permitting the measurement of electron density at roughly 250,000 points in the molecule. This provided a resolution of 1.4Å, which was sufficient to localize nearly every atom in the molecule. These data then served as a basis for the construction of a three-dimensional electron density contour map (Figure 4–8, Panel B), which was then translated into a molecular model (Figure 4–8, Panels C and F). The principle of a highly ordered, specifically folded, compact structure of a globular protein is quite evident. It is important to note that this tortuous and irregular conformation does not represent a random or accidental orientation. On the con-

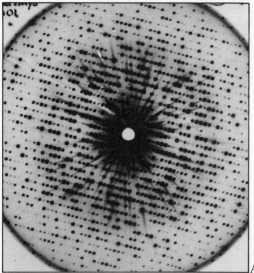

A

B

Figure 4–8 Myoglobin structure. *Panel A:* X-ray diffraction photograph of a myoglobin crystal. The calculation of the intensity of each reflection (dots) is used as the basis for reconstructing a three-dimensional electron density distribution, which is most conveniently represented as a series of contour maps plotted on parallel transparent sheets as shown in *Panel B*. The intense doughnut-shaped area in the center right of Panel B corresponds to an alpha helix segment of the polypeptide chain viewed from one end. A similar but much clearer view of the same thing is shown in the upper left of *Panel C*, which is an enlarged photo of a three-dimensional electron density distribution contour map. Panel C also shows a side view of the planar heme grouping. Also visible are the linkages of the heme grouping to the imidazole side chain of a histidine residue (at seven o'clock) and to a water residue (at one o'clock). *Panel D* diagrammatically summarizes the extent of alpha helical conformation along the polypeptide chain. *Panel E* shows a model of the twists and folds of the polypeptide chain (sausage-shaped) and the orientation of the heme grouping (dark disc at top). *Panel F* is a skeleton model of the myoglobin molecule derived from the contour maps. The white cord follows the course of the polypeptide chain; the heme grouping is located at the upper center with the iron atom (gray sphere) associated with a histidine residue at the left and a water molecule to the right (white sphere). The many projections represent the side chains of the amino acid residues. (Panels A, B, C, E, and F taken with permission from "Myoglobin and the Structure of Proteins," Kendrew, J. C., **Science,** *139,* 1259–1266 (1963). Photographs generously provided by J. C. Kendrew.)

C

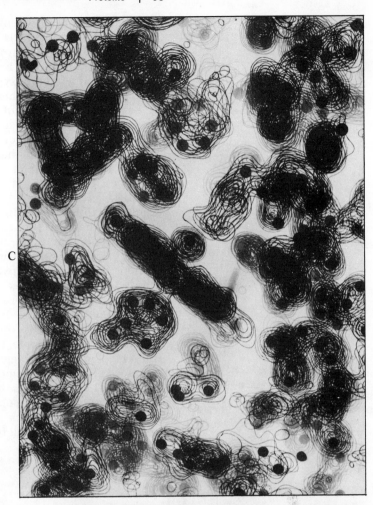

D

Helical segments (70–80%)

Random coil segments (non-helical)

E

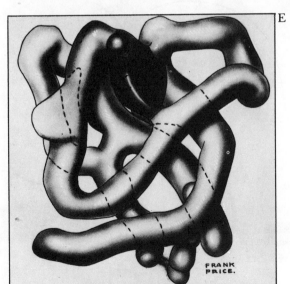

FRANK PRICE.

F

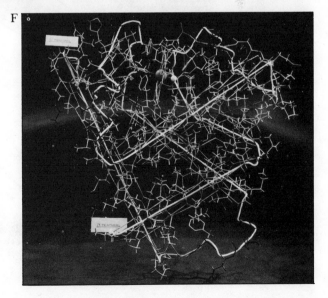

trary, it is quite specific, being assumed every time a myoglobin molecule is synthesized. The same is true of other proteins.

The success with myoglobin is not isolated. To date, the complete structures of hemoglobin, insulin, cytochrome c, lysozyme, ribonuclease, chymotrypsinogen, carboxypeptidase, and lactate dehydrogenase have also been resolved, and others are currently being studied. The latter five are enzymes. Knowledge of their three-dimensional structure promises to contribute immensely to our understanding of how enzymes work. The structure and action of lysozyme are examined in the next chapter.

The specification that the tertiary structure of proteins is an *ordered conformation* of a severely distorted and constrained poly-peptide chain obviously dictates a necessity for *stabilizing forces*. In several cases the presence of one or more disulfide bridges in the primary structure fulfills this function. Such is the case in insulin and lysozyme (page 121, Chapter 5), for example. The covalent disulfide linkage is not the only stabilizing force, however, and in fact is not present at all in several proteins. On the whole, stabilization is mediated largely by non-covalent interactions between certain amino acid side chains. The primary stabilizing forces are: (a) *electrostatic forces of attraction,* localized near the periphery of the molecule, between side chains which possess oppositely charged groups such as lysine and glutamic acid; (b) *non-peptide bond hydrogen bonding* between tyrosine and glutamic acid residues, for example; (c) *peptide bond hydrogen bonding* between different pleated-sheet segments of the chain; and (d) *hydrophobic interactions* among the non-polar side chains of LEU, VAL, ILE, ALA, and PHE. The hydrophobic bond is based on the mutual attraction of the similarly structured non-polar groups, resulting in the mutual exclusion of polar solvent molecules. This type of interaction, proposed to be the most important stabilizing force, is generally found localized within the

Figure 4–9 A diagrammatic representation of stabilizing forces in proteins. Only one of each type of bond is shown. The frequency of occurrence of each type varies from protein to protein.

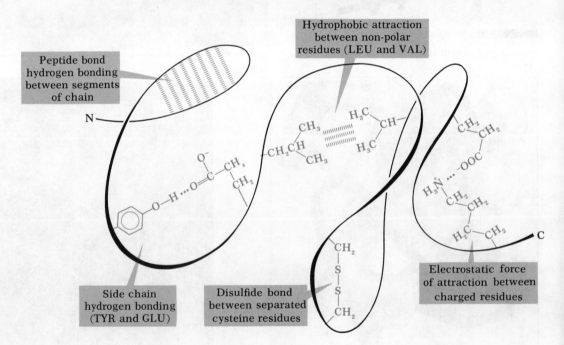

Peptide bond hydrogen bonding between segments of chain

Hydrophobic attraction between non-polar residues (LEU and VAL)

Side chain hydrogen bonding (TYR and GLU)

Disulfide bond between separated cysteine residues

Electrostatic force of attraction between charged residues

core of the molecule, performing the vital function of stabilizing the internal matrix. An illustration of each type of bond is in Figure 4–9.

QUATERNARY STRUCTURE

This level of structure refers to those native proteins which exist as *aggregates of more than one polypeptide chain that are not linked to each other by disulfide bonds or any other type of covalent linkage.* Dimers, trimers, and tetramers are most common. The nature of the interactions that stabilize the aggregate are not yet known with certitude, but electrostatic bonds and hydrogen bonding among side chains localized near the surface of each chain are probably involved. Hydrophobic forces are not likely, since the nonpolar residues are generally localized within the inner core of each globular unit, and thus would not be available for significant surface interactions.

The most classical and most studied example of this type of protein is hemoglobin (Figure 4–10), which is a tetramer consisting of two identical alpha (α) chains and two identical beta (β) chains. Each chain is associated with a heme prosthetic group and, as pointed out previously, is very similar to the myoglobin molecule. Recently, Perutz culminated his years of study on hemoglobin structure with a determination of all the residues that are in contact in both oxygenated and deoxygenated hemoglobin.

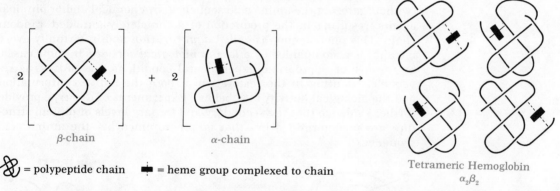

β-chain α-chain   Tetrameric Hemoglobin $\alpha_2\beta_2$

⚖ = polypeptide chain   ▪ = heme group complexed to chain

A special aspect of certain enzyme proteins of this type is their capacity to exist in a variety of hybridized forms called *isoenzymes* or *isozymes*. For example, the enzyme lactate dehydrogenase (LDH) is a tetramer which can contain all possible combinations of two different polypeptide chains designated H and M. The chains are so designated because of their preponderance in either heart (H) or muscle (M) preparations of the enzyme. The possible tetrameric species are HHHH, HHHM, HHMM, HMMM, and MMMM. All have the same enzymatic function (see page 279) but to a different degree. Because each hybridized form contains varying levels of two monomeric polypeptide units that differ in amino acid composition, an LDH preparation can be electrophoretically resolved to reveal the presence of each component. This type of analysis of various LDH tissue preparations followed by quantitative analysis of each component has proven to be a valuable clinical tool in the diagnosis of many respiratory diseases (see page 281).

Figure 4–10 A schematic drawing illustrating the formation of hemoglobin from its constituent units. Each heme-containing chain can be visualized as a molecular cousin to myoglobin, as represented in panel E of Figure 4–8.

CHANGES IN PROTEIN CONFORMATION

Students of biochemistry often interpret the ordered spatial conformation of a protein, as illustrated for myoglobin in Figure 4–8, to represent a rigid, inflexible conformation. This is a false impression, for indeed proteins are not rigid molecules; rather, they are <u>flexible</u> molecules capable of undergoing slight but significant transitions to other conformational states with distinctly different topographical features. Transitions of this type *in vivo* are generally induced through the interaction of the protein with other compounds in the cell. In certain instances, this type of transition may be accompanied by an activation or an inhibition of the biological activity of the protein. For example, the oxygen-binding activity of hemoglobin is stimulated by oxygen itself. The enhancement effect is believed to be mediated by the initial binding of oxygen at one or two of the four heme sites, which then promotes a structural transition of the whole tetrameric molecule, making the binding of oxygen at the remaining heme sites more favorable. Note that this type of structural modification is not permanent and does not involve changes in the primary structure of the protein, but rather a subtle reordering in the spatial arrangment of the polypeptide chain(s). This important principle, termed *allosterism,* will be analyzed further in our discussion of enzyme action in the next chapter.

In addition to being highly ordered and flexible, the optimum conformation of a protein is a very delicate state subject to destruction (without altering the amino acid sequence) by chemical and/or physical agents, resulting in the production of a completely unfolded, random chain. This phenomenon is called *denaturation* and in virtually every instance is accompanied by a *loss in biological activity*. In some cases, by the use of appropriate experimental conditions, the process is reversible, resulting in the restoration of both the native conformation and the biological activity (see below). Experiments of this type provide further evidence that the secondary and tertiary levels of protein structure are predetermined by—that is, programmed by—the amino acid sequence.

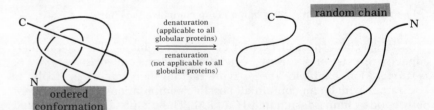

The biochemist must make every effort to prevent denaturation in order to insure substantive studies into the activity of a protein. Accordingly, most of the handling is done at reduced temperatures to avoid thermal denaturation, buffers are employed to maintain the natural polyionic character of the protein, and physical trauma such as shaking is avoided or kept to a minimum. Laboratory investigations dealing with the isolation, purification, and analysis of proteins are truly representative of the art of biochemical analysis.

PROTEIN ISOLATION AND PURIFICATION

Isolation and purification are necessary prerequisites for the study of a protein, whether it be to characterize its structure or its biological function. Despite the relatively advanced state of biochemical methodology, these tasks are easier said than done. Several different steps are generally required, with each designed to eliminate a greater portion of unwanted material from the fraction of the previous step until ultimately the desired protein is obtained in pure, uncontaminated form. Since there is no universally applicable procedure for every protein, the choice of each step must be determined solely on the basis of trial and error. Of course, the most desirable situation is to develop a scheme involving the smallest number of operations required to yield a pure material. Generally speaking, if the investigator can accomplish this objective with three to five steps, he should be pleased. As you might suspect, each step of the procedure requires analyses on the fraction obtained in that step for the total protein concentration and for the activity of the protein being isolated. A demonstration of the purity of the protein in the final fraction is also required.

A typical isolation scheme is illustrated by the data given in Table 4–4 showing the isolation of a protein from bacterial cells. (The protein in question is partially responsible for the movement of simple sugars such as galactose and glucose across the bacterial cell membrane. The proposed function of the protein is to bind with the sugar and then, in conjunction with other membrane components, to transport the sugar to the inside of the cell.) As indicated, the isolation procedure consists of six separate steps. As in any protein isolation procedure, the first step involves rupture of the intact cells to yield a *cell-free extract* (see page 232, Chapter 9). The procedure used in this case was osmotic shock. Washed cells were suspended in a 40% sucrose solution and then transferred to water. The cells lose internal water and shrink in the first phase and then burst when water rushes in during the second phase. The particulate cell debris is removed by centrifugation and the resultant supernatant is the cell-free extract. Other procedures for the preparation of cell-free extracts are discussed in Chapter 9. The treatment with *protamine* does not seem to have accomplished very much in terms of protein enrichment. What does occur is not represented by the data of Table 4–4. Protamine is a very basic protein (high arginine content) and carries a large net positive charge. Therefore, it is a good precipitating agent of substances such as nucleic acids which possess a large net negative charge. This is the role of protamine in this procedure where it removes about 95% of the nucleic acid present in the cell-free extract. The third step consists of an *ammonium sulfate fractionation,* a tactic commonly utilized in protein isolation. Addition of ammonium sulfate to protein solutions decreases the solubility of proteins in that solution. The effect, generally called the *"salting-out" phenomenon,* is dependent on the concentration of ammonium sulfate added and the nature of the protein. The last three steps are *column chromatographic methods* (see Chapter 2) based on anion exchange (DEAE-cellulose), adsorption (hydroxyapatite), and anion exchange plus molecular sieve (DEAE-Sephadex).

Table 4–4 Isolation of galactose-binding protein from *Escherichia coli*.

Steps of isolation	Total protein[a] (mg)	Total binding activity[b] (units)	Specific activity (units/mg)	% yield[c]
1. Cell-free extract	2600	940	0.39	100
2. Protamine precipitation	2352	798	0.34	85
3. Ammonium sulfate precipitation	1664	728	0.43	75
4. DEAE-cellulose chromatography	432	488	1.15	52
5. Hydroxyapatite chromatography	46	322	7.0	34
6. DEAE-Sephadex chromatography	18	208	12.0	22

a. Protein measured by the Lowry method
b. Activity of protein was assayed by placing protein fraction in a semi-permeable tubing and dialyzing for several hours against a solution containing a known amount of C^{14}-galactose. The amount of radioactive galactose bound to the protein was calculated by subtracting the radioactivity of the dialyzate from that in the tubing. Radioactivity measurements were made by liquid scintillation. One unit of binding activity represents the binding of 1×10^{-9} mole of galactose.
c. (Total activity of any step/total activity of initial extract) × 100.
(Data taken with permission; see legend to Figure 4–11.)

The course of the isolation is readily apparent from Figure 4–11. Note the gradual elimination of protein until only one band is observed in disc polyacrylamide gel electrophoresis of the last fraction, suggesting that the sample is pure. The presence of only one symmetrical peak in the analytical ultracentrifuge pattern confirms the purity. The molecular weight of the binding protein computed from the latter is 35,000.

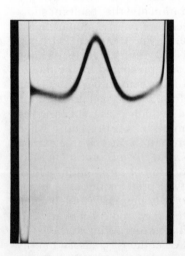
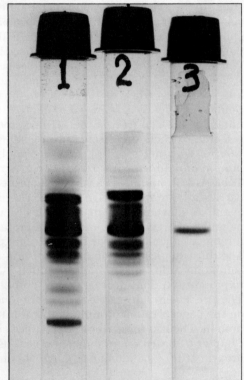

Figure 4–11 *Right:* Photograph of stained polyacrylamide gels showing the progress of the isolation for galactose-binding protein. Tube 1: electrophoresis of the original cell-free extract; tube 2: electrophoresis of the ammonium sulfate fraction; tube 3: electrophoresis of the DEAE-Sephadex fraction. *Left:* Photograph of the optical pattern observed in the analytical ultracentrifuge of boundary movement for the DEAE-Sephadex fraction. (Reproduced with permission from "Transport of Sugars and Amino Acids in Bacteria," Anraku, Y., *J. Biol. Chem.*, **243**, 3116–3122; 3123–3127 (1968). Photographs generously supplied by Y. Anraku.)

LITERATURE

AGRANOFF, B. W., "Memory and Protein Biosynthesis," *Scientific American,* **216,** 115–122 (1967). A synopsis of an interesting series of experiments illustrating that trained goldfish forget learned tasks when injected with certain drugs that block the manufacture of protein in brain cells.

ANFINSEN, C. B., "Molecular Structure and the Function of Proteins," in *Molecular Organization and Biological Function,* J. M. Allen, Editor, 1–19. New York: Harper & Row, Publishers, 1967. A brief and informative statement on the relationship of amino acid sequence to three-dimensional conformation and biological function of proteins.

ANFINSEN, C. B., M. L. ANSON, K. BAILEY, J. T. EDSALL, and F. M. T. RICHARDS (eds.), *Advances in Protein Chemistry.* New York: Academic Press. A multi-volume reference work (annual volumes) begun in 1944 and devoted to the proteins. Advanced reading.

DICKERSON, R. E., and I. GIES, *The Structure and Action of Proteins.* New York: Harper & Row, Publishers, 1969. A lucid and modern introduction to the structure and function of proteins. The book contains a wealth of imaginative and highly informative drawings, many of which are available in color slides.

GLASSMAN, E., "The Biochemistry of Learning: An Evaluation of the Role of RNA and Protein," in *Annual Review of Biochemistry,* Volume 38, 605–646 (1969). A review article of a fascinating subject mentioned briefly in this chapter.

HIRS, C. H. W. (ed.), *Enzyme Structure.* Volume 11 of *Methods in Enzymology,* Colowick, S. P., and N. O. Kaplan (eds.). New York: Academic Press, 1967. Part of a multi-volume work devoted to practical aspects of biochemical studies, particularly those dealing with the isolation and assay of enzymes. Volume 11 contains much information on the techniques available for the study of primary level of protein structure such as amino acid composition; end group analysis; separation of polypeptide subunits; cleavage of disulfide bonds; separation of peptides; and sequence determination.

KENDREW, J. C., "Myoglobin and the Structure of Proteins," *Science,* **139,** 1259–1266 (1963). A paper adapted from the author's address on accepting the Nobel Prize in Chemistry in 1962. Emphasis is given to the use of X-ray crystallography in deciphering protein structures. The treatment is non-mathematical and suitable for beginning students. Several figures from this paper are reproduced in this chapter.

KLOTZ, I. M., N. R. LANGERMAN, and D. W. DARNALL, "Quaternary Structure of Proteins" in *Annual Review of Biochemistry,* Volume 39, 25–62 (1970). A review article summarizing the subunit aspect of protein structure. This article contains the most complete listing (through 1969) of proteins composed of two or more polypeptide chains.

LEHNINGER, A., *Biochemistry.* New York: Worth Publishers, Inc., 1970. A new and acclaimed biochemistry textbook. Chapters 3, 4, 5, 6, and 7 deal with various aspects of proteins. The treatment is general and less rigorous than that in the text by Mahler and Cordes.

MAHLER, H. R., and E. H. CORDES, *Biological Chemistry,* Second Edition. New York: Harper & Row, Publishers, 1971. A highly regarded but advanced textbook. Chapters 2 and 3 are devoted to amino acids, peptides, and proteins. The treatment is primarily physicochemical.

MEISTER, A., *Biochemistry of the Amino Acids,* Second Edition. New York: Academic Press, 1965. An authoritative two-volume work devoted exclusively to the isolation, occurrence, structure, and metabolism of the amino acids. Many references to the original literature.

MERRIFIELD, R. B., "The Automatic Synthesis of Proteins," *Scientific American,* **218,** 56–74 (1968). A synopsis of the chemical methodology of solid-phase peptide synthesis, with specific details on the synthesis of insulin.

NEURATH, H. (ed.), *The Proteins.* New York: Academic Press. A five-volume reference work begun in 1963 and dealing with the isolation, composition, structure, and function of proteins. Volumes 1 and 2 treat most of the subjects dealt with in this chapter and more. Later volumes are devoted to specific types of proteins.

NOLAN, C., and E. MARGOLIASH, "Comparative Aspects of Primary Structure of Proteins," in *Annual Review of Biochemistry,* Volume 38, 727–790 (1968). An excellent and thorough review article discussing comparative studies of the amino acid sequences of proteins as they relate to evolutionary, developmental, and genetic mechanisms as well as to the structure–function principle.

PAULING, L., R. B. COREY, and H. R. BRANSON, "The Structure of Proteins: Two Hydrogen-Bonded Helical Configurations of the Polypeptide Chain," *Proc. Natl. Acad. Sci., U.S.,* **37,** 205–211 (1951). The original paper describing the nature of the alpha helix.

PERUTZ, M. F., "The Hemoglobin Molecule," *Scientific American,* **211,** 64–76 (1964). A description of the three-dimensional structure of the hemoglobin molecule by the primary investigator.

STEWART, J. M., and J. D. YOUNG, *Solid Phase Peptide Synthesis.* San Francisco: W. H. Freeman and Company, 1969. A detailed description of the technique developed by R. B. Merrifield.

ZUCKERHANDL, E., "The Evolution of Hemoglobin," *Scientific American,* **212,** 110–118 (1965). An article comparing the amino acid sequences of the alpha and beta chains of hemoglobin molecules from different species and showing how this provides a basis of establishing evolutionary relationships among organisms on a chemical level in terms of the evolution of a molecule common to these organisms.

EXERCISES

4-1 For each of the amino acids given below, write the equilibrium reactions that would apply at a pH corresponding to each of the pK_a values for each amino acid.
a) alanine
b) glutamic acid
c) arginine

4-2 Would the three amino acids listed in exercise 4–1 be completely separated from each other by electrophoresis in an electrolytic buffer solution at pH 2, pH 7, or pH 12? Explain.

4-3 At what approximate pH would each of the amino acids listed in exercise 4–1 exist almost exclusively in an isoelectric form? Write the structures of the isoelectric species.

4-4 Write the complete structure of the following peptides.
a) glutamyl-valyl-glycine
b) leucyl-methionyl-alanine
c) phenylalanyl-arginyl-tryptophanyl-serine
d) ileu-asn-gly-his-lys-glu-gln-arg

4-5 Classify each of the peptides given in exercise 4–4 as (a) a basic peptide; (b) an acidic peptide; or (c) a neutral peptide.

4–6 For each of the peptides given below, indicate which bonds would be cleaved by the action of (a) trypsin; (b) chymotrypsin; (c) cyanogen bromide; (d) hydrazine; (e) aminopeptidase; and (f) dilute hydrochloric acid and heat. (Assume that the specificity of trypsin and chymotrypsin is limited to text description.)

a) arg-lys-gly-ala-ser-asp-asp-arg-ala-ser-cySH

b) glu-tyr-lys-met-lys-phe-gly-val-thr-met-leu-val

c) phe-trp-lys-tyr-ileu-arg-val-ile-val-trp-glu

4–7 How many peptide fragments would be obtained from the treatment of the globin moiety of myoglobin with (a) trypsin, and (b) chymotrypsin? (Assume that the specificity of each enzyme is ideally limited to text description.)

4–8 A pentapeptide obtained from treatment of a protein with trypsin was shown to contain arginine, aspartic acid, leucine, serine, and tyrosine. To determine the amino acid sequence, the peptide was cycled through the Edman degradation procedure three times. The composition of the peptide remaining after each cycling was as follows:

After Cycle 1:   arginine, aspartic acid, leucine, serine

After Cycle 2:   arginine, aspartic acid, serine

After Cycle 3:   arginine, serine

What is the sequence of the pentapeptide?

4–9 What information—not given in this chapter—would you need to predict whether the total length of a polypeptide chain existing entirely in the alpha helix conformation should be greater than or less than if it existed in the pleated-sheet conformation? Explain.

4–10 Summarize the nature of each type of bond listed below and its role in protein structure.

a) peptide bond

b) disulfide bond

c) hydrogen bond

d) electrostatic bond

e) hydrophobic bond

4–11 Explain why the carbonyl oxygen and the imino hydrogen atoms contributed by the same peptide bond do not enter into hydrogen bond formation with each other.

4–12 If a mixture containing (1) the coat protein of tobacco mosaic virus, (2) lysozyme, and (3) cytochrome C were applied to the top of a polyacrylamide gel and then analyzed by electrophoresis at pH 6, which of the following patterns would best represent the appearance of the gel after staining to detect the positions of the proteins? (The data given in Table 4–2 will be helpful in solving this problem. Assume that each acidic and basic residue would contribute a +1 and −1 charge, respectively, to each intact protein.)

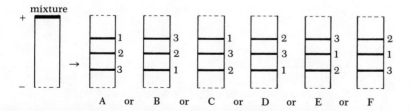

4–13 If a mixture containing proteins A, B, and C were analyzed by gel permeation column chromatography, which of the following elution profiles would best represent the differential movement of A, B, and C through the column? (Given: Molecular weights of A, B, and C are 150,000, 75,000, and 65,000, respectively. The swollen gel granules had an exclusion limit of approximately 100,000).

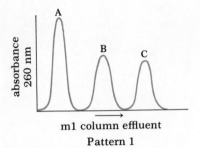

Pattern 1

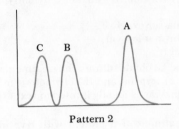

Pattern 2

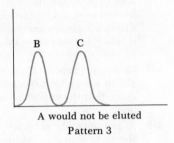

A would not be eluted

Pattern 3

4-14 Two pure proteins (A and B), each with a molecular weight of 60,000, underwent dissociation in the presence of urea. Sedimentation analysis in the ultracentrifuge showed that the urea-treated A sample gave two separate boundaries, neither of which corresponded to the original untreated A protein. The urea-treated B sample, on the other hand, gave only one boundary, but it likewise did not correspond to the original untreated B sample. What conclusions can you draw from these statements concerning the structures of proteins A and B?

4-15 The complete hydrolysis of an unknown nonapeptide revealed the presence of glutamic acid, 2 valine, glycine, 2 lysine, tyrosine, threonine, and phenylalanine residues. The first amino acid to be detected as a phenylthiohydantoin derivative on Edman degradation of the peptide was glutamic acid. The only amino acid detected after treating the peptide with hydrazine was threonine. Treatment of the peptide with trypsin and chymotrypsin gave three fragments in each case: T1, T2, T3 and C1, C2, C3, respectively. None of the trypsin fragments were identical to the chymotrypsin fragments. C2 and T2 proved to be dipeptides; C1 and T1 were tripeptides; and C3 and T3 were tetrapeptides. Hydrolysis of C3 followed by paper chromatography revealed only three ninhydrin-sensitive spots. The N-terminal residue of T3 was shown to be phenylalanine and the C-terminus was threonine. The N-terminus of C1 was glycine and the C-terminus was the same as in T3. C2 was shown to contain tyrosine and glutamic acid. T1 was composed of lysine, tyrosine, and glutamic acid. The N-terminus of T2 was valine and the N-terminus of C3 was lysine. At basic pH the C3 fragment migrated with a net charge of +2. Use all of this information to construct a sequence for the original nonapeptide. (Assume that the specificity of trypsin and chymotrypsin is limited to text description.)

5

Enzymes

The most distinguishing feature of reactions that occur in a living cell is the participation of biocatalytic proteins, called *enzymes*. The basic property of an enzyme—as with any catalyst—is to increase the rate of a reaction. Enzymes, however, are characterized by three unequalled catalytic effects. First, they are the *most efficient* catalysts yet known to man, with micromolar quantities accelerating cellular reactions at extremely fast rates. Second, the majority of enzymes are distinguished by a *specificity of action*. Virtually every conversion of a reactant, termed a *substrate*, to a product is catalyzed by a preferred enzyme. The third and perhaps most remarkable characteristic is that the *activity of enzymes is subject to regulation,* with the regulatory stimulus or agent being either intracellular or extracellular. In either case the effect is the same, namely, the catalytic activity of an enzyme, or in many cases a group of enzymes, is reduced or enhanced, resulting in the metabolic control of the whole organism.

Although the study of enzymes and enzyme action (enzymology) is a biochemical specialization in itself, it is not an isolated domain with the acquired knowledge being of interest and utility only to the enzymologist. On the contrary, the study of enzymes is central to all of the biological sciences. This central position is a consequence of the phenomenon stated in the preceding chapter, that is, that the biochemical genetic individuality of any cell can, to a large degree, be extrapolated to its unique complement of enzymatic proteins with their regulatory properties.

The first enzyme to be isolated was urease in 1923 by Sumner. In the half-century that has elapsed since then, the number of enzymes that have been isolated has grown to approximately 1000. Most have

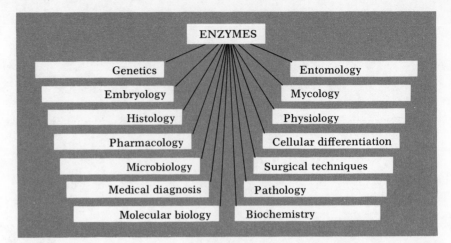

been isolated and studied as purified aqueous preparations and several have been crystallized. At the time of this writing, models of three-dimensional conformation based on X-ray analyses have been proposed for seven, with the enzyme lysozyme being the most clearly understood.

In this chapter we will examine the basic principles of enzymes and their action. Particular attention will be given to relating how the catalytic function of an enzyme is related to its chemical structure, and to an analysis of how certain enzymes are regulated at the cellular level. Both subjects, however, will be preceded by a development of the classical *Michaelis-Menten theory of enzyme kinetics,* which has guided the study of enzymes for approximately 40 years.

CLASSIFICATION OF ENZYMES

TRIVIAL AND SYSTEMATIC METHODS

Enzymes are distinguished and hence classified on the basis of the type of chemical reaction that they catalyze. Prior to 1965 enzymes were designated by descriptive but relatively non-systematic methods of nomenclature. The most direct tactic was to merely add the suffix *-ase* to the name of the substrate. For example, the enzyme which converts the disaccharide *maltose* to two glucose units was called *maltase.* Another ramification was to similarly modify a word to indicate the type of chemical change that the substrate undergoes. For example, the enzyme converting lactic acid to pyruvic acid would be named *lactic acid dehydrogenase,* since the process can be described as a dehydrogenation of an alpha hydroxy acid to an alpha keto acid. Many were given trivial names that were totally non-descriptive, such as the proteolytic enzymes of the intestinal tract—chymotrypsin, trypsin, and pepsin. As more enzymes were discovered, this system generated a lot of confusion and resulted in the formulation of a new systematic scheme by the International Enzyme Commission in 1964.

The new system, outlined in Table 5–1, categorizes all enzymes into six main classes in terms of the general type of chemical reaction

maltose

$\downarrow$ *maltase*

2 (glucose)

$$\underset{\text{H}}{\overset{\text{OH}}{\text{CH}_3-\overset{|}{\underset{|}{\text{C}}}-\text{COOH}}}$$

lactic acid

$\downarrow$ *lactic acid dehydrogenase*

2H's $\leftarrow$

$$\text{CH}_3-\overset{\text{O}}{\overset{||}{\text{C}}}-\text{COOH}$$

pyruvic acid

in which they participate. It is interesting to note that, of the thousands of reactions that occur in nature, chemically speaking, they can be grouped into only six classes. Each main class contains subclasses, sub-subclasses, and sub-sub-subclasses which are designed to classify each enzyme as a unique entity. In addition, a numbering system is used throughout the scheme which permits the designation of each enzyme by a numerical code system such as 2.1.3.4., where the first number specifies the main class and the remaining numbers respectively correspond to specific subdivisions. An example is given in Table 5–1.

Table 5–1 A partial outline of the systematic classification of enzymes.

1. **Oxidoreductases** (oxidation–reduction reactions of all types)

   1.1.   Acting on $\diagdown$CH—OH group of substrate

   1.1.1.   Requires NAD^+ or $NADP^+$ as hydrogen acceptor
   1.1.1.1. Specific substrate is ethyl alcohol

   Example

   Reaction: $CH_2CH_2OH + NAD^+ \rightarrow CH_3CHO + NADH + H^+$ (see page 267)
   Systematic Name: alcohol:NAD oxidoreductase (1.1.1.1.)
   Trivial Name: alcohol dehydrogenase (see Table 5–2)

2. **Transferases** (reactions involving the transfer of an intact group of atoms from a donor to an acceptor molecule)
   2.1. Transfer of methyl groups
   2.4. Transfer of glycosyl groups
   2.7. Transfer of phosphorus-containing groups

   Example

   Reaction: creatine + ATP $\rightarrow$ phosphocreatine + ADP (see page 290)
   Systematic Name: ATP:creatine transferase (2.7.3.2)
   Trivial Name: creatine kinase (see Table 5–2)

3. **Hydrolases** (reactions involving the hydrolytic cleavage of chemical bonds)
   3.1 Hydrolysis of ester bonds
   3.2 Hydrolysis of glycoside bonds
   3.4 Hydrolysis of peptide bonds

   Example

   Reaction: glucose-6-phosphate + $H_2O \rightarrow$ glucose + phosphate (see page 286)
   Systematic Name: glucose-6-phosphate phosphohydrolase (3.1.3.9)
   Trivial Name: glucose-6-phosphatase

4. **Lyases** (reactions involving the addition of groups to substrates containing double bonds, or the non-hydrolytic removal of groups from substrates to yield products with double bonds)
   4.1 Carbon-carbon lyases
   4.2 Carbon-oxygen lyases
   4.4 Carbon-sulfur lyases

   Example

   Reaction: L-histidine $\rightarrow$ histamine + CO_2 (see page 421)
   Systematic Name: histidine decarboxylase (4.1.1.)
   Trivial Name: same as systematic name

Table 5-1 (Continued)

5. **Isomerases** (reactions involving any type of isomerization such as racemization, epimerization, and *cis-trans* isomerizations)
   5.1 Racemization and epimerization
   5.2 *Cis-trans* isomerization

   Example

   Reaction: D-ribulose-5-phosphate → D-xylulose-5-phosphate (see page 294)
   Systematic Name: D-ribulose-5-phosphate 3-epimerase (5.1.3.1)
   Trivial Name: phosphoribuloepimerase

6. **Ligases** (reactions involving the formation of a product resulting from the condensation of two different molecules coupled with the breaking of a pyrophosphate linkage in ATP)
   6.1 Forming carbon-oxygen bonds
   6.2 Forming carbon-sulfur bonds
   6.3 Forming carbon-nitrogen bonds
   6.4 Forming carbon-carbon bonds

   Example

   Reaction: L-amino acid + tRNA + ATP → amino acyl ~ tRNA + AMP + PP$_i$
   (see page 501)
   Systematic Name: L-amino acid:tRNA ligase (AMP) (6.1.1.1)
   Trivial Name: aminoacyl~tRNA synthetase

Although many of the trivial and non-systematic names are recognized as accepted synonyms due to their wide familiarity resulting from prolonged usage, the modern classification is now demanded and utilized in most of the professional chemical and biochemical journals and scientific abstract services. However, the older system is still widely practiced, most commonly in monographs and textbooks. Despite the limitations of the older system, it probably has more pedagogical value and thus it will be employed in this book. Accordingly then, the main groupings of the older scheme are outlined in Table 5–2. It is of basic importance that you become familiar with these terms as well as with those of Table 5–1. Imperfect as they may be in appearance, they are part of the routine language of enzymology and they will be used extensively in future chapters.

COFACTOR-DEPENDENT ENZYMES

Another classification scheme is possible on the principle that all enzymes can be broadly segregated into two groups according to the basis for their catalytic activity. One group would include any enzyme whose function is due solely to its protein nature. The second group would include all other enzymes whose catalytic properties, though indeed still related to their protein nature, are dependent for optimal activity on the presence of a heat-stable, non-protein structure called a *cofactor*. Cofactors may vary in nature from simple inorganic ions such as Zn^{++}, Mg^{++}, Mn^{++}, Fe^{++}, Fe^{+++}, Cu^{++}, K^+, and Na^+ to more complex organic materials such as the cobamide derivatives (see page 441). The organic cofactors—many of which are derivatives of *vitamins*—are generally termed *coenzymes*.

Dehydrogenases (1): Loss of hydrogen from substrate (S) with the acceptor (A) being something other than molecular oxygen.

$$SH_2 + A \leftrightarrow S + AH_2$$

Oxidases (1): Loss of hydrogen with acceptor being molecular oxygen.

$$SH_2 + \tfrac{1}{2}O_2 \leftrightarrow S + H_2O$$

or

$$SH_2 + O_2 \leftrightarrow S + H_2O_2$$

Kinases (2): Transfer of phosphate group from nucleoside triphosphate (commonly ATP) to substrate molecule.

$$S + ATP \leftrightarrow S{-}OPO_3^= + ADP$$

Phosphatases (3): Hydrolytic cleavage of phosphate esters.

$$S{-}OPO_3^= + H_2O \leftrightarrow S{-}OH + HOPO_3^=$$

Mutases (2): Transfer of a functional group between two positions in the same molecule.

$$\text{glucose-1-phosphate} \leftrightarrow \text{glucose-6-phosphate}$$

Synthetases (6): Condensation of two separate molecules coupled with the cleavage of ATP.

$$\overset{\displaystyle O}{\overset{\|}{CH_3C}}COO^- + CO_2 + ATP \rightarrow {}^-OOCCH_2\overset{\displaystyle O}{\overset{\|}{C}}COO^- + ADP + P_i$$

pyruvate   oxaloacetate

Decarboxylases (4): Decarboxylation of substrate.

$$\overset{\displaystyle O}{\overset{\|}{CH_3C}}COO^- \rightarrow CH_3CHO + CO_2$$

pyruvate   acetaldehyde

Thiokinases (6): ATP-dependent formation of thiol esters.
$$R{-}S{-}\overset{\displaystyle O}{\underset{\|}{C}}{-}R'$$ from Coenzyme A (CoASH) and carboxylic acids.

$$R{-}COO^- + ATP + CoASH \rightarrow RCSCoA + AMP + \text{pyrophosphate (PP}_i)$$
$$\overset{\|}{O}$$

Carboxylases (6): ATP-dependent addition of CO_2 to acceptor substrate.

$$CH_3\overset{\displaystyle}{\underset{\|}{C}}SCoA + ATP + CO_2 \rightarrow {}^-OOCCH_2\overset{\displaystyle}{\underset{\|}{C}}SCoA + AMP + PP_i$$
$$\quad\ O \qquad\qquad\qquad\qquad\qquad\ O$$

(acetyl-SCoA)   (malonyl-SCoA)

Table 5–2 A partial listing of traditional groupings of enzymes. (Numbers in parentheses are for cross-reference to the main classes of the systematic scheme.)

Generally speaking, most cofactors are not tightly bound to the enzyme protein and frequently are lost in the process of isolating the enzyme itself. For example, prolonged dialysis against a small-pore membrane is sufficient to strip the cofactor from the protein if it is

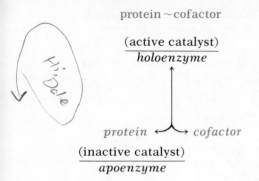

protein ~ cofactor

(active catalyst)

holoenzyme

protein ←→ cofactor

(inactive catalyst)

apoenzyme

loosely bound. In certain cases, however, the cofactor is known to be firmly bound to the protein moiety via a covalent linkage and cannot be removed by simple dialysis. In the classical jargon of enzymology, the complete enzyme-cofactor complex is termed a *holoenzyme,* and the protein component stripped of its cofactor is termed an *apoenzyme.* The apoenzyme is generally inactive as a catalyst.

The cofactors function (a) by complexing with the surface of the enzyme protein to provide an optimal conformation for interaction of the enzyme with the substrate; (b) by actually coordinating themselves between the substrate and the enzyme, thus positioning the two in proper spatial alignment; or (c) by actually participating in the overall reaction as an active agent that accepts a chemical group from the primary substrate and subsequently transfers it to a second substrate in the same or a different reaction. The metal ions participate by any one of these mechanisms, whereas the organic coenzymes normally function as *group transfer agents.* In some cases the original form of the coenzyme is regenerated during the course of the reaction, while in others the coenzyme actually undergoes structural modification. In the latter instance, the original form is usually regenerated by a *coupled reaction.* For example, if the oxidized form of a coenzyme is converted to the reduced form by acting as a hydrogen acceptor for a dehydrogenase in one reaction, the reduced form may then function as a coenzyme by acting as a hydrogen donor in another reaction catalyzed by a different dehydrogenase. The two reactions are thus linked—that is, coupled—to each other by a common participant which is a product in one reaction and a reactant in the other.

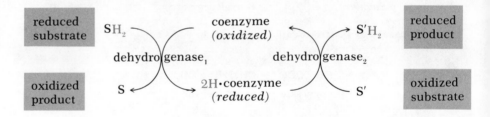

On the coenzyme level, the net effect of the coupled reaction is the metabolic regeneration of the original form of the coenzyme. The coupling phenomenon will be developed more thoroughly in subsequent chapters, especially in the context of energy transfer between separate reactions (see Chapter 10).

Rather than devote a separate chapter to a structural and functional analysis of the coenzymes, we will integrate these principles with appropriate material in future chapters. As a preliminary exposure, however, a listing of the important coenzymes, together with a brief description of their metabolic function, is given in Table 5–3. Note the relationship to the essential vitamins. In some cases the coenzyme is a biosynthetic derivative of the vitamin, whereas in other instances the coenzyme and the vitamin are one and the same.

To recapitulate—the great majority of reactions in any living organism are catalyzed by enzymes, many of which require the simultaneous participation of a cofactor. In the absence of the cofactor, the activity of the enzyme is significantly reduced and even nil. Finally, it should be noted that any one coenzyme will serve as a cofactor for many different proteins. However, the converse is not true, and any one enzyme protein will depend on a specific cofactor or a specific set of cofactors.

CHEMICAL KINETICS

Every enzyme is unique in terms of its structure as a protein. In terms of their function, however, enzymes are less individualistic, as evidenced by the small number of reaction types that they catalyze. That is to say, many enzymes, each with a different structure, catalyze the same type of chemical reaction. It is possible to go one step further and discuss enzymes in a more homogeneous manner by describing their catalytic properties in the language of *chemical kinetics*, a specialized branch

Table 5–3 Coenzymes: Name, function, and vitamin origin.

Coenzyme	Type of Reaction	Group Transferred	Vitamin Precursor*
Nicotinamide adenine dinucleotide (NAD+)	Oxidation–reduction	H (electrons)	Niacin
Nicotinamide adenine dinucleotide phosphate (NADP+)	Oxidation–reduction	H (electrons)	Niacin
Flavin adenine dinucleotide (FAD)	Oxidation–reduction	H (electrons)	Riboflavin
Coenzyme Q	Oxidation–reduction	H (electrons)	—
Cytochrome heme groups	Oxidation–reduction	Electrons	—
Coenzyme A	Activation and transfer of acyl groups	$R-\overset{\overset{O}{\|}}{C}-$	Pantothenic acid
Lipoic acid	Acyl group transfer	$R-\overset{\overset{O}{\|}}{C}-$	Lipoic acid
Thiamine pyrophosphate	Acyl group transfer	$R-\overset{\overset{O}{\|}}{C}-$	Thiamine
Biotin	CO_2 fixation	CO_2	Biotin
Pyridoxal phosphate	Transamination of amino acids	$-NH_2$	Pyridoxal
Tetrahydrofolic acid	Metabolism of one-carbon fragments	$-CH_3$; $-CH_2-$; or $-CHO$	Folic Acid
Cobamide coenzymes	Specialized (see page 441)		B_{12}
Nucleoside triphosphates:			
Adenosine triphosphate (ATP)	Phosphorylation	$-OPO_3$	—
Uridine triphosphate (UTP)	Biosynthesis and interconversion of carbohydrates	glycosyl	—
Cytidine triphosphate (CTP)	Phospholipid biosynthesis	Conjugated glyceride	—

* All the substances listed constitute what is generally termed the group of B vitamins.

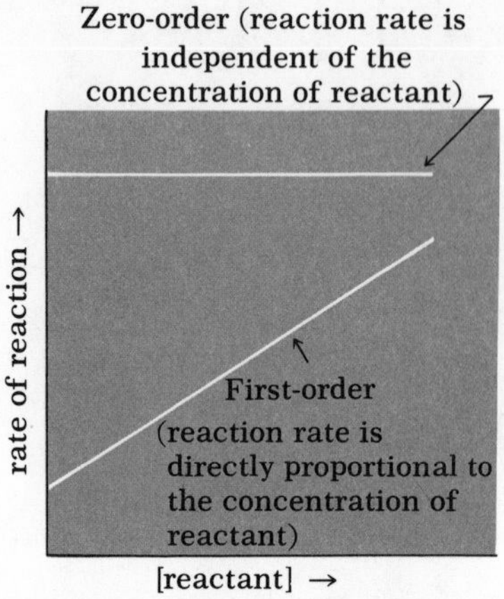

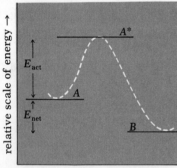

Zero-order (reaction rate is independent of the concentration of reactant)

First-order (reaction rate is directly proportional to the concentration of reactant)

rate of reaction →

[reactant] →

Figure 5–1 A graphical representation of zero-order and first-order chemical kinetics.

of physical chemistry concerned with the study of *reaction rates*. Despite the unifying nature of this approach, however, a comparison of kinetic properties also serves as an additional basis for differentiating the enzymes. The value of a kinetic study cannot be overemphasized for it is the only means whereby the mechanism of a reaction can be determined.

REACTION ORDER

On a molecular level, chemical reactions are classified as being monomolecular reactions, bimolecular reactions, and so on, depending on the number of molecules that must interact prior to product formation. On a kinetic level, reactions are distinguished by their kinetic order, which specifies the dependence of reaction rate on the concentration of reactants. In this context the overall reaction may be termed zero order, first order, and so forth.

The kinetic order of a reaction is determined by experiment and represents a fitting of the experimental data to the rate equation for the reaction in question. As an example, for the reaction, $aA \rightarrow bB$, one can write a general mathematical expression defining the rate of reaction (or velocity of reaction), v, in terms of the disappearance of reactant A with respect to time, $-d[A]/dt$, or the formation of product B with respect to time, $+d[B]/dt$, as follows:

$$v = -\frac{d[A]}{dt} = +\frac{d[B]}{dt} = k_r[A]^n$$

Here k_r corresponds to the *rate constant*, which has a fixed value for the system under a specified set of conditions, with the only variable being the concentration of reactant. The exponent, n, corresponds to the *kinetic (reaction) order*. Thus, by determining the reaction rate with different concentrations of A, the value of n can be determined. Once n is known, k_r can be calculated.

By assigning values to n, the meaning of reaction order becomes apparent and the resultant conclusions are obvious.

when $n = 0$ (zero order): $\qquad v = k_r[A]^0 = k_r$

when $n = 1$ (first order): $\qquad v = k_r[A]^1 = k_r[A] \quad$ or $\quad v \propto [A]$

From these relationships we can see that a *zero-order* reaction is one in which the rate is constant and independent of reactant concentration. A *first-order* reaction, on the other hand, is one in which the rate is directly proportional to the concentration of reactant raised to the first exponential power. Thus, an increase in concentration will result in a linear increase in reaction velocity. These conclusions are graphically depicted in Figure 5–1. These basic principles of chemical kinetics will be most useful in developing the basic principles of enzyme kinetics.

TRANSITION STATE THEORY AND CATALYSIS

Any chemical reaction represents a transition from one state (reactants) to another (products); these states may or may not be distinguished by different energy levels. In either case, however, the progress of the

relative scale of energy →

A^*

E_{act}

A

E_{net}

B

some parameter representative of the progress of reaction →

Figure 5–2 An energy profile diagram of a hypothetical reaction, $A \rightarrow B$. The finite difference between the energy levels of the ground state of reactants and the excited (transition) state of reactants is the energy of activation, E_{act}, for A. The illustration depicts an energy-yielding reaction, with the net output of energy, E_{net}, corresponding to the difference between the ground states of A and B.

reaction—energetically speaking—does not proceed directly from re-actants to products. On the contrary, modern kinetic theory proposes that in every reaction the formation of products is preceded by the formation of a *transition state* representing an *activated (high-energy) state* of the reactant(s), as shown in Figure 5-2. Furthermore, a more important fact is that one of the primary rate-limiting factors of a re-action is the rate at which the concentration of this activated species is produced. This in turn is controlled by three determining elements: (a) the difference between the energy of the transition state and the ground state of the reactants, namely, the *energy of activation,* with large differences generally commensurate with low rates; (b) the num-ber of effective energy-transferring collisions among reacting molecules, with a low frequency favoring reduced rates; and (c) a requirement for a proper spatial orientation of all participants involved in the formation of the transition state, with a strict and highly ordered arrangement reducing the probability of higher rates. A more precise and math-ematical analysis of each factor is possible, but would be beyond the scope of this book.

In the context of transition state theory, a catalyst functions in effect by increasing the rate of production of the transition state inter-mediate. In view of the discussion above, the simplest explanation to account for this is that the presence of a catalyst reduces the energy of activation, resulting in an increase in the percentage of effective col-lisions which yield the activated intermediate (see Figure 5-3). The net energetics of the overall reaction remain unchanged. The explanation of why and how the energy of activation is reduced is a topic of con-siderable complexity and variation and will not be discussed here. The important point to recognize is that the increased rate of production of the activated intermediate is due to the effect of the catalyst on the alteration of one or more of the deterministic elements stated above.

The unequaled catalytic effect of enzymes can be similarly ex-plained. However, there is one distinguishing dimension of enzyme catalysis, namely, the relative ease with which an enzyme can orient the reacting substrate(s) into the required spatial conformation. This point will be developed more thoroughly in the following sections.

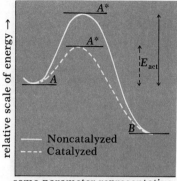

some parameter representative of the progress of reaction →

Figure 5-3 Energy profile diagrams of the reaction, $A \rightarrow B$, illustrating the *smaller* energy of activation in the pres-ence of a catalyst. The presence of the catalyst has *no effect* on the net energy of the reaction.

ENZYME KINETICS

MICHAELIS-MENTEN KINETIC THEORY OF ENZYME ACTION

In 1913 I. Michaelis and M. L. Menten investigated the reaction kinetics of the following system:

$$\text{sucrose} \xrightarrow[\text{H}_2\text{O}]{\text{invertase}} \text{glucose} + \text{fructose}$$

By measuring the initial velocity (v_0) of the reaction under different experimental conditions, they made two basic discoveries: (1) when the initial substrate concentration was held constant and the amount of enzyme was varied, the velocity was observed to be directly proportional to the concentration of enzyme present, as shown in Figure 5-4; and (2) in reciprocal experiments, when the enzyme concentration was held constant and the amount of substrate was varied, the relationship be-

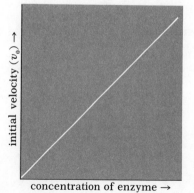

Figure 5-4 Kinetics of an enzyme-catalyzed reaction: constant substrate concentration and variable enzyme concentration.

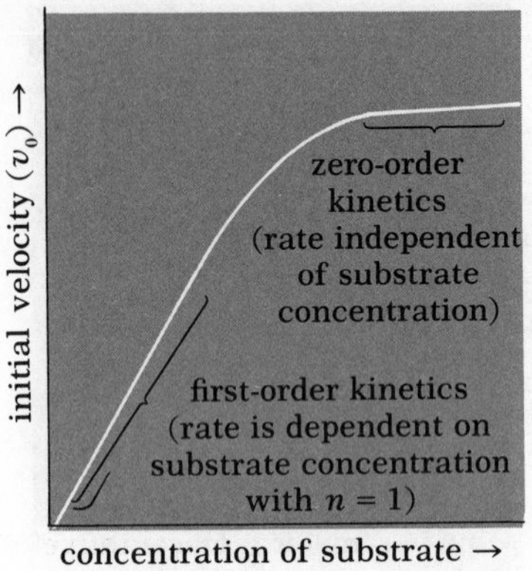

Figure 5-5 Kinetics of enzyme-catalyzed reaction: constant enzyme concentration and variable substrate concentration.

tween initial velocity and substrate concentration was hyperbolic, as shown in Figure 5-5. (Because of several variables—frequently quite different from one system to another and particularly so with enzyme-catalyzed reactions—that cause alterations in the reaction rate with time, the initial velocity, that is, the rate soon after the reaction has started, is the most accurate measurement of enzyme activity.)

Both of these relationships have since been found to have a general applicability to enzyme-catalyzed reactions. In terms of classical chemical kinetics, the two distinct slopes of the hyperbolic plot (Figure 5-5) correspond to first-order and zero-order kinetics, respectively. Michaelis and Menten described this as a rate transition from a *substrate-dependent phase* to a *substrate-independent phase*. This fundamental conclusion was a key factor in the formulation of their theory for enzyme action.

In retrospect, the theory of Michaelis and Menten was remarkably simple. They proposed that the enzyme (E) reversibly combined with the substrate (S) to form an *intermediate enzyme-substrate complex* (ES), which then irreversibly decomposed to yield products (P) and the free enzyme in its original form. Kinetically speaking, each reaction is defined by a specific rate constant, designated below as k_1, k_2, and k_3.

$$E + S \underset{k_2}{\overset{k_1}{\rightleftharpoons}} ES \overset{k_3}{\rightarrow} E + P$$

They reasoned that, if their proposal was valid, a mathematical equation of state could be derived that would be consistent with the empirical data represented by Figures 5-4 and 5-5. In developing the rate equation, several other assumptions were made in addition to the postulated formation of an intermediate complex. The most important are the following:

1. A *steady-state equilibrium* is attained very rapidly. Under the steady-state condition, which basically corresponds to a balance of all the reactions in a living organism, the rate of substrate disappearance ($-d[S]/dt$) is equalled by the rate of product formation ($+d[P]/dt$). Alternatively, the rate of formation of the intermediate complex ($+d[ES]/dt$) and the rate of its disappearance ($-d[ES]/dt$) are balanced. Thus,

$$+\frac{d[ES]}{dt} = -\frac{d[ES]}{dt}$$

or

$$k_1[E][S] = k_2[ES] + k_3[ES]$$

2. The *total* enzyme concentration $[E_t]$ is the sum of the enzyme combined with substrate $[ES]$ and free enzyme $[E_f]$ not so complexed.

$$[E_t] = [ES] + [E_f]$$

3. The *rate-limiting factor* will be the decomposition of the enzyme-substrate complex, and thus the initial velocity (v_0) will always be directly proportional to the concentration of the intermediate complex. That is,

$$v_0 \propto [ES]$$

4. As a corollary to point 3, the *maximum initial velocity* (V_{max}) will be attained when the concentration of ES reaches a maximum, which will occur when all of the available enzyme is complexed

with substrate, that is, when $[E_f] = 0$. This condition is termed *saturation of the enzyme with substrate*. When $[E_f] = 0$, however, $[ES] = [E_t]$, and thus the maximum velocity will be directly proportional to the total enzyme concentration.

$$V_{max} \propto [E_t]$$

Given these conditions, the development of the rate equation relating v_0 and $[S]$ is straightforward. Beginning with the equation based on the steady-state assumption (see item 1), but designating $[E]$ more specifically as $[E_f]$ and then solving for $[ES]$, we obtain

$$[ES] = \frac{k_1}{k_2 + k_3}\,[E_f][S] \qquad (i)$$

Now, since the proportionality constants of $v_0 \propto [ES]$ and $V_{max} \propto [E_t]$ must be the same, it follows that

$$\frac{v_0}{V_{max}} = \frac{[ES]}{[E_t]} \qquad \text{and} \qquad [ES] = \frac{v_0}{V_{max}}\,[E_t]$$

Substituting for $[ES]$ with this relationship into equation (i) yields

$$\frac{v_0}{V_{max}} = \frac{k_1}{k_2 + k_3}\,\frac{[E_f][S]}{[E_t]} \qquad (ii)$$

The multiple rate constant term can be treated as one constant and was originally manipulated in that fashion by Michaelis and Menten as follows:

$$\frac{k_2 + k_3}{k_1} \equiv K_m$$

Termed the *Michaelis-Menten constant*, K_m has a special significance to enzyme kinetics that will be developed shortly. This substitution into equation (ii), coupled with a substitution for $[E_f]$ and a slight rearrangement, yields

$$v_0 = \frac{V_{max}}{K_m}\left(\frac{[E_t][S]}{[E_t]} - \frac{[ES][S]}{[E_t]}\right) = \frac{V_{max}}{K_m}\left([S] - \frac{[ES][S]}{[E_t]}\right)$$

A second substitution for $[ES]$ according to $[ES] = (v_0/V_{max})[E_t]$ yields

$$v_0 = \frac{V_{max}}{K_m}\left([S] - \frac{v_0[E_t][S]}{V_{max}[E_t]}\right) = \frac{V_{max}}{K_m}\left([S] - \frac{v_0[S]}{V_{max}}\right)$$

which finally, on collection of terms and solving for v_0, gives

$$v_0 = \frac{V_{max}[S]}{K_m + [S]}$$

This last statement is the form of the classical Michaelis-Menten kinetic equation corresponding to that of a rectangular hyperbola (Figure 5–5) with v_0 and $[S]$ as coordinates and with the constant V_{max} as the asymptotic, maximum value of v_0. The equation is also consistent with the plot of v_0 versus enzyme concentration in Figure 5–4.

Although the classical Michaelis-Menten theory does not always apply to every enzymatic reaction, it is generally applicable and has provided the most useful insight into the problem of how enzymes function. The concept of an enzyme-substrate complex has been firmly established and has been substantiated in some cases by the actual isolation of same. Although there has been a progressive advancement in the field of enzyme kinetics, the original proposal, which serves as the nucleus for contemporary theories, still retains in its own right a general validity and utility in the study of enzymes.

SIGNIFICANCE OF MICHAELIS-MENTEN CONSTANT

The operational definition of $K_m = (k_2 + k_3)/k_1$ is not very enlightening. If we assume, however, that k_2 is much greater than k_3, the value of K_m—now approximated by k_2/k_1—will correspond to a constant representing the affinity of the enzyme for the substrate. Since the rate constant for the formation of the enzyme-substrate complex (k_1) is in the denominator, large K_m values are interpreted as representative of a small affinity, and small K_m values represent a strong affinity. A more informative and more accurate meaning of K_m is obtained by solving the Michaelis-Menten equation for the substrate concentration when the initial velocity is one-half the maximum velocity, that is, $v_0 = V_{max}/2$. Such a calculation yields $[S]_{v_0 = V_{max}/2} = K_m$. Now we can see that the Michaelis-Menten constant has units of concentration and specifically corresponds to the concentration of substrate required to saturate one-half of the enzyme molecules present in solution.

Although the first interpretation is not always valid, it is possible by combining both lines of reasoning to determine the relative substrate specificity of the enzyme from a measurement of K_m's with different substrates. This approach further assumes that the binding affinity and saturation of a given enzyme for a substrate are a reflection of the catalytic specificity of the enzyme. For example, the listing of K_m values for brain hexokinase (Table 5–4) with three isomeric sugars (hexoses) illustrates that the binding with allose is different from that of glucose or mannose by a factor of 10^3. That is to say, the amount of allose required for half-saturation of the enzyme is 1000 times greater than that for glucose and mannose. The K_m values for glucose and mannose indicate that they are bound to approximately the same extent. Thus, one may conclude that the structural feature which differentiates glucose and mannose from allose is in part a measure of the specificity of action of the hexokinase toward different hexose sugars. Inspection of their

Table 5–4 K_m values of hexokinase (brain)

sugar + ATP $\xrightarrow{\text{hexokinase}}$ sugar phosphate + ADP

Sugar	$K_m \times 10^6$ (molarity)	Structure		
D-allose	7000	¹CHO H—²C—OH H—³C—OH H—⁴C—OH H—⁵C—OH ⁶CH₂OH allose	CHO H—C—OH HO—C—H H—C—OH H—C—OH CH₂OH glucose	CHO HO—C—H HO—C—H H—C—OH H—C—OH CH₂OH mannose
D-glucose	8 } difference not significant			
D-mannose	5 }			

structure suggests that the spatial orientation of merely one hydroxyl group on one carbon atom is critical (carbon atom number 3).

MEASUREMENT OF K_m

The evaluation of K_m by graphically determining $[S]_{v_0 = V_{max}/2}$ from a plot of velocity versus substrate concentration is at best only an approximation because of the inherent uncertainty in estimating the asymptotic value, V_{max}. The Lineweaver-Burk plot, initially proposed in 1934, is the most commonly used alternative method. It is based on a rearrangement of the original hyperbolic rate equation to permit a plot of coordinates that will correspond to a straight-line function. This can be done by simply taking the reciprocal of both sides of the Michaelis-Menten equation, multiplying both sides by V_{max}, and finally solving for $1/v_0$ which yields

$$\frac{1}{v_0} = \frac{K_m}{V_{max}}\left(\frac{1}{[S]}\right) + \frac{1}{V_{max}}$$

This equation has the form $y = mx + b$, which is that of a straight-line relationship between two variables (y and x) where m is the slope of the line and b is the intercept of the line on the y axis. In the equation above, $y = 1/v_0$, $x = 1/[S]$, $m = K_m/V_{max}$, and $b = 1/V_{max}$. Figure 5–6 shows a typical Lineweaver-Burk plot of these coordinates. By first determining the value of the $1/v_0$ intercept through extrapolation, the K_m can be evaluated from the slope of the line. Alternatively, the K_m can be directly determined by further extrapolation of the plot to $1/v_0 = 0$ (that is, through the x axis) where the intercept on the abscissa is equal to $-1/K_m$. Because of some statistical limitations with this type of plot, other linear formulations have been devised which in statistical terms place an equal emphasis on all experimental data; such a formulation is the Eadie-Hofstee plot (Figure 5–7). Some problems in the use of these principles are provided at the end of the chapter.

ENZYME INHIBITION

The kinetic analysis of enzymes in the presence of their natural substrates is not the only method that has contributed to the current understanding of enzyme action. Equally important, if not more so, is the kinetic analysis of enzymes in the presence of materials that inhibit the activity of the enzyme. On first thought, the significance and wisdom of this negative approach may seem somewhat questionable. However, the rationale becomes evident by recognizing that the most direct method to determine the essential role of any part of a multi-component system is to remove it from the system, thus preventing its normal participation in same. If the system is inhibited, that is, if there is a reduction in its normal activity, then the essential role of the component in question is established. These general remarks express the basic philosophy of enzyme inhibition studies wherein we are particularly interested in determining two elements of enzyme action: (1) the identity of the amino acid residues that are involved in the substrate-enzyme protein

$$\frac{1}{v_0} = \frac{K_m}{V_{max}}\frac{1}{[S]} + \frac{1}{V_{max}}$$

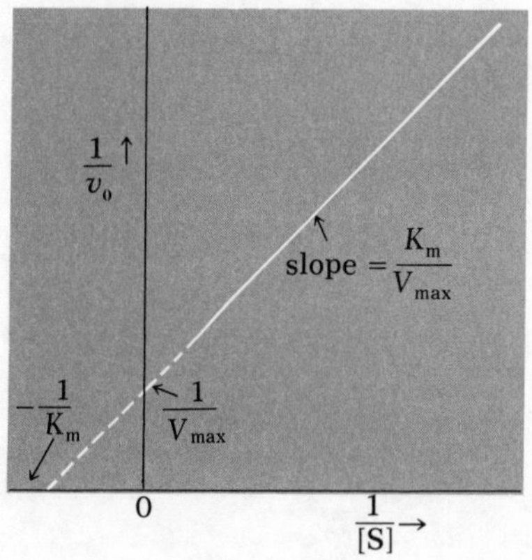

Figure 5–6 Lineweaver-Burk plot of Michaelis-Menten kinetics.

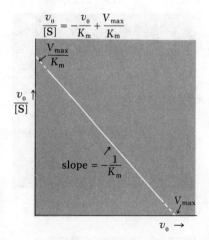

$$\frac{v_0}{[S]} = -\frac{v_0}{K_m} + \frac{V_{max}}{K_m}$$

Figure 5–7 Eadie-Hofstee plot of Michaelis-Menten kinetics.

interaction and are thus largely responsible for the activity of the enzyme, and (2) the extent to which there may be a specific interaction between enzyme and substrate. In addition to providing useful information for a working hypothesis for the distinctive features of how an enzyme works (its mechanism of action), enzyme inhibition studies have also been instrumental in the development of a variety of chemotherapeutic agents and in the understanding of how they function on a molecular basis.

The two most common types of enzyme inhibitors are classified as *competitive* and *non-competitive* inhibitors. In discussing the characteristics of each type, we will make use of an important principle which we have implied but have not yet specifically stated in this chapter, namely, that *the interaction of a substrate with an enzyme occurs at a specific, localized region on the surface of the enzyme protein termed the active site.* This concept will be treated separately in the next section. For the moment it is necessary only to understand its basic meaning. To recapitulate using other terminology, the formation of the enzyme-substrate complex is mediated through the interaction of the substrate with a small group of specific amino acid residues arranged in a particular spatial order and localized at or near the periphery of the globular enzyme protein. Now let us examine each type of inhibition.

COMPETITIVE INHIBITION

Competitive inhibitors are substances that bear a strong structural resemblance to the natural substrate. This results in a molecular competition for binding to the active site when both inhibitor and substrate are together in the presence of an enzyme. The formation of an enzyme-inhibitor complex reduces the population of free enzyme molecules that are available for interaction with the natural substrate. Relative to the kinetics of the same system in the absence of inhibitor, this results in a reduction in the amount of substrate converted to product in a given time. A competitive inhibitor normally combines reversibly with the enzyme at its active site and is not converted to any product(s). Hence, this type of inhibition can be reversed or minimized by merely increasing the concentration of the natural substrate, with the greater population of substrate molecules competitively favoring the formation of a larger percentage of the normal intermediate complex.

The Michaelis-Menten kinetics, which distinguish and serve as a means of empirically determining competitive inhibitors, are depicted in the Lineweaver-Burk plot of Figure 5–8. Notice that the normal V_{max} is unchanged, whereas the K_m in the presence of inhibitor is increased. These kinetic characteristics are consistent with the explanation given above and are also a verification of the original Michaelis-Menten theory. If the molecules do continually compete for the same active site, then a greater amount of substrate should be required for half-saturation (higher K_m). When the system is saturated, however, the maximum velocity should be unaffected as though no inhibitor were present.

One of the most classical examples of competitive inhibition is shown by *succinic acid dehydrogenase,* an enzyme of the citric acid cycle (page 313) previously introduced in Chapter 3, which catalyzes the

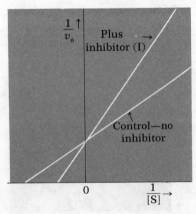

$$E + S \rightleftarrows ES \rightarrow E + P$$
$$E + I \rightleftarrows EI$$

Figure 5–8 Lineweaver-Burk plot of kinetics of competitive inhibition.

conversion of succinic acid to fumaric acid. The enzyme is dependent on the coenzyme participation of *flavin adenine dinucleotide* [FAD] as a hydrogen acceptor.

$$^-OOC-CH_2-CH_2-COO^- + FAD \xrightarrow[\text{dehydrogenase}]{\substack{\text{succinic} \\ \text{acid}}} {}^-OOC-\overset{\overset{\displaystyle H}{|}}{C}=\underset{\underset{\displaystyle H}{|}}{C}-COO^- + FADH_2$$

succinate

fumarate

$^-OOC-CH_2-COO^-$ (competitive inhibitor of succinate)

malonate

A variety of competitive inhibitors of this enzyme are known, but the most effective is malonic acid, the next lower methylene homologue of succinic acid. Specifically, if only 2% of the molecules present are malonic acid, there is a 50% inhibition in the rate of production of fumarate.

Many chemotherapeutic drugs function as competitive inhibitors. For example, several of the *sulfa drugs,* used to combat microbial infections in man, are structurally related to *para-aminobenzoic acid* (PABA). PABA is a vital precursor in the microbial biosynthesis of *folic acid,* which in turn is converted to *tetrahydrofolic acid* (see page 439, Chapter 16), an extremely important coenzyme for several enzymes. A few of these enzymes catalyze crucial steps in the biosynthesis of purine and pyrimidine nucleotides, which in turn are used in the biosynthesis of the nucleic acids, RNA and DNA (next chapter). When the sulfa drug is administered, the immediate effect is the inhibition of the PABA-incorporating enzyme step in the production of folic acid. This results in a decreased cellular production of tetrahydrofolic acid, which in turn reduces the production of the purine and pyrimidine nucleotides, thus limiting the production of nucleic acids. The eventual result of all this is that the organism dies. The selective action of the drugs on the infectious organism is due to the fact that, although man is also critically dependent on folic acid, he does not have the biochemical capacity to synthesize this material from PABA and other precursors. Rather, man depends on an external dietary source and/or an internal supply from the

several enzymatic steps involved with one enzyme catalyzing the incorporation of para-aminobenzoic acid

H_2N—⬡—COOH

precursors $\rightarrow \rightarrow \rightarrow \xrightarrow{\quad} \rightarrow \rightarrow \rightarrow$ folic acid $\rightarrow \rightarrow$ tetrahydrofolic acid

competitive inhibition

H_2N—⬡—SO_2NH_2

sulfanilamide
(a sulfa drug)

essential coenzyme for metabolism of purines and pyrimidines
see pages 452 and 457

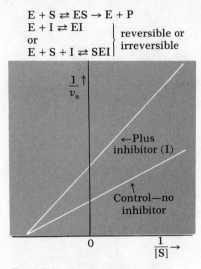

$$E + S \rightleftarrows ES \rightarrow E + P$$
$$E + I \rightleftarrows EI$$
or
$$E + S + I \rightleftarrows SEI$$
⎰ reversible or
⎱ irreversible

Figure 5–9 Lineweaver-Burk plot of kinetics of non-competitive inhibition.

non-infectious intestinal bacteria. One of the dangers of sulfa drug therapy is that an excessive amount can annihilate the intestinal bacteria, resulting in a loss of their many symbiotic life-sustaining functions. The antibiotic *puromycin* is also a competitive inhibitor in the process of protein biosynthesis (see pages 147 and 510).

NON-COMPETITIVE INHIBITION

Inhibitors of this type interact with the enzyme in a variety of ways. The binding may be reversible or irreversible, may occur at the active site or at some other region on the surface of the enzyme protein, and may or may not prevent the binding of substrate. In any case the resultant complex is generally inactive, and the effect cannot be reversed by merely increasing the ratio of substrate to inhibitor. Recall that this is just the opposite of competitive inhibition. The Michaelis-Menten kinetic characteristics of classical non-competitive inhibition are shown in Figure 5–9. Note the reverse effect on the K_m and V_{max} relative to competitive inhibition. The molecular explanation of the generally recognized poisonous character of many substances such as cyanide, carbon monoxide, azide, Hg^{++}, Pb^{++}, and arsenicals is derived from their potent non-competitive inhibition of certain enzymes.

The use of non-competitive inhibitors can provide valuable information concerning the catalytic nature of enzymes. For example, p-*chloromercurobenzoate* and *diisopropylfluorophosphate* covalently and irreversibly attach to cysteine sulfhydryl groups and serine hydroxyl groups, respectively. Thus, if inhibition is detected with either material, this is strong experimental evidence for the essential participation of the R groups of cysteine or serine. If the binding of the inhibitor also prevents the binding of the substrate, it is quite likely that the amino acid is actually part of the active site.

Enzyme —CH₂—SH + Cl—Hg—⟨◯⟩—COO⁻ ⟶ Enzyme —CH₂—S—Hg—⟨◯⟩—COO⁻

para-chloro-mercurobenzoate

Enzyme —CH₂OH +

$$(CH_3)_2CH \quad CH(CH_3)_2$$
$$O \quad O$$
$$\backslash P \diagup$$
$$F \quad O$$

diisopropylphospho-fluoridate

⟶ Enzyme —CH₂—O—P—OCH(CH₃)₂ with OCH(CH₃)₂ above and O below

PHYSICAL FACTORS

Because enzymes are proteins, their catalytic activity is very sensitive to temperature and pH, with deactivation common to high and low extremes of each parameter. The effect may be reversible or irreversible. Of course, denaturation of the protein conformation (see page 96,

Chapter 4) is common to each condition except at low temperature. Consistent with the nature of the physiological environment, the optimum temperature and optimum pH associated with maximum activity generally lie in the ranges of 35–40°C and pH 6–8.

ENZYME SPECIFICITY AND ACTIVE SITE

It was mentioned previously that one of the most characteristic and remarkable properties of enzymes is their preferential action toward certain substrates. Generally this property is simply called enzyme specificity. In some instances *absolute specificity* is observed, with the enzyme acting on only one substrate. The enzymes urease and succinic acid dehydrogenase are two examples. However, most enzymes demonstrate a *relative specificity,* with a broader but still limited preference for a finite number of chemically related materials. Even in this case, however, the reaction rates and the K_m values will frequently differ due to the preference of an enzyme for a certain member(s) of the group. For example, hexokinase will catalyze the ATP-dependent phosphorylation of a large number of hexoses, but one observes a maximum rate with glucose (see page 114, this chapter).

A more striking aspect of specificity is evidenced by the action of certain enzymes that catalyze the asymmetric degradation of a symmetrical compound, resulting in the formation of a specific isomeric form of the product. With succinic acid dehydrogenase (SDH), for example, the dehydrogenation of succinic acid occurs specifically via *trans* elimination to yield fumarate, the *trans* isomer of the unsaturated dicarboxylic acid. Despite the fact that the four hydrogens in succinate are structurally identical, the other potential isomer, maleate, which would be formed by the *cis* elimination of hydrogens, is not produced. In other words, the enzyme recognizes the four equivalent hydrogens of the symmetrical succinate molecule in a non-equivalent fashion. As we

will discuss shortly, it is the spatial orientation of the hydrogens that is recognized as being different after the formation of the enzyme-substrate intermediate complex. Another example of this phenomenon is the conversion of citrate to isocitrate, catalyzed by *aconitase* (p. 308).

All aspects of enzyme specificity are based on the existence of an *active site in the enzyme molecule consisting of a spatially ordered but structurally asymmetric constellation of a small number of amino acid residues.* This localized region is stabilized by, and indeed a consequence of, the conformation of the complete protein molecule. This concept can be more clearly understood by considering the anatomy of an enzyme protein in terms of four types of amino acid residues: (1) *nonessential residues* which can be replaced and in some cases even

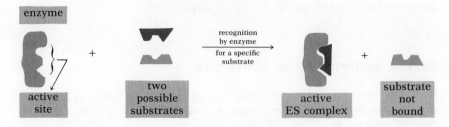

Lock and Key Theory

removed without any commensurate loss in conformation or function of the enzyme; (2) *structural residues* which are essential to the maintenance of an ordered conformation of the intact protein molecule; (3) *binding residues* which are responsible for the interaction of the enzyme with its substrate; and (4) *catalytic residues,* which may or may not be identical to binding residues, that participate in the chemical transformation of the substrate. The so-called active site will encompass binding and catalytic residues that are maintained in a localized array because of the interaction of the structural residues that direct and stabilize the foldings of the polypeptide chain.

One of the original theories to account for the ordered formation of the active site-substrate complex was the *"lock and key"* hypothesis. The crux of this suggestion is that there is a topographical, structural compatibility between enzyme and substrate which optimally favors the recognition of the substrate (see above). The principal limitation of the lock-key hypothesis is the implication that the conformation of the enzyme protein is *fixed* or *rigid*. A more current suggestion is Koshland's *"induced-fit theory,"* which is based on the premise that the conformational structure of a protein is *flexible*. The approach of the substrate initiates a subtle shift in conformation of the protein, producing the proper orientation of the active site residues. With enzymes

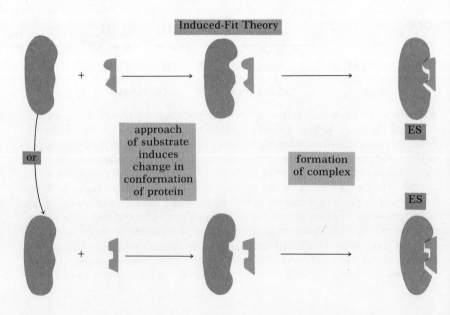

Induced-Fit Theory

that are cofactor dependent, this change may be induced by the initial binding of the cofactor, thus rendering the binding of the substrate more likely. Although both theories may account for the operation of enzymes *in vivo*, the induced-fit proposal more adequately explains the high degree of relative specificity exhibited by several enzymes. The lock and key theory, on the other hand, though it is obviously well suited to explain those instances of absolute specificity, is less appropriate in explaining a broad range of substrate specificity because of its postulation of a rigid active site.

The amino acid residues of the active site need not be adjacent, but can be contributed by different segments of the molecule that are brought close together by the intricate folds and twists of the polypeptide backbone. Because this region of the enzyme actively participates in the binding and the catalytic processes, it is only logical that the constituent residues should include amino acids with chemically reactive side chains such as cysteine, serine, or the acidic and basic amino acids. These residues are capable (a) of complexing with a substrate via ionic or covalent interactions that may further contribute to the establishment of bond strains within the substrate; (b) of participating as donors or acceptors of electrons and protons in the actual mechanism; or (c) of merely providing a centralized location for the interaction of substrate and coenzyme.

These principles are clearly represented by the current state of knowledge concerning the mechanism of action of *lysozyme,* a simple protein consisting of 129 amino acids in a single polypeptide chain with four intrachain disulfide linkages. First discovered (accidentally) by Alexander Fleming in 1922 as the active antibacterial agent of nasal mucus, lysozyme has since been detected in many body tissues and secretions, in plants, and most abundantly in egg whites. Being one of the natural defense mechanisms against infections, the enzyme is so named because of its lytic action on bacterial cells. The action of lysozyme is due to its ability to destroy the structural integrity of the bacterial cell wall by cleaving specific chemical linkages in the polymeric carbohydrate (substrate) which is one of the main constituents of the cell wall (see page 188). The microbe, stripped of the protective wall and shielded only by a fragile plasma membrane, is then readily subject to lysis, i.e., destruction.

The key to our understanding of the action of lysozyme was the determination of its complete tertiary structure—a first for an enzyme— by D. C. Phillips and coworkers in 1965. This was truly a milestone in modern biochemical research. Aside from providing the basis for defining how lysozyme works, it resulted in the categorical validation of the active-site principle. The existing theories, which had been formulated on less convincing evidence, were correct. The study of Phillips provides us with a distinct opportunity to analyze the structure–function principle as it applies to biocatalysts.

Three-dimensional models of lysozyme both as a free enzyme and complexed with a segment of the polysaccharide substrate are shown in Figure 5–10. The ordered, asymmetric structure of the protein is obvious. The distinct cleft (or if you prefer, crevice or invagination) that appears vertically through the center of the model constitutes the active site. To repeat, it exists because of the ordered folding of the polypeptide chain, which in turn is intimately dependent on the amino acid sequence. The attachment of the carbohydrate substrate is believed to occur via

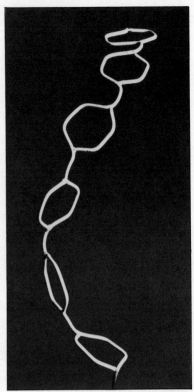

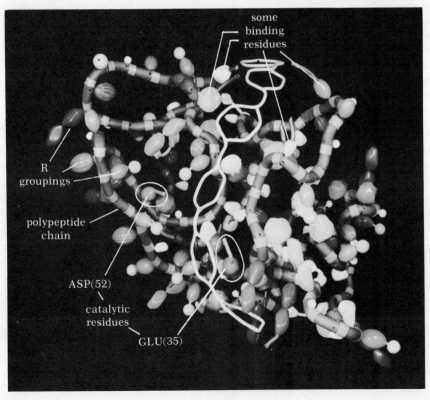

Figure 5–10 The three-dimensional structure of lysozyme. *Upper left:* model of the free enzyme showing a large cleft in the center of the molecule from top to bottom. *Upper right:* model of a hexameric segment of the polysaccharide portion of the bacterial cell wall which serves as the substrate. *Bottom:* model of the enzyme-substrate complex formed between lysozyme and the carbohydrate substrate. Binding residues are present all through the cleft. The aspartic acid and glutamic acid catalytic residues can be seen just below the midpoint of the cleft, oriented at the sensitive bond in the substrate which will ultimately be cleaved. (The Biobit model of lysozyme was generously supplied by The Ealing Corporation. Photographs by Charles Blumle.)

hydrogen bonding at specific sites in the cleft. These are identified by white wires projecting from the R group bits. The catalytic residues are believed to be ASP (52) and GLU (35), which are localized near the center of the cleft (see legend of Figure 5–10). From studies of models such as these, a satisfactory fit of model substrates in the cleft requires a slight structural distortion of part of the substrate. This observation has been incorporated into the formulation of a mechanism of action.

The suggested mechanism is diagrammed below. The hexameric sequence of six-membered rings, which corresponds to a brief segment of the polymeric carbohydrate portion of cell wall material, represents the substrate. Each ring is a substituted glucose molecule. They are consecutively attached to each other by acid-labile glycosidic bonds. See Chapter 7 for additional details. Phillips' proposed mechanism proceeds as follows. There is a localized production of a proton mediated by the glutamic acid residue in position 35. The proton attacks the acid-labile glycosidic bond, already destabilized by ring distortion in the initial binding of the substrate. (The distortion itself is not illustrated.) The bond is cleaved, generating a carbonium ion (C^+), which in turn is stabilized via an electrostatic interaction with the aspartic acid residue in position 52. The reaction is completed by the interaction of the carbonium ion with a hydroxide ion. These events are followed by dissociation of the enzyme molecule, which seeks out another site on the cell wall surface, and the process is repeated. The net result is the solubilization of the polymeric cell wall.

Since the success with lysozyme, other enzymes have been similarly studied and our understanding of biocatalysis is becoming progressively more definitive. Detailed knowledge of this sort promises to open new frontiers in man's ability to control and regulate life processes.

NATURAL REGULATION OF BIOCATALYSIS—ALLOSTERISM

In a previous section we discussed how the sulfa drugs, certain antibiotics, and a host of other chemical agents—all of which have a natural or man-made origin—can inhibit the progress of enzyme-catalyzed reactions via competitive or non-competitive effects. In effect, their use as chemotherapeutic agents permits the control of enzyme activity or, more generally, the control of metabolism, with the desired objective being the selective destruction of the viability of the infectious organism.

Within the past ten or fifteen years it has become increasingly apparent that metabolic control is also a *natural phenomenon* common to all types of organisms. The bulk of this regulation is likewise exerted at the level of the enzyme-catalyzed reaction via low-molecular-weight materials that are normally present and in fact are actually produced within the cell itself. The natural regulatory mechanisms, however, are generally not characterized by competitive or non-competitive inhibition, and furthermore, the effects are not all inhibitory but include the enhancement of enzymatic activity as well. These control mechanisms are currently treated under the *theory of allosterism* and the resultant effects are termed *allosteric effects*.

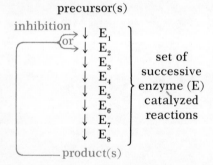

EXPERIMENTAL BACKGROUND

The theory of allosterism was essentially an outgrowth of investigations in the early 1960's designed to determine the mechanism of *feedback inhibition*. The latter term was coined to refer to a specific regulatory phenomenon wherein an initial enzyme(s) of a biosynthetic reaction sequence—often consisting of several steps, each catalyzed by a different enzyme—is susceptible to deactivation by the natural end product of the pathway. An organism benefits immensely from feedback inhibition, because it avoids wasteful production of metabolic end products under physiological conditions in which their biosynthesis is not needed in large amounts. Thus, an organism can utilize all of its important basic resources such as carbon, nitrogen, sulfur, phosphorus, and energy in a most efficient manner.

The first systematic study of feedback inhibition was performed by J. C. Gerhart and A. B. Pardee in 1962. The enzyme studied was *aspartate transcarbamylase* (ATCase), which catalyzes the first of a series of reactions in the biosynthesis of the pyrimidine nucleotides. The specific reaction in question is shown in Figure 5–11. In this section we will examine the data and primary conclusions of their classical experiments. This approach will serve as an empirical basis for introducing the theory of allosterism, which attempts to formulate a model to explain the mechanism of feedback inhibition and related regulatory phenomena. Finally, the theory will be applied to aspartate transcarbamylase.

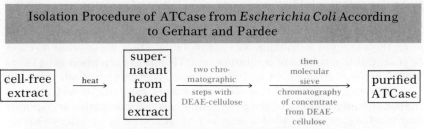

carbamyl
phosphate   aspartate   carbamyl
                                       aspartate

several steps
catalyzed by
different enzymes
comprise the rest
of the pathway

cytidine triphosphate (CTP)

Figure 5–11 A schematic diagram of the feedback inhibition of pyrimidine bio-synthesis in *Escherichia coli.* The heavy broken arrow indicates feedback inhibition. The succession of smaller arrows repre-sents a multitude of intermediate enzyme-cataiyzed reactions between the initial reaction and the terminal product, CTP.

ATCase was chosen for study by Gerhart and Pardee because (a) its activity was known to be subject to a strong feedback control by the end product, *cytidine triphosphate* (CTP), as depicted in Figure 5–11; (b) the enzyme can be readily obtained in a highly purified form as out-lined below; and (c) the enzyme preparation can be stored for several months with no appreciable loss in activity or in sensitivity to inhibitors.

Isolation Procedure of ATCase from *Escherichia Coli* According to Gerhart and Pardee

| cell-free extract | → heat | super-natant from heated extract | two chro-matographic steps with DEAE-cellulose → | then molecular sieve chromatography of concentrate from DEAE-cellulose → | purified ATCase |

(0.001 *M* mercaptoethanol and 0.0001 *M* EDTA were present in all steps to prevent oxidation of the enzyme and any damage to the enzyme from heavy metal ions, respectively.)

Before examining the experimental results, we should first under-stand how the data were collected. Accordingly, the assay system is outlined below. Note that the original reaction mixture contained all participants required for formation of carbamyl aspartate and was suitably buffered at pH 7.0. In assays of this type (fixed-time), the enzyme is generally the last component to be added. After a 30-minute incubation at 28°C, the reaction was terminated by the addition of an acid-containing reagent (X), which also forms a colored complex (absorp-tion maximum at 560 nm) with carbamyl aspartate. Thus, the extent of reaction was measured in terms of the increase in absorption at 560 nm which reflected the appearance of product. The effects of other materials

composition of initial reaction mixture

a) carbamyl phosphate (3.6×10^{-3} M)
b) aspartate (5×10^{-3} M)
c) 0.5 ml of ATCase in
   phosphate buffer (pH 7.0)
d) other materials as
   required (2×10^{-3} M)
   Total Volume = 0.5 ml

$\xrightarrow[28°C]{30 \text{ min}}$ then add reagent X $\xrightarrow{}$ then measure absorbancy at 560 nm $\xrightarrow{}$

on the activity of the enzyme were determined by simply including each material in the original reaction mixture and comparing the change in absorbancy to that of a control system containing only the normal substrates and the enzyme. Experiments of this type with additions of different purine and pyrimidine derivatives constituted the first phase of the study. A partial compilation of the results is given in Table 5–5. Since the purines and pyrimidines have not yet been discussed, a brief description of each substance is included in the tabulation. The triphosphonucleotides differ from each other in terms of the nitrogen base attached to ribose. Cytosine (C) and uracil (U) are pyrimidines, whereas guanine (G) and adenine (A) are purines.

Inspection of the data reveals that in the pyrimidine family the inhibition was relatively specific for cytidine nucleotides, the maximum effect occurring with CTP. Cytosine, the free nitrogen base, showed no inhibition at all. The requirement for the pyrimidine moiety to be cytosine is reflected by the low inhibitory effect of the sister pyrimidine nucleotide, UTP. Purine derivatives caused opposite effects. In one case GTP was a mild inhibitor. However, the extent of inhibition was significantly less than with CTP. Subsequent investigations revealed that the amount of inhibition observed with GTP could be equaled by using CTP in an amount about 1/50th that of GTP, thus confirming that CTP is a more potent inhibitor. Additions of ATP proved extremely interesting in that this purine nucleotide acted as an *activator* (expressed as negative inhibition) of ATCase activity rather than as an inhibitor. Moreover, the extent of activation was appreciable. Thus, we see that ATCase is susceptible not only to inhibition by CTP but to activation by ATP as well. The activation effect will also be discussed as part of our analysis.

Having established that the most potent inhibitor of ATCase was indeed the end product of the pyrimidine biosynthetic pathway, Gerhart and Pardee then performed a series of kinetic studies in order to ascertain whether the inhibition was competitive, non-competitive, or of some other type. Similar studies were performed on the ATP activation. In order to apply classical Michaelis-Menton kinetics to this bimolecular reaction, it was necessary to maintain one of the primary substrates in excess and vary the concentration of the other. In this case the analyses were performed under conditions of *varying the concentration of aspartate* and *holding carbamyl phosphate in excess*. The concentrations of the enzyme and of the inhibitor or activator were, of course, held constant. The results of the kinetic analyses are summarized in Figure 5–12. Immediately apparent from the data on the *control system* (no CTP or ATP added) is that the kinetic behavior of ATCase was not completely consistent with the Michaelis-Menten theory. The expected rectangular hyperbolic curve was not observed. Rather, the curve possessed a *sigmoid character* ($\mathcal{S}$-shaped) due to the very slow increase

Table 5–5 Inhibition of aspartate transcarbamylase.

Compound	Structure	% Inhibition
Cytosine (free pyrimidine)	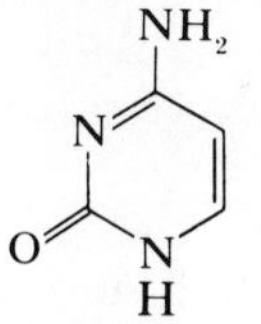	0
Cytidine (nucleoside)	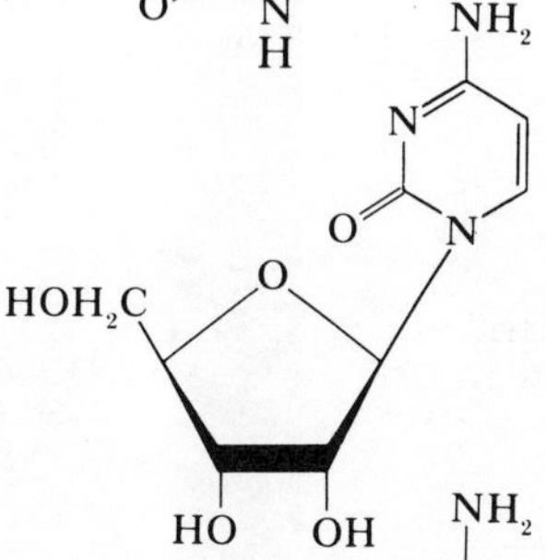	24
Cytidine mono-phosphate (CMP)	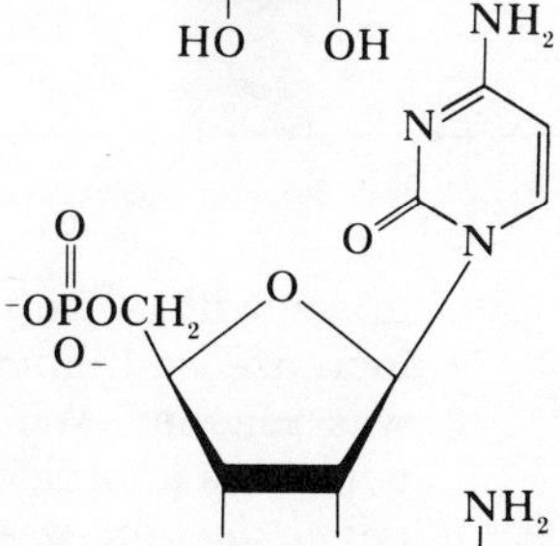	38
Cytidine di-phosphate (CDP)	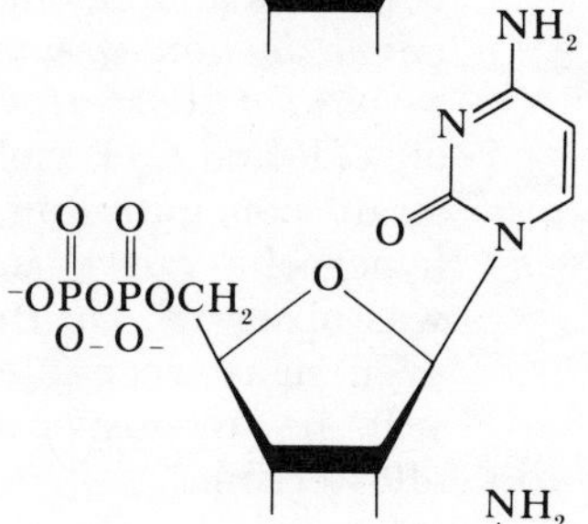	68
Cytidine tri-phosphate (CTP)	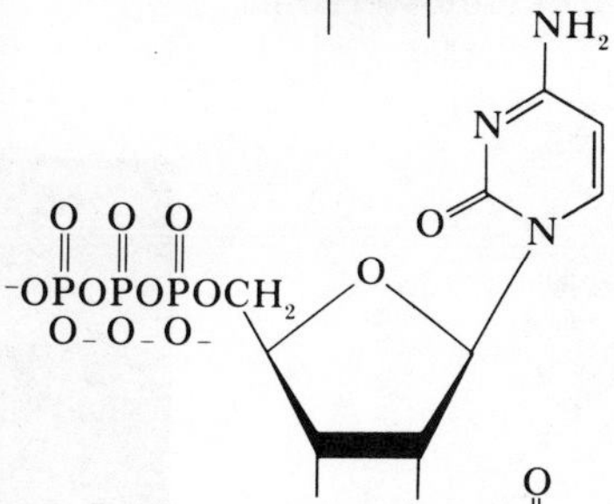	86 ←
Uridine tri-phosphate (UTP)	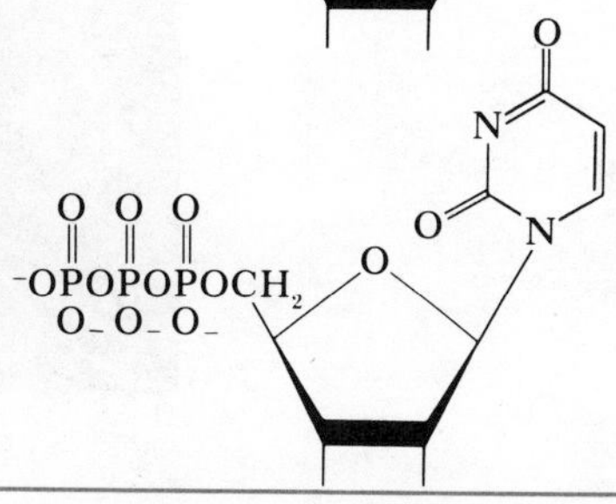	8

PYRIMIDINE FAMILY

NUCLEOTIDES

Table 5-5 *(Continued)*

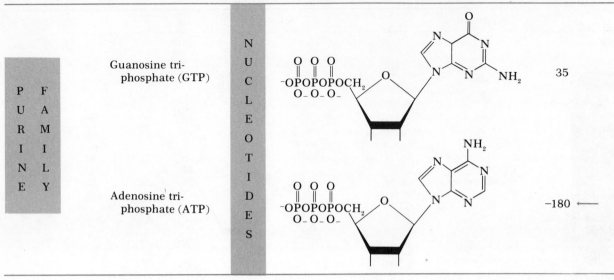

P U R I N E **F A M I L Y**	Guanosine tri-phosphate (GTP)	35
	Adenosine tri-phosphate (ATP)	-180 ⟵

in velocity at low concentrations of aspartate, followed by a greater increase at higher substrate concentrations until a maximal velocity was reached. While we are not in a position at the moment to pursue what this anomalous behavior means, suffice it to say that the *sigmoid curve is now generally regarded as the distinctive kinetic characteristic of allosterically controlled enzymes.* Note also that the presence of ATP and CTP yielded different patterns of rate dependence on substrate concentration. With ATP the sigmoid character was lost and a hyperbolic curve indicative of classical Michaelis-Menten kinetics was observed. On the other hand, the presence of CTP resulted in an even more accentuated sigmoid curve. These empirical observations will be reconsidered after we have developed the principles of allosterism.

Figure 5-12 Kinetic analysis of ATCase in the absence and presence of CTP and ATP. Velocity = units of activity per mg of protein × 10^{-3}. (1 unit of enzymatic activity produces 1 μmole of carbamyl aspartate per hour.) The reaction mixture contained 3.6 × 10^{-3} M carbamyl phosphate; aspartate varied as indicated; 2.0 × 10^{-4} M CTP when used; 2 × 10^{-3} M ATP when used; 0.04 M potassium phosphate buffer, pH 7.0; and 9.0 × 10^{-2} μg of enzyme protein per ml. (Data taken with permission from "The Enzymology of Control by Feedback Inhibition," Gerhart, J. C. and A. B. Pardee, *J. Biol. Chem.*, **237,** 891–896 (1962).)

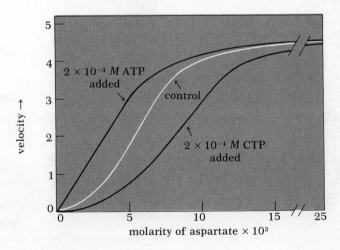

Further analysis of inhibition by CTP relative to the control system *suggests competitive inhibition*, since the presence of the nucleotide did not appreciably change the V_{max} but did alter the K_m. In fact, a comparison of K_m's reveals that the inhibition was rather extensive, as evidenced by the twofold increase in K_m when CTP was added. In the context of our previous interpretation of the Michaelis-Menten constant, this suggests that the binding of aspartate required for half-saturation was increased by a factor of approximately two in the presence of CTP. Since the presence of CTP did not appreciably affect the V_{max}, the complete data suggest that CTP functioned as a competitive inhibitor. *However, it is difficult to reconcile how CTP could function as a competitive inhibitor of aspartate, since they are definitely not structurally related chemical species* (see Figure 5–11). Furthermore, previous studies on the specificity of ATCase showed the enzyme to be rather specific for binding L-aspartate. It shows little or no activity, for example, with L-glutamate or L-β-methyl aspartate. (The enzyme will, however, bind succinate. In this case though, that is all that happens, and no actual reaction of succinate with carbamyl phosphate occurs. This property of ATCase was exploited to full advantage in subsequent studies.) The activation of the enzyme by ATP is readily apparent from Figure 5–12. Kinetically, the effect of ATP can be explained as above for CTP. That is, the presence of ATP reduced the amount of substrate required for half-saturation, and hence the velocity is greater with smaller levels of aspartate.

In order to explain the unusual inhibition kinetics observed with CTP, Gerhart and Pardee proposed that there are *two separate,* localized regions in the enzyme molecule; one selectively binds with the normal substrates—aspartate and carbamylphosphate—and the other selectively binds with CTP. Furthermore, they suggested that the binding of CTP is independent of the binding of aspartate. Finally, they argued that, if this is so, it should be possible to selectively disrupt one site without damaging the other. For example, if the CTP binding site were disrupted and the aspartate site were not, then the enzyme would be less sensitive to inhibition by CTP, but would still possess enzymatic activity. If, however, both substrate and inhibitor depended on the same site for binding, or if the two sites were mutually dependent on each other, the separation of inhibition and normal enzymatic activity would not be possible. This major premise of the hypothesis was successfully tested, as revealed by the data of Table 5–6 and Figure 5–13. The denaturing methods used were thermal treatment and exposure of the enzyme to

Treatment	% inhibition by CTP 2×10^{-4} M	V_{max} maximum velocity	Aspartate for half-saturation (molarity $\times 10^3$)
1. None	70	4.5	6
2. 10^{-6} M HgNO₃	0 ⎫	10.0 ⎫	12
3. Preheat with 4 minutes at 60°C	0 ⎬ inhibitor binding destroyed	9.0 ⎬ substrate binding not destroyed	12
4. 0.8 M urea	0 ⎭	~4.5 ⎭	—

Table 5–6 Selective destruction of feedback inhibition.

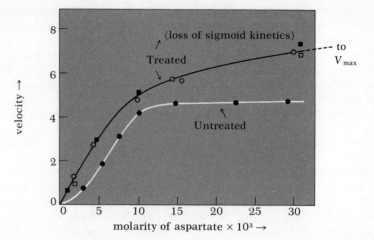

Figure 5–13 Dependence of reaction rate on aspartate concentration after loss of feedback inhibition. ● = untreated (native) enzyme; ■ = 10^{-6} M HgNO$_3$ present during assay; O = enzyme heated for 4 minutes at 60°C and cooled before assay with no CTP present; □ = heated enzyme assayed in the presence of CTP. (Data taken with permission from "The Enzymology of Control by Feedback Inhibition," Gerhart, J. C. and A. B. Pardee, *J. Biol. Chem.,* **237,** 891–896 (1962).)

mercurials (mercury-containing compounds). Similar results were obtained with other methods as well, such as treatment with urea.

Inspection of the effects of heating the enzyme and exposing it to mercurous nitrate and urea reveals that the inhibitor site was, in fact, selectively destroyed. That is, there was no difference observed in the response of the treated enzyme in the presence or absence of CTP, but the enzyme was still active. Thus, it can be concluded that the *binding site of the inhibitor was largely independent of the site for the normal substrates.* A comparison of the treated and untreated systems indicates, however, that the sites are *not entirely independent,* since the maximum velocity differed. In fact, the increase in velocity in the treated systems was nearly twofold. In addition, the concentration at which the enzyme was half-saturated by aspartate doubled. Finally, the kinetics of the treated systems were no longer characterized by the sigmoid curve common to the native enzyme. Thus, although the data suggest that the sites are independent in the sense that they are defined as separate and distinct regions of the enzyme surface, they also indicate that the *activity of the aspartate (substrate) binding site is profoundly affected by disruption of the inhibitor site.* One might argue, however, that the sites may be truly independent and that the activity of the active site was caused by the heat or mercury treatment and was not related to the disruption of the inhibitor site. A possible rebuttal to this argument is that the alteration in activity of the active site is not consistent with the nature of treatments employed, since the activity should be *reduced rather than increased.* One characteristic of the treated systems has not yet been mentioned, namely, that the structure of the treated enzyme is most probably different from that of the native enzyme. This was verified by comparing sedimentation characteristics, which revealed a considerable difference. The treated enzyme had a sedimentation constant of 5.9S compared to 11.6S for the native enzyme. Therefore, Gerhart and Pardee suggested that it is quite probable that *the interdependency of one site on the other is a consequence of favorable or unfavorable structural changes in the protein molecule.*

A final experiment designed to determine whether the activator, ATP, could cause a reversal of the inhibitory effect of CTP was then performed. The results are shown in Figure 5–14 and definitely illustrate

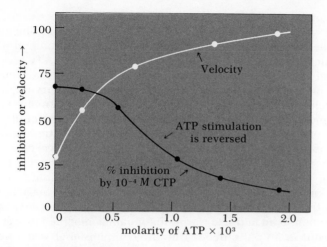

Figure 5–14 Reversal of CTP inhibition by ATP. The velocity curve refers to the stimulation of the enzyme by ATP. The extent to which stimulation was reduced by 10^{-4} M CTP is described by the percentage inhibition curve. Concentration of ATP was varied as indicated. The concentration of aspartate was 2.5×10^{-3} M. (Data taken with permission from "The Enzymology of Control by Feedback Inhibition," Gerhart, J. C., and A. B. Pardee, *J. Biol. Chem.*, **237**, 891–896 (1962).)

that the inhibition of CTP was significantly lessened in the presence of ATP. Gerhart and Pardee then suggested that it is likely that ATP and CTP *competitively bind at the same site* on the enzyme. This is not unreasonable, since the two molecules are structurally similar. Recent investigations have supported this, but it has not been categorically established. Assuming, however, that ATP and CTP do indeed bind at the same site, we are then provided with a clear example of the sensitive relationship between structure and function. In other words, this would mean that two *structurally similar materials, ATP and CTP, can bind to the same enzyme at the same site and cause opposite effects on the enzymatic activity—activation and inhibition.*

All of the foregoing data can be recapitulated and summarized by considering the primary conclusions of Gerhart and Pardee.

1. Aspartate transcarbamylase is representative of a group of enzymes that possess more than one binding site. In addition to the primary active site which binds the natural substrates, there also exist, in the same molecule, separate *secondary sites* which can bind other substances that function as inhibitors and/or activators.
2. Both the primary and secondary sites can be occupied simultaneously.
3. The secondary sites are not necessarily specific in their action and different materials can bind, resulting in different effects.
4. The binding at the secondary sites may cause a subsequent shift in the topographical features (conformation) of the protein molecule, which can affect the catalytic activity of the primary active site.
5. The secondary site effects constitute the basis of feedback control mechanisms that serve as an effective means of regulating metabolism.

BIRTH OF THE ALLOSTERIC THEORY

In 1963 Monod, Changeux, and Jacob formulated a theory to explain the mechanism of enzyme regulation. Although studies of the type described above for aspartate transcarbamylase served as the experimental basis for the theory, the theory is not confined to enzymes subject only to feedback inhibition control. Rather, it is a theory that was intended to have general applicability to any protein which may be subject to *secondary site effects* resulting in either its inhibition or activation. The architecture of the theory was guided by the following experimental observations, which of course are represented by the studies on ATCase. (1) In a number of cases a plot of enzyme activity against substrate concentration does not yield the classical rectangular, hyperbolic curve (⌢) according to Michaelis-Menten kinetics, but approximates a sigmoid curve (⌡). (2) Enzymes showing this type of kinetic behavior are generally subject to inhibition or activation by other substances. The kinetics of inhibition are not of the classical competitive or non-competitive type and are generally associated with an exaggerated sigmoid curve. On the other hand, the kinetics of activation more closely approximate Michaelis-Menten kinetics. (3) The unusual kinetic behavior is observed with enzymes that have more than one binding site. (4) The sensitivity of a native protein to an activator or inhibitor can be modified by treatments which result in an alteration of the three-dimensional structure of the protein. In addition, this desensitization of the enzyme to a secondary effector can also be accompanied by changes in the kinetics and activity of the enzyme towards the normal substrate, as evidenced by the loss of the sigmoid curve and the enhanced maximum velocity of ATCase following thermal or mercurial treatment.

The theory developed by Monod, Changeux, and Jacob is called the *allosteric theory* or the *theory of allosterism*. A key to the basic understanding of its design can be provided by an analysis of the word "allosterism," which refers to *variations* (allo-) *in three-dimensional conformation* (-steric; -sterism). Consequently, it should be apparent that the emergence of the *theory of allosterism* to explain metabolic regulation *was based on the premise that regulation is effected by an agent (termed an allosteric effector) which can bind to a secondary site and thus mediate transitions of an enzyme (a protein molecule) between different (variable) molecular conformations*.

The primary principles of the theory were subsequently incorporated by Monod, Wyman, and Changeux in 1965 into a conceptual model which attempts to explain the observations enumerated above. The model has been subjected to a detailed theoretical analysis, and mathematical equations of state are available which embody the principles of the model. While the theory has not been accepted by all with total commitment, it has been received with considerable enthusiasm and since its appearance has generated and guided a substantial amount of research in the field of enzyme kinetics in general and enzyme regulation in particular. In one case the model has been successfully tested. It seems appropriate that the first verification of the model should involve the first allosteric enzyme to be studied in detail, namely, aspartate transcarbamylase. Let us now examine the key features of the theory, the proposed model, and the current state of knowledge of aspartate transcarbamylase.

Monod and coworkers proposed that proteins subject to allosteric effects are *oligomeric* in nature (that is, they are aggregates of more than one polypeptide chain) and that the *monomeric units are identical*. Furthermore, they proposed that, in the intact oligomeric molecule, all the monomers occupy *equivalent positions*. In other words, the allosteric protein was visualized as being a structurally symmetrical, homogeneous oligomer. Finally, each monomer contains only one binding site corresponding to each possible effector. The maximum number

According to allosteric theory, the monomeric units are termed *protomers* and a protomer may be composed of one or more polypeptide chains. When the latter applies, the polypeptide chains may also be different (see pages 136 and 137).

of sites would, therefore, correspond to the number of different types of effectors. For example, if an enzyme catalyzed the conversion of $A \to B$, but was also inhibited or activated by some other material, C, then each monomer would contain two sites—one for A and one for C. If the enzyme were inhibited by one effector (C) and also activated by another (D), and if both effectors required different binding sites, then each monomer would contain three sites. If, on the other hand, both inhibitor and activator bound at the same site with different effects, then each monomer would contain only two sites. Note that the actual substrate of the enzyme is also to be considered as an allosteric effector. If the same enzyme were not subject to activation or inhibition by some other material, but did show the unusual sigmoid kinetics as the concentration of A was varied, then each monomer would possess only one stereospecific site for the natural substrate, A.

It was further postulated—and this is the major feature of their theory—that the allosteric protein, uncomplexed to substrates, activators and inhibitors, exists in *two different states* that are in *equilibrium* with each other. In other words, it is hypothesized that the component monomers can interact with each other to yield two different oligomeric complexes with subtly but significantly different spatial conformations. Whether the equilibrium favors one conformation or the other, or involves equal populations of both conformations, would be controlled by differences in stability contributed by differences in the interactions of the monomeric subunits. Putting it simply, a *two-state model* is proposed, with each state representing a different conformational structure of the same protein. Most important is the corollary that, because the conformation of each state is different, each protein state will exhibit different binding and catalytic properties. One state with a high degree of substrate binding and catalytic action would represent the *active* conformation. If the protein were subject to activation, the active conformation would also possess optimum binding sites for the activator. The second state with a low degree of substrate binding and catalytic action would represent the *inactive* conformation. If the protein were subject to inhibition, the inactive conformation would also possess the optimum binding sites for the inhibitor(s). Regardless of the number of types of allosteric effectors, the theory states that the actual binding of an effector to its preferred site in the preferred conformation will cause a *transition* of the protein from one conformational state to the other. This aspect of the theory is discussed further below.

The theory also distinguishes between what are called *homotropic* and *heterotropic effects*. Homotropic effects are those observed when only *one kind of effector is binding with the enzyme*. This, of course, will always be the situation when allosteric effects are observed in the presence of the normal substrate alone. The effect of binding of the substrate at equivalent sites in different monomers is said to be *cooperative* in that additional binding results in a favorable transition to a conformation which increases the rate of enzymatic activity. Kinetically, the cooperative effect is ascribed to the *initial stages* of the sigmoid curve when there is a definite transition in the dependence of reaction velocity on the substrate concentration. Heterotropic effects are due to the *binding of more than one type of effector* to each monomer at different sites. Whereas homotropic effects will always be cooperative, heterotropic effects may be cooperative or antagonistic depending on whether the secondary binding material is an inhibitor or an activator.

INACTIVE CONFORMATION

Sites 1 and 3:

unfavorable sites for
substrate binding

Sites 2 and 4:

favorable sites for
inhibitor binding;
unfavorable sites for
activator binding

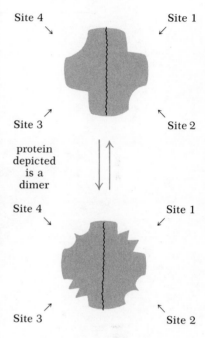

protein
depicted
is a
dimer

ACTIVE CONFORMATION

Sites 1 and 3:

favorable sites for
substrate binding

Sites 2 and 4:

favorable sites for
activator binding;
unfavorable sites for
inhibitor binding

Note: In this diagram it is implied that Sites 1 and 3 correspond to the same localized region in both conformations and that it is the orientation of amino acid residues in these regions that differs (indicated by different contour surfaces) in each conformation. The same applies to Sites 2 and 4.

An explanation of activation and inhibition can now be given in more specific language. The *activation* with ATP, for example, can be explained in terms of the binding of ATP, which causes a *favorable transition* resulting in a considerable diminution of the cooperative effect in terms of aspartate binding. That is to say, the binding of ATP to a secondary site is the driving force which results in the availability of a greater population of optimal sites for aspartate binding. In the absence of ATP binding (control), the driving force is the binding of aspartate itself, and hence we observe the cooperative effect, that is, the sigmoid kinetics. The binding is with the active conformation of the protein, forming an effector-enzyme complex. This in turn displaces the equilibrium of uncomplexed protein, which then readjusts itself. This means that more of the inactive state shifts to the active state. Thus, the effect of ATP as an activator of ATCase activity is *indirect*. The enzyme is presumed to already exist in an active state. The presence and binding of ATP result in more of the active conformation being produced from the inactive conformation. The inhibition with CTP can be similarly explained, but in reverse. In the presence of CTP binding, an *unfavorable transition* occurs which results in a smaller number of optimal sites for aspartate binding. To counteract this, a greater amount of aspartate will be required to make the optimal sites again available. That is to say, the cooperative effect in terms of aspartate binding will require a larger amount of aspartate. Kinetically, this is reflected by the greater concentration of aspartate required for half-saturation of ATCase in the presence of CTP than in the control with no CTP present (Figure 5–12).

In order to clarify any confusion generated by the verbal description of the allosteric effects, the same principles are depicted in the diagrammatic representation shown in Figure 5–15. For the sake of simplicity, a dimeric protein is used in the diagram. Inspection of the model reveals that it can be used to explain all of the theoretical features attributed to allosteric systems by merely applying fundamental principles of the law of mass action. An equilibrium of at least two conformational states of the dimeric protein molecule is represented at the top of the diagram. Note closely that each state preferentially binds to different allosteric effector substances. This tendency for preferential binding is symbolically represented by the complementary relationship between the structural topography of the allosteric effectors and that of their binding sites present in each conformational state. In effect, the diagram summarizes the statement that the presence of an allosteric inhibitor (*I*) with a preferred binding for the inactive conformation will serve as the driving force that will shift the original pre-existing equilibrium to favor the formation of additional protein molecules in the inactive conformation and fewer molecules in the active conformation. Alternatively, the presence of the natural substrate (*S*) and/or an allosteric activator (*A*), both with a preferred binding for the active conformation, will shift the original equilibrium to favor the formation of additional molecules in the active conformation and fewer molecules in the inactive conformation.

As previously stated, the two-state model has been subjected to a rigorous mathematical analysis. It is beyond the scope of this book, however, to investigate this aspect of the theory. Suffice it to say that the theoretical conclusions have been supported by recent experimentation

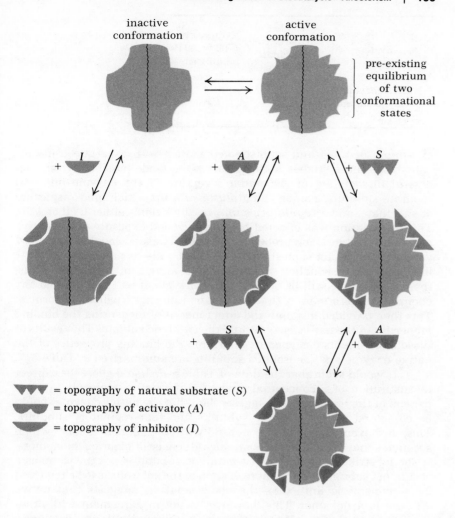

= topography of natural substrate (*S*)

= topography of activator (*A*)

= topography of inhibitor (*I*)

a) As the level of substrate (∨∨∨) increases,
   a favorable transition (⟶) will occur;
   a cooperative effect will also be observed.
b) As the level of activator (∨∨) increases,
   a favorable transition will likewise occur; this will reduce
   the extent of the cooperative effect in the binding of
   substrate.
c) If inhibitor (▬) were present, its binding would cause
   an unfavorable transition (⟵) to occur; this binding
   would also result in a greater cooperative effect of
   substrate binding to reverse the transition; the transition
   could be reversed by the presence of activator.

Figure 5–15 A diagrammatic summary of
allosteric interactions and their effects in
terms of the two-state model. The hypothetical protein molecule represented is
a dimer.

Table 5–7 Comparison of binding properties of native enzyme and isolated subunits.

System	Number of aspartate or succinate binding sites	Number of CTP or ATP binding sites
Native enzyme	4	4
Catalytic subunit	2	0
Regulatory subunit	0	1

of a more detailed and sophisticated nature with aspartate transcarbamylase. These studies with ATCase were made possible by the successful dissociation of the native structure of the enzyme into two separate subunits, namely, a *catalytic subunit* which binds aspartate or succinate, and a *regulatory subunit* which binds either CTP or ATP. This dissociation was effected by the controlled exposure of the native enzyme to *p*-chloromercurobenzoate. The ATCase molecule also proved very appropriate for such studies because it will—as previously stated— bind succinate, which is a non-reactive analog of aspartate. Thus, though succinate will be bound by the enzyme, it will not undergo any chemical transformation, that is, carbamyl succinate will not be formed. This then provided a simple and direct means of measuring the binding properties of the native enzyme and the catalytic subunit. The results of those experiments designed to determine the binding properties of the native enzyme and the isolated subunits are summarized in Table 5–7.

It would seem that the data of Table 5–7 should allow for a direct reconstitution of a conceptual model for the native molecule. A comparison of the binding data suggests then that the native enzyme should be composed of two catalytic subunits and four regulatory subunits. This, however, constitutes a *non-fit* with the Monod theory, which stipulates that the native molecule should consist of identical monomers. It should strike the reader that a catalytic subunit is *not* the same as a regulatory subunit. Furthermore, if each of the subunits is to be regarded as a monomeric unit, then the above analysis suggests that native ATCase is a hexamer. This, however, is not in agreement with other studies which have indicated that the native molecule is a tetramer. These inconsistencies can be resolved by assuming that the isolated subunits do not really represent one of the monomeric units in intact form. This is not an unrealistic assumption and is supported by other data. For example, the molecular weights of the isolated subunits are significantly different. To resolve these inconsistencies, the workers proposed that the native molecule be visualized as a *tetramer of identical monomers* by assuming *each monomer* (A in the diagram below)

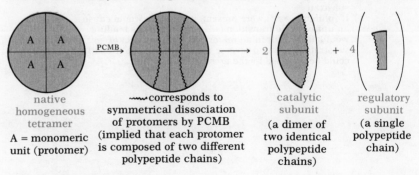

native homogeneous tetramer

A = monomeric unit (protomer)

⌇⌇ corresponds to symmetrical dissociation of protomers by PCMB (implied that each protomer is composed of two different polypeptide chains)

catalytic subunit

(a dimer of two identical polypeptide chains)

regulatory subunit

(a single polypeptide chain)

to consist of one regulatory subunit and one-half of a catalytic subunit which are bonded together such that they are susceptible to attack by *p*-chloromercurobenzoate (PCMB). More recent investigations by Rosenbusch and Weber, however, have provided strong evidence favoring a hexameric structure with each monomeric unit consisting of one regulatory subunit and one catalytic subunit for a total of twelve polypeptides per native ATCase molecule. Continued investigations will be necessary to substantiate this. Whatever the final outcome, here is but one example of the constantly changing state of biochemical knowledge.

In closing, it should also be noted that the theory of Monod still requires further confirmation and perhaps modification. Additional support now exists from recent reports that the allosteric properties of hemoglobin (it too displays a cooperative effect with respect to the binding of oxygen) also fit the two-state model. Although this theory has enjoyed wide acceptance, there are still those who favor alternative explanations to account for allosteric effects. Koshland, for example, proposes that the protein may exist in only one form and that the binding of one substance to one site on the native protein may *directly* cause conformational changes to occur elsewhere in the molecule (induced-fit theory) which may favor or disfavor subsequent binding. While knowledge in this field is still minimal, this lack of unanimity is a healthy and even necessary prerequisite for productive research.

The treatment given the subject of allosterism was by deliberate design meant to be extensive. Although the regulation of enzyme activity by allosteric effects is important in itself, since many enzymes exhibit this phenomenon, and although the principles enumerated here will be referred to repeatedly in subsequent chapters, other factors motivated this in-depth analysis. First of all, the complex nature of the principle of allosterism necessarily demands more than a superficial treatment, even in introductory textbooks. The more superficial the treatment, the greater is the probability that its understanding will remain obscure. In addition, the subject provides an excellent opportunity to illustrate the *modus operandi* of biochemical research and also illustrates in a limited fashion the scientific method at work. A problem is formulated; some initial data are collected; a working hypothesis is formed; additional observations are performed to support the hypothesis; the hypothesis is then revised, if necessary; a theory is formulated; and the theory is tested. Finally, the inclusion and interpretation of actual experimental data should serve to catalyze development of an analytical attitude, which is too often lacking in students upon their first exposure to biochemistry. Usually the material is approached basically as a conglomeration of descriptive material to be memorized. The last section of this chapter was designed to counteract that attitude.

Because this detailed analysis of allosterism (secondary-site effects) may have detracted from an understanding of its biological significance, it seems wise to recapitulate. A living cell is characterized by a multitude of enzyme-catalyzed reactions, the sum of which define the biochemical dynamics of the cell and, indeed, are responsible for its very existence. As we will discover in ensuing chapters, all of these reactions are interrelated, and frequently many can be categorized as a functional set (*metabolic pathway*) designed for the concerted degradation or biosynthesis of specific substances. However, despite the critical nature of this multitude of reactions, we now know that an organism is

hexameric native state

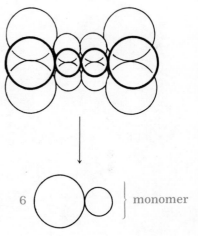

6   monomer

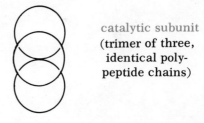

catalytic subunit
(trimer of three,
identical poly-
peptide chains)

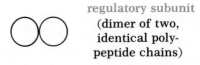

regulatory subunit
(dimer of two,
identical poly-
peptide chains)

not dependent on their continual operation at a constant level. On the contrary, a variety of natural checks and balances do exist that operate on a molecular level to regulate the dynamics of cellular metabolism. This self-regulatory capacity confers to the living organism an efficiency level unequaled by any chemical machine and, indeed, makes the cell seem like a microscopic, molecular computer.

LITERATURE

BERNHARD, S., *The Structure and Function of Enzymes,* New York: W. A. Benjamin, Inc., 1968. An introductory treatment of enzymes with emphasis on kinetics and reaction mechanisms.

BLOW, D. M., and T. A. STEITZ, "X-Ray Diffraction Studies of Enzymes," in *Annual Review of Biochemistry,* Volume 39, 63–100 (1970). A good review of structural details of seven enzymes in terms of the mechanism and specificity of their catalytic action.

BOYER, P. D., H. LARDY, and K. MYRBACK (eds.), *The Enzymes,* Second and Third Edition. New York: Academic Press. A valuable multi-volume work covering most aspects of biocatalysis with emphasis on reaction types. Volume 1 (second edition, 1960) is devoted to fundamentals of enzyme catalysis. Volumes 1 and 2 (third edition, 1970) contain the latest information on general principles including structure, control, kinetics, and mechanism.

CHANGEUX, J. P., J. C. GERHART, and H. K. SCHACHMAN, "Allosteric Interactions in Aspartate Transcarbamylase: Binding of Specific Ligands to the Native Enzyme and its Isolated Subunits," *Biochemistry,* 7, 531–538 (1968). A research article describing the binding properties of catalytic and regulatory subunits and the first proposed model of the quaternary structure of the native enzyme.

DAWES, E. A., *Quantitative Problems in Biochemistry.* Baltimore: The Williams and Wilkins Company, 1967. A problem-oriented textbook covering various physicobiochemical subjects. Chapters 5 and 6 are devoted to reaction kinetics and enzyme kinetics.

DIXON, M., and E. C. Webb, *Enzymes,* Second Edition. New York: Academic Press, 1964. A textbook dealing exclusively with enzymes. Although somewhat out of date, it is still an excellent reference for a detailed coverage of general principles.

GERHART, J. C., and PARDEE, A. B., "The Enzymology of Control by Feedback Inhibition," *J. Biol. Chem.,* 237, 891–896 (1962). The first study providing evidence for the existence of secondary sites in enzymes and their role in the modulation of catalytic activity.

KOSHLAND, D. E., "Correlation of Structure and Function in Enzyme Action," *Science,* 142, 1533–1541 (1963). A review article defining the nature of the catalytic process from the standpoint of protein structure. Included is a definitive summary of the induced-fit theory, of which the author is the chief proponent.

KOSHLAND, D. E., and K. E. NEET, "The Catalytic and Regulatory Properties of Enzymes," in *Annual Review of Biochemistry,* Volume 38, 359–410 (1968). An excellent and current review article.

MAHLER, H. R., and E. H. CORDES, *Biological Chemistry,* Second Edition. New York: Harper & Row, Publishers, 1971. A textbook with an advanced and authoritative treatment of enzyme kinetics, mechanism of enzyme action, and coenzymes.

MARKUS, G., D. K. McCLINTOCK and J. B. BUSSEL, "Conformational Changes in Aspartate Transcarbamylase: A Functional Model for Allosteric Behavior," *J. Biol. Chem.,* 246, 767–771 (1971). A research paper offering the most recent proposal on the structural organization of ATCase and its relationship to the allosteric properties of the enzyme.

MONOD, J., J. P. CHANGEUX, and F. JACOB, "Allosteric Proteins and Cellular Control Systems," *J. Mol. Biol.*, **6,** 306–329 (1963). The original article describing the theory of allosterism.

MONOD, J., J. WYMAN, and J. P. CHANGEUX, "On the Nature of Allosteric Interactions: A Plausible Model," *J. Mol. Biol.*, **12,** 88–118 (1965). Original article explaining the formulation of the two-state equilibrium model for enzyme regulation.

NORD, F. F. (ed.), *Advances in Enzymology*. New York: John Wiley Interscience. A publication composed of annual volumes (since 1942) devoted to reviewing progress in enzymology. The articles, written by authorities, deal with general and specific subjects. This is an extremely useful reference work for researchers, teachers, students, and writers of biochemistry textbooks. The last-cited article on regulatory mechanisms is a particularly good example.

ROSENBUSCH, J. P., and K. WEBER, "Subunit Structure of Aspartate Transcarbamylase from *Escherichia coli*," *J. Biol. Chem.*, **246,** 1644–1657 (1971). Experimental evidence for a hexameric structure of the native protein.

STADTMAN, E. R., "Allosteric Regulation of Enzyme Activity," in *Advances in Enzymology*, Volume 28, 41–154 (1966). A thorough review of regulatory mechanisms.

EXERCISES

5–1 From the final form of the Michaelis-Menten equation as given on page 113, prove that K_m is equal to the substrate concentration when the enzyme is 50% saturated.

5–2 The enzyme glutamic acid dehydrogenase catalyzes the reaction:

$$\underset{\text{L-glutamate}}{^-OOCCH_2CH_2\overset{\overset{\displaystyle NH_3^+}{|}}{C}HCOO^-} + NAD^+ \rightarrow \underset{\alpha\text{-ketoglutarate}}{^-OOCCH_2CH_2\overset{\overset{\displaystyle O}{\|}}{C}COO^-} + NH_3 + NADH + H^+$$

The dependence of initial velocity on the concentration of L-glutamate is given below. The initial concentration of NAD$^+$ was held constant in each case. Calculate the K_m and V_{max} of the enzyme by the classical Michaelis-Menten plot and also by the Lineweaver-Burk method, and compare the values. (*Note:* The reaction velocity is expressed in terms of the rate of change in the absorbance at 360 nm. This is a measure of the rate of product formation, specifically NADH. See page 26, chapter 2, for a review of the absorbance of NAD$^+$ and NADH).

L-glutamate concentration (millimolar)	initial velocity (change in absorbance at 360 nm/min)
1.68	0.172
3.33	0.250
5.00	0.286
6.67	0.303
10.0	0.334
20.0	0.384

5–3 Glycogen is a polymeric carbohydrate composed of several glucose residues. Glycogen synthetase is the enzyme responsible for lengthening the glycogen molecule according to the following reaction. The structures of UDP-glucose (the metabolically active substrate form of glucose in this reaction) and

$$\text{UDP-glucose} + (\text{glucose})_n \rightarrow (\text{glucose})_{n+1} + \text{UDP}$$

acceptor   chain lengthened

glycogen will be considered in Chapter 7. The data below can, however, be analyzed without this knowledge. The results of two separate studies on the catalytic action of glycogen synthetase are given under conditions where the concentration of UDP-glucose was varied and the concentration of the acceptor polyglucose was held constant. In one case no further additions were made, while in the other, ATP was added (2.5 mM). From a Lineweaver-Burk graphical analysis, determine the apparent type of inhibition by ATP on the activity of the enzyme.

UDP-glucose (millimolar)	initial velocity μmoles $(\text{glucose})_{n+1}$ formed/min	
	no additions	ATP added (2.5 mM)
0.8	10.0	2.0
1.4	12.5	3.3
3.3	22.0	6.7
5.0	25.0	10.0

5-4 The catalytic activity of most enzymes is a sensitive function of pH. A plot (activity versus pH) of the data given below will clearly illustrate the degree of this sensitivity. What is the optimum pH for the enzyme in question?

units of enzyme activity	24.8	33.0	66.7	56.2	41.3	27.5
pH	7.2	7.6	8.0	8.6	8.8	9.0

5-5 After a pre-incubation with p-chloromercurobenzoate, the binding of an enzyme with its substrate was no different from that of the untreated enzyme, but the catalytic activity of the treated enzyme was found to be 40% less. What conclusion can one draw from this type of observation?

5-6 The enzyme 6-phosphogluconate dehydrogenase catalyzes the oxidative decarboxylation of 6-phosphogluconate according to the following reaction (see Chapter 11, page 294).

6-phosphogluconate $+ \text{NADP}^+ \rightarrow$ ribulose-5-phosphate $+ \text{CO}_2 + \text{NADPH} + \text{H}^+$

From the following kinetic data, determine what effect rose bengal has on the activity of the dehydrogenase. The data were obtained under conditions

Concentration of NADP+ (10^{-5} M)	initial velocity (units of enzyme activity/min)	
	no additions	+ rose bengal (1.5 × 10^{-5} M)
2	2.12	1.11
3	2.70	1.47
4	2.94	1.73
6	3.33	2.32
10	3.85	2.78

where the concentration of glucose-6-phosphate was constant and that of NADP$^+$ was varied. (Rose bengal is an organic dye that has been used successfully as a probe into the mechanism of action of certain enzymes. Your analysis of the data will partially indicate why this is so. Note the extremely low concentration of rose bengal used in these studies.) Briefly discuss the data in view of the fact that rose bengal forms strong complexes with imidazole-containing substances.

5–7 Phosphofructokinase is an enzyme, widespread in nature, catalyzing the reaction given below, which is an important step unique to the degradation of carbohydrates by the glycolytic pathway (Chapter 11).

fructose-6-phosphate
(F6P)

fructose-1,6-diphosphate
(FDP)

Under conditions where the concentration of ATP was held constant, the dependency of the initial velocity on the concentration of fructose-6-phosphate as measured at two different pH's (6.9 and 8.2) is represented by the data below. Plot the data according to the classical Michaelis-Menten method and interpret what effect the pH has on the activity of the enzyme.

fructose-6-phosphate (millimolar)	0.3	0.5	0.8	1.0	1.3	1.5	1.7	2.5	3.5
initial velocity (micromoles F6P reacted/min) pH 6.9	1.0	2.7	3.0	12	22	46	68	77	80

fructose-6-phosphate (millimolar)	0.02	0.04	0.05	0.07	0.1	0.15	0.25	0.40
initial velocity (micromoles F6P reacted/min) pH 8.2	35	47	60	68	80	90	92	95

5–8 Using Figure 5–12 as a reference, what type of Michaelis-Menten plot would be obtained if the concentration of CTP were increased above that specified in the legend of Figure 5–12? Explain the reason for this in terms of the two-state model for allosteric effects.

6

Nucleotides and Nucleic Acids

In the organization of this textbook, the principles of protein chemistry and biocatalysis were treated first because of their pre-eminent role in the living processes. Yet, despite their vital importance, the proteins constitute only one of four main classes of naturally occurring organic compounds. The other three are nucleic acids, carbohydrates, and lipids. Beginning with this chapter and continuing through Chapter 8, we will consider each remaining class in that order. Having explored the chemical nature of these molecules, we will then begin a systematic analysis of their participation in the dynamic operations of a cell.

Every living organism contains two types of nucleic acids, termed *ribonucleic acid (RNA)* and *deoxyribonucleic acid (DNA)*. Viruses, on the other hand, contain only one type—either RNA or DNA. The molecular weights of nucleic acids cover a wide spectrum. Transfer-RNA, a particular species of RNA and the smallest known nucleic acid, has a molecular weight of approximately 25,000, whereas individual molecules of DNA—constituting some of the largest single molecules yet known to man—range in molecular weight from 10^6 to 10^9.

Both RNA and DNA are polymeric substances with the monomeric unit termed a *nucleotide*. Consequently, a nucleic acid is synonymously referred to as a *polynucleotide*. A single nucleotide consists of three chemical parts—inorganic phosphate, a simple sugar, and a *purine* or *pyrimidine* nitrogen base. All parts are covalently attached in the following order: phosphate—sugar—nitrogen base. In a nucleic acid, successive nucleotides are linked together via *phosphodiester bonds* between the sugar moiety of adjacent nucleotides. The nitrogen bases are not involved in any covalent linkages other than their attachment to the sugar-phosphate backbone.

In terms of chemical composition, the most distinguishing difference between RNA and DNA is the type of sugar molecule found in the monomeric nucleotides. *D-ribose* is present in the nucleotides of *ribo*nucleic acids, whereas *D-deoxyribose* is present in the nucleotides of *deoxy*ribonucleic acids. A second compositional distinction is based on the purine and pyrimidine nitrogen bases that are present. The situation is, however, considerably simpler than with the proteins, where 18–20 different side chains are possible. To be specific, a nucleic acid consists primarily of only four different nitrogen bases. Furthermore, each type of nucleic acid contains two purines and two pyrimidines. In terms of their purine composition, RNA and DNA are identical; that is, they both contain *adenine* (A) and *guanine* (G). The difference exists in the pyrimidine composition. Although both contain *cytosine* (C), RNA contains *uracil* (U) while DNA contains *thymine* (T). Parallel to our previous discussion of amino acid sequence in proteins, it is the *sequence of nitrogen bases* along the invariant sugar-phosphate backbone which controls both the three-dimensional conformation and the biological properties of the nucleic acids.

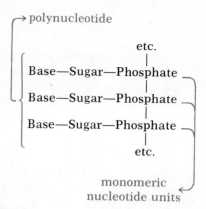

The biological function of nucleic acids is basically twofold. First, they serve as the *molecular mechanism for the storage and transmission of genetic information.* Secondly, they *control and direct the biosynthesis of proteins.* In fulfilling these functions, the nucleic acids constitute the molecular agents responsible for (a) the constancy of cellular replication, (b) the regulated metabolic shifts of a cell due to physiological demands or a changing environment, (c) the natural and induced changes in the genetic constitution of an organism, and (d) the continued maintenance of a viable organism.

NUCLEOTIDES

Before analyzing nucleic acid structure, it is necessary to first consider the structure of the monomeric nucleotides. Furthermore, aside from their occurrence in nucleic acids, the nucleotides are important biological materials in their own right and thus deserve our attention. Our objective here is to investigate the chemical structures of the constituent parts of a nucleotide and also how they are linked to each other. Since the carbohydrates have not yet been discussed, let us begin by briefly considering the sugar unit. Chapter 7 treats the structure of carbohydrates in greater detail.

RIBOSE AND DEOXYRIBOSE

As previously mentioned, the two sugars that distinguish the nucleotides of RNA and DNA are D-ribose and D-deoxyribose, respectively. Each sugar is shown below in a linear structural formula and in a *Haworth* formula, named after the individual who first proposed such cyclic drawings as convenient and reasonably representative projections of their structural conformation in solution. Note that each sugar contains five carbon atoms (called pentoses), but that deoxyribose contains one fewer functional hydroxyl groups, specifically at C^2. The Haworth formula depicts a completely planar system, with groups attached to the ring carbons projected upwards or downwards relative to the plane of the ring. The accompanying systematic names of the sugars contain a *-furanose* suffix because of the structural similarity to the five-membered cyclic organic molecule, *furan.*

The Greek letter β is used to refer to a subtle but significant structural feature. To be specific, *it designates the spatial orientation of the hydroxyl group at* C^1. Whereas the orientation of the C^2 and C^3 groups is nonvariant—indeed, it defines the very structural reality of the pentoses—the C^1—OH can assume either one of two possible conformations, each corresponding to a different isomeric form of the sugar. If the C^1 hydroxyl is directed upward in the Haworth formula, the sugar is said to be in the β *form.* If the C^1 hydroxyl is directed downward, the sugar is in the α *form.* As absurdly minute as it may seem to you, this is an extremely relevant aspect of carbohydrate structure. Several examples of this principle will be given in the next chapter. At present it is significant for us to note that only the β form of D-ribofuranose and D-deoxyribofuranose is found in nucleic acids.

In regard to the structure of a nucleotide, the nitrogen base is always linked to the pentose via the C^1—OH (β) group, while the phosphate group is in ester linkage with one of the remaining hydroxyls, generally at the C^5—OH. We will consider both aspects in more detail in subsequent sections.

NITROGEN BASES

The nitrogen bases found most frequently in RNA and DNA are *adenine, guanine, cytosine, thymine,* and *uracil.* The first two (A and G) are *substituted purines,* and the remaining three (C, T, and U) are *substituted pyrimidines.* Their structures, systematic names, and occurrence in nucleic acids are given below. The possibility of *tautomeric* forms of each base (with the exception of adenine) is also indicated. In this regard, it is important to note that the *keto* isomer predominates in nature. Another distinguishing structural feature of these molecules is

purine

pyrimidine

Major purines and pyrimidines of nucleic acids

adenine (A)
6-aminopurine
(RNA + DNA)

guanine (G)
2-amino-6-oxypurine
(RNA + DNA)

uracil (U)
2,4-dioxypyrimidine
(RNA)

thymine (T)
5-methyl-2,4-
dioxypyrimidine
(DNA)

cytosine (C)
2-oxy-4-amino
pyrimidine
(RNA + DNA)

tautomerism:

keto form   enol form

evident from the space-filling models, namely, the coplanarity of all atoms in the ring and of any atom immediately attached to the ring. The significance of both the keto tautomeric form and the planar conformation will be discussed shortly.

Examples of some nitrogen bases occurring less frequently in nature are shown below. Some, such as 5-methylcytosine, are minor components of DNA while others, such as 4-thiouracil and dihydrouracil, are minor components of RNA. Others of synthetic rather than natural origin are exemplified by 5-bromouracil (a potent mutagenic agent) and 6-mercaptopurine (an antitumor agent). Unlike the amino acids, the nitrogen bases do not occur in nature in the free state to any great extent. Rather, they are found largely in covalent linkage with ribose or deoxyribose as nucleosides and nucleotides.

Other Nitrogen Bases

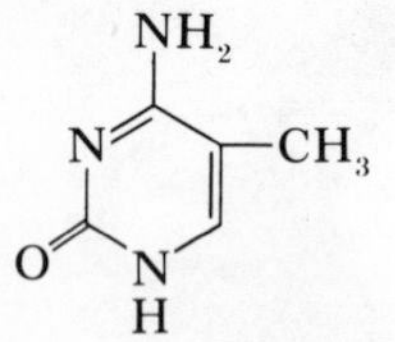

5-methyl-cytosine (DNA) 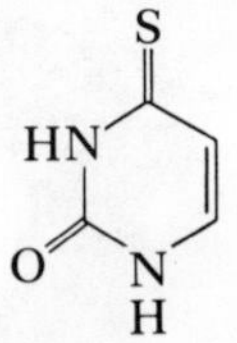 4-thiouracil (RNA) 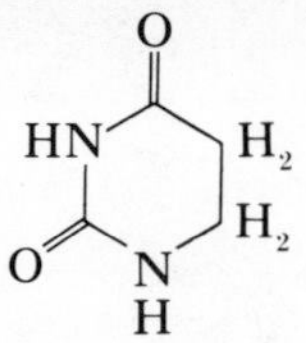 dihydrouracil (RNA) 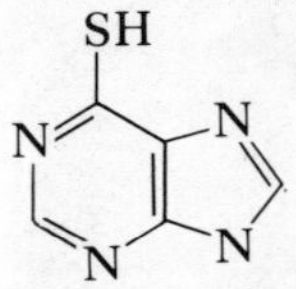 6-mercaptopurine 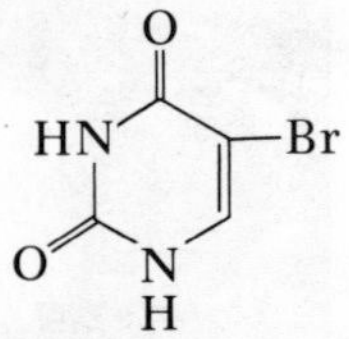 5-bromouracil

Due to their heterocyclic, aromatic nature, the nitrogen bases characteristically absorb energy in the UV region of the electromagnetic spectrum (see page 25, Chapter 2). Although each substance has a unique absorption spectrum, one of the absorption maxima in each is close to 260 nm. This property of nitrogen bases accounts for the strong absorption of nucleic acids at 260 nm, a characteristic that is frequently utilized in the *quantitative estimation* of nucleic acid concentration.

NUCLEOSIDE STRUCTURE

A nucleoside is a substance which on hydrolysis yields two chemical units: a sugar (D-ribose or D-deoxyribose) and a nitrogen base. More specifically, a nucleoside can be considered as an *N-glycoside* of the nitrogen base with the glycosidic linkage involving the $C^{1'}$ hydroxyl group of the sugar and the N^1 atom of the pyrimidine ring or the N^9 atom of the purine ring. To avoid confusion in numbering, the atoms of the carbohydrate unit are differentiated by a prime superscript. The accepted trivial names of the common ribonucleosides are adenosine, guanosine, uridine, and cytidine. The common deoxyribonucleosides are named deoxyadenosine, deoxyguanosine, deoxycytidine, and thymidine. Thymidine is not prefixed because of its infrequent occurrence as an N-riboside; it would be named ribosylthymine. This is another example of the confusion that often exists when using a non-systematic nomenclature. On a more systematic basis, the nucleosides are named as β-D-ribosyl or β-D-2-deoxyribosyl derivatives of the nitrogen base, as indicated on the following page.

a pyrimidine ribonucleoside

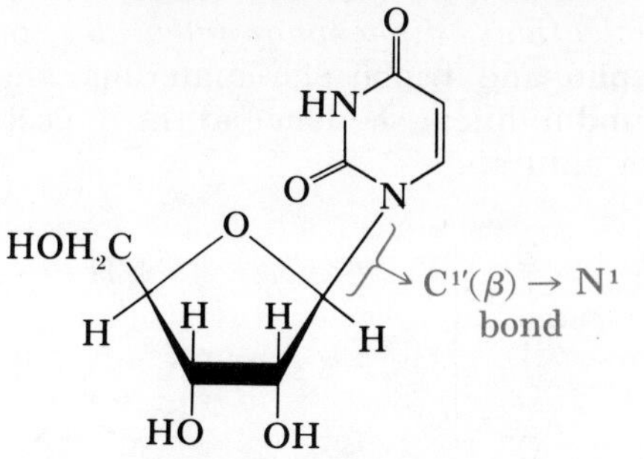

a purine deoxyribonucleoside

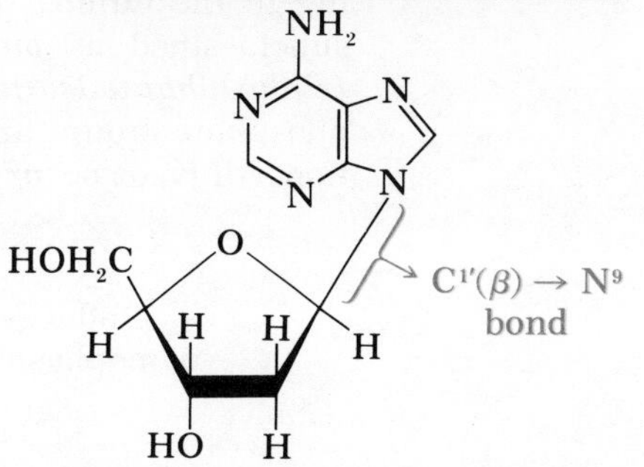

uridine
1-β-D-ribofuranosyluracil

deoxyadenosine
9-β-D-2-deoxyribofuranosyladenine

The nucleoside family is not without structural variety. Representative of some unique materials are *pseudouridine*, a C-glycoside of uracil found in transfer-RNA, and *puromycin*, a potent antibiotic excreted by a *Streptomyces* organism. The latter has a rather exotic structure containing an N-methylated adenine residue attached to aminoribose, which in turn possesses a phenylalanine residue in amide linkage. The mechanism of action of puromycin is discussed in Chapter 18 (page 510).

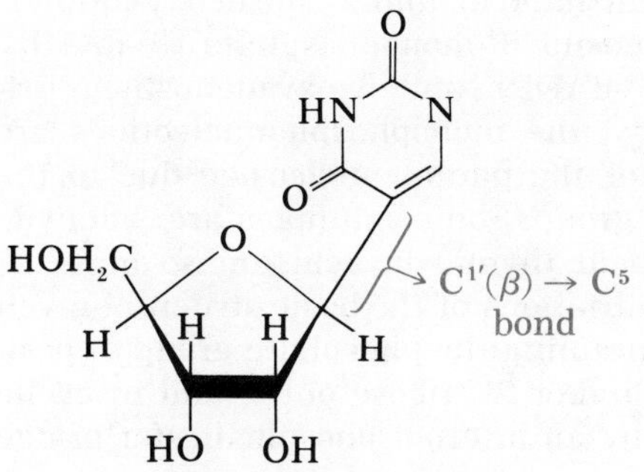

pseudouridine
5-β-D-ribofuranosyluracil
(RNA)

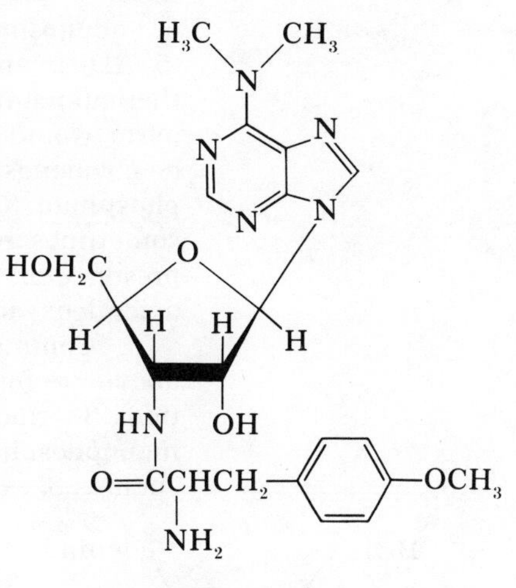

puromycin
(antibiotic: inhibits protein
biosynthesis)

NUCLEOTIDE STRUCTURE

The simplest way of defining a nucleotide is to say that it is a phosphorylated nucleoside with *one, two,* or *three* phosphate residues that are generally attached via ester linkage at the 5'—OH group of the pentose. Depending on the identity of the pentose, all nucleotides can be categorized as either ribonucleotides or deoxyribonucleotides. According to the number of phosphate residues present, nucleotides can be subclassified as *monophosphonucleotides, diphosphonucleotides,* or *triphosphonucleotides.* In diphospho and triphospho materials, the phosphate groups are generally found in linear sequence at the 5' position. All types occur ubiquitously in nature.

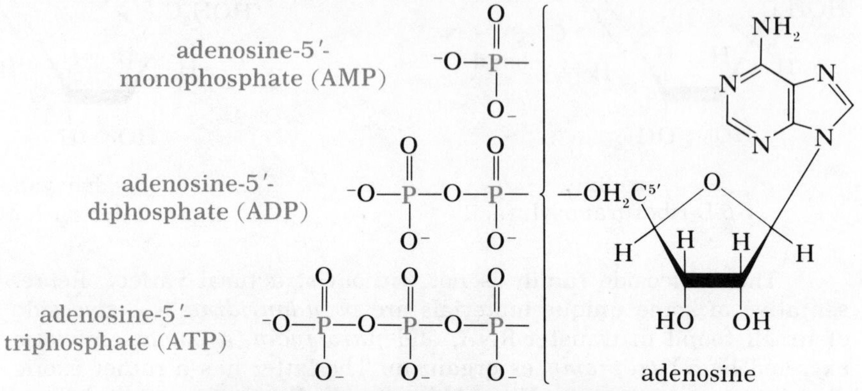

mono-, di-, triphosphonucleotides (5')
of adenosine

Nucleotides are named in a variety of ways. One method considers them as phosphate esters. Thus, the adenosine family would consist of adenosine-5'-monophosphate (5'-AMP), adenosine-5'-diphosphate (5'-ADP), and adenosine-5'-triphosphate (5'-ATP) where the parenthetical notation has an obvious shorthand meaning. The deoxy counterparts would be named deoxyadenosine-5'-monophosphate (5'-dAMP), deoxyadenosine-5'-diphosphate (5'-dADP), and deoxyadenosine-5'-triphosphate (5'-dATP). Alternatively, the monophosphonucleotides are sometimes named as acyl acids of the parent nucleoside due to the presence of the acidic phosphate group. Some examples are: adenylic acid, deoxyadenylic acid, uridylic acid, thymidylic acid, and so on.

Common but less frequent variations of the basic structure given above are found in nucleotides containing the phosphate group at positions 3' (ribose and deoxyribose) and/or 2' (ribose only), and in cyclic monophosphonucleotides formed by an internal phosphodiester bridge such as 3' → 5'.

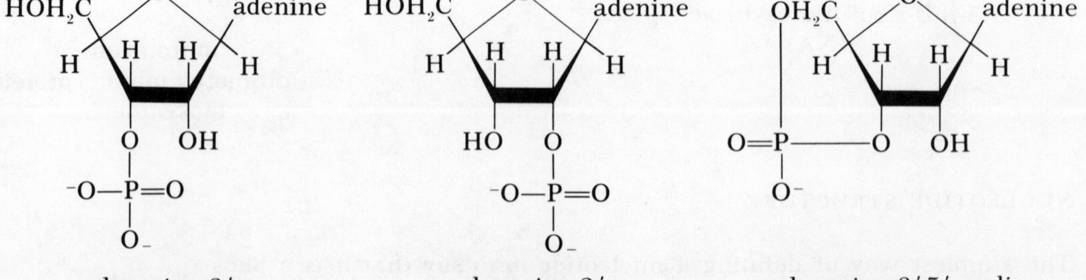

adenosine-3'-
monophosphate

3'-AMP

adenosine-2'-
monophosphate

2'-AMP

adenosine-3',5'-cyclic
monophosphate

3',5'-cyclic AMP

Cyclic-AMP, first isolated in 1959, has proved to be a compound of immense biological importance. Specifically, it appears that cyclic-AMP is involved in many diverse processes as a major *regulator* of metabolic and physiological activity in all types of organisms. In mammalian organisms, in particular, its action is intimately connected with many hormones. In fact, there is extensive evidence showing that the primary and immediate effect of many hormones is to activate the enzyme responsible for the production of cyclic-AMP. The cyclic-AMP then acts in turn to control the activity of other enzymes, frequently by an allosteric activation. In other words, cyclic-AMP acts as a secondary regulator carrying the message of the primary regulator, a hormone. Thus, cyclic-AMP is often called a *secondary messenger* of hormonal control. In Chapter 11 we will discuss a specific example of such a relationship involving the control of carbohydrate metabolism by the hormone adrenalin (see page 275).

HYDROLYSIS OF TRIPHOSPHONUCLEOTIDES

In addition to their utilization in nucleic acid biosynthesis (see next section), the triphosphonucleotides participate in many enzyme-catalyzed reactions involved in the metabolism of all types of compounds. In some cases their involvement is rather specific. For example, CTP participates in phospholipid biosynthesis (see page 405), and UTP functions in the biosynthesis and interconversions of various carbohydrates (see page 281). On the whole, however, their participation in metabolism is of a more general nature described in terms of the reversible hydrolysis of a terminal phosphate residue. The importance of this type of reaction to what goes on inside a living cell cannot be overstated. Using ATP as an example, the pertinent chemistry can be represented as shown below. Chemically speaking, the nature of this reaction is quite simple—a *phosphoanhydride* bond is cleaved (forward process) and formed (reverse process). It will become apparent that our choice of ATP to illustrate this system was deliberate rather than random.

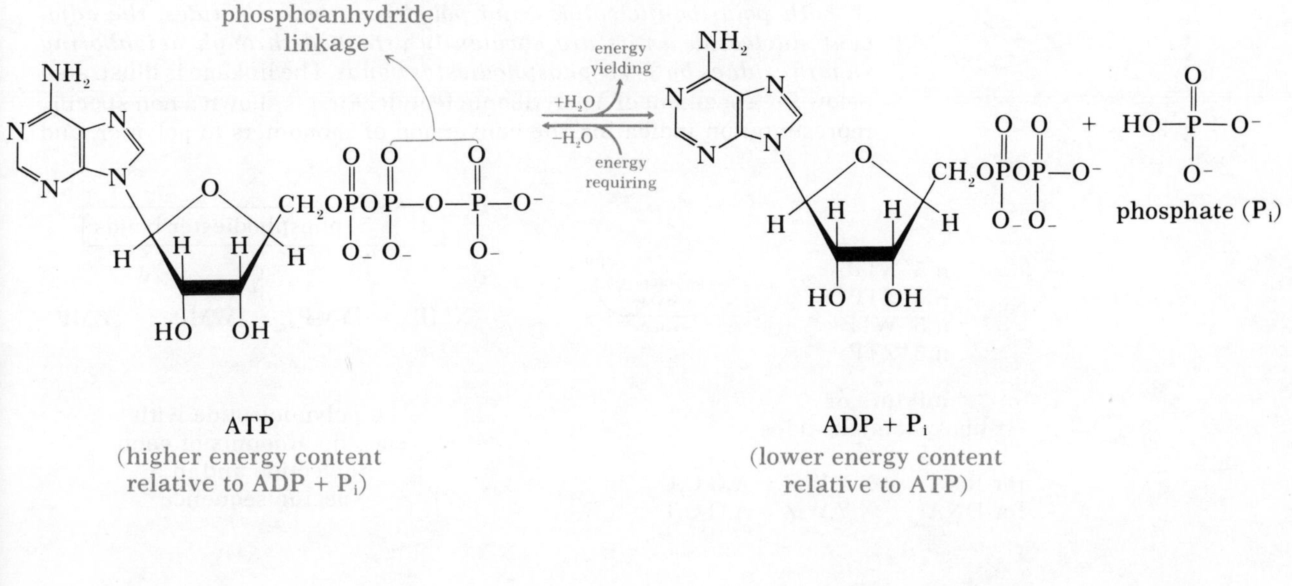
phosphoanhydride linkage
energy yielding
$+H_2O$
$-H_2O$
energy requiring
phosphate (P_i)
ATP
(higher energy content relative to ADP + P_i)
ADP + P_i
(lower energy content relative to ATP)

The energetics of the ATP $\rightleftarrows$ ADP interconversion are extremely important. Simply put, this represents the key to understanding the flow of energy within a cell. Although the net chemistry and energetics would apply to all of the triphosphonucleotides, the choice of ATP was deliberate because the ATP $\rightleftarrows$ ADP system is synonymous with the transfer of useful chemical energy during cellular metabolism. There are two aspects to this involvement. First, the formation of ATP from ADP and P_i (reverse process) is synonymous with the *conservation* of chemical energy from metabolized foodstuffs. That is to say, the chemical energy supplied by the degradation of high-energy dietary foodstuffs is utilized to bring about the formation of ATP. Secondly, the subsequent degradation of ATP to ADP (forward process) is synonymous with the cellular *use* of the chemical energy now stored in ATP by all energy-requiring processes needed to sustain the life of an organism. This completes a brief sketch of the central theme of bioenergetics. It is not restricted to any one organism or group of organisms. On the contrary, the ATP $\rightleftarrows$ ADP + P_i system is the *primary basis of the dynamic flow of energy in all cells.* As such, it is a good example of biochemical unity in our tremendously diverse biosphere. The analysis given here of this subject is meant to be only an initial exposure. The principles of bioenergetics and particularly the biochemistry of ATP will be probed in greater depth in Chapter 10. In fact, they will be referred to throughout our analysis of metabolism.

FORMATION OF POLYNUCLEOTIDES

One of the most significant biological reactions involving the triphosphonucleotides is their condensation to yield RNA and DNA. The enzymes involved, termed *RNA polymerases* and *DNA polymerases,* are specific for the triphosphonucleotides as substrates. In addition, both require a mixture of all the nucleotides, sometimes called a "cellular pool." RNA is syntheisized from a pool of ATP, GTP, CTP, and UTP, whereas DNA is produced from a pool of dATP, dGTP, dCTP, and dTTP. The details of both processes will be described later (Chapter 18). For the moment we are most interested in establishing only one point, namely, *in both polyribonucleotides and polydeoxyribonucleotides, the adjacent nucleotide units are covalently attached through neighboring sugar residues by 3'→5' phosphodiester bonds.* The linkage is illustrated below for a segment of a polyribonucleotide. First is shown a non-specific representation indicating the conversion of monomers to polymer, and

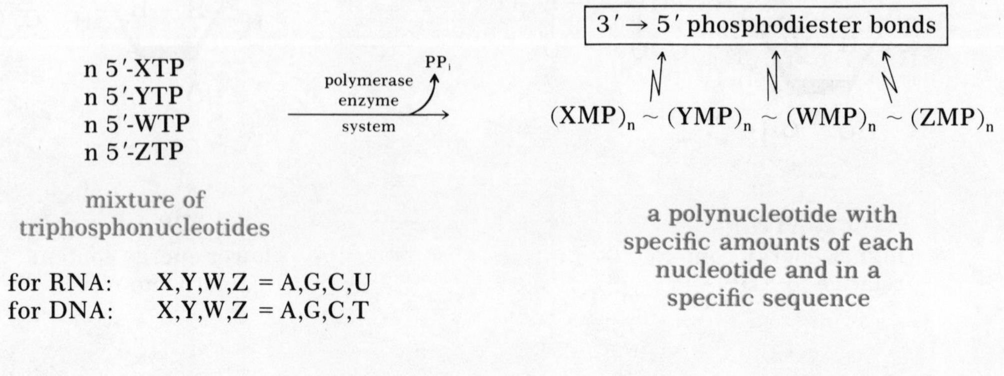

$$
\begin{array}{c}
\text{n } 5'\text{-XTP} \\
\text{n } 5'\text{-YTP} \\
\text{n } 5'\text{-WTP} \\
\text{n } 5'\text{-ZTP}
\end{array}
\quad
\xrightarrow[\text{system}]{\overset{PP_i}{\underset{\text{enzyme}}{\text{polymerase}}}}
\quad
$$

$$\boxed{3' \rightarrow 5' \text{ phosphodiester bonds}}$$

$$(XMP)_n \sim (YMP)_n \sim (WMP)_n \sim (ZMP)_n$$

mixture of
triphosphonucleotides

a polynucleotide with
specific amounts of each
nucleotide and in a
specific sequence

for RNA: X,Y,W,Z = A,G,C,U
for DNA: X,Y,W,Z = A,G,C,T

second, a specific segment of a nucleotide chain illustrating the nature of the repeating phosphodiester bond.

A segment of a polynucleotide chain illustrating $3' \to 5'$ phosphodiester bonds between adjacent nucleotides.

Note the anionic phosphate groups which would exist at pH ~ 7.

The large polynucleotides are termed nucleic acids because of the presence of several mildly acidic phosphate groups within their structure. Since the latter groupings are appreciably ionized at pH 7, the nucleic acids are polyanionic in nature. To conclude this introduction to nucleic acid structure, let us summarize a few basic facts. The two naturally occurring nucleic acids are homogeneous in terms of the pentose sugar moiety found in each. DNA contains only deoxyribose and RNA only ribose. In terms of nitrogen base content, the two are heterogeneous, with both containing varying amounts and sequences of the major bases common to each type: A,G,C, and T in DNA, and A,G,C, and U in RNA. Finally, the number of nucleotide monomers in DNA is generally much greater than in RNA. That is to say, the length of naturally occurring polydeoxyribonucleotide chains is greater than that of polyribonucleotide chains. Exceptions to this latter generalization are the large RNA molecules found in certain viruses.

SYMBOLIC FORMULAE OF POLYNUCLEOTIDES

It should be obvious that complete line drawings of polynucleotide structures would be too cumbersome for normal use. Hence, shorthand designations are frequently employed. One popular convention utilizes a pN notation to represent a ribonucleoside (designated by the letter N) with a 5′ phosphate and a free 3′—OH, and an Np notation to represent a ribonucleoside with a 3′ phosphate and a free 5′—OH. Deoxyribonucleosides are symbolized as dN, with pdN and dNp similarly representing 5′ and 3′ deoxyribonucleotides. A polynucleotide is represented simply as a linear series of the appropriate notation where NpN corresponds to a 3′→5′ phosphodiester bond between adjacent nucleotides. If the identity of the nitrogen bases is known, the letter N is replaced by the appropriate code letter.

	5′-terminus	3′-terminus
For a polyribo-nucleotide	. . . pNpNpNpNpNpNpNpNpNpNpN . . .	
	. . . pA pG pC pA pG pG pA pC pC pG pA . . .	
For a polydeoxy-ribonucleotide	. . . dpNdpNdpNdpNdpNdpNdpNdpN . . .	
	. . . dpA dpT dpG dpC dpA dpG dpC dpC . . .	

A second, more illustrative convention utilizes a vertical line to represent the sugar unit. The top and bottom of the line represent the 1′ and 5′ positions in the sugar, respectively. Diagonal dashes on the right represent the 2′ and 3′ hydroxyls, and the lone dash on the left designates the 5′—OH. Nitrogen bases are represented by N or the appropriate code letter and are shown at the 1′ position. The notation of 3′→5′ phosphodiester bonds is obvious.

pentose   5′-NMP   3′→5′ phosphodiester bond
               (nucleotide)

NUCLEIC ACID STRUCTURE

ISOLATION OF NUCLEIC ACIDS

A systematic study of nucleic acids is largely dependent on one's ability to isolate the material in as pure a state as possible. The first problem in this regard is to extract the material from its natural source, whether cellular or viral. (The conditions of nucleic acid extraction are not treated in this text. The interested student is referred to more comprehensive textbooks, monographs on the nucleic acids, and the literature in general.) If the extract is heterogeneous, that is, if it contains several different species of nucleic acid, the second problem is one of resolving the individual components. The most frequently used technique for this is density gradient ultracentrifugation (see page 23, Chapter 2). A separation of three RNA components obtained from bacterial ribosomes (see later section) is diagrammed in Figure 6–1. Once a particular nucleic acid component is isolated, the same method is generally used for confirmation of purity and additional characterization studies such as the determination of molecular weight.

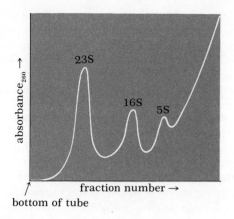

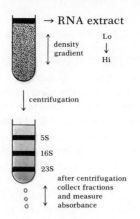

Figure 6-1 A typical velocity density gradient ultracentrifugation pattern of RNA extracted from intact ribosomes of *Escherichia coli.* The absorbance pattern of the tube contents after centrifugation illustrates the presence of three different RNA's distinguished by different sizes: 23S (heavy), 16S (intermediate), and 5S (light).

PRIMARY STRUCTURE

The primary level of nucleic acid structure is defined in terms of the composition and sequence of the purine and pyrimidine bases covalently attached to the sugar-phosphate backbone. Whereas much data are available on base composition of both RNA and DNA from virtually every conceivable biological source, information on base sequence is scarce. In fact, sequence studies (both complete and partial) have been successful only with low-molecular-weight species of RNA (see page 163 and page 498). Because of its tremendously large size, not one intact DNA molecule has been sequenced. Indeed, it is quite probable that one never will be sequenced. The fact that one of the smallest DNA molecules known—namely, the DNA chromosome of a tiny bacterial virus designated ϕX174—contains approximately 5500 nitrogen bases typifies the problem.

The DNA from ϕX174 is also known to be a circular molecule in the native state. Thought at one time to be unique to this virus, circular DNA's are now known to be present in many other viruses and in several bacteria. Actually, the DNA from all sources including those of higher organisms may exist in a circular state which is broken during isolation to give linear strands and thus never detected. No circular forms of RNA have been isolated. Whatever the case may be, linear strands of a nucleic acid (native or otherwise) do contain characteristic terminal groupings, namely, a *5'-terminus* and a *3'-terminus.* As we pointed out earlier, the 5' end is most generally phosphorylated whereas a free —OH grouping exists at the 3' end.

The problem of determining base composition is relatively straightforward. The nucleic acid is first degraded into its monomeric nucleotide units via a chemical (base hydrolysis) or biological (enzymatic) process. RNA is susceptible to both techniques whereas DNA is resistant to base hydrolysis. The resolution and quantitative analysis of the nucleotide mixture are then performed via ion exchange chromatography (recall that nucleotides are ionic substances) coupled with a detection procedure based on UV absorption. In the case of DNA, the ultracentrifugal sedimentation properties in a cesium chloride density gradient have also been used as a sensitive measure of base composition. To repeat: one of the truly remarkable characteristics of nature is that only A,G,C, and T and small quantities of 5-methylcytosine are found in DNA, regardless

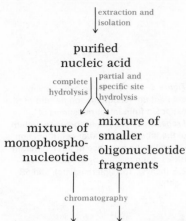

intact cells

|extraction and
|isolation

purified
nucleic acid

complete | partial and
hydrolysis | specific site
| hydrolysis

mixture of
monophospho-
nucleotides

mixture of
smaller
oligonucleotide
fragments

chromatography

separation and
quantitative
measurement
of individual
nucleotides

separation of
fragments with
each then
sequenced
separately

of its biological source. A greater variety of bases have been detected in RNA, but A,G,C, and U are the most abundant.

The determination of base sequence is more difficult. The principles of the experimental approach are basically the same as those used to elucidate the amino acid sequence of proteins. The nucleic acid is selectively degraded into smaller oligonucleotide fragments by treatment with hydrolytic enzymes, called *endonucleases,* which cleave specific phosphodiester bonds within the main chain of the polymer. The fragments are then isolated (by ion exchange and/or molecular sieve chromatography), analyzed for base composition, and sequenced separately. The complete sequence is constructed by aligning the sequenced fragments according to common overlapping regions. The specificity of the hydrolytic endonucleases is based on the nitrogen base attached on the 3′ or 5′ side. *Exonucleases,* which selectively attack 3′- or 5′-terminal residues, permit the sequential removal of monophosphonucleotides from the fragments. Once again, nature has provided the experimental tools and man has provided the experimental ingenuity.

The functional properties of certain nucleases are given in Table 6–1 together with an example of their use. The five listed represent only a small fraction of the total that occur in nature. Approximately 100 additional enzymes have been isolated from various sources, and their specificity or lack of it has been characterized. Obviously, the natural function of RNAases and DNAases is to break down RNA and DNA. In this context we can identify five natural processes in which they participate: (1) the digestion of extracellular nucleic acids supplied to the organism from the surroundings, that is, the diet or growth medium; (2) a self-defense mechanism against infection from foreign agents such as viruses; (3) the degradative phase of the continuing cyclic operation of nucleic acid turnover in the cell; (4) the process of genetic recombination wherein a segment of one DNA molecule is removed and replaced by a segment of another DNA molecule; and (5) the process of repair to damaged DNA wherein a defective segment of DNA is removed and then degraded, with a new segment being synthesized with the aid of DNA polymerase (see page 470). The nature of the regulatory factors that initiate and control these operations remain obscure, as do other possible functions of nuclease enzymes.

The first nucleic acid to be sequenced was a *transfer-RNA* molecule done by Holley and coworkers in 1965. Further discussion will be deferred to a later section. The sequence of a light fraction from ribosomal-RNA has also been reported. Although the massive size of an intact DNA molecule prohibits actual sequencing through the use of specific nucleases, or through any other approach for that matter, the ingenious technique of *nearest-neighbor analysis* does permit a direct determination of the frequency of occurrence of every conceivable dinucleotide sequence along the DNA chain. A discussion of this technique is given in Chapter 17.

SECONDARY AND TERTIARY STRUCTURE—DNA

Nearly two decades ago in 1953, J. D. Watson and F. H. C. Crick, while working together at the Cavendish Laboratory in England, proposed a model for the three-dimensional conformation of DNA. Their suggestion

Table 6–1 Functional characterization of some nucleases.

Enzyme	Substrate	Mode of Attack	Specificity	Cleavage sites
1. Pancreatic ribonuclease	RNA	Endo	Linkage between pyrimidine (Py) and a nonspecific base (X) on the 3' side; phosphodiester bond cleaved at 5' position	$..PypXp..$ ↑
2. Takadiastase T₁ (isolated from fungi)	RNA	Endo	Linkage between guanine (G) and nonspecific base (X) on 3' side; phosphodiester bond cleaved at 5' position	$..GpXp..$ ↑
3. Micrococcal nuclease	RNA, DNA	Endo	Linkage between adenine (A) and nonspecific base (X) on 5' side; phosphodiester bond cleaved at 5' position	$..XpAp..$ ↑
4. Snake venom nuclease	RNA, DNA	Exo	Attack starts from 3' hydroxyl end with phosphodiester bond cleaved at 3' position; no base specificity	$..XpYpZ(3'—OH)$ ↑₂ ↑₁
5. Spleen nuclease	RNA, DNA	Exo	Attack starts from and requires a free 5' hydroxyl terminus; phospho-diester bond cleaved at 5' position; no base specificity; 5'—OH generated by initial treatment with 5'-monoesterase	$[5'—OH]XpYpZ..$ ↑₁ ↑₂

EXAMPLE:

```
          2  1  1
          ↓  ↓  ↓
    pApGpCpTpApApGpC
    ↑   ↑    ↑  ↑    ↑
    |   ↑    3  3    4  (repetitive from
    |   5 (repetitive from    right to left)
    |      left to right)
    5'-monoesterase then
      spleen nuclease
```

numbers designate
enzymes listed
in table

was as follows: *DNA consists of two right-handed, helical polynucle-otide chains, each coiled around a common perpendicular axis but running in opposite directions.* They further proposed that the super-coiled *double helix is stabilized by interchain hydrogen bonding between specific pairs of nitrogen bases which are projected from each chain towards the core of the helix and perpendicular to the vertical axis.* A generalized representation of their model is shown in Figure 6–2. Their brilliant proposal has proven correct and is generally recognized as the single achievement which has revolutionized twentieth century biological science. In particular, it has given birth to the scientific discipline of *molecular biology,* which attempts to explain the storage, replication, and expression of genetic information in terms of par-ticipating molecules.

With no intent to detract from the talents of Watson and Crick, it is interesting to note that their activities in this effort were not exactly representative of the layman's concept of how brilliant discoveries are made or how brilliant suggestions evolve. In fact, they did very little

Figure 6-2 A diagrammatic representation of DNA according to Watson and Crick. The two ribbons symbolize the two phosphate-sugar chains, and the horizontal rods the pairs of hydrogen-bonded nitrogen bases holding the chain together. The vertical line marks the central axis. (Reproduced with permission: *Nature,* **171,** No. 4356, 737–738 (1953).)

laboratory work in the literal sense. Their genius in this endeavor is described in terms of their interpretation of data available to them, and the formulation of a model consistent with the data and their interpretation. In addition, they happened to be at the right place at the right time. The critical empirical data were provided by earlier reports by E. Chargaff on the nitrogen base composition of DNA, and by X-ray diffraction studies being performed at that time on crystalline DNA by M. Wilkins and R. Franklin at nearby King's College of London.

The studies of Chargaff revealed some remarkably simple generalizations about the base composition of DNA. First, the number of purine bases (A + G) was balanced by the number of pyrimidine bases (T + C); that is, the ratio of purines to pyrimidines was approximately one (Pu/Py = 1.0). Second, the number of adenine residues was balanced by the number of thymine residues; that is, the ratio of adenine to thymine was approximately one (A/T = 1.0). Third, the number of guanine residues was balanced by the number of cytosine residues; that is, the ratio of guanine to cytosine was approximately one (G/C = 1.0). Fourth, the sum of adenine and cytosine residues was balanced by the sum of guanine and thymine residues; that is, (A + C) = (G + T). Fifth, each of these relationships was found to be true of all DNA samples examined, regardless of biological source. Each of these points is summarized in Table 6–2; the information listed here is only a small fragment of available data. Note that each source has a unique composition of each nitrogen base.

The X-ray diffraction analysis of crystalline DNA suggested a high degree of symmetry. However, though the data were important and in-

Table 6-2 Distribution of purines and pyrimidines in dioxyribonucleic acids (a partial listing).

Biological Source	%				Ratios		
	A	G	Cᵃ	T	A/T	G/Cᵃ	Purine/Pyrimidine
VIRUSES							
Lambda (*E. coli*)	26.0	23.8	24.3	25.8	1.01	0.98	0.99
Adenovirus (human)	24.5	25.2	24.8	25.5	0.96	1.02	0.99
Fowlpox	32.3	18.0	17.2	32.6	0.99	1.05	1.01
BACTERIA							
Escherichia coli	23.8	26.0	26.4	23.8	1.00	0.98	0.99
Bacillus subtilis	28.9	21.0	21.4	28.7	1.01	0.98	1.00
Pseudomonas fluorescens	18.2	33.0	30.0	18.8	0.97	1.10	1.05
PLANTS							
Carrot	26.7	23.1	23.2	26.9	0.99	1.00	0.99
Tobacco leaf	29.7	19.8	20.0	30.4	0.98	0.99	0.98
Peanut	32.1	17.6	18.0	32.2	1.00	0.98	0.99
ANIMALS							
Frog	26.3	23.5	23.8	26.4	1.00	0.99	0.99
Chick embryo	28.9	23.7	21.2	26.2	1.10	1.12	1.11
Chicken (liver)	30.3	22.0	19.7	28.0	1.08	1.12	1.10
Rat (liver)	28.6	21.4	21.5	28.4	1.01	1.00	1.00
Human (liver)	30.3	19.5	19.9	30.3	1.00	0.98	0.99
Human (spleen)	28.1	24.7	21.1	26.1	1.08	1.11	1.12
Human (thymus)	29.8	20.2	18.2	31.8	0.94	1.11	1.02

a. Includes any contribution from 5-methylcytosine.

compatible with all previously proposed conformations, data alone did not permit an unequivocal conclusion as to the double helical conformation. One of the other proposals, suggested a few weeks earlier by Linus Pauling, was a triple helix with the phosphate residues within the core of the fiber and the bases projected outward. In all likelihood, this caused Pauling, who was and still is a giant in the scientific community, a considerable amount of embarrassment. Pauling's error probably would not have been made if he had had access to the X-ray data of the King's College group. After considerable discussion, debate, and manipulation of models, Watson and Crick finally proposed the right-handed double helix conformation as described above, and to their excitement discovered that it was consistent with all of the available data. Furthermore, the model seemed to fit the biological function ascribed to DNA. The model has proven consistent with more exact studies performed since then and is now universally accepted. For their contribution, Watson, Crick, and Wilkins were awarded the Nobel Prize in 1962. An extremely interesting and controversial narrative account of this period in scientific history and of the personalities involved is given by Watson himself in his book, *The Double Helix*.

The *novel feature of the double helix conformation is the interchain hydrogen bonding between nitrogen bases on different chains directly opposite each other, with a purine always bonded with a pyrimidine*. More specifically, *adenine is always bonded to thymine* (A≡≡≡T) and *guanine is always bonded to cytosine* (G≡≡≡C). This bonding arrangement is in agreement with the base composition data and is also consistent with the structures of the nitrogen bases. In fact, it represents an optimum spatial fit. Accordingly, the A≡≡≡T and G≡≡≡C pairings are termed *complementary base pairs*. Line drawings and space-filling models of each pair are given in Figure 6–3. The latter are especially informative in that they clearly illustrate the *structural compatibility of the planar bases* in forming linear hydrogen bonds. Without question, this is one of the most striking examples of the molecular logic that exists in nature. If you conclude that the bond strength of a G≡≡≡C pair with three hydrogen bonds should be greater than that of the A≡≡≡T pair with one less hydrogen bond, you are correct.

The specification of the two helical chains running in opposite directions is most important, because this provides the proper alignment of all bases required for hydrogen bond formation. In structural jargon, this feature is referred to as *opposite polarity* because of the non-identity of the terminal groups at each end (pole) of the double helix. Since the propagation of one chain is 3′→5′ and the other is 5′→3′, each terminus will consist of a 3′—OH and 5′—phosphate. Another noteworthy feature relative to the interaction of the two chains is that *base pairing* is not confined to localized regions within the molecule, but rather is *present along the entire length*. Hence, the *entire base sequence of one chain is complementary to that of the other.*

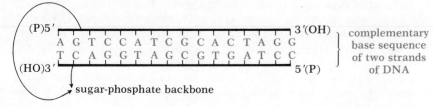

complementary
base sequence
of two strands
of DNA

sugar-phosphate backbone

Guanine ≣≣≣ Cytosine

(three hydrogen bonds)

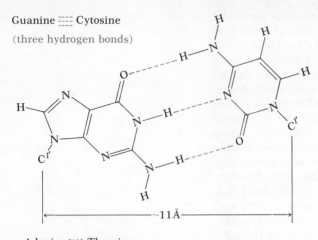

Adenine ⋮⋮⋮ Thymine

(two hydrogen bonds)

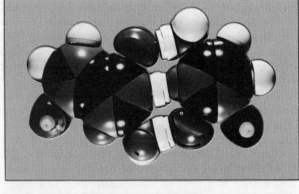

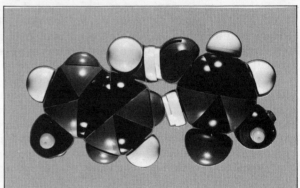

Figure 6–3 Purine-pyrimidine base pairs in deoxyribonucleic acids.

To summarize: DNA is a double-helix fibril consisting of two complementary, right-handed, helical, polynucleotide chains of opposite polarity intertwined around the same axis and held together by internal purine-pyrimidine hydrogen-bonded base pairs which are projected within the central core from a sugar-phosphate backbone. The polyanionic character of the molecule permits an additional mode of stabilization via electrostatic interaction with appropriate cations such as Mg^{++}, or with basic proteins such as the histones (see page 80) containing large numbers of positively charged amino acid side chains. The important molecular dimensions of DNA, determined originally by Wilkins and since confirmed, are: (1) each complete turn of the helix transcribes 34Å; (2) the distance between adjacent base pairs is 3.4Å, a measurement which, in combination with point 1, yields 10 base pairs per turn; (3) the diameter of the double-helical fiber is approximately 20Å, with the distance between the peripheral phosphorus atoms and the central axis being approximately 10Å; (4) the two grooves in the surface of the helix have approximate widths of 12Å and 22Å, respectively, each sufficient to accommodate a polypeptide chain. All aspects of DNA structure are summarized in Figures 6–4 and 6–5. Because of the large molecular dimensions, it is possible to view single DNA molecules with an electron microscope. The electron micrograph of Figure 6–6 shows the circular double helix common in some bacteria and viruses. A circular form of *single-stranded* DNA has also been found in the ϕX174 bacterial virus. The latter, an interesting exception to the Watson-Crick structure, has recently been synthesized by A. Kornberg (see Chapter 17, page 471).

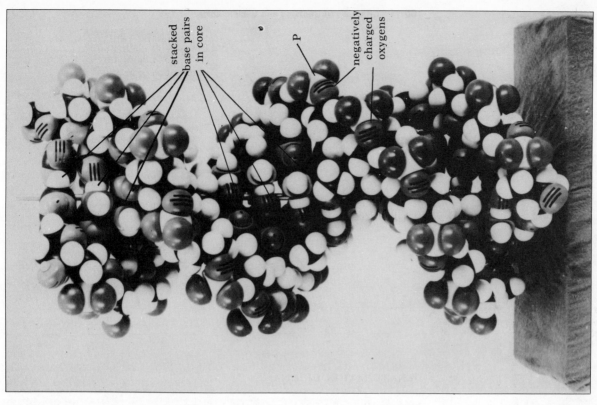

stacked
base pairs
in core

P

negatively
charged
oxygens

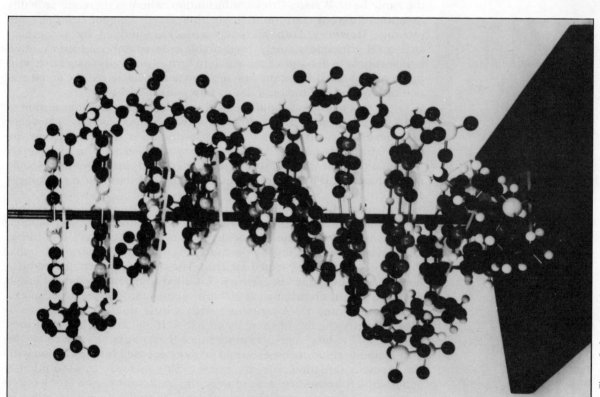

Figure 6—4 Left: A skeleton model of a segment of a DNA duplex molecule. (Photograph supplied through the courtesy of METALOGLASS, INC..
Boston, manufacturers of biological and crystal structure models.) Right: A space-filling model of a segment of a DNA duplex molecule.
(Photograph supplied through the courtesy of The Ealing Corporation, Cambridge, Mass.)

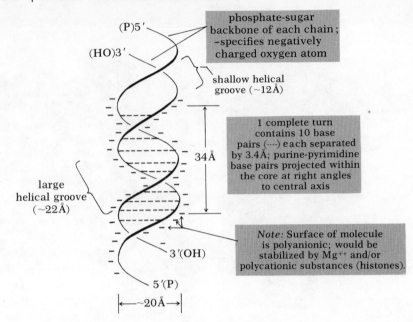

(P)5′

(HO)3′

phosphate-sugar backbone of each chain; –specifies negatively charged oxygen atom

shallow helical groove (~12Å)

1 complete turn contains 10 base pairs (----) each separated by 3.4Å; purine-pyrimidine base pairs projected within the core at right angles to central axis

34Å

large helical groove (~22Å)

Note: Surface of molecule is polyanionic; would be stabilized by Mg⁺⁺ and/or polycationic substances (histones).

3′(OH)

5′(P)

|←—~20Å—→|

Figure 6–5 A schematic representation of DNA double helix including significant molecular dimensions.

DENATURATION OF DNA

Nearly all of the DNA molecules found in nature are thought to exist in the same basic Watson-Crick conformation, whereas there are probably as many different conformations in the protein kingdom as there are proteins. However, both materials are characterized by a common structural principle, namely, their highly ordered natural conformation is susceptible to denaturation, which in turn is generally associated with a loss of biological function. Having previously discussed the denaturation of proteins in Chapter 4, let us now consider DNA.

At this point you should realize that the complete denaturation of DNA would involve treatment with some chemical or physical agent that destabilizes hydrogen bonds, resulting in a transition from the double-stranded, helical conformation to any partially or completely unfolded random state. If you do not understand this statement, you do not understand DNA structure and it is advised that you reread pages 155–59.

A most effective physical method of disrupting DNA is to heat it. The input of thermal energy contributes to greater molecular motion, making the required spatial localization of nitrogen bases less likely, and hence ultimately causing the unfolding of the double-stranded helix. This process has been termed *melting*. The course of thermal denaturation of DNA is depicted in Figure 6–7. Called a *melting curve*, the graph depicts a plot of absorbance at 260 nm versus temperature. Once again, if you understand DNA structure, with a little thought you should be able to justify the use of these coordinates. If you argue that denatured DNA should exhibit a greater absorbance than native DNA because the purine and pyrimidine bases would be more exposed for interaction with the incident radiation, you are correct. This increase in absorption is called *hyperchromicity*. Accordingly, the important region of the curve is the steep sigmoid area that corresponds to the temperature range in which the complete transition in conformation occurs. The midpoint of this region is termed the *transition* or *melting temperature* (T_m) and is a distinctly reproducible physical property of a DNA molecule. In fact, extensive studies have shown that the T_m is a relatively reliable approximate measure of DNA base composition. The discovery and development of this simple technique are testimony to the ingenious exploitation of a seemingly unimportant physicochemical phenomenon.

As a final observation, we should note that the absolute value of T_m, which may range anywhere from 85–100°C, is extremely high. By comparison, the ordered conformation of proteins is disrupted at much lower temperatures. This is not too surprising, since the actual number of stabilizing forces per typical protein molecule is much less than that of a DNA molecule. Thus, we can conclude that the presence of thousands of hydrogen bonds does, in fact, contribute considerable stability to the Watson-Crick conformation of DNA.

SECONDARY AND TERTIARY STRUCTURE—RNA

The current state of knowledge concerning the structural conformation of RNA is less complete than that pertaining to DNA. In part this is due to the fact that there are four different types of RNA: *transfer-RNA* (tRNA), *messenger-RNA* (mRNA), *ribosomal-RNA* (rRNA), and *viral-RNA* (vRNA). The first three types, believed to be present in every cell, vary in both structure and function, although they are all single stranded and participate in the process of protein biosynthesis. In RNA viruses, the RNA has the added role of carrying the genetic information of the virus. That is to say, the viral RNA is the viral chromosome. Recall that in other organisms this is the sole function of DNA.

In this chapter we will not consider the function of each RNA type in any great detail. This is more appropriate to the subjects of protein biosynthesis and biochemical genetics, both of which will be discussed in Chapters 17 and 18. At this time the following capsule description will serve as a preliminary introduction and contribute some meaning to the basis of naming the different RNA's. The events of protein biosynthesis can be segregated into two sequential phases: first, *transcription*; second, *translation*. *Transcription is a DNA-dependent process*—occurring in the nucleus where DNA is located—resulting in the production of RNA molecules with a nitrogen base sequence that is complementary to segments of DNA and that functions as a template that is copied. Due to this complementarity with DNA, the product RNA is termed *messenger-RNA,* indicating that the genetic message originally in DNA, coded as a base sequence, is now transcribed and carried by an RNA molecule. In the complex RNA-dependent process of translation, the mRNA migrates out of the nucleus and becomes attached to a cluster of ribonucleoprotein particles called *ribosomes,* which are the cellular site of polypeptide biosynthesis. The RNA in the ribosomes is called *ribosomal-RNA.* Amino acids are carried to this ribosomal assembly site via covalent attachment to small RNA molecules called *transfer-RNA.* At the ribosomal assembly site, the amino acids are positioned in a certain sequence directed by a coded recognition between mRNA and the tRNA component of the tRNA-amino acid adduct (see diagram). The code is based in the sequence of bases in mRNA, which was patterned after the sequence of bases in chromosomal DNA. Hence, the nitrogen base

Figure 6–6 An electron micrograph of a DNA molecule. The DNA is a circular duplex molecule obtained from *Proteus mirabilis,* a bacterium. This DNA is representative of extrachromosomal genetic elements, called R factors, that are found in certain bacteria. They carry genetic determinants controlling resistance to a number of antibiotics and can be transferred from one bacterium to another. Since this may account for the acquired resistance of certain bacteria to chemotherapeutic agents, the study of R factors is potentially of considerable importance. (Taken with permission from "Composite Circular Forms of R Factor Deoxyribonucleic Acid Molecules," Nisioka, T., M. Mitani, and R. Clowes, *J. Bacteriol.,* **97,** 376–385 (1969). Photograph supplied through the courtesy of R. Clowes and prepared by M. Mitani).

sequence of a nucleic acid is translated into a sequence of amino acid residues in the ultimate product, a protein. The general sequence of DNA→RNA→protein is today a universally accepted dogma of molecular biology (see page 447). Now let us return to a consideration of the individual RNA's.

The study of mRNA structure is restricted because (a) many different species—perhaps on the order of 10^3—are possible; (b) cellular levels are quite low; and (c) it undergoes a rapid turnover within the cell. Consequently, it is difficult to isolate appreciable quantities of a homogenous mRNA preparation; hence our limited knowledge. We do know that it exists as a *single* polynucleotide strand of varying chain length. No ordered spatial conformation, helical or otherwise, has been proposed.

Figure 6-7 A typical melting curve profile of DNA depicting the hyperchromic effect observed on heating.

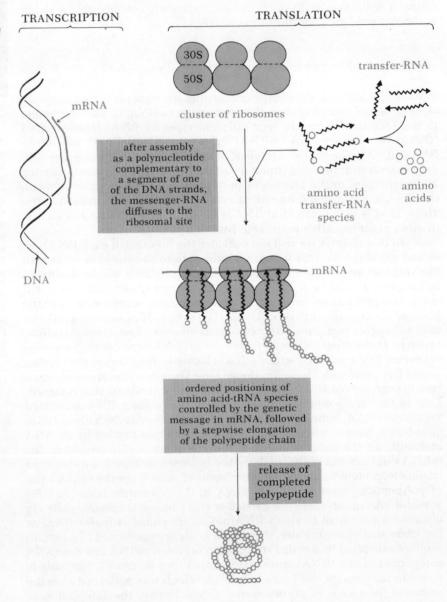

By contrast, our current understanding of rRNA, though not extensively detailed, is more complete. We know, for example, that the intact ribosome (70S in bacteria) is a complex of two distinctly sedimenting nucleoprotein subunits—one heavy (50S) and one light (30S). We also know that the RNA isolated from each subunit is different—the RNA from the heavy subunit sediments at 23S and 5S, while the RNA from the light subunit sediments at 16S. What we do not know is whether the RNA sedimenting at either 23S or 16S is a homogeneous mixture of identical molecules or a heterogeneous mixture of slightly different molecules. Also unknown is whether rRNA, which exists largely in a single-stranded state, has an ordered conformation in the native state. Although these questions and many others exist at the moment, continued studies promise to yield some answers. For example, rapid progress has been made on the study of a purified 5S RNA preparation first isolated from the 50S subunit in 1963. Although its function remains obscure, it has been shown to be largely homogeneous, and the major component has been isolated and its nitrogen base sequence determined. Ribosome structure is discussed in more detail in Chapter 18 (page 491).

Relative to mRNA and rRNA, the structure of tRNA is most clearly understood; this, despite the fact that approximately 60 different species are known to exist. Meaningful structural studies have proven successful for basically two reasons: (1) in comparison to mRNA and rRNA, molecules of transfer-RNA are relatively small, containing approximately 75–85 nitrogen bases; and (2) they can be readily isolated in appreciable quantities. The first real breakthrough was made by Holley and coworkers in 1965 when they successfully sequenced a transfer-RNA molecule. Since then progress has been astounding, and at the time of this writing, the sequences of approximately 15 different tRNA's, purified from various sources, have been reported. In 1969, for outstanding contribution in the initial development of methodologies for the sequence analysis of nucleic acids, Holley received the Nobel Prize.

The results of these sequence studies and other investigations have strongly suggested that tRNA, which is single stranded, exists in some type of ordered, folded conformation. Support for this is exemplified by a significant hyperchromic effect observed on heating tRNA preparations, suggesting an increased exposure of nitrogen bases brought about by the melting of hydrogen bonds between base pairs in different regions of the tRNA molecule. Thus, the crux of proposed models for tRNA conformation emerges, namely, that the native molecule consists of one or more *intramolecular double-stranded* segments which originate from complementary sequences of bases that are brought into the appropriate spatial juxtaposition for hydrogen bonding via folds and twists along the main chain. The proponents of this hypothesis were no doubt especially delighted when the first tRNA was sequenced, because, lo and behold, the results did confirm that the chain could, in fact, be folded to reveal complementary regions in different parts of the molecule in accordance with the rules of base pairing, that is, A pairs with U, and G pairs with C. The complete phenomenon is illustrated in Figure 6–8 depicting a proposed cloverleaf conformation with four distinct double-stranded segments separated by three peripheral loops and the two termini. This particular conformation is quite popular, because the sequence of every tRNA species reported to date permits the polynucleotide to be so folded. Based on recent X-ray diffraction studies of crystalline

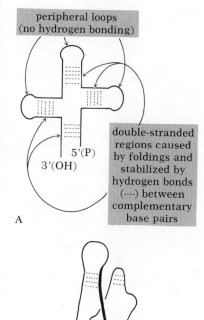

Figure 6–8 Proposed models of the partial double-stranded conformation of single-stranded transfer-RNA molecules. A: a generalized and ideal planar representation of the cloverleaf model frequently used in discussing tRNA structure. B: a representation of a more elongated and compact structure, such as that suggested by Kim and Rich, which more accurately approximates the actual native conformation, as yet unknown. (The structure and function of transfer-RNA are discussed in greater detail in Chapter 18.)

tRNA, however, Kim and Rich have taken issue with the cloverleaf conformation. They interpret their data as representative of a molecule with a more elongated structure containing intrachain double-helical segments that are folded together in a fairly compact form and generally lie along the same axis of the molecule, as diagrammed in Figure 6–8. Only a tracing of the polymeric chain is shown for reasons of simplicity. The positioning of double-stranded segments and protrusions is hypothetical. Whatever the final outcome, an appreciable amount of evidence does exist indicating that the biological activity of tRNA is unquestionably related to its molecular conformation. In this context, the fine details of its participation in protein biosynthesis will be discussed in Chapter 18. At that time, we will once again discover a remarkable facet of the structure–function relationship on a molecular level. In addition, we will examine the remarkable relationship of DNA structure to its biological function. Although we have introduced the fundamental premise of the structure–function principle in our analysis of polypeptides, it is by no means restricted in application to the proteins. To employ an oft-used phrase—the game remains the same; only the players change.

NUCLEOPROTEINS

In our discussion of the double-helix conformation of DNA, it was mentioned that the alternating helical grooves could easily accommodate polypeptide chains. This was by no means merely a passing observation, but rather a point of fact that is relevant to the known *in vivo* association of DNA with protein. In fact, chemically speaking, the chromosomes of animal, plant, and microbial cells are just that—deoxyribonucleoprotein particles. The phenomenon is not restricted to DNA; all nucleic acids, with the exception of mRNA and tRNA, are generally believed to exist *in vivo* as nucleoproteins. For example, a ribosome consists roughly of 60% RNA and 40% protein, and is more accurately termed a ribonucleoprotein particle.

Although the existence of nucleic acid-protein complexes in all types of living cells is firmly established, we do not yet know with certainty how the polypeptides are arranged in the complex. Exceptions are some well-defined viruses. With DNA the suggestion that the polypeptides may be localized in the surface grooves is just that—a suggestion. The manner in which rRNA is complexed with ribosomal protein is completely obscure. However, in both instances information is available concerning the nature of the protein component. The proteins isolated from deoxyribonucleoproteins are generally of low molecular weight and rich in basic amino acid residues. For these reasons, they are classified as histones. Upon dissociation from DNA, the histone preparations display considerable heterogeneity, containing several polypeptide species. A probable physical role of the polycationic histones as a secondary stabilizing force of DNA conformation was mentioned previously (see page 158). Although no clear biological function has yet been categorically established, some evidence suggests that the histones may function as regulators in the expression of the chromosomal DNA at the level of transcription in protein biosynthesis.

In comparison to our knowledge of the histones, our understanding of ribosomal protein is more complete. In recent years there have been reports of the isolation, purification, and structure–function studies of these proteins from various sources (see page 494). It is known, for example, that both the heavy (50S) and light (30S) subunits each contain a very heterogeneous but characteristic set of proteins, with the combined total of different proteins being in the range of 30 to 40. Generally speaking, they are all of low molecular weight, with a broader distribution of amino acids than the histones of DNA. In fact, they are not histones. An insight into the function of ribosomal proteins has been gained through *in vitro* reconstitution studies. The design of such studies is simple in principle: ribosomes are isolated and purified; the rRNA is separated and purified from the protein fraction; the constituent proteins of the latter are then isolated in purified form; and finally, the purified rRNA is added back to a mixture of the purified proteins, and assays are made for restoration of normal ribosomal activity. Incredible as it may seem, reassociation with an accompanying restoration of biochemical function does occur. By attempting reconstitution with various combinations of the isolated proteins from the original mixture and then assaying for the extent of restoration of function, it is possible to equate the presence of specific proteins with specific properties of the complete ribosome. With this approach, it has been demonstrated that certain proteins are, indeed, completely essential to various aspects of ribosomal activity. For example, one particular protein is known to be responsible for the ribosomal binding of the antibiotic streptomycin. The binding of streptomycin to ribosomes is the basis for its mode of action as an antibiotic. Briefly, the binding renders the ribosome inactive and thus impedes protein biosynthesis. When streptomycin is used in the treatment of microbial infections, the ultimate effect is the death of the infectious organism.

VIRUSES

It is probably common knowledge to you that a virus is not considered as a true life form but rather as a parasite which depends on the infection of a host organism for its replicative existence. What you may not realize is that most viruses consist only of protein and nucleic acid, that is, they are nucleoprotein particles. Chemically speaking, there are two classes of viruses—those that contain RNA and those that contain DNA. Depending on the virus, the nucleic acid (either RNA or DNA) exists in either a linear or a circular form with a single- or double-stranded helical conformation. Physically speaking, the viruses constitute a heterogeneous lot with varying sizes and shapes. Biologically speaking, we have animal, plant, and bacterial viruses with several types of each class. The properties of some viruses are given in Table 6–3.

The experience of the average layman teaches that viruses are the natural enemy of living organisms. This attitude is well founded as evidenced by the countless diseases that have been attributed to viral infection. Many of the viruses produce tumors, some have been implicated with cancer, others are responsible for encephalitis and influenza, and still others cause polyoma, leukemia, chicken pox, mumps, measles, smallpox, and rabies. Frequently overlooked, however, is the

Table 6–3 Nucleic acids of some RNA and DNA viruses.

Host	Virus	Nucleic Acid (Mol. Wt.)	Nucleic Acid Conformation
ANIMAL VIRUSES			
Man	Adenovirus	DNA (16×10^6)	Double-stranded helix; linear
Mammals	Polyoma	DNA (7.5×10^6)	Double-stranded helix; circular
PLANT VIRUSES			
Tobacco	Tobacco Mosaic Virus (TMV)	RNA (2×10^6)	Single-stranded helix; linear
Turnip	Turnip Yellow Mosaic Virus (TYMV)	RNA (2×10^6)	Single-stranded helix; circular
BACTERIAL VIRUSES			
E. coli	T$_2$	DNA (1.6×10^8)	Double-stranded helix; circular
E. coli	λ	DNA (3×10^7)	Double-stranded helix; linear
E. coli	φX174	DNA (1.6×10^6)	Single-stranded helix; circular (see page 471)

fact that special viral preparations have proven to be of great benefit to mankind, e.g., the vaccines against polio, smallpox, and measles. In addition to this applied aspect of viral biotechnology, basic research into the molecular biology and biochemistry of viral particles and their action has been in progress for years. In fact, at the present time the viruses are one of the most studied biological systems.

As evidenced by the diseases listed above, it is rather obvious that the presence of viral material can produce profound biochemical alterations in the host organism. As part of modern viral research, the mechanisms that underlie these alterations are actively being studied. In addition, however, considerable research on a much more basic level is being performed, inasmuch as the viruses represent a miniaturized and simplified model of the essential life-giving biochemical processes that are characteristic of more complex organisms. To understand this premise, we need to examine briefly the virus–host relationship. The initial event is the attachment of the virus to the host cell, followed by injection of the viral nucleic acid into the cytoplasm of the host cell. Within the cell, the foreign nucleic acid is replicated many times and begins to act as a controlling chromosome. In addition, the genes of the viral chromosome will be translated into viral mRNA, which will in turn be transcribed into viral proteins for assembly with the newly produced viral nucleic acid to yield new viral particles. Thus, the replication of a virus consists basically of three steps: nucleic acid biosynthesis, protein biosynthesis, and self-assembly. In addition, both biosynthetic processes are regulated by the viral chromosome itself. Now the use of viruses as model biochemical research systems is not simply due to the fact that all processes including the regulatory mechanisms are common to higher organisms, but primarily because they are believed to occur via the same mechanisms.

Certain bacterial viruses have proven extremely valuable subjects because of their small size. For example, the ϕX174 bacterial virus which infects *Escherichia coli* contains but one type of DNA molecule (MW $\sim 10^6$) with only five or six separate genes. Although the great majority of bacterial viruses contain larger nucleic acid molecules with roughly 50–200 genes, this is still far removed from the number of genes in the mammalian cell, which may be as high as 10^6–10^7. The single DNA chromosome of *E. coli* itself may contain approximately 1000 genes. Thus, in viral replication there are fewer genes being transcribed, and hence the molecular events are easier to monitor. Since viral genes —like the genes of all higher life forms—are capable of mutation and recombination, much has been learned about these phenomena from the study of viruses. In addition, methodologies have been developed to permit mapping of the relative positions of genes along a chromosome. In fact, the very foundation of contemporary thinking about the nature and function of the gene is provided by studies with bacterial viruses. This abbreviated survey of this subject should provide you with some preliminary material to reflect upon. In future chapters we will analyze in greater depth the biosynthesis of nucleic acids and proteins as well as the nature of the gene.

LITERATURE

BURTON, K., "Sequence Determination in Nucleic Acids," in *Essays in Biochemistry* (Volume 1), Campbell, P. N., and G. D. Greville (eds.). New York: Academic Press, 1965. A review article summarizing the strategy for determining the sequence of nucleotides in a polynucleotide.

CRICK, F. H. C., "The Structure of the Hereditary Material," *Scientific American,* **191,** 54–61 (1954). The first pedagogical article to be published on the structure of DNA.

FRAENKEL-CONRAT, H., *The Chemistry and Biology of Viruses.* New York: Academic Press, 1969. An excellent introduction to the principal facts known about the structure and function of bacterial, plant, and animal viruses. Several hundred references are given to the original literature.

FRAENKEL-CONRAT, H., *Design and Function at the Threshold of Life: The Viruses.* New York: Academic Press, 1962. A somewhat dated but still very informative introduction at the basic level. Available in paperback.

GROSSMAN, L., and K. MOLDAVE, (eds.), *Nucleic Acids.* Volume 12 of *Methods in Enzymology,* Colowick, S. P., and N. O. Kaplan (eds.). New York: Academic Press, 1968. A collection of papers from many contributors dealing with practical aspects in the study of nucleosides, nucleotides, and nucleic acids.

HOLLEY, R. W., "The Nucleotide Sequence of a Nucleic Acid," *Scientific American,* **214,** 30–39 (1966). A description of how the first nucleic acid molecule, a species of transfer-RNA, had its primary structure determined.

HORNE, R. W., "The Structure of Viruses," *Scientific American,* **208,** 48–56 (1963). A description of the structure of various types of viral particles as revealed by high-resolution electron microscopy.

ROBISON, G. A., R. W. BUTCHER, and E. W. SUTHERLAND, "Cyclic AMP," in *Annual Review of Biochemistry,* Volume 38, 149–174 (1968). A review article emphasizing the biochemistry of cyclic-AMP in mammalian organisms.

WATSON, J. D., *The Double Helix.* New York: Atheneum, 1968. An interesting and revealing narrative account of the events and persons associated with the discovery of DNA structure. Became a best seller.

EXERCISES

6-1 Draw the structural formula for each of the following substances.
a) guanosine-3'-monophosphate
b) deoxyadenosine-5'-diphosphate
c) 5'-dADP
d) 5'-dTMP
e) thymidine
f) cytosine-5'-triphosphate
g) ....pUpGp....

6-2 Shown below is an oligonucleotide segment of a ribonucleic acid molecule. What type of cleavage pattern (if any) would result in this segment by treating the RNA with
a) sodium hydroxide
b) pancreatic ribonuclease
c) micrococcal nuclease
d) spleen nuclease after 5'-monoesterase
e) takadiastase
(P-5').... pGpGpCpUpApCpGpUpApGpApUpCpAp.... (3'-OH)

6-3 A purified DNA preparation was found to contain 30.4% adenine and 19.6% cytosine. The adenine-thymine ratio was 0.98 and the guanine-cytosine ratio was 0.97. Calculate the amount of guanine and thymine in this DNA and also the ratio of purine bases to pyrimidine bases.

6-4 Draw a representation of the complementary base pair found in RNA that would correspond to the adenine-thymine pair in DNA.

6-5 The length of the chromosome of *Escherichia coli* cells has been measured by electron microscopy to be approximately 1.2 millimeters. Assuming that the chromosome consists of a single DNA molecule, how many complementary base pairs are present in the chromosome? (1 angstrom = 1×10^{-8} centimeters.)

6-6 The data given below are representative of the point made in our discussion of melting temperatures (T_m) of DNA, namely, that the T_m is a sensitive function of the overall base composition. Plot the data (% G+C versus T_m) to determine the type of relationship, and then calculate the %A+T of a DNA with a T_m of 85°C.

DNA Sample	T_m(°C)	G+C(%)
A	92.5	55.0
B	83.5	35.0
C	94.2	60.0
D	87.0	44.0
E	81.3	28.7
F	90.3	51.0

6-7 How would you account for the fact that the T_m of DNA preparations increases with increasing amounts of guanine and cytosine?

7

Carbohydrates

All organic material in our biosphere is derived from the reductive, energy-requiring fixation and conversion of atmospheric CO_2 into carbohydrate, $(CH_2O)_n$, through the process of *photosynthesis*. The primary carbohydrate end products of photosynthesis are the polymeric celluloses and starches. In addition to serving specific functions in the plant organism, the photosynthetically produced carbohydrates are ingested by higher animals and utilized as substrates in the oxidative, energy-yielding process of *respiration*. Thus, the two processes of photosynthesis and respiration are complementary and partially represent the marvelous design of nature for the maintenance of a chemical and energy balance in the biosphere—a balance in danger of destruction by modern civilization. The scheme given below summarizing this relationship is rather deceiving, since it depicts only the net chemistry and net energetics of both processes. For the moment, however, the essential message is just that. We will examine in greater detail the intricate biochemistry of each process in future chapters.

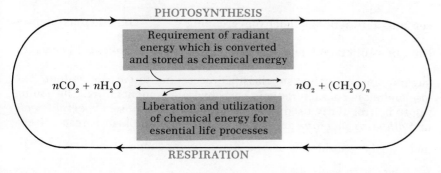

PHOTOSYNTHESIS

Requirement of radiant energy which is converted and stored as chemical energy

$$nCO_2 + nH_2O \rightleftharpoons nO_2 + (CH_2O)_n$$

Liberation and utilization of chemical energy for essential life processes

RESPIRATION

The most important function of the carbohydrates is their centralized metabolic role in the dynamic flow of carbon and energy in an organism. In fact, in most organisms carbohydrate material—largely in the form of the simple sugar, *glucose*—is the primary foodstuff, which upon degradation supplies the bulk of the energy and carbon skeletons required in the biosynthesis of proteins, nucleic acids, lipids, and other carbohydrates.

Other more specific biological roles of the carbohydrates are many and varied, as are the types of carbohydrates that occur in nature. Our objective in this chapter will be to examine a few principles of each aspect. Of necessity, our treatment will be brief and introductory. As in previous chapters, our approach to the subject will be based on the theme of structure and function and will follow a basic outline, considering three classes of carbohydrates in logical sequence: (1) the *monosaccharides* and important derivatives (monomeric units), (2) the *oligosaccharides* (2–10 monomers in glycosidic linkage), and (3) the *polysaccharides* (high-molecular-weight polymers). The term *saccharide* (derived from Greek: *sakchar* meaning sugar or sweetness) is related to the characteristic taste of many of the simple carbohydrates. Conjugated carbohydrates, complexes of carbohydrate and other types of biomolecules, will be discussed briefly.

Methods of carbohydrate separation and isolation will not be discussed. Suffice it to say that mono- and oligosaccharides can be analyzed by any of the chromatographic methods considered in Chapter 2. Gel permeation chromatography and ultracentrifugation are quite useful in the analysis of polysaccharides.

MONOSACCHARIDES

BASIC STRUCTURE AND STEREOISOMERISM

Chemically speaking, the monomeric carbohydrates—that is, the monosaccharides—can be described as polyhydroxy aldehydes, polyhydroxy ketones, and derivatives thereof. We will start our analysis by first considering the unsubstituted and unmodified simple sugars. Important derivatives will be discussed later. All simple monosaccharides have the *general empirical formula*, $(CH_2O)_n$, where n is a whole number ranging from 3 to 8. Regardless of carbon number, all monosaccharides can be grouped into one of two general classes—*aldoses* or *ketoses*. Aldoses contain a functional aldehyde grouping $\left(-\overset{\overset{\text{H}}{|}}{C}=O\right)$, whereas ketoses contain a functional ketone grouping $\left(\diagdown C=O\right)$. As indicated below, the sugars can be further subclassified according to carbon content. The *-ose* ending is characteristic in carbohydrate nomenclature. The ending *-ulose* is irregularly used to designate a simple ketose. *Glyceraldehyde* and *dihydroxyacetone* are the simplest aldose and ketose, respectively, and can be considered as the parent compounds of higher $\diagdown$CHOH homologues in each class.

ALDOSE FAMILY

$C_3H_6O_3$	$C_4H_8O_4$	$C_5H_{10}O_5$	$C_6H_{12}O_6$
			CHO
		CHO	CHOH
	CHO	CHOH	CHOH
CHO	CHOH	CHOH	CHOH
CHOH	CHOH	CHOH	CHOH
CH_2OH	CH_2OH	CH_2OH	CH_2OH
Aldotriose	Aldotetrose	Aldopentose	Aldohexose
Glyceraldehyde			
(simplest aldose)			

KETOSE FAMILY

$C_3H_6O_3$	$C_4H_8O_4$	$C_5H_{10}O_5$	$C_6H_{12}O_6$
			CH_2OH
		CH_2OH	C=O
	CH_2OH	C=O	CHOH
CH_2OH	C=O	CHOH	CHOH
C=O	CHOH	CHOH	CHOH
CH_2OH	CH_2OH	CH_2OH	CH_2OH
Ketotriose	Ketotetrose	Ketopentose	Ketohexose
Dihydroxyacetone			
(simplest ketose)			

Aside from the obvious chemical distinction between the parent trioses, note that glyceraldehyde contains an asymmetric carbon atom whereas dihydroxyacetone does not. What is true of dihydroxyacetone, however, is not true of all other ketoses. In fact, as revealed by close inspection of the general structures shown above, the absence of an asymmetric center is unique to dihydroxyacetone, with all other classes of simple carbohydrates having at least one asymmetric center, the total number being equal to the number of internal 〉CHOH groups. Since the number of stereoisomers for any asymmetric molecule is given by 2^n, where n equals the number of asymmetric carbons, it is obvious that a progression through the homologous families of aldoses and ketoses will yield greater numbers of isomeric forms. For example, an aldohexose with a general formula of $C_6H_{12}O_6$ and four asymmetric carbons—that is, four 〉CHOH groups—could exist in any one of 16 possible isomeric forms, with eight L forms and eight D forms. The basis of designating the L and D forms in terms of the two possible stereoisomers of glyceraldehyde was previously described in Chapter 4 (page 64).

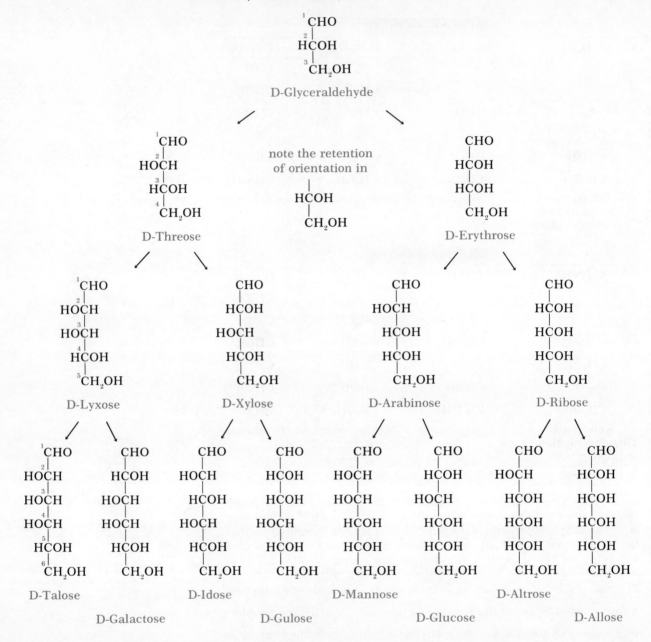

Figure 7-1 Structural relationships among D-aldoses.

As shown in Figure 7–1, with D-glyceraldehyde as the parent compound, it is possible to construct a chart illustrating the structures of all D-aldoses through the aldohexose group. The diagram illustrates the sugars of one homologous family as originating from the next lower homologous group, with the chain extended by the generation of a new CHOH at position 2. Note that every time this occurs, the hydroxyl group at C^2 can assume two possible orientations, while the orientation

of all other ⟩CHOH groupings remains unchanged. The same phenomenon occurs in the chemical synthesis of sugars when the chain
length of a lower homologue is extended. The overall configuration of
each sugar is fixed by the orientation of the ⟩CHOH group most distant
from the functional aldehyde group. This would be —C^5 in hexoses;
—C^4 in pentoses; and —C^3 in tetroses. A similar diagram can be constructed for the L series, beginning with L-glyceraldehyde. Diagrams for
the ketoses are also possible.

     At this point, a question that should come to mind is whether the
D or L form predominates in nature. The question is valid, and yes, one
form does predominate—the D configuration. Thus, through the first
four homologous classes of aldoses and ketoses, the number of biologically important simple sugars has been reduced from 45 to 23. To
further simplify matters, we can note that only a few monosaccharides
participate most frequently in the living process. A dozen of the more
common ones are listed in Table 7–1. Each occurs in the free state, in
oligomeric and/or polymeric linkage, or in a modified form. The structures of those sugars not previously given are also shown in Table 7–1.
Included among the latter is sedoheptulose, a seven-carbon ketose.

ANOMERIC ISOMERS

Consider the following facts. Two separate aqueous solutions containing equal amounts of pure D-glucose may exhibit widely different optical
properties when analyzed in a polarimeter. On prolonged standing, the
specific rotation of each solution would gradually change and ultimately
attain the same equilibrium value. The latter phenomenon is accelerated by the presence of small quantities of acid. This type of behavior
is not restricted to D-glucose, but is common to all of the simple monosaccharides.

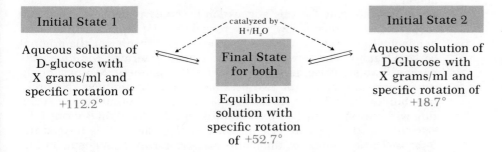

The obvious questions are: (a) How can identical solutions have different
optical properties? and (b) How can both solutions attain the same
specific rotation? Well, it should occur to you that, in fact, the samples
must be *not* identical, and that the observed differences of "identical"
solutions would be most logically explained by proposing that each
solution probably contains a different isomeric form of D-glucose.
Furthermore, since the two solutions differ only in their ability to rotate
a ray of polarized light, in all probability they contain two different

Table 7–1 Common monosaccharides.

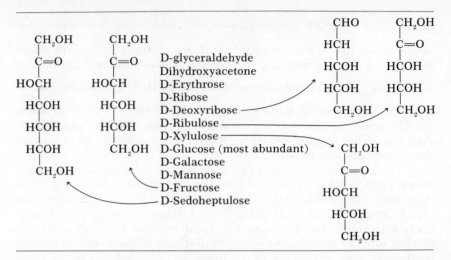

stereoisomeric forms of D-glucose. With regard to the second question, we can interpret the data as representative of the interconversion of these two forms to yield an equilibrium mixture containing each isomer in quantities characteristic of D-glucose.

The above description and accompanying interpretation of data are representative of the first encounter with this apparent anomaly when it was observed 75 years ago. To account for the existence of two stereoisomeric forms of D-glucose, it was proposed that *in solution very few sugar molecules exist with free aldehyde or ketone functional groups but rather as cyclic hemiacetals,* due to the intramolecular interaction of the carbonyl grouping with a distant hydroxyl grouping. For reasons of chemical stability, only five- and six-membered rings are most common. (Generally, aldohexoses form six-membered rings via a C^1–C^5 interaction; ketohexoses form five-membered rings via a C^2–C^5 interaction; aldopentoses form five-membered rings via a C^1–C^5 interaction.)

The rationale for this suggestion becomes evident by inspecting the structures shown below, which reveal that the formation of a cyclic hemiacetal generates an additional asymmetric center at the original carbonyl atom. The new asymmetric center is termed the *anomeric carbon.* Two stereoisomers exist because the anomeric hydroxyl group can assume either one of two possible spatial orientations. No other possibilities exist. In the linear Fischer projection formulae, the structure with the anomeric hydroxyl group oriented to the right is termed the *α-form,* and the opposite orientation (—OH to the left) is termed the *β-form.* The existence of anomeric isomers for all simple sugars has been confirmed by many lines of evidence and is an indisputable fact of carbohydrate chemistry. As we will see in later sections, this is an extremely significant structural phenomenon relative to naturally occurring carbohydrates. We have already encountered one example in Chapter 6. Can you identify it without cross-reference?

The interconversion of the α and β anomers is termed *mutarotation.* The conversion is not direct, but is bridged by the non-cyclic form containing a free carbonyl group. An equilibrium mixture of unchanging optical properties does not imply 50–50 amounts of each anomer.

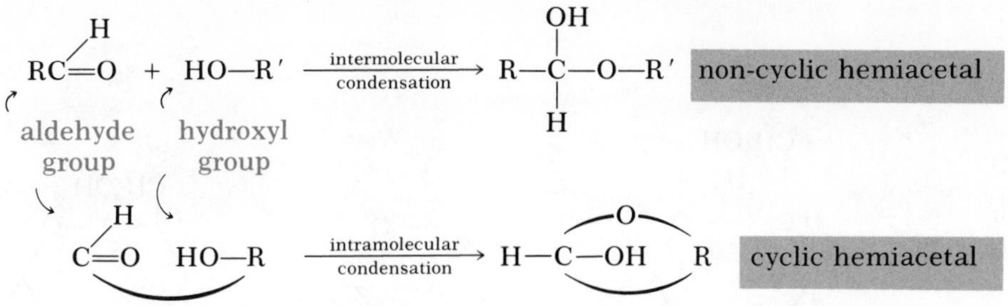

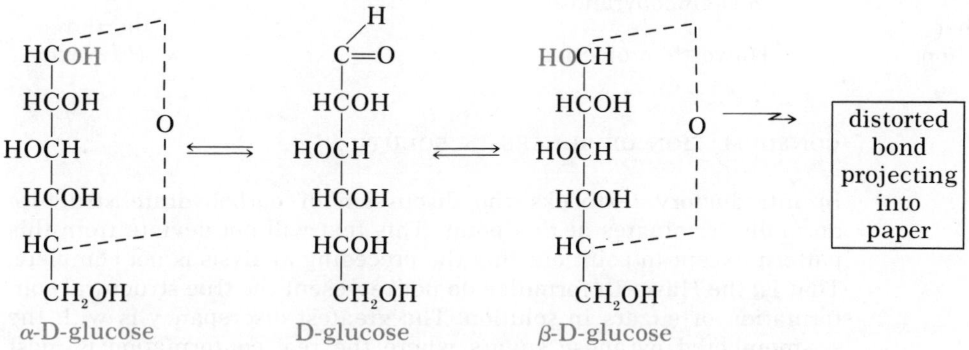

α-D-glucose   D-glucose   β-D-glucose

One form is usually in excess, with the relative amounts being deter-mined by differences in chemical stability.

HAWORTH PROJECTION FORMULAE

In depicting hemiacetal ring structures, Fischer projection formulae are inadequate and, indeed, very inaccurate. A more realistic represen-tation (previously introduced in Chapter 6) was suggested by Haworth in 1929. To review: the Haworth convention depicts the sugar as a planar ring system with hydroxyl groups oriented above or below the plane. Because of the similarity to furan and pyran, five- and six-mem-bered cyclic sugars are termed *furanose* and *pyranose,* respectively. In view of our previous encounter with the furanose form (see page 144), only the pyranose structure is shown (next page). The guideline for con-version of Fischer projections (as drawn here) to Haworth projections is simple. First, the terminal —CH$_2$OH grouping in the Fischer formula is projected above the plane of the ring in the Haworth representation. Then all hydroxyl groups that appear to the right and left in the Fischer formula—including those at the anomeric carbon—are respectively directed below and above the plane of the ring in the Haworth represen-tation. A frequently used shorthand form of the Haworth projection eliminates the H's and indicates OH's solely by dashes projected above or below the plane of the ring.

HCOH
|²
HCOH
|³
HOCH   O
|⁴
HCOH
|⁵
HC----
|⁶
CH₂OH

α-D-glucose

Fischer
projection

⁶CH₂OH
            H
    ⁵|
H C------O----H
  |⁴ |¹
  C OH   H C
HO |³ |² OH
   C-------C
   H   OH

α-D-glucopyranose

Haworth projection

Pyran

CH₂OH

shorthand
Haworth

CONFORMATION OF SUGARS IN SOLUTION

In introductory textbooks the discussion of carbohydrate structure normally terminates at this point. This text will not deviate from this pattern except to point out that the preceding analysis is not complete. That is, the Haworth formulae do not represent the true structural conformation of sugars in solution. The greatest discrepancy is with the six-membered pyranose sugars where the real conformation is most accurately represented by the classical *chair* or *boat* forms of cyclohexane, with hydroxyl groups existing in axial or equatorial orientations. A line drawing and a model of the chair conformation of β-D-glucopyranose are shown below. The planar Haworth projection of furanose sugars (see page 144) is also slightly inaccurate, since the ring system is slightly puckered. Despite the inaccuracy of the Haworth representations, they are used routinely because they are less cumbersome to draw and somewhat easier to interpret.

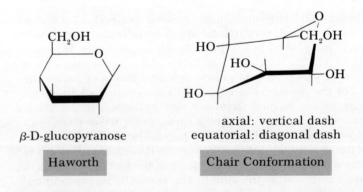

β-D-glucopyranose

Haworth

axial: vertical dash
equatorial: diagonal dash

Chair Conformation

PHOSPHATE ESTERS

Due to the presence of reactive hydroxyl-groups and to the potential aldehyde or ketone functions, the monosaccharides exhibit a broad spectrum of chemical activity. Many reactions of incomplete definition have been exploited as a basis for colorimetric assay procedures for carbohydrates or carbohydrate-containing materials. For example, treatment of ribose with an acidified *orcinol* solution produces a colored complex. This reaction has been incorporated into a qualitative and quantitative test for RNA. Deoxyribose yields a blue complex on treatment with a *diphenylamine* reagent. This is similarly used for DNA assays. Two particular reactions of biological importance, and more specifically defined, are the formation of *phosphate esters* and *glycosides*. We will consider these reactions in that order.

In nature the phosphate esters are generally formed in an ATP-dependent reaction catalyzed by a *kinase* enzyme (see page 107), with phosphorylation occurring at the anomeric hydroxyl or at the distal hydroxymethyl group. Diphosphoesters, formed by two successive kinase-catalyzed reactions, are quite common. The biological significance of phosphate esters is simply stated—they represent the metabolically active form of sugars. In other words, whenever a carbohydrate participates as a substrate in an enzyme-catalyzed reaction, it does so primarily as a phosphate ester. The primary exceptions to this generalization are, of course, the kinase-catalyzed reactions wherein the phosphorylated species are themselves formed from the neutral sugars. Sugar phosphates are optimal enzyme substrates for two basic reasons. First, the presence of the phosphate group renders the molecule ionic—a condition which will favor its binding to the active site of enzymes. This is a kinetic reason. Secondly, on an energetic basis, the phosphate esters are more unstable than the non-phosphorylated sugars—a condition which favors the directional flow of carbohydrates through a multi-faceted metabolic pathway, be it degradation or synthesis. This is a thermodynamic reason. The basis for the thermodynamic argument will become clear in subsequent chapters.

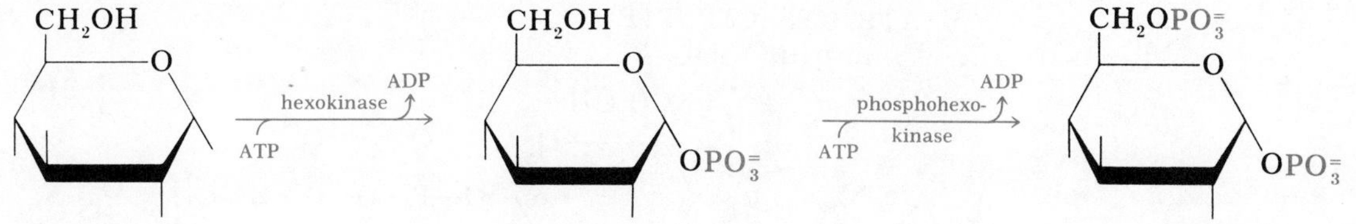

α-D-glucopyranose
or simply
α-D-glucose

α-D-glucopyranose-1-phosphate
or
glucose-1-phosphate (G1P)

α-D-glycopyranose-1,6-diphosphate
or
glucose-1,6-diphosphate (GDP)

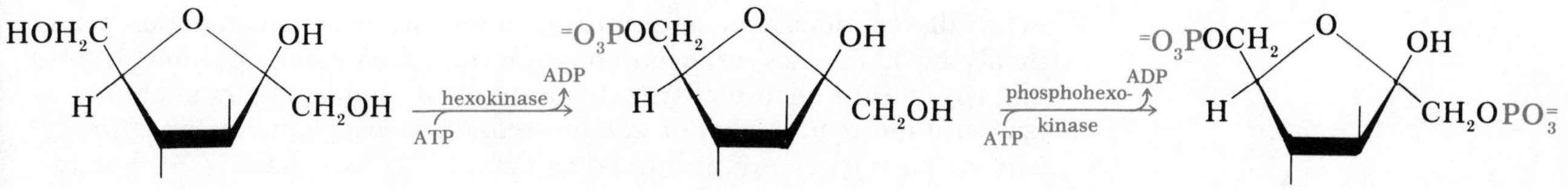

β-D-fructofuranose
or
β-D-fructose

β-D-fructofuranose-6-phosphate
or
fructose-6-phosphate (F6P)

β-D-fructofuranose-1,6-diphosphate
or
fructose-1,6-diphosphate (FDP)

The fact that the cell membrane is not very permeable to the transport of sugar phosphates is another significant aspect of phosphorylation. In effect, this means that once they are formed within the cell, the sugar phosphates are more or less trapped inside.

NUCLEOSIDE DIPHOSPHO SUGARS

One of the most important reactions that the sugar-1-phosphates undergo is a reaction with another unit of a nucleoside triphosphate to yield nucleoside diphospho sugar derivatives. The general reaction, catalyzed by an enzyme referred to as either a *NuDP-sugar pyrophosphorylase* or a *nucleotidyl transferase*, is shown below. In effect, the reaction consists of the phosphorylysis of the nucleotide, with the formation of a new phosphoanhydride bond between the resultant monophosphonucleotidyl grouping and the sugar-1-phosphate. Although all types of nucleoside diphospho sugars are found in nature, the most abundant are the *UDP-sugars*.

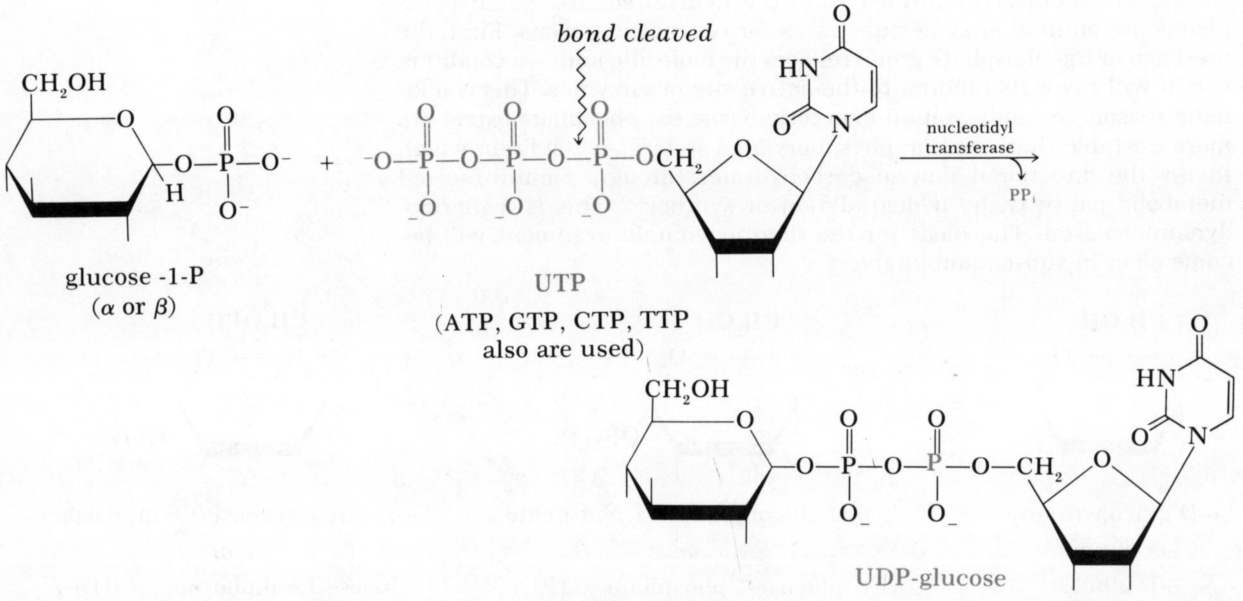

glucose -1-P
(α or β)

bond cleaved

UTP
(ATP, GTP, CTP, TTP
also are used)

nucleotidyl transferase → PP$_i$

UDP-glucose

The NuDP-sugars participate in many reactions. Basically, however, all reactions can be grouped under either of two reaction types involving (a) the biosynthesis of oligomeric and polymeric carbohydrates, and (b) certain chemical transformations of simple sugars such as the isomeric interconversion of galactose and glucose, which is an epimerization. Both types are discussed in Chapter 11 (see page 282). For his

(a) (glucose)$_n$ + UDP-glucose → (glucose)$_{n+1}$ + UDP
(b) UDP-glucose ⟷ UDP-galactose

many contributions in furthering the understanding of carbohydrate metabolism, and especially for the discovery and elucidation of the role of UDP-sugars, L. F. Leloir was awarded the Nobel Prize in 1970.

GLYCOSIDES

A glycoside is a sugar containing a substituent in ether linkage at the anomeric carbon. Whereas the unsubstituted sugar is termed a hemiacetal, the glycoside is a full acetal. In the laboratory, glycosides can be easily prepared by treatment of hemiacetals with an acidified alcohol solution. The alkylation of the hydroxyl groupings at other carbons to yield a fully substituted glycoside requires further treatment with an alkyl sulfate and sodium hydroxide.

Glycoside Synthesis

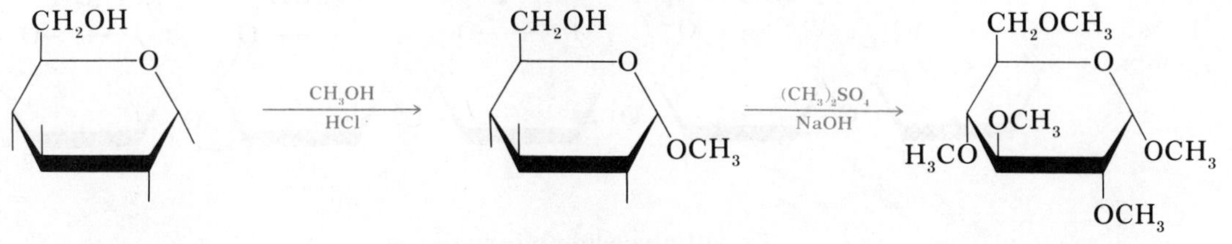

α-D-glucopyranose
(hemiacetal)

methyl-α-D-glucopyranoside
anomeric glycoside
(full acetal)

methyl-2,3,4,6-
tetra-O-methyl-α-D-
glucopyranoside

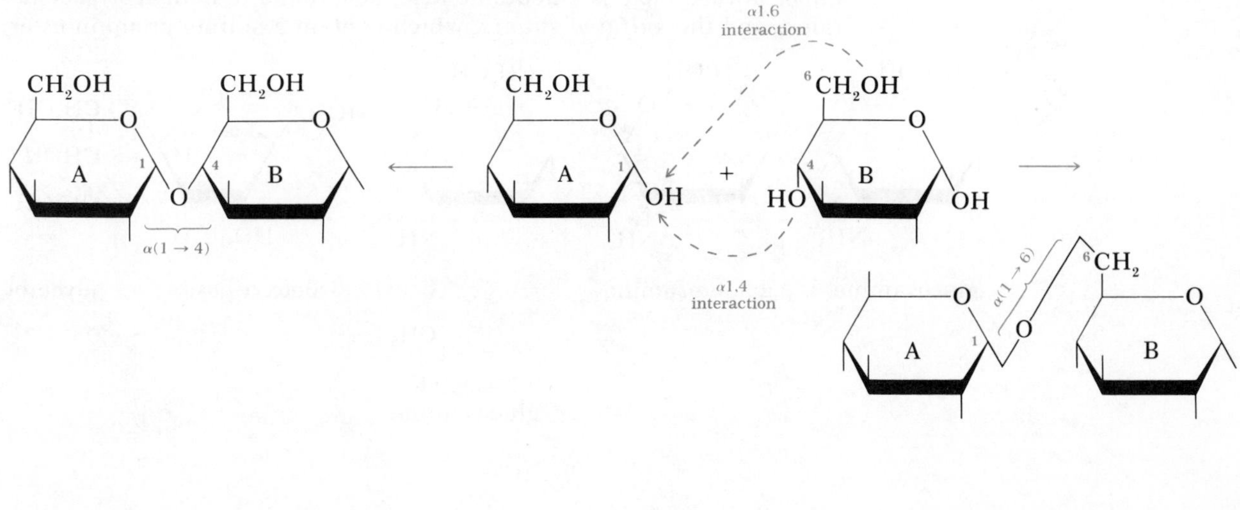

The glycosidic linkage is of extreme biological significance, since, neglecting some obscure exceptions, it represents the covalent bond of nearly all monosaccharide-monosaccharide interactions. Consequently, the glycoside bond is to carbohydrates as the peptide bond is to proteins and as the phosphodiester bond is to nucleic acids. The glycoside linkage between two sugars normally involves the anomeric hydroxyl group (α or β) of one monosaccharide and any available hydroxyl group in the second monosaccharide. The formation of glycosidic linkages between the α-hydroxyl group of one glucose molecule and the C^4 and C^6 hydroxyl of a second glucose molecule is diagrammed below. The respective bonds are symbolized as $\alpha(1 \rightarrow 4)$ and $\alpha(1 \rightarrow 6)$, respectively. Although all combinations ($\alpha(1 \rightarrow 3)$, $\alpha(1 \rightarrow 2)$, $\beta(1 \rightarrow 4)$, $\beta(1 \rightarrow 6)$, and so on) are found in the naturally occurring oligo- and polysaccharides, each particular oligosaccharide and polysaccharide contains a specific glycosidic linkage. Indeed, in some instances this is the primary structural difference between otherwise identical oligomers or polymers. With the exception of disaccharides, all oligomers or polymers will contain monomeric residues involved in two glycosidic linkages. Some residues may be involved in three glycosidic bonds—a situation common to branched polymers such as glycogen. Of course, the terminal residues of the chain are involved in only one.

Polyglucose Molecule

all glycoside bonds are $\alpha(1 \rightarrow 4)$

ADDITIONAL SUGAR DERIVATIVES

Phosphate esters and glycosides, albeit important, represent only two of many derivatives of the simple sugars. Other types are found throughout nature and many have important biological functions. We have already encountered one such example in the preceding chapter, namely, the *deoxy sugars* as exemplified by 2-deoxyribose, a constituent of DNA. Others of significance are: the *sugar alcohols*—important examples are glycerol, a principal constituent of lipids, and D-ribitol, a constituent of the coenzyme FAD; the *amino sugars*, where an —NH_2 group replaces a hydroxyl group, generally at position C^2—important examples are glucosamine and galactosamine, both found in many polysaccharides, frequently as N-acetyl derivatives; the *uronic acid sugars*, which consist of a terminal —COOH grouping in place of —CH_2OH—an important example is glucuronic acid, also found in many polysaccharides; and the *sulfated sugars*, which contain a sulfate group in ester

glucosamine   galactosamine   N-acetyl-glucosamine   deoxyribose   glycerol

linkage—an example is glucuronic acid-2-sulfate, found in heparin. As a final example, consider *muramic acid,* a derivative of N-acetyl-glucosamine containing a *lactic acid* substituent in ether linkage at position C^3. Muramic acid is a component of bacterial cell walls.

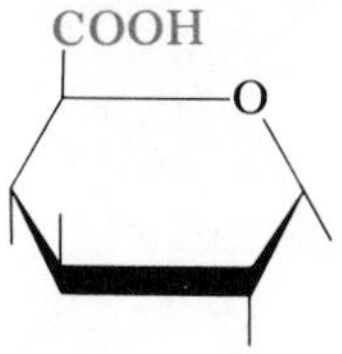

glucuronic acid

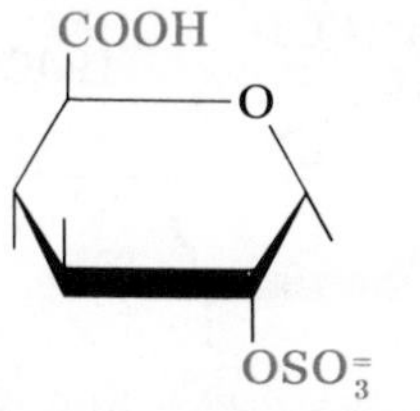

glucuronic acid-2-sulfate

CH₂OH
HCOH
HCOH
HCOH
CH₂OH

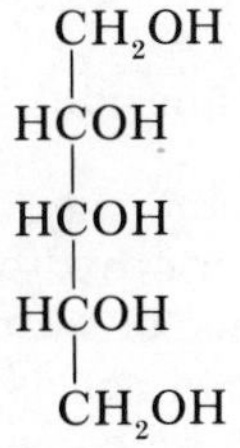

D-ribitol

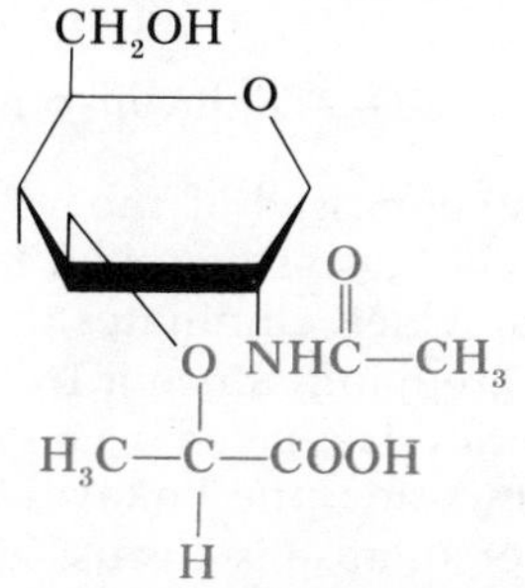

muramic acid

OLIGOSACCHARIDES

Oligosaccharides contain two or more monosaccharides linked to each other via glycosidic bonds. Depending on the number of monomeric residues, an oligosaccharide is termed a disaccharide, trisaccharide, and so on, with an upper limit of ten residues generally accepted as the distinction from polysaccharides. Most oligosaccharides are comprised of hexose sugars. If all residues are identical, the substance is termed a *homogeneous oligomer.* Obviously then, the presence of two or more different types of monomers characterizes a *heterogeneous oligomer.* Both types occur in nature and examples of each are given in this section. The coverage will be primarily descriptive and confined to disaccharides.

DISACCHARIDES

Among the many disaccharides of natural origin that occur in the free state, *sucrose* and *lactose* are the most abundant and most important. Both are heterogeneous disaccharides. Sucrose is found throughout the plant kingdom, but is most abundant in sugar cane, sugar beets, and maple syrup. Of course, it is the primary granulated product obtained from the processing of sugar cane and is commonly known as table sugar. In addition to its sweetening and flavor-enhancing properties, the monomeric residues (D-glucose and D-fructose) produced during the hydrolytic process of digestion serve as major dietary sources of carbon and energy. Lactose is the primary carbohydrate of milk. Likewise, the monomeric residues (D-glucose and D-galactose) released in digestion are major dietary sources of carbon and energy.

The Haworth formula of sucrose is

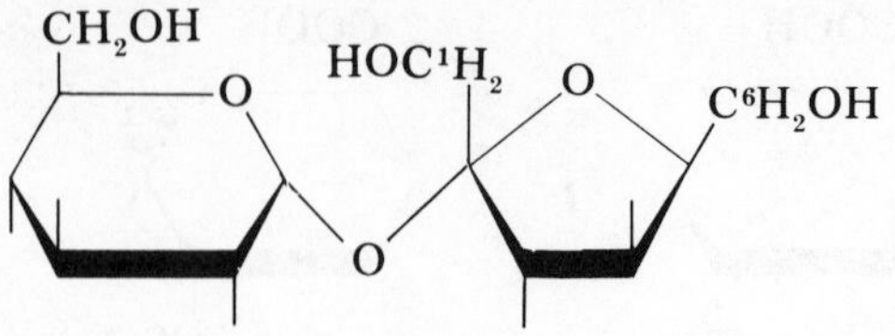

Sucrose

2-O-β-D-fructofuranosyl-α-D-glucopyranoside

or

2-O-α-D-glucopyranosyl-β-D-fructofuranoside

Sucrose is comprised of the α form of D-glucose and the β form of D-fructose. The glycosidic bond involves the anomeric hydroxyl of both monomers, which eliminates the potential existence of a free aldehyde or ketone grouping. Since a free carbonyl group can act as a reducing agent, sucrose is termed a non-reducing sugar. If we consider sucrose as an α-glucoside, the linkage will be specified as α, $\beta(1 \rightarrow 2)$. The biosynthesis of sucrose is discussed briefly on page 256.

The Haworth formula of lactose is

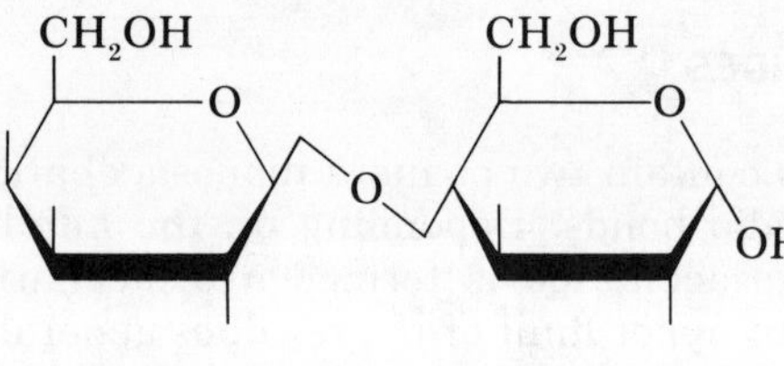

Lactose (α form)

4-O-β-galactopyranosyl-α-D-glucopyranose

Lactose is composed of the β form of D-galactose and either the α or β form of D-glucose and is generally referred to as a β-galactoside. Since the anomeric carbon of the glucose residue is not involved in the glycosidic linkage, the potential for a free aldehyde group does exist, and thus lactose is classified as a reducing sugar. After its formation from lactose during digestion, the metabolic utilization of D-galactose is preceded by conversion to D-glucose in a multi-step, UTP-dependent process. Normal operation of this process is critical, since high levels of blood galactose contribute to severe physiological disturbances which can be fatal, especially in the milk-ingesting young. The condition, termed *galactosemia,* is a genetic disease whose molecular basis is a malfunctional enzyme in one of the steps in the D-galactose $\rightarrow$ D-glucose conversion (see page 282).

Other disaccharides occurring primarily as repeating units in various polysaccharides are *cellobiose, maltose,* and *isomaltose.* These sugars are identical in that each is a diglucose molecule, but they differ in the nature of the glycosidic linkage. Cellobiose $\beta(1 \rightarrow 4)$ is the sole repeating unit in cellulose; maltose $\alpha(1 \rightarrow 4)$ is the sole repeating unit of the amylose fraction of starch; isomaltose $\alpha(1 \rightarrow 6)$, though not a repeating unit, is found in the amylopectin fraction of starch and glycogen.

Cellobiose (β form)
4-O-β-D-glucopyranosyl-β-D-glucopyranose

Maltose (α form)
4-O-α-D-glucopyranosyl-α-D-glucopyranose

Isomaltose (α form)
6-O-α-D-glucopyranosyl-α-D-glucopyranose

POLYSACCHARIDES

Based on the arbitrary limit mentioned earlier, an oligomer containing more than 10 monosaccharide residues is categorized as a polysaccharide. However, the number of residues in polysaccharides of natural origin is frequently much larger, i.e., in the approximate range of 200 to several hundred thousand. In addition to variance in size among different materials, the residue count frequently varies among samples of the same material. For example, molecules of cellulose may contain anywhere from 30,000 to 500,000 or more glucose residues. Thus, contrary to what was true of proteins, the molecular weight of polysaccharides is not a well-defined parameter and has minimal physicochemical value.

The structural features that essentially determine the functional properties of any given polysaccharide are (a) the identity of the constituent monomers, and (b) the nature of the glycosidic linkages between them. Relative to the first point, polysaccharides can be classified as *homopolysaccharides* (all residues identical) or *heteropolysaccharides* (two or more different residues). Contrary to the proteins, however, in the latter case the number of different residues occurring in polymeric linkage is much smaller, and frequently only two are present. Furthermore, the residue sequence is not random but usually *repetitive*.

The situation with glycosidic linkages is the same as for oligosaccharides, namely, a variety exists. Polysaccharides exist in the free state and also conjugated with other materials such as lipids, peptides, and proteins. Generally the conjugation is covalent.

This brief introduction summarizes a considerable amount of material. In the next few pages, we will examine most aspects, considering homopolysaccharides (cellulose, chitin, starch, glycogen), heteropolysaccharides (hyaluronic acid and heparin), and conjugated polysaccharides (peptidoglycan material of bacterial cell walls and glycoproteins) in that order. Although our approach will be basically descriptive, an attempt will be made to relate and contrast chemical structure with biological function.

HOMOPOLYSACCHARIDES: CELLULOSES

Cellulose is the most abundant organic compound of natural origin on the face of the earth. As a minute piece of information, note that the seed hairs of the cotton plant are particularly rich sources, containing 98–99% cellulose. The molecules are typically large fibrils consisting of a variable number of unbranched polyglucose chains intertwined with each other. If your eyes had the resolving power of a microscope, the pages these words are printed on would serve as a good visual aid for such fibrils. Since the number of glucose residues per chain is also variable, it is unrealistic to refer to molecular weight. All glucose residues are in the β-D configuration linked via $\beta[1 \rightarrow 4]$ glycosidic bonds as illustrated below.

repeating disaccharide unit
β-Cellobiose

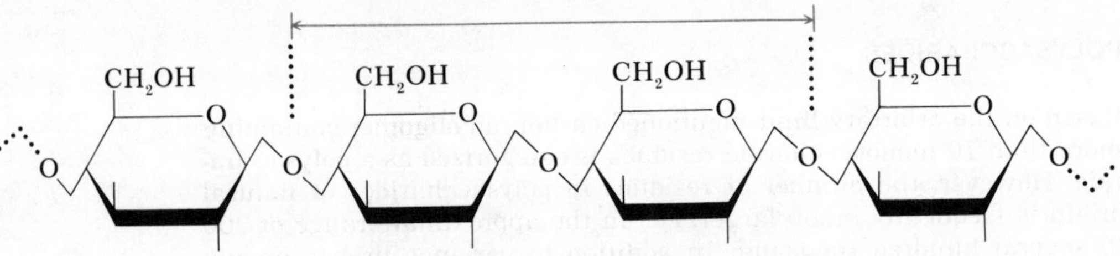

representative segment of one polyglucose chain
of cellulose molecule

With the exception of ruminants, the direct nutritional value of cellulose is virtually nil for the higher animals. The basic reason for this is that the combined digestive secretions of the mouth, stomach, and intestine do not contain a *cellulase* that would cleave the glycosidic bonds, yielding free glucose units. However, cellulases are found in nature, most commonly in ruminants, various insects, snails, fungi, algae, and bacteria. For obvious reasons, such organisms are referred to as *cellulolytic*. Think about this the next time you see a grazing cow, a moth-eaten piece of clothing, a rotted piece of wood, or a damp, odor-ridden basement.

In the plant world, the celluloses are found primarily as components of the cell wall, functioning chiefly as structural materials. The molecular structure of cellulose is well suited for this purpose. For the most part, the individual chains of cellulose fibers are close packed and strongly held together by numerous secondary forces such as hydrogen bonding. Accordingly, the fibers are quite stable and have a high tensile strength. Thus, we have another illustration of the remarkable logic of the structure–function relationship in terms of naturally occurring molecules.

CHITIN

A subtle variation on the structure of cellulose is found in chitin, which is a linear homopolysaccharide consisting of *N-acetyl-glucosamine* residues linked by $\beta(1 \rightarrow 4)$ bonds. Because it is a close structural relative of cellulose, we might argue that it should have a biological function similar to that of cellulose. Indeed, such is the case, since chitin is the major organic structural component of the exoshells of the invertebrates.

Disaccharide repeating unit of chitin

STARCHES

The starches comprise a group of polyglucose materials of varying size and shape. Occurring exclusively in plants, they exist inside the plant cell as granules dispersed in the cytoplasm. Like the celluloses, all starches are homogeneous, containing only D-glucose residues. Unlike the celluloses, the starches are not single molecules but normally mixtures of two structurally distinct polysaccharides. One component is termed *amylose,* the other *amylopectin.* Both are poly-α-D-glucose molecules. Amylose is a linear molecule with all residues linked via $\alpha(1 \rightarrow 4)$ bonds. Amylopectin, on the other hand, is a branched molecule due to the presence of a small number of $\alpha(1 \rightarrow 6)$ linkages at various points along a core chain consisting of $\alpha(1 \rightarrow 4)$ linkages. Amylose appears to prefer a helical-coiled conformation. No preferred conformation of amylopectin has been suggested. A diagrammatic representation of each material is shown in Figure 7–2. For simplicity, the glucopyranose units are represented by a hexagon with the attached dash corresponding to —C^{6}H$_2$OH. The periodic inversion of hexagon units is necessary to depict several branching points along the center core. This maneuver is perfectly legitimate because free rotation does exist around the glycosidic bond.

Legend:

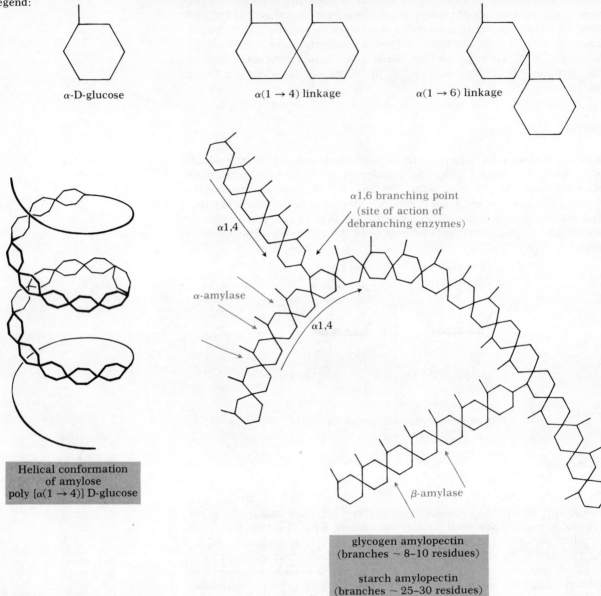

α-D-glucose

α(1 → 4) linkage

α(1 → 6) linkage

Helical conformation
of amylose
poly [α(1 → 4)] D-glucose

α1,4

α-amylase

α1,4

α1,6 branching point
(site of action of
debranching enzymes)

β-amylase

glycogen amylopectin
(branches ~ 8–10 residues)

starch amylopectin
(branches ~ 25–30 residues)

Figure 7–2 Diagrammatic representations of starch amylose and glycogen amylopectin. A lesser frequency of branching in glycogen amylopectin characterizes the amylopectin fraction of starch.

As we pointed out earlier, the starches are molecular storage reservoirs. When the proper functioning of the plant requires, the starches are enzymatically degraded to simpler sugars, which are then metabolized further to supply needed energy and carbon skeletons. Most plants contain two distinct hydrolyzing enzymes, trivially named *α-amylase* and *β-amylase*. Both attack the amylose and amylopectin fraction at α(1 → 4) sites but in a different pattern. Cleavage with α-amylase is random, occurring at different loci to yield a mixture of glucose and maltose. The action of β-amylase is more ordered, characterized by successive removal of only maltose units, beginning at a non-reducing terminus (see Figure 7-2). Neither enzyme is capable of hydrolyzing the $\alpha(1 \rightarrow 6)$ linkages. Thus, whereas the combined action of the two enzymes will completely degrade amylose to glucose and maltose, amylopectin is only partially degraded. However, other catalysts, called *debranching enzymes,* specific for hydrolyzing the $\alpha(1 \rightarrow 6)$ linkage, do exist in nature.

Starch is present to varying degrees in the diet of all animals. Unlike cellulose, however, starch is digestible by man due to the presence of salivary amylase and pancreatic amylase in the digestive secretions. Both enzymes are similar in action to the α-amylase of plants. In combined action with other digestive enzymes (notably *maltase* and debranching enzymes), starch is completely degraded to α-D-glucose, which is absorbed and metabolized further. As some of you may have experienced or are now experiencing, on diets high in starch (carbohydrate), the bulk of the absorbed glucose is converted into fat (lipid).

GLYCOGEN

The storage of carbon and energy as polyglucose materials in dynamic equilibrium with other cellular materials is not a biochemical phenomenon unique to plants. An identical role is fulfilled by glycogen in animals and most bacteria. In higher animals, glycogen granules are most abundant in cells of liver and muscle tissue. Structurally, glycogen is a branched polyglucose molecule identical to the amylopectin fraction of starch in all respects except one—glycogen is more highly branched. Branch points on glycogen occur every 8–10 residues along the central core. In starch amylopectin, branch points are believed to occur every 25–30 residues. Refer to the legend of Figure 7-2. Within the cell, the glycogen molecule is degraded by *glycogen phosphorylase,* an enzyme which sequentially removes one glucose residue at a time, yielding glucose-1-phosphate (see page 272).

HETEROPOLYSACCHARIDES: HYALURONIC ACID

Hyaluronic acid is a heteropolysaccharide of major importance in higher animals. In connective tissue, it is the primary component of *ground-substance,* a gelatinous material filling the extracellular spaces of tissue. Another abundant source is synovial fluid, a viscous packing around bone joints serving as a lubricant and shock absorber. The vitreous humor and umbilical cord are also rich in hyaluronic acid. Since aqueous solutions of this material are gelatinous, it is synonomously termed a *mucopolysaccharide.* Structurally, the molecule is largely a linear polymer of a disaccharide repeating unit composed of *D-glucuronic acid* and *N-acetyl-D-glucosamine,* two sugar derivatives, linked together by a $\beta(1 \rightarrow 3)$ bond. Adjacent repeating units are linked by $\beta(1 \rightarrow 4)$ linkages. Thus, $\beta(1 \rightarrow 3)$ and $\beta(1 \rightarrow 4)$ bonds alternate along the chain. The high viscosity of hyaluronic acid is probably in part related to its polyanionic character at physiological pH, which would favor excessive hydration and interchain hydrogen bonding.

Disaccharide repeating unit of hyaluronic acid

HEPARIN

Found in many mammalian tissues, heparin is another interesting mucopolysaccharide. The exact structure is not yet resolved, but most evidence favors a linear or nearly linear molecule composed of a disaccharide repeating unit of *sulfated glucuronic acid* and *disulfated galactosamine* residues linked via an $\alpha(1 \rightarrow 4)$ bond. Adjacent repeating units are similarly linked. Heparin is a good blood anticoagulant and is widely used as such in medical practice.

Suggested disaccharide repeating unit of heparin

CONJUGATED POLYSACCHARIDES

BACTERIAL CELL WALLS

All unicellular bacteria contain a rigid cell wall. For years it was thought that the only notable function of the wall was a protective one, but recently this view has changed considerably and many diverse functions are now associated with the cell wall. In accord with the structure–function theme of modern biochemical research, it was only logical that studies should be initiated to ascertain the chemical structure of this cytological unit. Success was first reported in 1965 by Strominger on the cell wall material of *Staphylococcus aureus*. Since then, cell wall preparations of other organisms have been similarly examined. On a comparative basis, the picture that has emerged is that bacterial cell walls are both heterogeneous and homogeneous in composition. They are heterogeneous in the sense that the total composition of wall preparations differs from one genus to another, with varying levels of peptides, proteins, lipids, and carbohydrates being the major components. They are homogeneous in the sense that all sources possess a similar (not identical) polymeric unit which acts as the basic structural framework of the wall. Variations in composition result from different types and amounts of accessory material associated with this substance. The common unit is a network of polysaccharide chains covalently cross-linked to each other via small polypeptide bridges. Due to this conjugation of peptide and carbohydrate, the material is conventionally termed a *peptidoglycan*. Figure 7–3 accompanies the following descriptive material. The polysaccharide moiety, which you will recall is the

Figure 7–3 Peptidoglycan material of bacterial cell wall.

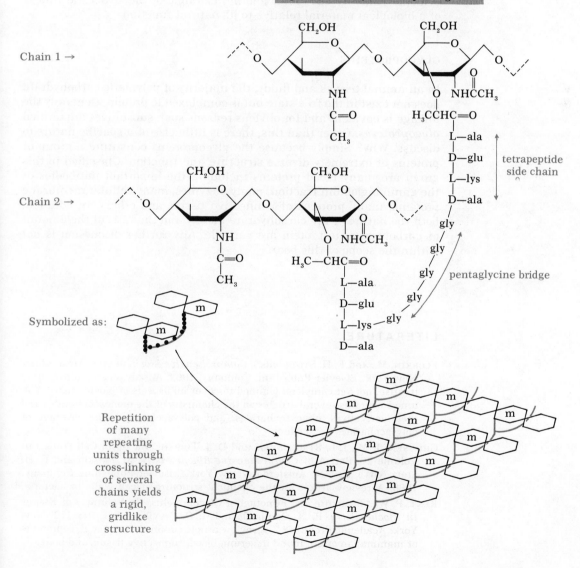

Peptide–Carbohydrate Repeating Unit

Chain 1 →

Chain 2 →

tetrapeptide side chain

L—ala
D—glu
L—lys
D—ala
gly
gly
gly   pentaglycine bridge
gly
L—lys—gly
D—ala

Symbolized as:

Repetition of many repeating units through cross-linking of several chains yields a rigid, gridlike structure

substrate of lysozyme (page 121, Chapter 5), is heterogeneous, composed of a repeating disaccharide unit of *N-acetyl-D-glucoasamine* and *N-acetylmuramic acid* with a $\beta(1 \rightarrow 4)$ linkage. Successive units are also attached via $\beta(1 \rightarrow 4)$ linkages. The peptide portion can be considered as consisting of two parts. First, we can identify a tetrapeptide unit composed of both D- and L-amino acids and covalently attached to the C^3 lactic acid side chain of the muramic acid residue. In fact, every muramic acid residue in every chain is so characterized. Secondly, we can distinguish a pentaglycine unit which acts as a bridge between the terminal alanine residue of one peptide branch on one chain and the L-lysine residue of a second branch attached to a neighboring parallel polysaccharide chain. As shown in Figure 7–3, the repetition of such linkages among several chains confers a grid pattern on the complete peptidoglycan structure. Considering the extensive presence of covalent bonds in criss-cross fashion, the basic rigidity of the cell wall should be evident. Thus, we encounter another example of the structural fitness of a biological material relative to its natural function.

GLYCOPROTEINS

In all animal tissues and fluids, the majority of polymeric carbohydrate does not exist in the free state but is complexed to protein. Generally the linkage is covalent and for obvious reasons such substances are termed *glycoproteins*. Other than this, there is little else of a specific nature to discuss. Why? Simply because the glycoproteins constitute a group of proteins of extremely diverse structure and function. Classified in this group are many blood proteins including the important antibodies of the gamma globulin fraction, many enzymes, many cellular membrane proteins, many proteins of connective tissue, and others. In addition, both the nature of the carbohydrate moiety and the ratio of the amount of carbohydrate to protein are variable. Any further discussion is not within the scope of this book.

LITERATURE

FLORKIN, M., and E. H. STOTZ (eds.), *Comprehensive Biochemistry*. Amsterdam-New York: Elsevier Publishing Company, 1963. An advanced multi-volume treatise, not yet complete, planned to cover all aspects of biochemistry. Volume 5 contains several articles on the chemistry of the monosaccharides and their derivatives, oligosaccharides, and polysaccharides. The coverage of polysaccharides is excellent.

GHUYSEN, J. M., J. L. STROMINGER, and D. J. TIPPEN, "Bacterial Cell Walls," in Volume 26, Part A of *Comprehensive Biochemistry*, M. Florkin and E. H. Stotz (eds.), 53–104. Amsterdam-New York: Elsevier Publishing Company, 1968. A review article on the chemical structure of cell walls in bacteria.

KENT, P. W., "Structure and Function of Glycoproteins," in Volume 3 of *Essays in Biochemistry*, P. N. Campbell and G. D. Greville (eds.), 105–152. New York: Academic Press, 1967. A review article confined to major glycoproteins of mammalian origin found in serum, blood, connective tissue, and bone.

MORRISON, R. T., and R. N. BOYD, *Organic Chemistry,* Second Edition. Boston: Allyn and Bacon, Inc., 1966. Acclaimed as the best organic chemistry text available. Chapters 33 and 34 contain a superb introductory treatment of carbohydrate chemistry.

SHARON, N., "The Bacterial Cell Wall," *Scientific American,* **220,** 87–98 (1969). Description of the chemical structure of the cell wall in bacteria and the action of lysozyme and penicillin.

EXERCISES

7-1 Draw the Haworth formula for each of the following carbohydrates.
   a) α-D-galactopyranose
   b) α-D-glucopyranose-1,6-diphosphate
   c) β-D-galactopyranose-1-phosphate
   d) β-D-ribofuranose-5-phosphate
   e) α-D-mannopyranose
   f) α-L-mannopyranose
   g) UDP-α-D-galactopyranose
   h) O-α-D-glucopyranosyl-(1 → 1)-α-D-glucopyranose
   i) O-α-D-galactopyranosyl-(1 → 6)-β-D-glucopyranose
   j) O-α-D-glucopyranosyl-(1 → 1)-α-D-glucosaminopyranose
   k) O-α-D-galactopyranosyl-(1 → 6)-O-α-D-glucopyranosyl-
   (1 → 2)-β-D-fructofuranose

7-2 β-D-mannose has a specific rotation of −16.3°, and an equilibrium mixture of the α and β isomers of D-mannose has a specific rotation of +14.5°. What conclusion can be drawn with respect to the specific rotation of α-D-mannose relative to the value given for β-D-mannose?

7-3 Give a brief description of the catalytic role of the following enzymes.
   a) hexokinase
   b) α-amylase
   c) β-amylase
   d) UDP-sugar pyrophosphorylase

7-4 Methylene blue is an organic dye capable of existing in an oxidized (blue) and a reduced (colorless) state. Consequently, if the oxidized form of methylene blue were added to a solution containing a reducing sugar such as

(a)

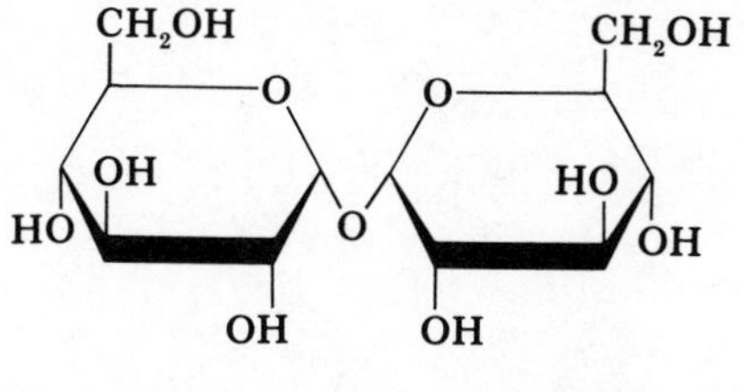

(b)

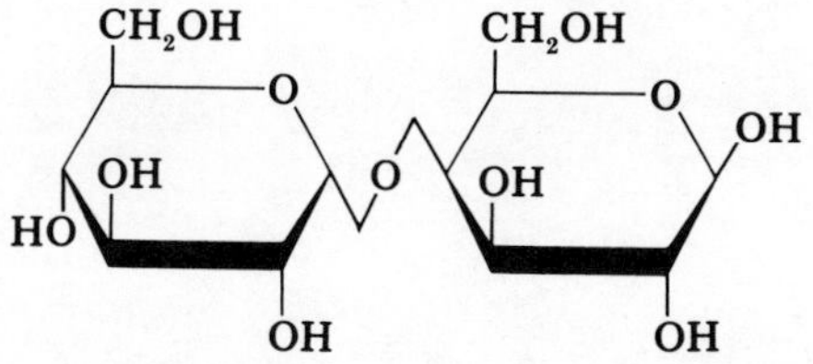

(c)

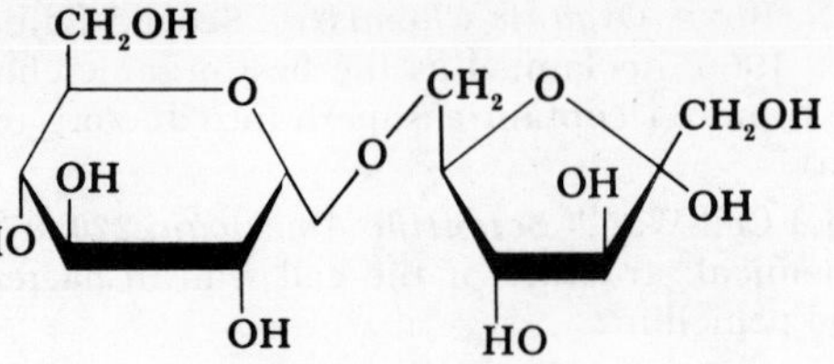

lactose, a blue to colorless transition would be observed. With this information, predict what would occur if the solution contained either of the disaccharides shown below. Explain your answer in each case.

7-5 How would you describe the similarities and differences between potato starch and liver glycogen?

7-6 The repeating disaccharide unit of chondroitin, a linear mucopolysaccharide found in many mammalian tissues, is composed of D-glucuronic acid and N-acetyl-galactosamine linked by a $\beta(1 \rightarrow 3)$ glycosidic bond. The repeating units are then known to be linked to each other by $\beta(1 \rightarrow 4)$ bonds. Draw the structure of the repeating unit in chondroitin.

7-7 Draw a complete structure corresponding to the linkage between the C-terminal residue of the pentaglycine bridge and the L-lysine residue of the tetrapeptide side chain in the peptidoglycan material of the bacterial cell wall.

8

Lipids

A lipid is any naturally occurring non-polar substance, or a product of same, that is nearly or totally insoluble in water but soluble in the so-called non-polar lipid solvents such as chloroform, carbon disulfide, ether, and hot ethanol. This somewhat vague and very generalized definition is not without cause, for the lipids—found in all organisms—represent a most heterogeneous group of materials in terms of both structure and function. Despite the lack of reference to specific structural features, the definition does focus on a particular physicochemical property related to lipid structure, namely, their *non-polar* nature. In most cases, this non-polarity is conferred upon lipid molecules by the presence of one or more *fatty acid* residues containing long aliphatic hydrocarbon chains. As we will discover, the biological function of many lipids of natural origin is predicated to a large extent on this structural characteristic of non-polarity.

During the past ten to fifteen years, a heightened interest—due largely to the development and refinement of biochemical methodologies such as thin-layer and gas–liquid chromatography (see pages 18–20, Chapter 2)—has given impetus to accelerated research in lipid biochemistry. In part, the yield of this effort can be measured by the discovery of many lipids of previously unknown occurrence. However, much effort has also been spent in attempting to unravel the details of how lipids function in living cells. In view of such studies, the major biological roles of lipids can now be listed with some confidence: (a) in association with proteins and carbohydrates, they serve as a basic *structural unit of cellular membranes* of all cells and of the membranes of cytologically distinct subcellular bodies such as mitochondria and chloroplasts; (b) as a component of membranes, they aid in the establishment and maintenance of an orderly arrangement or *compart- mentalization* of metabolically active proteins localized in the membrane; (c) on a metabolic level, they constitute one of the chief *storage* forms of chemical energy and of carbon; and (d) they serve as a primary *transport* system of nonpolar materials through biological fluids. This list should not be interpreted as complete. Other more specific functions, represented by the physiological properties of lipid *hormones* and lipid *vitamins,* will be encountered within the body of the chapter.

The design of this chapter will parallel a classification based on structure which segregates the lipids into three broad groups: (a) *simple lipids;* (b) *compound lipids;* and (c) *derived lipids.* The simple lipids include only those materials that are esters of fatty acids and the C_3 trihydroxyalcohol, glycerol, or long-chain monohydroxyalcohols. The compound lipids include a host of materials which contain other substances in addition to an alcohol and fatty acids. They are so named because their structures can be thought of—to varying degrees—as compound variations of the structural theme of a simple lipid. The derived lipids represent an outright hodge-podge group which includes any material that meets the operational definition given above, but is not classifiable in either of the previous groups. Steroids, carotenoids, and the water-insoluble vitamins are examples. The basis of this classification may seem just as nebulous as the above definition of a lipid, but it is a useful approach for a brief discussion. Furthermore, it focuses attention on a structural characteristic common to most lipids, namely, the presence of fatty acids.

SIMPLE LIPIDS

The simple lipids can be subdivided into two groups: (1) the *neutral acylglycerols* (glycerides), and (2) the *waxes.* We will consider each in that order and also analyze the important fatty acids as a chemical group in itself.

NEUTRAL ACYLGLYCEROLS

An acylglycerol is an *ester of a fatty acid* and the trihydroxyalcohol, *glycerol.* Depending on the number of esterified hydroxyl groups, we have monoacylglycerols, diacylglycerols, and triacylglycerols. The triacyl species is the most abundant in nature. In any case, a simple acylglycerol does not contain any ionic functional groups and hence, is said to be a *neutral lipid.* The structures of a mono-, a di-, and a triacyl-glycerol are shown on the next page; the R groups, which are usually different, designate the acyl side chains of the aliphatic fatty acids. In an older nomenclature scheme, the acylglycerols were less precisely called *glycerides.* The latter term is gradually fading from use. Depending on their physical state at room temperature, triacylglycerols are termed *neutral fats* (solids) or *neutral oils* (liquids). Their water insolubility is common knowledge.

In animals the triacylglycerols fulfill three basic functions. First, they constitute the so-called *fat depots* which are the primary storage

$$
\begin{array}{cccc}
\alpha \quad 1 \quad H_2C\text{—OH} & H_2C\text{—O—}\overset{\displaystyle O}{\overset{\|}{C}}R & H_2C\text{—O—}\overset{\displaystyle O}{\overset{\|}{C}}R & H_2C\text{—O—}\overset{\displaystyle O}{\overset{\|}{C}}R \\
\beta \quad 2 \quad HC\text{—OH} & HC\text{—OH} & HC\text{—O—}\overset{\displaystyle O}{\overset{\|}{C}}R' & HC\text{—O—}\overset{\displaystyle O}{\overset{\|}{C}}R' \\
\alpha' \quad 3 \quad H_2C\text{—OH} & H_2C\text{—OH} & H_2C\text{—OH} & H_2C\text{—O—}\overset{\displaystyle O}{\overset{\|}{C}}R'' \\
\text{glycerol} & \text{1-acylglycerol} & \text{1,2-diacylglycerol} & \text{triacylglycerol}
\end{array}
$$

a monoacylglycerol

*R groups may be different
or identical*

reservoirs of lipid material. In this context, the term "lipid" is synonymous with "fatty acids," and hence, to be more specific, the triacylglycerols are storage forms of the fatty acids. Since the complete oxidative degradation of the fatty acids to CO_2 produces a sizeable amount of useful energy, the fat depots are also termed energy reserves. In animal cells they are the major energy reserves. Although the fat depots are in dynamic equilibrium with all metabolic processes, their degradation is favored under normal conditions when the level of dietary carbohydrate is low. On the other hand, a high level of dietary carbohydrate coupled with a low rate of respiration favors their formation. Secondly, in the form of lipoprotein particles called *chylomicrons,* the triacylglycerols serve as the means whereby ingested *fatty acids are transported* via the lymphatic system and blood for distribution within the animal body. Thirdly, they provide *physical* and *thermal insulation* to the various body organs.

There is only one relevant reaction of the simple acylglycerols, namely, their hydrolysis to yield free glycerol and the fatty acids. Chemically, this is readily accomplished by treatment with dilute acid or dilute alkali. When alkali is used, the process is termed *saponification.* Biologically, the same effect is achieved via enzymes termed *lipases* (see page 390, Chapter 15). As you might anticipate in view of our previous discussion on enzymes, the enzymatic hydrolysis is characterized by some degree of specificity, with different lipases preferentially acting on different linkages.

$$
\begin{array}{c}
H_2\text{COC}\overset{\displaystyle O}{\overset{\|}{}}R_1 \\
|\\
H\text{COC}\overset{\displaystyle O}{\overset{\|}{}}R_2 \\
|\\
H_2\text{COC}\overset{\displaystyle O}{\overset{\|}{}}R_3
\end{array}
$$

$$
\xrightarrow[\text{or}\ \ H^+/H_2O]{OH^-/H_2O}
$$

$$
\begin{array}{ccc}
H_2\text{COH} & & R_1\text{COOH} \\
| & & + \\
H\text{COH} & + & R_2\text{COOH} \\
| & & + \\
H_2\text{COH} & & R_3\text{COOH}
\end{array}
$$

WAXES

A wax is an ester distinguished from all other esters by the nature of the constituent alcohol and acid—both contain *long* hydrocarbon chains. Generally speaking, all waxes are totally insoluble in water. Commercial applications of synthetic and naturally occurring waxes are widespread. In nature the waxes are generally metabolic end products, with the most important biological role being to serve as protective chemical coatings on the surfaces of animals and plants. Did you ever wonder why a duck, or your own skin, never really gets wetted? The surface feathers and skin are coated with a waxy covering that acts as a waterproofing agent.

general formula
of wax

$$R—\overset{\displaystyle O}{\overset{\|}{C}}—O—R'$$

(R and R' are long
hydrocarbon chains)

example:

$$CH_3(CH_2)_{14}\overset{\displaystyle O}{\overset{\|}{C}}—O—CH_2(CH_2)_{28}CH_3$$

myricyl palmitate

(primary component of beeswax)

The waxy coating on the leaves and fruits of plants prevents loss of moisture and probably also prevents infection.

FATTY ACIDS

Since all acylglycerols contain glycerol, it should be obvious that any and all variations in their physical and chemical properties will be exclusively dependent on the nature of the side chain acyl residues. Equally obvious is a similar but lesser contribution of the acyl moiety of the waxes. These conclusions lead us directly into a discussion of the fatty acids. Aside from being components of the neutral acylglycerols and the waxes, fatty acids are also present in most of the compound lipids. Furthermore, in Chapter 15 we will discover that a most important phase of lipid metabolism is largely based on the degradation and synthesis of the fatty acids themselves—the degradation providing both carbon skeletons and energy for many biosynthetic processes, and the synthesis serving as the means of storing energy for future utilization.

Other than a traditional reference to their isolation from fats, the term "fatty acid" has no precise meaning. Chemically speaking, the fatty acids constitute a rather extensive family of *aliphatic carboxylic acids*. However, based on extensive compositional data, we can simplify matters by providing generalizations concerning those acids that occur most frequently in nature: (a) most are monocarboxylic acids containing linear hydrocarbon chains with an even number of carbon atoms generally in the range of C_{12}—C_{18}; shorter and longer chain acids, branched and cyclic chain acids, and acids of odd-number carbon content do occur but at a much lower frequency; (b) unsaturation is common but largely confined to the C_{18} acids, with one, two, or three double bonds being most frequent; in the latter two cases, the double bonds are almost exclusively present as neighboring bonds separated by a single methylene group, that is, —CH=CH—CH$_2$—CH=CH— and —CH=CH—CH$_2$—CH=CH— CH$_2$—CH=CH—; (c) in the unsaturated acids, the double bonds are nearly always in the *cis* orientation. The names and structural formulae of those acids consistent with these generalizations are given in Table 8–1 (I and II). Some exceptions (III) are also listed as a useful frame of reference. Note that palmitic, stearic, oleic, linoleic, and linolenic acids are most abundant in nature.

Volumes have been written on the chemistry and biochemistry of fatty acids. In this introductory text, we will consider only three aspects —one is structural, the second is analytical, and the third is metabolic. Using stearic acid as an example, the structural principle becomes evident by recalling some basic descriptive chemistry. Suppose you are

Table 8–1   Naturally occurring fatty acids—a partial listing.

Fatty Acid (Carbon Content)	Number of Double Bonds	Formula	Extent of Occurrence
I. Even-numbered—straight-chain—fully saturated			
Lauric acid (C_{12})	0	$CH_3(CH_2)_{10}COOH$	small
Myristic acid (C_{14})	0	$CH_3(CH_2)_{12}COOH$	intermediate
Palmitic acid (C_{16})	0	$CH_3(CH_2)_{14}COOH$	abundant
Stearic acid (C_{18})	0	$CH_3(CH_2)_{16}COOH$	abundant
Arachidic acid (C_{20})	0	$CH_3(CH_2)_{18}COOH$	trace
II. Even-numbered—straight-chain—unsaturated			
Palmitoleic acid (C_{16})	1	$CH_3(CH_2)_5CH{=}CH(CH_2)_7COOH$	intermediate
Oleic acid (C_{18})	1	$CH_3(CH_2)_7CH{=}CH(CH_2)_7COOH$	abundant
Linoleic acid (C_{18})	2	$CH_3(CH_2)_4CH{=}CHCH_2CH{=}CH(CH_2)_7COOH$	abundant
Linolenic acid (C_{18})	3	$CH_3CH_2CH{=}CHCH_2CH{=}CHCH_2CH{=}CH(CH_2)_7COOH$	small
III. Miscellaneous Acids (very limited occurrence)			
Ricinoleic acid (C_{18}) (Hydroxy-containing)	1	$CH_3(CH_2)_5\underset{\underset{OH}{\mid}}{C}HCH_2CH{=}CH(CH_2)_7COOH$	castor oil and cerebrosides
Tuberculostearic acid (C_{19}) (Branched)	0	$CH_3(CH_2)_7\underset{\underset{CH_3}{\mid}}{C}H(CH_2)_8COOH$	tubercle bacillus
Lactobacillic acid (C_{19}) (Cyclic branch)	0	$CH_3(CH_2)_5CH{-}\!\!-\!\!{-}CH(CH_2)_9COOH$ with CH_2 bridge	*Lactobacillus* genus

given the structural formula of stearic acid and asked to predict its water solubility. How would you proceed? Well, you should remember that the dissolution of any solute in any solvent is based on the formation of mutual attractive forces between the two substances, which in turn is controlled by the structural similarity of the solute and solvent. To dust off some classical generalizations: like dissolves like; polar dissolves polar; non-polar dissolves non-polar. The exercise is now straightforward. You know that water is highly polar. All that is required is an evaluation of the polarity or non-polarity of stearic acid. This presents no problem. Study this structural formula of stearic acid for a moment.

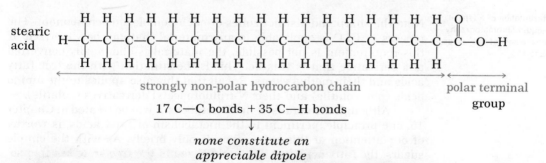

stearic acid

strongly non-polar hydrocarbon chain

17 C—C bonds + 35 C—H bonds

polar terminal group

↓

none constitute an appreciable dipole

Most conspicuous are the many C—C bonds (17) and C—H bonds (35). Because of the minimal difference in electronegativity between C and H, and because there is obviously none at all between C and C, we deduce that there is a total of 52 extremely non-polar linkages which completely

mixture of fatty acids

RCOOH
R′COOH
R″COOH

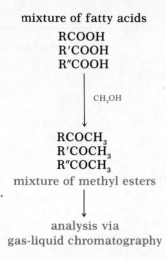

CH₃OH

RCOCH₃
R′COCH₃
R″COCH₃

mixture of methyl esters

analysis via
gas-liquid chromatography

overshadow the one polar COOH group. We conclude then that stearic acid is a very non-polar substance and thus very insoluble in water. It should be obvious that the same characteristic applies to other fatty acids and to any material containing one or more fatty acids in ester linkage. In addition to explaining water insolubility, this is a physico-chemical phenomenon most basic to a discussion of lipid function, particularly the ordered complexing of protein and lipids in cellular membranes (see page 203).

The analytical aspect is noteworthy, because it exemplifies the fantastic resolving power and sensitivity of gas–liquid chromatography (GLC), the principles of which were previously discussed in Chapter 2 (page 18). With GLC, fatty acid composition studies of simple or compound lipids are now rapid and routine. After hydrolysis, the reaction mixture is chemically treated to effect the conversion of the non-volatile, free fatty acids to volatile ester derivatives—generally methyl esters. The esters are then separated and a small sample is injected into the gas chromatograph. A typical GLC pattern is shown in Figure 8–1.

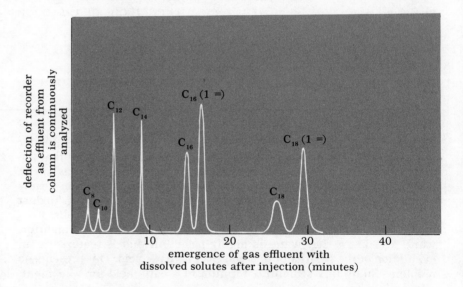

Figure 8–1 A representation of a typical separation by gas–liquid chromatography of a mixture of methyl esters of fatty acids. (See Figure 2–6, page 19.)

Note the sharp and distinct zones of each homologous component. The process of GLC is applicable to any material that can be vaporized. If this requirement is not possible, the material is chemically converted to a derivative that *is* volatile. This is the situation with the free fatty acids and their methyl esters. Recall that this also applies to the amino acids (non-volatile) and their N-trifluoroacetyl derivatives (volatile).

Although the details of lipid metabolism will be treated in Chapter 15, one principle, pertinent to the metabolism of fatty acids, is worthy of our attention at this point, even if only briefly. As with the simple sugars, the fatty acids are not metabolized in the free state but in a so-called *active form*. Whereas the simple sugars are processed as sugar phosphates, the fatty acids are metabolized as *acyl esters of Coenzyme A*. The complete structure of Coenzyme A can be found on page 250. As shown below, formation of the active species occurs in an ATP-dependent reaction catalyzed by a *thiokinase*. Note that the active group of Coenzyme A (symbolized as CoASH) is a *free sulfhydryl group,* and hence the ester of the fatty acid and Coenzyme A is more precisely called

a *thioester.* The acyl thioester linkage $\left(\begin{matrix} O \\ \parallel \\ -C-S- \end{matrix}\right)$—to be examined more

extensively in Chapter 10—is most important and will be encountered repeatedly. A clue to the relative energy content of acyl-Coenzyme A esters is provided in the following reaction.

$$
\underset{\substack{\text{fatty acid}}}{\overset{\displaystyle O}{\overset{\displaystyle \parallel}{\text{RCOH}}}} + \underset{\substack{\text{coenzyme A}}}{\text{HSCoA}} \xrightarrow[\text{ATP} \quad \text{AMP} + \text{PP}_i]{\text{thiokinase}} \underset{\substack{\text{acyl-SCoA} \\ \text{(thioester)}}}{\overset{\displaystyle O}{\overset{\displaystyle \parallel}{\text{R}-\text{C}-\text{SCoA}}}}
$$

Can you identify the clue and also contrast the energy states of the free fatty acid and the thioester?

PROSTAGLANDINS

In recent years considerable interest has been shown in a special group of lipid materials called the *prostaglandins.* Biologically synthesized from the unsaturated fatty acids, the prostaglandins occur in many body organs, with relatively high concentrations being found in the seminal plasma and genital glands. Their biological role appears to be hormonal in nature, with several different physiological phenomena as the targets of their control. For example, the prostaglandins are known to stimulate smooth muscle contraction and to lower blood pressure. Current interest is high because of studies that have shown purified prostaglandins to be physiologically active as labor-inducing agents in pregnant women, abortion-inducing agents, and birth control agents. Domestic marketing of pharmaceutical preparations is currently awaiting FDA approval. The structure of one of six known prostaglandins is shown below. Variations in the structure of the two side chains and/or the reduction of the keto group in the cyclopentanone ring define the other prostaglandins.

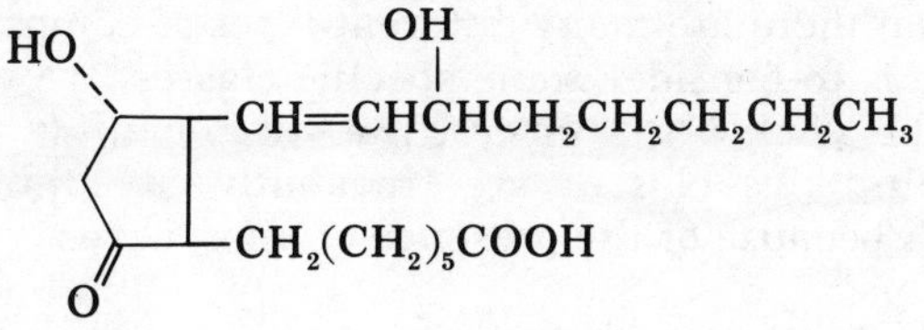

prostaglandin E_1

One very beneficial use of the prostaglandins may emerge from recent studies demonstrating that one of them, prostaglandin E_1, is very effective, when added in very small amounts, in improving the ability to prepare and store concentrated suspensions of human platelet cells from plasma and from whole blood. Platelets are small cells in the blood, performing various functions, including playing a role in the clotting of blood. Clinical studies have shown that platelet suspensions are very effective in treating hemorrhage due to thrombocytopenia, a condition characterized by a deficiency of platelets. Platelet concentrates have also been studied for use as supplements in various programs of chemotherapy and immunosuppressive therapy to minimize rejection of transplanted tissue. Consequently the demand for platelet concentrates is growing steadily, but they are in increasingly short supply. One serious difficulty arises from the loss in viability of platelets at the low temperatures used in chilling blood immediately upon its collection. The addition of prostaglandin E_1 to freshly drawn blood not only greatly reduces this loss in viability upon chilling, it also yields a bonus effect—the harvested platelets show a better ability to survive in storage.

It also appears that the prostaglandins are intimately associated with the therapeutic properties of aspirin. Aspirin, long considered a safe drug, has long been used as an effective analgesic for the relief of minor pain as well as for the treatment of inflammation and fever. Ironically, however, the biochemical bases of these effects were largely unknown until recent studies conducted by J. R. Vane and coworkers in London. These investigators have reported evidence suggesting that the effect of aspirin may be linked to its ability to cause the inhibition of the biosynthesis of the prostaglandins by various organs. Although the biochemical basis of this inhibition and of the precise role played by the prostaglandins in normal processes such as the regulation of body temperature is not yet understood, this breakthrough has opened the door to understanding so that future research into the mode of action of aspirin and related drugs can now proceed with some direction.

COMPOUND LIPIDS

The complete hydrolysis of a compound lipid yields one or two fatty acids, a substance with one or more functional hydroxyl groups, and one or more additional materials. Other than highlighting the general composition of a compound lipid, this definition is not very informative. What are these hydroxy-containing substances? What are these additional materials? The difficulty in giving a more precise definition is due to the fact that there are many different types of compound lipids. Our only recourse is to consider some specific classes. We will confine our analysis to the *phosphoglycerides*, the *sphingolipids*, and the *glycolipids*. The first two classes are frequently called *phosphatides* or *phospholipids* because of the presence of phosphorus.

PHOSPHOGLYCERIDES

Phosphoglycerides are the major compound lipids of natural origin and occur most abundantly in membranes—all types of membranes in all types of cells. Their presence is easily demonstrated by treatment of cells with a chloroform-methanol solvent. Because of their appreciable non-polar character, the phosphoglycerides are easily extracted from the cells with this non-polar solvent. The chloroform-methanol extract (that is, the phosphoglyceride fraction) can then be easily analyzed by thin-layer chromatography (TLC: see Chapter 2, page 19). The extract is nearly always a mixture of several different phosphoglycerides. Depending on the type of cell and its physiological state, the number of components and their relative concentrations are quite variable. Despite this diversity, there are what can be called major and minor components. The former include *phosphatidyl choline, phosphatidyl ethanolamine,* and *phosphatidyl glycerol.* The latter include *phosphatidyl serine, cardiolipin (diphosphatidyl glycerol), phosphatidyl inositol,* and the parent compound of all phosphoacylglycerols, *phosphatidic acid.* In view of the last statement, our analysis of structure most logically begins with phosphatidic acid.

Phosphatidic acid consists of a diacylglycerol moiety with a terminal phosphoric acid residue in ester linkage. Structurally speaking, it is the simplest phosphoglyceride. The free acid occurs in nature only in small quantities, with the bulk found in ester linkage as the phosphatidyl component of other phosphoglycerides. In other words, the remaining phosphoglycerides are esters of phosphatidic acid. As indicated above and illustrated below, the different phosphoglycerides are distinguished from one another by the nature of the grouping esterified to phosphatidic acid. The fatty acid composition of the various phosphoglycerides follows no clear pattern. In fact, variations in fatty acid composition occur for each species of phosphoglyceride. Thus, ten molecules of phosphatidyl choline obtained from ten different sources most generally will have ten different sets of fatty acids esterified with the glycerol moiety. The same even applies to phosphatidyl choline molecules obtained from the same source. In other words, phosphatidyl choline is phosphatidyl choline not because of its fatty acid composition but because of the presence of choline.

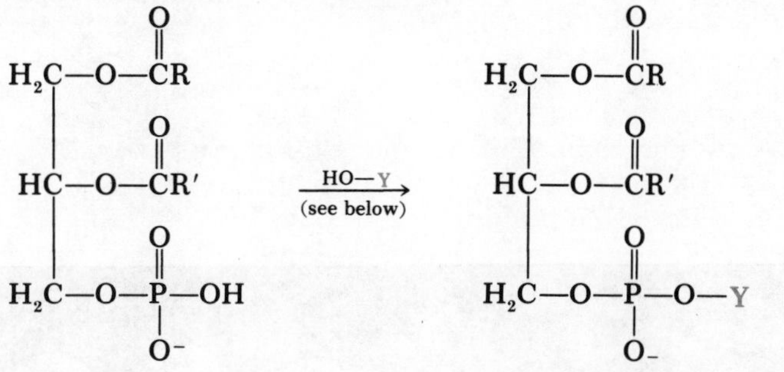

phosphatidic acid   phosphatidyl *derivative*

HO—Y

ethanolamine: HO— $CH_2CH_2\overset{+}{N}H_3$

glycerol: HO— CH_2CHCH_2OH
                        |
                        OH

choline: HO— $CH_2CH_2\overset{+}{N}(CH_3)_3$

serine: HO— CH_2CHCOO^-
                    |
                    $\underset{+}{N}H_3$

phosphatidyl glycerol: HO— $CH_2CHCH_2OPOCH_2CHCH_2$

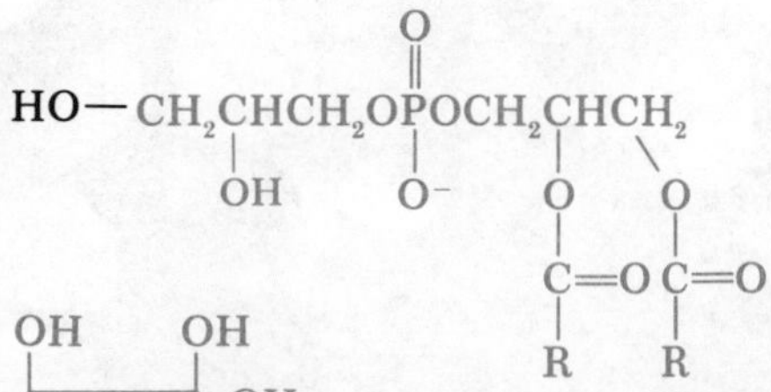

inositol:

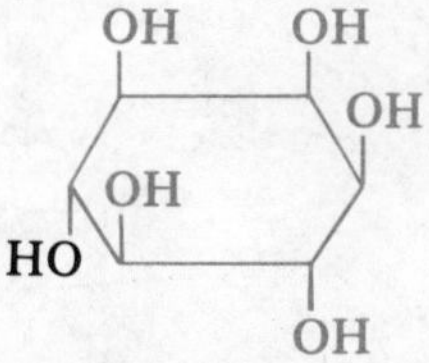

In discussing the phosphoglycerides, our purpose will not be to survey their known participation in many processes, but rather to explore on a preliminary basis their involvement with only one, namely, their role as structural components in membranes. The key principle in understanding this function is physicochemical in character and related to the structure of the lipids themselves. In this context, we put aside the distinguishing structural features specified above and alternatively focus attention on gross structural similarities. In so doing, we note—as represented below by phosphatidyl choline—that the phosphoglycerides are by their nature *amphipathic* (Greek amphi—of both sides; pathos—feeling) molecules containing distinct regions which have been termed the *hydrophobic, non-polar "tail"* and the *hydrophilic, polar "head."* The tail region includes the fatty acid hydrocarbon chain, whereas the head region includes the negatively charged (at physiological pH) phosphate group with its ester component. At a minimum, the polarity of the head region is limited to the anionic phosphate group.

$$CH_2OCCH_2CH_2CH_2CH_2CH_2CH_2CH_2CH_2CH_2CH_2CH_2CH_2CH_2CH_2CH_2CH_3$$

$$CHOCCH_2CH_2CH_2CH_2CH_2CH_2CH_2CH=CHCH_2CH_2CH_2CH_2CH_2CH_2CH_2CH_3$$

non-polar "tail"

$$(CH_3)_3\overset{+}{N}CH_2CH_2OPOCH_2$$

polar "head"

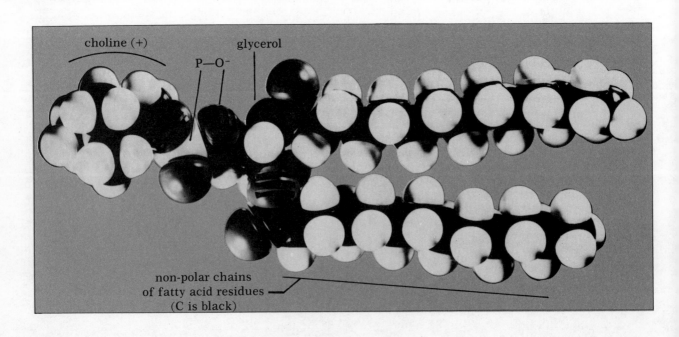

choline (+)   glycerol

P—O⁻

non-polar chains
of fatty acid residues
(C is black)

However, if the alcohol moiety is also charged at physiological pH, as is the case with the quaternary amino grouping of choline (see above), the polarity of the head portion is correspondingly greater. The same would also apply to phosphatidyl ethanolamine and phosphatidyl serine. As amphipathic molecules, the phosphoglycerides have the capacity to act as surface-active agents by orienting themselves between a polar aqueous phase and a non-polar lipid phase. As a result, the complete system is neither distinctly polar nor distinctly non-polar, but a blend of the two.

BIOLOGICAL (CELLULAR) MEMBRANES

The latter principle is extremely relevant to biological membranes, which are basically conglomerates of globular proteins and lipids, primarily phosphoglycerides. Although there is appreciable evidence to indicate that the protein and lipid portions exist as lipoprotein complexes, the exact arrangement has yet to be determined with certainty. In fact, the nature of membrane ultrastructure is presently a topic of considerable debate. The most popular model proposes a *unit bilayer structure* composed of two phospholipid-protein monolayers wherein the lipid and protein are complexed to each other via polar-polar interactions between the hydrophilic head of the phosphoglyceride and the polar amino acid residues at or near the surface of the globular protein.

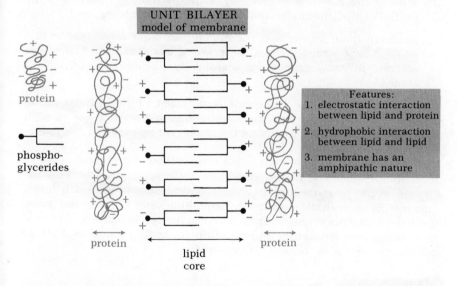

UNIT BILAYER
model of membrane

protein

phospho-
glycerides

Features:
1. electrostatic interaction between lipid and protein
2. hydrophobic interaction between lipid and lipid
3. membrane has an amphipathic nature

protein   protein

lipid
core

In turn, each lipoprotein monolayer is proposed to interact with the next via a non-polar–non-polar interaction between the hydrophobic hydrocarbon tails of adjacent monolayers. Thus, the complete membrane is envisioned as having a highly ordered ultrastructure consisting of a phospholipid core sandwiched between two protein layers. One protein layer would be exterior to the cell whereas the other would be interior to the cell. The complete arrangement has been termed the *unit membrane.* Since drawings of the unit bilayer membrane structure may imply otherwise, we should point out that there is extensive evidence that different proteins with different functions are present in the inner and outer layers of the intact membrane. In other words, the biochemistry of the inner and outer layers is different.

The unit membrane hypothesis has proven consistent with many experimental studies including the electron microscopy of red blood cell membranes, which has revealed the presence of a continuous, nearly transparent, inner zone distinctly bounded on both sides by more opaque regions (see Figure 8–2). Although the unit membrane model is in agreement with this and other observations, it is not universally accepted as representative of membrane ultrastructure, and other models have been proposed. It is not important for us to debate the alternative suggestions, nor to proceed at any great length in analyzing all the data supporting the unit membrane model. What is important is that we recognize that

(a) biological membranes are composed of a lipoprotein complex;

(b) the membrane as a unit will have an amphipathic character, thus allowing for passage of both polar and non-polar materials;

(c) the membrane is indeed a barrier, but less rigid than the cell wall due to the lack of a repetitive sequence of covalent bridges;

(d) there may be various ultrastructural arrangements between lipid and protein;

(e) some of these arrangements may be highly ordered, resulting in the spatial compartmentalization of lipoprotein complexes; and

(f) although many of the lipoprotein complexes are associated with a passive structural function, there are others that participate more actively in membrane transport and as membrane-localized enzymes.

A vivid example of the last point is provided by the mitochondrial membrane, which is an extremely active metabolic unit involved with many cellular activities, including the important process of ATP production from ADP (Chapter 13).

Although the phosphoglyceride composition of membranes varies from source to source, phosphatidyl ethanolamine and/or phosphatidyl choline occur most frequently as the major components with lesser amounts of phosphatidyl glycerol, cardiolipin, and other minor phosphoglycerides. Other neutral lipids, such as the cerebrosides and cholesterol, occur less frequently and generally in smaller amounts. Certain cell membranes also contain sphingolipids.

SPHINGOLIPIDS

The complete hydrolysis of a sphingolipid yields one fatty acid, choline, phosphoric acid, and a *sphingosine*. No glycerol is present. The sphingosines are a family of long-chain, unsaturated *amino alcohols* varying in terms of carbon length. A common representative is shown below. The most abundant sphingolipid is sphingomyelin, found in considerable quantities in the cellular membranes of nerve and brain tissue. Although the exact mechanism of action is yet to be resolved, sphingomyelin is

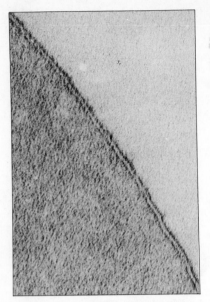

Figure 8–2 An electron micrograph of a portion of the cytoplasmic membrane of a red blood cell showing the unit bilayer ultrastructure. The dense granular area at the right represents the inside of the cell; the light gray area at the right represents the outside of the cell. The two electron-dense lines represent the inner and outer protein layers of the membrane sandwiching the less electron-dense phospholipid region. Magnification: 240,000 ×. (Photograph generously supplied by J. David Robertson.)

known to participate as an insulator for nerve fibers, preventing short circuits in the transmission of impulses by the nerves.

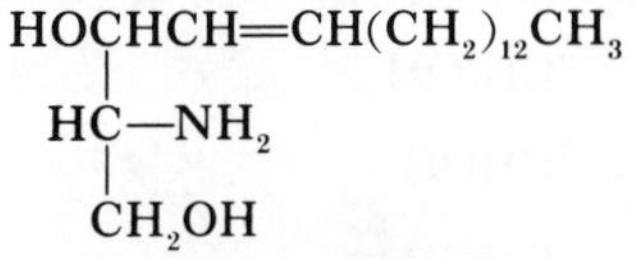

$$HOCHCH{=}CH(CH_2)_{12}CH_3$$

sphingosine

$$HOCHCH{=}CH(CH_2)_{12}CH_3$$

acyl group of fatty acid

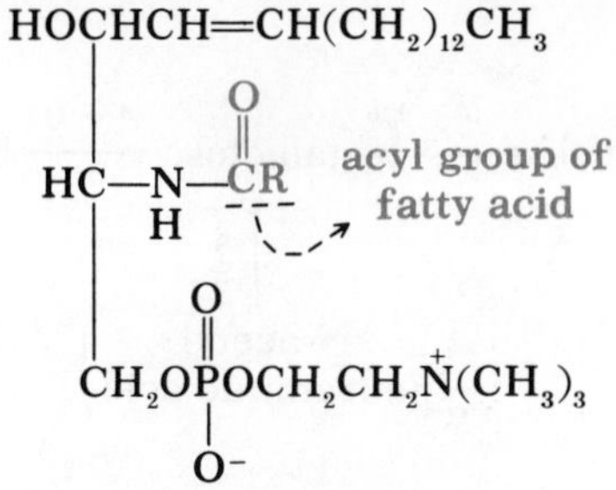

sphingomyelin
a sphingolipid

GLYCOLIPIDS

Glycolipids consist of carbohydrate and lipid moieties in covalent linkage. There are two important classes, namely, the *cerebrosides* and the *gangliosides*. Both are non-phosphorus containing and are considered neutral lipids owing to the absence of charged groups. They are somewhat polar, however, due to the presence of the carbohydrate residue.

The complete hydrolysis of a cerebroside yields one or two fatty acids, a sphingosine, and a simple sugar, generally glucose or galactose. Due to the presence of the sphingosine moiety, a more precise general term would be glycosphingolipid. Like sphingomyelin, the cerebrosides are most abundant in brain and nervous tissue, but have also been detected in membranous fractions from other sources such as liver, kidney, erythrocytes, and chloroplasts of plants.

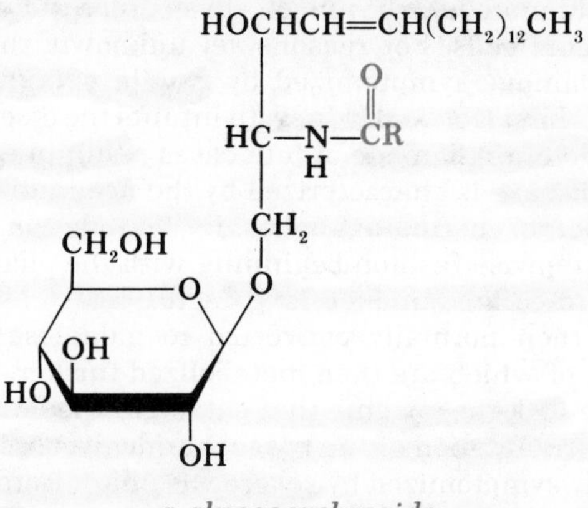

$$HOCHCH{=}CH(CH_2)_{12}CH_3$$

a glucocerebroside

The gangliosides—also widely distributed—are derivatives of cerebrosides containing a more complex carbohydrate moiety that includes acetylated derivatives of amino hexoses and *neuraminic acid*. The latter is a modified C_9 ketose which is sometimes called *sialic acid*.

$$\text{HOCHCH}=\text{CH(CH}_2)_{12}\text{CH}_3$$

a ganglioside

$(6 \leftarrow 1)\beta$ $(4 \leftarrow 1)\beta$ $(3 \leftarrow 1)\beta$

$\text{CH}_2\text{O} \xleftarrow{\beta1} \text{glucose} \longleftarrow \text{galactose} \longleftarrow \text{N-acetylgalactosamine} \longleftarrow \text{galactose}$

N-acetyl neuraminic acid

$^9\text{CH}_2\text{OH}$
$^8\text{CHOH}$
$^7\text{CHOH}$

Although the glycolipids occur ubiquitously, their exact biological role(s) is as yet unknown. It is known, however, that their synthesis and breakdown in higher animals are required for normal life processes, and that defects in their metabolism can result in serious physiological diseases. Four such well-documented conditions in man are: *Gaucher's* disease, *Fabry's* disease, *Tay-Sachs* disease, and *Niemann-Pick* disease. In each instance, the problem is due to abnormal degradation of glyco-lipids because of defective genes that fail to direct the synthesis of specific required enzymes. Because they are genetic (and thus trans-ferable) diseases manifested by abnormal metabolism, conditions of this sort are frequently termed *"inborn errors of metabolism."*

In Gaucher's disease, the deficient enzyme is the one required to cleave the glucose moiety from a glucocerebroside. The blockage results in abnormally high cellular levels of glucocerebrosides, particularly in reticuloendothelial cells. For reasons yet unknown, this causes severe physiological damage symptomized by fragile bone structure and an enlargement of the spleen and kidney. In infants the disease is associated with irreversible brain damage. Acute cases result in early death.

Fabry's disease is characterized by the accumulation of an inter-mediate product of normal ganglioside degradation. Normally, this proceeds in a stepwise fashion beginning with the oligosaccharide por-tion. One intermediate product is galactosyl-galactosyl-glucosylcera-mide; this is then normally converted to galactose and galactosyl-ceramide, both of which are then metabolized further. Individuals with Fabry's disease lack the enzyme that catalyzes the latter reaction. This results in an accumulation of the trisaccharideglycolipid, an occurrence that is clinically symptomized by severe vascular disorders and cataract formation. Life expectancy is 30–40. The defect in Tay-Sachs disease is also associated with abnormal degradation of gangliosides. Infants suffer progressive mental retardation, blindness, and eventually death at an early age (3–4). The Niemann-Pick condition is related to abnormal degradation of sphingomyelin. The accumulation of sphingomyelin in the nerve cells has a destructive effect on them. The physiological symptoms—again manifested early in life—are acute mental and physical retardation. An early death (at 3–4) is likewise probable.

Unfortunately, these four conditions are not the only examples of inborn errors of metabolism. Recall that galactosemia, a disease associated with abnormal galactose metabolism, was mentioned in the last chapter. A few diseases related to abnormalities in the metabolism of amino acids are discussed in Chapter 16. Several other examples are listed in Appendix 3. In each case, research continues in an attempt to establish the precise biochemical basis for the disease, the cause–effect relationship, and possible treatment.

LIPOPROTEINS

Although we have emphasized that complexes of lipids and proteins (lipoproteins) are the primary structural components of membranes, such materials are also involved in other physiological and metabolic processes. For example, the active forms of many enzymes are lipoprotein complexes, as are many of the plasma proteins. In addition, the molecular events of vision involve an active complex of Vitamin A and protein (see page 209).

DERIVED LIPIDS

As stated previously, in terms of both structure and function, the derived lipids represent a truly heterogeneous group similar only in their water insolubility. In the following pages, we will briefly consider a few important representatives, namely, the *steroids,* the *carotenoids*, and related *lipid vitamins*.

STEROIDS

Steroids are found in all organisms, where they are associated with various functions. In man, for example, they function as sex hormones, as emulsifying agents in lipid digestion, and in the transport of lipids across membranes and through plasma fluids.

All steroids have a similar basic structure—unlike anything we have yet encountered—consisting of a *fused hydrocarbon ring system.* Due to its structural relationship to the aromatic hydrocarbon, *phenanthrene,* the basic ring structure is called *perhydrocyclopentanophenanthrene* (perhydro- meaning completely hydrogenated). The diversity

phenanthrene   cyclopentane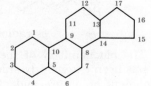

perhydrocyclopentanophenanthrene

of steroid structure is due to numerous structural variations of the per-hydrocyclopentanophenanthrene nucleus, which include varying levels of unsaturation, the presence of ring substituents, and various chemical modifications of the cyclopentano moiety in particular.

The presence of a C_8—C_{10} hydrocarbon side chain at position 17, and of a hydroxyl group at position 3, characterize a large number of steroids called the *sterols*. The most important member of this family—indeed, the most abundant sterol in the animal kingdom—is *cholesterol*. Note the distinct presence of one double bond between C_5 and C_6. Cholesterol is a structural component of cell membranes and is the primary metabolic precursor of other important steroids including the bile acids and the sex hormones. The complete biosynthetic pathway of cholesterol has been determined, as have many of the steps involved with its conversion to other steroids (see Chapter 15).

cholesterol

Three steroids of particular interest are the male sex hormone, *testosterone*, and the female sex hormones, *estradiol* and *progesterone*. Testosterone regulates the development of nearly all sex characteristics in the male, the maturation of the sperm, and the activity of the genital organs. Estradiol and progesterone—both products of the ovary glands—are largely responsible for regulation of the menstrual cycle. Progesterone is produced only during a certain period of the cycle, most notably *after the release of the ovum from the ruptured follicles,* at which time it begins to regulate the preparation of the uterine mucosa for the deposition of the fertilized ovum. If fertilization occurs, the production of progesterone continues through pregnancy. If the egg is not fertilized, the level of progesterone drops and production does not resume until the next cycle.

testosterone   estradiol   progesterone

The biochemistry of the hormonal regulation of the menstrual cycle has been extensively studied, with a primary objective being the development of a safe and effective method of fertility control. The pioneering studies were performed in the late 1930s, and the first significant discovery was that daily injections of the natural progesterone inhibited ovulation. In the past 30–35 years, hundreds of steroid preparations—mostly synthetic in nature—have been tested for inhibitory and/or regulatory properties for both ovulation and menstruation. Several of these materials are now available in oral "pill" form. Although these steroids have been declared safe by manufacturers and the Food and Drug Administration, our knowledge of possible undesirable effects on both a short- and a long-term basis is not precise or complete. Accordingly, even when conditions warrant their use, they should be employed only under advisement and with caution.

CAROTENOIDS

The carotenoids—consisting of two main groups: the *carotenes* and the *xanthophylls*—are water-insoluble pigments widely distributed in nature but most abundant in plants and algae. The carotenes are pure hydrocarbons, whereas the xanthophylls are oxygen-containing derivatives. The former are more abundant and only these are considered here.

The most common carotenoid is the carotene, *β-carotene*. As shown below, β-carotene is a C_{40} hydrocarbon consisting of a highly branched, unsaturated chain containing identical substituted ring structures at each end. Virtually all other carotenoids can be considered as variants of this structure. Although the carotenoids have been linked as participants in the photochemical phase of photosynthesis, the exact mechanism of their participation is yet to be resolved. The same is true of other plant and microbial processes known to involve carotenoids. More precisely documented is the enzyme-catalyzed oxidative cleavage of β-carotene to Vitamin A, which occurs with a stoichiometry of $1 \rightarrow 2$. That is, one molecule of β-carotene yields two molecules of Vitamin A. In animals this conversion represents a chief natural source of Vitamin A.

β-carotene

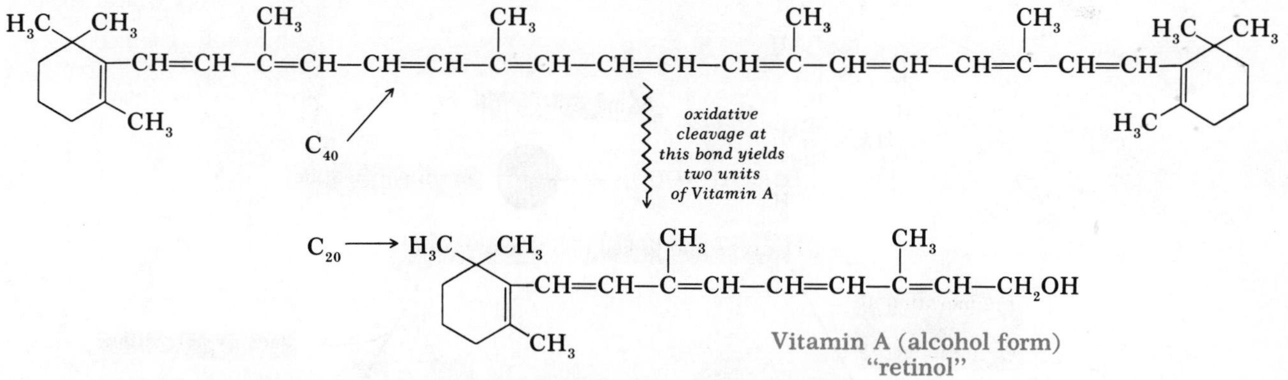

C_{40}

oxidative cleavage at this bond yields two units of Vitamin A

$C_{20} \longrightarrow$

Vitamin A (alcohol form) "retinol"

The only place where the physiological function of Vitamin A is understood on a molecular level is in the retina of the eye, where the reduced, alcohol form of Vitamin A (*retinol*) is enzymatically converted to the oxidized, aldehyde form (*retinal*), which then becomes complexed with different retinal proteins, called *opsins,* to constitute the active pigments that function in vision. The visual pigments are the primary photoreceptors of incident light in the visual cells, resulting in a transmission of information to the nervous system by a process not yet clearly understood. Most vertebrates contain two types of visual cells in the retina: (1) *rod cells*, which are dim-light receptors and do not perceive color, and (2) *cone cells,* which are bright-light receptors also responsible for color vision. In the rod cells, there appears to be only one opsin, and the active lipid-protein receptor complex is called *rhodopsin.*

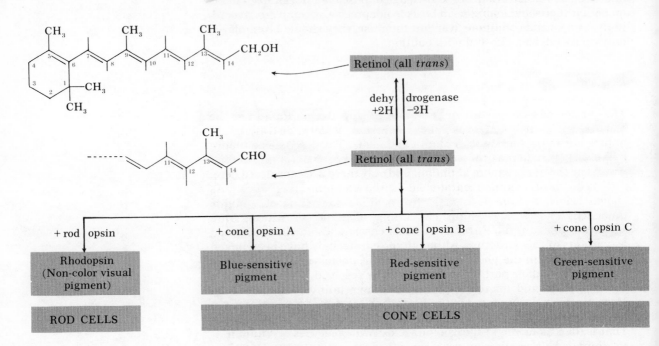

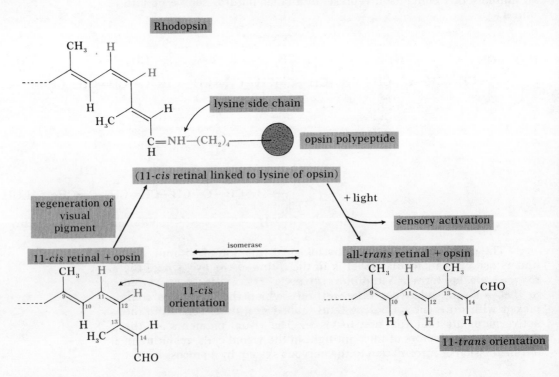

In cone cells, at least three different opsins are known to occur; these are complexed to retinal to constitute a blue-sensitive pigment, a red-sensitive pigment, and a green-sensitive pigment. In the case of rhodopsin, it has been established that the retinal is covalently attached to the protein via the side chain amino group of a lysine residue.

In order to understand the molecular events of the light-sensitive process, it is first necessary for us to investigate the structure of retinal, with particular emphasis on the geometric orientation of each double bond in the side chain. Note that there are four such bonds and that each has the potential to exist in a *cis* or *trans* orientation. In view of this potential for several isomeric forms, it is interesting to note that the most stable, and indeed the most prevalent, species in the retina is the all-*trans*. At one time it was thought that this was the only form of retinal associated with the visual cells. Subsequent studies proved this conclusion erroneous, and a second isomeric form was discovered, namely, 11-*cis* retinal. In fact, the latter isomeric form is the one that is complexed to the opsin protein.

The key to the chemistry of vision was the observation that 11-*cis* retinal, when exposed to light, was converted to the all-*trans* isomer. In accordance with these findings, the molecular events of vision are proposed to consist of a cycle of *cis-trans* isomerization, as shown below for the rod pigment. The distinguishing photochemical act is the cleavage of the lipoprotein pigment accompanied by the isomerization of retinal. The conversion is not direct, but involves many intermediates. There is reasonable evidence suggesting that one or more of these intermediate steps may be subsequently involved in generating extremely small electrical potentials that activate the nervous system. The vision cycle, in terms of the fate of the visual pigment, is completed by the regeneration of 11-*cis* retinal, which is required for the reformation of the active rhodopsin pigment. One possible route is a direct enzymatic conversion catalyzed by an isomerase.

As a fitting conclusion to the structural and functional heterogeneity exemplified in this chapter, the formulae of other lipid vitamins (E, K, and D) are shown below along with an indication of their primary physiological roles.

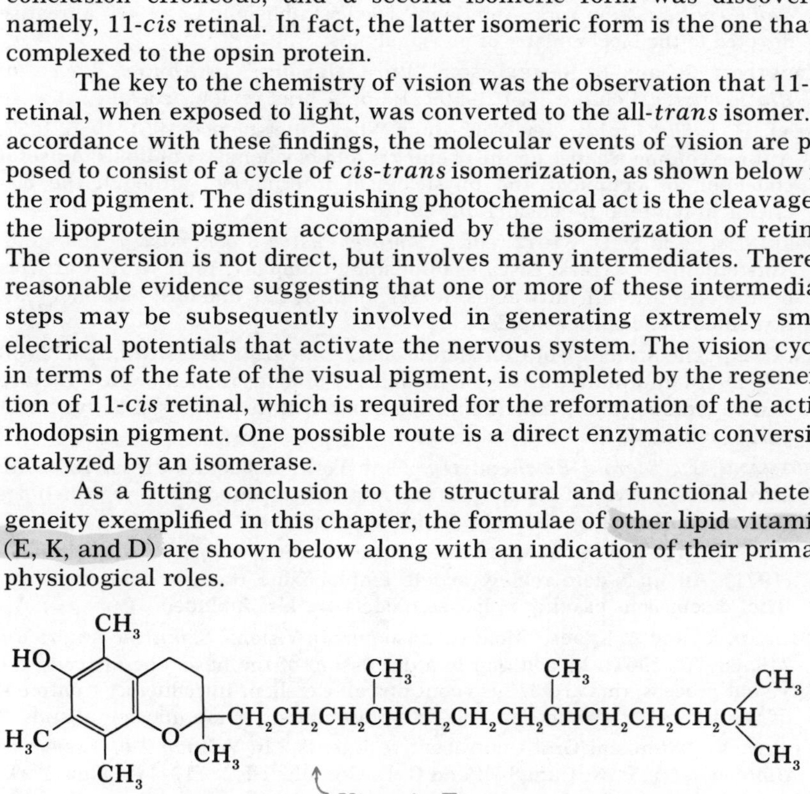

Vitamin E
(nutritional deficiency in mammals causes sterility)

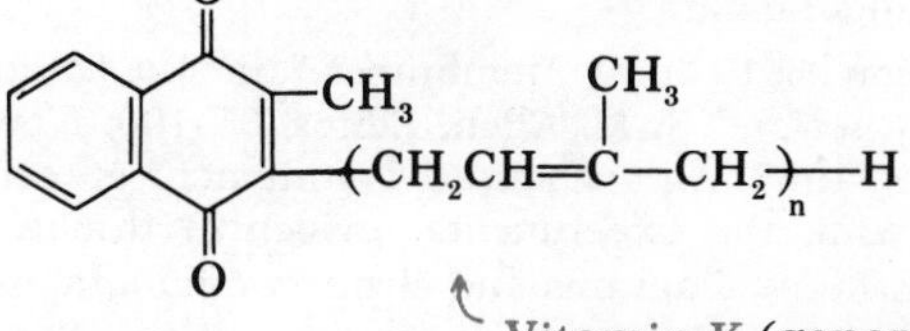

n is variable but usually < 10

Vitamin K (general structure)
(required for blood clotting)

Vitamin D
← (required for normal growth and developme
of bones and teeth)

LITERATURE

ANSELL, G. B., and J. W. HAWTHORNE, *Phospholipids: Chemistry, Metabolism, and Function.* New York: American Elsevier Publishing Co., 1964. A treatise devoted to the biochemistry of phospholipids.

BERGSTROM, S., and B. SAMUELSSON, "Prostaglandins," in *Annual Review of Biochemistry,* Volume 34, 101–109 (1965). A brief review article.

DEUEL, H. J., *The Lipids.* New York: John Wiley. Interscience, 1951, 1955, 1957. A three-volume treatise on the chemistry and biochemistry of lipids. A useful collection of chemical and physiological information, although the biochemical material is considerably dated.

FLORKIN, M., and E. H. STOTZ (eds.), *Comprehensive Biochemistry,* Volume 6. Amsterdam–New York: Elsevier Publishing Company, 1965. Review articles on the chemistry of fatty acids, waxes, neutral fats and oils, phospholipids, glycolipids, and sphingolipids.

FOX, C. F., "The Structure of Cell Membranes," *Scientific American,* 226, 30–38 (1972). An informative article on the roles of proteins in membrane structure and membrane function including a discussion of the process of active transport of materials across membranes.

HEFTMANN, E., *Steroid Biochemistry.* New York: Academic Press, 1970. An introductory survey of the steroids and related compounds. Coverage includes structure, metabolism, and physiological properties.

HENDLER, R. W., "Biological Membrane Ultrastructure," *Physiol. Rev.,* 51, 66–97 (1971). An up-to-date review article emphasizing the unit bilayer theory. Brief discussions of other proposed models are also included.

HUBBARD, R., and A. KROPF, "Molecular Isomers in Vision," *Scientific American,* 216, 64–76 (1967). In addition to a discussion of the basic chemistry of the visual process, this article also contains an excellent introductory treatment of the subject of geometrical (*cis-trans*) isomerism in organic compounds.

PETROW, V., "Steroidal Oral Contraceptive Agents," in Volume 2 of *Essays in Biochemistry,* P. N. Campbell and G. D. Greville (eds.), 117–146. New York: Academic Press, 1966. A review article surveying the structures and mechanism of action of natural and synthetic contraceptive steroids.

RAMWELL, D. W., and J. E. SHAW, "Biological Significance of the Prostaglandins," in Volume 26 of *Recent Progress in Hormone Research,* E. B. Astwood (ed.). New York: Academic Press, 1970. A recent and informative review article containing discussions of experimental data.

ROBERTSON, J. D., "The Organization of Cellular Membranes," in *Molecular Organization and Biological Function,"* J. M. Allen, Editor, 65–106. New York: Harper & Row, Publishers, 1967. An authoritative statement on cell membrane ultrastructure reviewing the experimental evidence (through 1965) for the unit bilayer theory. Many diagrams and electron micrographs are included.

Rothfield, L., and A. K. Finklestein, "Membrane Biochemistry," in *Annual Review of Biochemistry,* Volume 38, 463–496 (1968). A review article discussing the isolation, composition, structure, and function of biological membranes and studies with artificial membranes.

Vane, J. R., "Inhibition of Prostaglandin Synthesis as a Mechanism of Action for Aspirin-like Drugs," *Nature New Biology,* **231,** 232–235 (1971). Experimental evidence relating the therapeutic effects of aspirin and related drugs to the production of prostaglandins in the lung. Two succeeding articles report on similar effects with spleen cells and with human blood platelets.

Wacker, W. E. C., and T. L. Coombs, "Clinical Biochemistry," in *Annual Review of Biochemistry,* Volume 38, 539–568 (1969). A review article containing descriptions of over fifty genetic diseases with known enzymatic defects and the basis for the clinical detection of each.

Wald, G., "Molecular Basis of Visual Excitation," *Science,* **162,** 230–239 (1968). The address delivered by the author on receiving the Nobel Prize in 1967 for his work in the field.

EXERCISES

8-1 The melting points of a few fatty acids are listed below. On the basis of these data, explain the distinguishing characteristic between neutral fats and oils.

Acid	Melting Point (°C)
linoleic acid	−10.0°
linolenic acid	−5.0°
myristic acid	53.9
oleic acid	13.4
palmitic acid	63.1
stearic acid	69.6

8-2 What prediction can be made regarding the value of the melting point temperature for (a) palmitoleic acid, (b) lauric acid, and (c) arachidic acid. The data in the preceding problem provide the answer.

8-3 If a mixture consisting of a triglyceride and phosphatidyl choline were analyzed by thin-layer chromatography on silica gel in a chloroform-methanol-water developing solvent, one would observe complete separation, with the R_f of the triglyceride being approximately 1 and that of phosphatodyl choline approximately 0.4. Explain why the R_f values of these two lipids differ so widely. (Reference to Table 3–2 may be helpful; page 54).

8-4 Draw an idealized diagrammatic representation of the monolayer structure of a cell membrane according to the unit-membrane hypothesis. Identify and describe the physicochemical nature of the outer and inner surfaces and of the principal bonding regions existing within the monolayer.

8-5 Draw the structure of the intact lipid that would correspond to each of the following mixtures of products obtained from the complete hydrolysis of the lipid.
a) glycerol, palmitic acid, stearic acid, inorganic phosphate
b) glycerol, palmitoleic acid, oleic acid, ethanolamine, inorganic phosphate
c) sphingosine, palmitic acid, inorganic phosphate
d) sphingosine, glucose, oleic acid

8-6 Which would have a greater amphipathic character—a glucocerebroside or a sphingomyelin? Explain.

8-7 One alternate suggestion for the ultrastructure of bilayer biological membranes, different from that described in this chapter, proposes that each monolayer consists of phospholipid and protein interacting with each other by hydrophobic bonding. It is further proposed that the internal core of the intact membrane is composed primarily of protein contributed by each monolayer rather than being composed of lipid material. In this case, the lipid molecules are suggested to be oriented in each monolayer such that the polar heads are projected toward the surfaces of the membrane. The diagram below summarizes this description. How can you account for the possible existence of non-polar–non-polar (hydrophobic) interactions between phospholipid and protein in each monolayer?

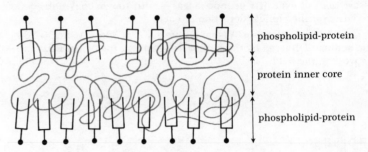

phospholipid-protein

protein inner core

phospholipid-protein

8-8 Draw the complete structure of the carbohydrate moiety of the ganglioside shown on page 206.

9

Organization of the Living Cell

In view of the attention given in preceding chapters to the chemistry of the major classes of biologically occurring compounds, let us not forget that the central subject of biochemistry is the living cell—the fundamental but complex unit of all living organisms. Common experience teaches that the living cell exists in many different models and displays many different functions. Indeed, most cells are quite specialized, displaying specific structural characteristics and performing specific physiological functions. For example, in the advanced multicellular organisms of the animal and plant kingdoms, we can identify liver cells, kidney cells, heart cells, muscle cells, retinal cells, nerve cells, brain cells, red blood cells, white blood cells, leaf cells, stem cells, root cells, and many, many more. The microbial world alone, which is composed of both multicellular (many-celled) and unicellular (single-celled) organisms, contains a countless number of individual cell types.

In view of this complexity, it may seem absurd for us to attempt to discuss the organization of the living cell within only a few pages. Well, if every cell were truly different from all other cells in every respect, it would be absurd. Indeed, it would be impossible. Fortunately, however, for you the student, for me the author, and for the scientist who investigates cellular phenomena, this is not the case. Rather, though our biosphere is certainly characterized by a vast amount of cellular diversity, there is also a distinct element of cellular unity. In other words, amidst all of the individuality of cell structure and function, there does exist a basic pattern of cellular organization. Recall that this same principle was stated in an earlier chapter in referring to the elements of biochemical diversity and biochemical unity regarding the dynamics of the living process.

The cell is the *fundamental unit* of life because, given a supply of exogenous nutrients and energy from the surroundings, it is the smallest biological entity capable of both growth and cell division. In other words, *all living organisms have a cellular structure, and the activity of the whole organism is the result of the individual and collective activities of cells.* It is interesting to note that the first meaningful statements of this *cellular theory of life,* now accepted as fact, were not made until 1838 by M. J. Schleiden and T. Schwaan, and then again in the late 1850's by R. Virchow. Now in the twentieth century, particularly during the past 20 years, the cellular basis of life has been extrapolated to the level of molecules. Thus, in a physiological or biochemical sense, a cell is what it is and does what it does only because it is composed of a certain set of molecules, all under the direction of the genes of the nucleic acid chromosomes. Nevertheless, the cell is regarded as the *basic unit* of life, since it is only at the cellular level that the basic characteristics of life are expressed. To reiterate: the nature of this expression of life is twofold, namely, *growth* and *multiplication* sustained by the ingestion and utilization of nutrients and energy from the environment.

The living cell, however, is not an amorphous, indivisible, continuous molecular blob. Quite the contrary; the cell is a highly organized entity consisting of separate and distinguishable parts, each of which performs an important function in the overall living process. In other words, the cell is like any other machine, with the operation of the complete unit being due to the combined and integrated operation of a particular set of individual component parts. In this sense, the cell is a *complex unit* of life. Furthermore, depending on the type and source of the cell, the degree of complexity is quite variable. Actually, *every type of living cell is unique.*

Despite this heterogeneity, most cells do share a fundamental level of organization in that they all possess a non-rigid but continuous molecular barrier (*cell membrane*) which separates the interior of the cell from the external surroundings. Many cells, mostly plants and bacteria, contain a second barrier in the form of a *cell wall* that is exterior to and more rigid than the cell membrane. Although both the structure and the function of the cell membrane and cell wall are variable from cell to cell, the *major basis for the differentiation among cells is the nature of the intracellular environment.* Here again, however, there is still a basic level of subcellular organization as represented by the fact that all cells can be classified as either of only two types—the *procaryotes* and the *eucaryotes.*

Procaryotic cells are distinguished by the *absence of any membrane-bound subcellular compartments.* In this type of cell, most of the functional biomolecules and particles are more or less dispersed in the aqueous intracellular fluid, called the *cytoplasm,* while the others are embedded in the main cell membrane. Most representative of this group of cells are the unicellular bacteria, believed to be the first type of living organisms, having evolved some 3–3.5 billion years ago. (*Note:* At present the most reliable estimate of the age of the earth is 4.8 billion years.) Eucaryotic cells, on the other hand, contain distinct subcellular particulate bodies, called *organelles.* These either are entirely membranous in nature or are organized units surrounded by a membrane. The most common membrane-bound organelle is the *cell nucleus.*

Others include the *mitochondrion,* the *chloroplast,* and the *lysosome.* The principal organelles that are basically membranous bodies are the *endoplasmic reticulum* and the *Golgi apparatus.* Eucaryotic cells represent a more advanced state of the living cell. Presumably they evolved from the smaller and less specialized procaryotes. The group includes nearly all animal and plant cells and advanced microbes such as the fungi, many algae, and some advanced forms of bacteria.

Our objective in this chapter will be to study the ultrastructural details of both groups of cells. Such an analysis is possible primarily because of the great strides that have been made in the past ten to twenty years both in the technological development of the electron microscope and in the laboratory preparation of biological samples for viewing (see Chapter 2). The specific coverage of this subject here is made possible only through the courtesy and generosity of several individuals who provided prints of electron micrographs from their personal files. As you will discover, the structure of a living cell—particularly that of a eucaryotic cell—is anything but a continuous blob. Rather, it is more like an expensive jeweled timepiece. The chapter concludes with a brief discussion of disruption and fractionation of whole cells into their constituent parts—a necessary prerequisite for the *in vitro* study of the specialized structure and functions of these parts.

PROCARYOTIC CELLS

The organization of a typical procaryotic cell is depicted in the electron micrographs of the bacterium, *Escherichia coli,* shown in Figures 9–1 and 9–2. *E. coli,* one of the simplest of the bacteria, is perhaps the organism best understood by man. We are interested in *E. coli* not merely because it is a normal and vital constituent of the intestinal tract of man, but primarily because it is an aerobic organism whose basic biochemistry is, for the most part, representative of that of all other aerobic organisms including man. Obviously, *E. coli* and man are different organisms, but remember that they are nevertheless composed of the same major classes of biomolecules. Moreover, if we neglect for the moment all of the specialized activities of each organism, recall further that the basic function of these biomolecules is the same in both. In view of the fact that *E. coli* evolved approximately 1.5 billion years before man, this is a rather fantastic generalization, to say the least. Other advantages in working with *E. coli* are that it is non-infectious, has a short generation time, and is easy to culture reproducibly in small or large quantities. For these reasons, it has proven to be and continues as an extremely useful model system for basic biochemical research.

The electron micrograph of Figure 9–1, showing the *surface* of two intact *E. coli* cells from different views, indicates that the organism has a cylindrical or rodlike shape. The cells are quite small, having a length of about $1-2\mu$ and a diameter of about $0.5-1\mu$. The cell surface actually corresponds to the *cell wall* of the organism, a rigid sheath with a lipid-polysaccharide-peptide composition (see page 188). Recall that this is the site of attachment (the substrate) of lysozyme, which ultimately solubilizes the polymeric nature of the wall, rendering the cell more susceptible to lysis. Specific components of the wall also serve

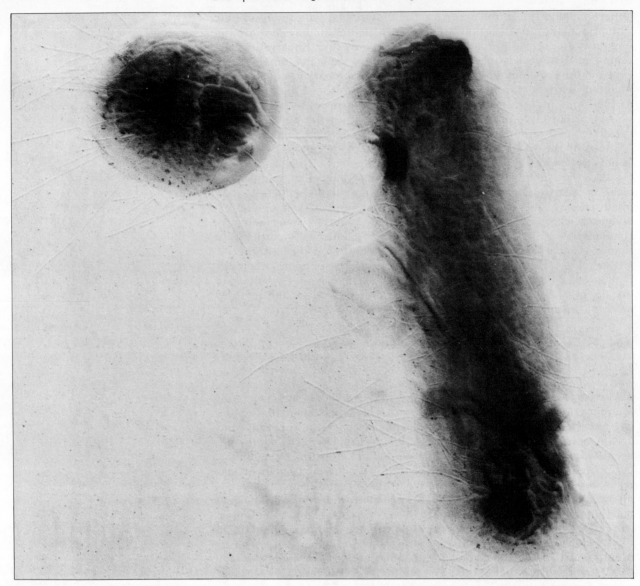

Figure 9–1 An electron micrograph of cells of *Escherichia coli* B. These are surface views depicting the rodlike shape of this organism. The image at the upper left represents a view from one end of the cell. The image at the right represents a view of the long axis of the cell. Faintly visible projections from each cell are pili (see text). Magnification: 45,500 ×.

as binding sites for bacterial viruses. The view of a sectioned *E. coli* cell in Figure 9–2 illustrates a single viral particle attached at the exterior wall. Although the primary function of the cell wall is to provide physical protection, recent studies suggest that the wall may have secondary functions in the general physiology of bacteria, such as participating in a molecular communication system between the exterior and the interior of the cell.

Figure 9–1 also reveals a second ultrastructural feature of the cell surface common to *E. coli* and several other bacteria, namely, the presence of long (up to several microns in length) and thin (approximately 100Å) filamentous strands, called *fimbriae* or *pili*. Known to consist primarily of protein and lipid, these appendages are postulated to be channels whereby DNA passes between two mating cells during

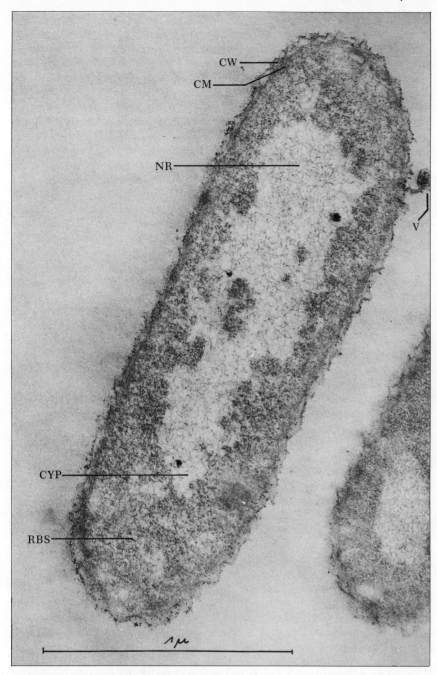

Figure 9–2 An electron micrograph of an *Escherichia coli* cell in cross-sectional view showing: the cell wall (CW); the cytoplasmic cell membrane (CM); the DNA-containing nuclear region (NR), and the ribosomes (RBS) distributed throughout the inner cytoplasm (CYP). The object attached to the cell at the upper right is a small bacterial virus (V). (See Figure 2–12, Panel D, page 29). Magnification: 68,000 ×. Horizontal line at the bottom represents a distance of 1 micron. (Photograph generously supplied by Carl Zeiss, Inc., New York.)

bacterial sexual conjugation. There is considerable debate as to whether the pili are specialized elaborations of the cell wall, of the interior cell membrane, or of the cytoplasm. Finally, the pili are similar in appearance to, but structurally distinct from, another group of specialized protein appendages, called *flagella,* which are responsible for the motility of certain bacteria.

The electron micrograph of a sectioned *E. coli* cell (Figure 9–2) clearly illustrates the non-specialized nature of the interior of a procaryotic cell. That is to say, the inside of the cell contains no specialized membrane-bound compartments. The appearance of distinct light and dark regions within the cell is created by selective fixing and staining methods in the preparation of the sample for viewing. The less dense region seen along the longitudinal axis of the cell corresponds to the *nuclear region* (NR) of the cell containing the DNA chromosomal material dissolved in the *cytoplasm* (CYP; see below). The massive and faintly visible filamentous network appearing against the light background is interpreted as representing DNA itself. (The three intense black spots are granules of unknown composition and function.) Depending on the growth conditions, an *E. coli* cell may contain 1, 2, or 4 *circular DNA molecules*, each of which is a single chromosome (see pages 167 and 471). The term *nuclear region* is used here because of the absence of a limiting membrane which would literally separate it from the rest of the cell interior. When the nuclear region is so bounded, the resulting entity is called a *nucleus* (see eucaryotic cells; page 221). The darker, more electron-dense area surrounding the nuclear region is interpreted to represent the presence of *ribosomes* (RB). The ribosomes, remember, are known to be the cellular site for the assembly of amino acids into protein molecules (see page 161, Chapter 6, and Chapter 18). It has been estimated that an actively metabolizing *E. coli* cell may contain anywhere from 10,000–15,000 ribosomes. The absence of ribosomes in the nuclear region of the cytoplasm may reflect the exclusion of these particles by the tightly packed strands of DNA molecules. Other than this exclusion from the nuclear region, the ribosomes display a fairly random localization, being scattered throughout the rest of the cellular cytoplasm. In addition to the dissolved DNA and dispersed ribosomal particles, the *cytoplasm* (cellular fluid) contains a host of other dissolved materials. The major components are proteins, with most functioning as enzymes. In electron micrographs this colloidal aqueous solution appears only as a background of low electron density against the remainder of the cell structure. In the picture of Figure 9–2, the cytoplasm is clearly evident only in the nuclear region, being for the most part camouflaged in the rest of the cell.

Although not clearly, Figure 9–2 also reveals the exterior *cell wall* (CW) and the *cell membrane* (CM) immediately adjacent to the interior of the wall. The dual structure is most visible at left center. At both the upper left and top of the cell, the wall appears irregularly detached from the membrane. On close inspection, note that the cell membrane appears to be composed of two electron-dense parallel lines separated by a lighter region. This pattern is typical of the bilayer model of membrane structure—that is, the *unit-membrane hypothesis*—that we discussed earlier in Chapter 8 (see page 203). Presumably, the dense parallel lines correspond to protein and the sandwiched light area corresponds to the lipid region.

The conspicuous body at the upper right of the cell represents an infecting bacterial virus (V) that has become attached to the cell wall. Following attachment, the virus injects its own chromosome into the cell, whereupon the viral genes begin to express themselves, resulting in the production of new viral particles within the host cell. Since no viral particles appear in this view of the cell, one would conclude that infection has not yet occurred or that, if it has, viral assembly within the cell has not yet taken place to any appreciable degree.

EUCARYOTIC CELLS

Whereas a procaryotic cell is conspicuous by the absence of distinct membrane-bound particulates within the cytoplasm, just the opposite is true of a eucaryotic cell. Such is represented by the drawing in Figure 9–3 illustrating an idealized cross-sectional view of a typical eucaryotic cell. Although there is really no such thing as a typical cell of any

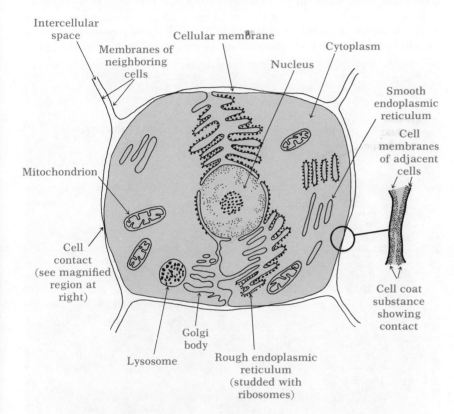

type, the subcellular organization depicted in Figure 9–3 is common to most eucaryotic cells. In other words, neglecting any specialized characteristics such as many cells display, it is a valid generalization that most specimens of eucaryotic cells contain those features identified in Figure 9–3, namely, the *nucleus,* the *mitochondrion,* the *endoplasmic reticulum,* the *Golgi apparatus,* the *lysosome,* and of course the *cell membrane* and the *cytoplasm.* With the aid of high-magnification electron micrographs, let us now examine each of these organelles in greater detail. In addition, we will also consider the *chloroplast,* a specialized organelle of photosynthetic cells.

Figure 9–3 A simplified sketch of a generalized eucaryotic cell. Photosynthetic cells would also contain chloroplasts (not shown here). See text for descriptive information and representative electron micrographs. (Solid continuous lines correspond to membranes and membranous systems.)

NUCLEUS

The nucleus of a cell (generally there is only one per cell) is the largest and hence the most conspicuous subcellular organelle. It is easily seen with a good light microscope and suitable stains. Yet it is only with the electron microscope that the ultrastructure of the nucleus is revealed.

An excellent example is given in Figure 9–4. Note first that the nucleus is enveloped by, and thus segregated from, the rest of the cell interior by a distinctly visible membranous system, seen as two electron-dense lines separated again by a lighter space. This is called the *nuclear membrane,* or sometimes the *nuclear envelope.* Presumably, *each* dense line represents a unit lipoprotein membrane. Hence, the nuclear envelope is a *double membrane* separated by an *intramembranous space.* The separation of the nucleus from the rest of the cell by this membrane is not absolute, however. That is to say, the nucleus is not totally isolated from the remainder of the cell. One reason for this is seen in Figure 9–4, which shows that the nuclear membrane is not con-

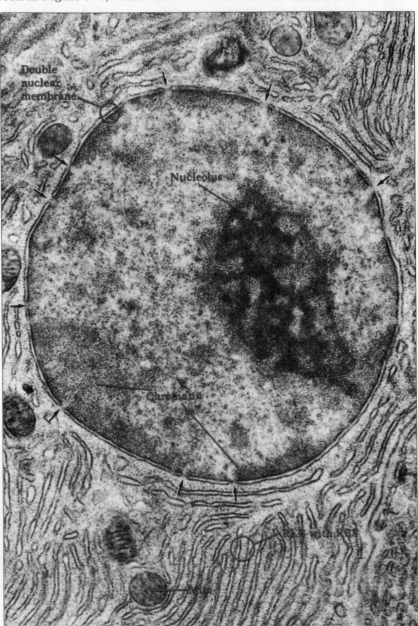

Figure 9–4 An electron micrograph of a cross-sectional view of an intact cell nucleus. Clearly visible are the two membranes of the nucleus, with several pores indicated by the arrows around the circumference of the nucleus. Visible within the nucleus and dispersed in the nucleoplasm are the nucleolus and chromatin regions. A large population of rough endoplasmic reticulum (RER) with attached ribosomes (RBS) is visible in the cytoplasm surrounding the nucleus. A small number of mitochondria (MITO) are also present. Specimen was obtained from the pancreas of a bat. Magnification: 17,000 ×. (Taken with permission from *An Atlas of Fine Structure: The Cell,* Fawcett, D. W., Philadelphia: W. B. Saunders Company, 1966. Photograph generously supplied by D. W. Fawcett.)

tinuous, but has several interruptions (arrows). These spacings are interpreted as representing *nuclear pores* that allow material synthesized within the nucleus, namely RNA, to pass into the surrounding cytoplasm. These nuclear pores are not necessarily openings in the true sense of the word, but rather are regions of less dense composition than the rest of the membrane proper. Although it is not visible in Figure 9–4, a second reason for this non-isolation of the nucleus is the suggestion that the outer layer of the double nuclear membrane is actually continuous throughout the cell as the endoplasmic reticulum, which in turn is continuous with the cell membrane itself (see Figure 9–3 and discussion below). Some convincing electron microscopic evidence for the continuity of the outer nuclear membrane and the cell membrane proper has recently been reported. Refer to the paper by Carothers listed at the end of this chapter for a clear micrograph of this phenomenon.

The inside of the nucleus, called the *nucleoplasm,* also contains a degree of internal organization. Particularly evident is the very electron-dense *nucleolus,* a somewhat spherical region that is quite rich in RNA. Current belief is that the nucleolus is the site within the nucleus where RNA molecules are synthesized from the monomeric nucleotides, using the sequence of nitrogen bases in DNA as a template. The process is called *transcription* and requires the participation of a DNA-dependent-RNA polymerase enzyme (see page 161, Chapter 6, and page 480, Chapter 17). Also note that, throughout the nucleoplasm but particularly near the nuclear membrane, there appear regions of electron density less than that of the nucleolus. These are termed *chromatin* and are known to contain the major portion (95% or more) of the total DNA found in the cell. Presumably, the DNA of the chromatin is associated with histone proteins. The more or less random distribution of the chromatin is characteristic of the nucleus when the cell is not dividing. At the onset of cell division and during the staged mitotic process, the chromatin regions become highly organized into the hereditary units commonly known to all as the *chromosomes.* Ultimately, the chromosomes replicate to produce two identical sets. The enzyme required for the replication of DNA, presumably a DNA-dependent–DNA polymerase (see page 466, Chapter 17), is also found in the nucleoplasm.

In describing the structural organization of the nucleus, note that we have also established the primary functions of this specialized organelle. To summarize: the nucleus is the cellular site where *genetic information* is (a) *stored* as DNA, (b) *transmitted* to the rest of the cell—DNA → RNA → proteins of cytoplasm, and (c) *replicated* to insure perpetuation of the cell line—DNA → DNA.

MITOCHONDRION

Although mitochondria are found in virtually all eucaryotic cells, their size, shape, and number are quite variable from one cell to another. In animal cells, the mitochondrion is frequently a rod-shaped particle with a length of 1.5–2μ and a diameter of 0.5–1μ. In other words, it is approximately 1/20 the size of the cell nucleus and about equal in size to that of a procaryotic bacterial cell such as *E. coli.* Certain generalizations can also be made regarding the cellular population of mitochondria. In cells characterized by a high degree of aerobic metabolism, the number per cell may be quite large. For example, each cell of liver tissue contains close to a thousand mitochondria. On the other hand, cells participating primarily in anaerobic metabolism, such as the cells of skeletal muscle tissue, contain only a few mitochondria. There is nothing special about their position within the cell.

The origin of the word mitochondrion (Greek: *mitos*—threadlike; *chondros*—grain) was based on the gross structural features of this organelle when it was first observed as a stained body under a light microscope some 65 years ago. In view of our current understanding of mitochondrial structure, the name is pitifully inappropriate. The electron micrograph of Figure 9–5, showing a cross-section of a typical mitochondrion magnified approximately 70,300 times, illustrates why.

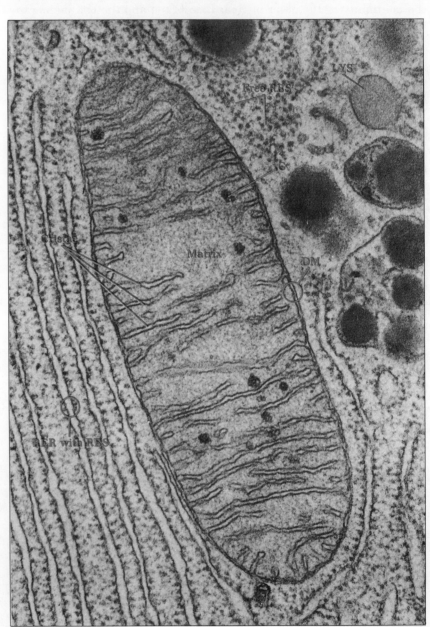

Figure 9–5 Electron micrograph of a longitudinal section of a mitochondrion and surrounding cytoplasm from the pancreas of a bat. Note the distinct double membrane (DM) of the mitochondrion and the numerous foldings (cristae) of the inner membrane that project into the matrix (M) of the mitochondrion. The heavily stained small granules (G) in the matrix are of unknown composition and function. They are not found in all mitochondria. Visible at the left from top to bottom is a region of rough endoplasmic reticulum (RER) with attached ribosomes (RBS). Free ribosomes are also present in the upper portion of the micrograph. A lysosome (LYS) can be seen in the upper right corner. Magnification: 70,300 ×. (Taken with permission from *An Atlas of Fine Structure: The Cell*, Fawcett, D. W., Philadelphia: W. B. Saunders Company, 1966. Photograph generously supplied by D. W. Fawcett. Original micrograph prepared by Dr. K. R. Porter.)

Observe that the particle is much more than a threadlike grain. Immediately apparent are the presence of a defining membrane system and also an extensive amount of *intramitochondrial* structure. Close inspection reveals that the membrane system is actually a *double membrane*—two unit membranes separated by an intramembranous space. Whereas the outer membrane appears to be smooth and continuous around the mitochondrion, the inner membrane undergoes an extensive and irregular folding within the mitochondrion. In cross-section, the numerous foldings of the inner membrane, called *cristae,* appear as two electron-dense invaginations. The region surrounding the cristae and having a homogeneous granular appearance represents the inner fluid of the mitochondrion, called the *mitochondrial matrix.* The very dense spots that appear within the matrix are small granules of unknown composition and function. They do not represent DNA (see below).

Mitochondria are responsible for the bulk of the aerobic (oxygen-dependent) metabolism of the cell, which includes the crucial biochemical processes of the *citric acid cycle* and *oxidative phosphorylation.* Together these activities produce nearly all of the energy (that is, ATP) required to sustain the growth and viability of the entire cell. For these reasons, the mitochondrion is sometimes termed the "powerhouse of the cell." Among other important activities known to be associated with mitochondria is the degradation of fatty acids by the process of *β-oxidation.* The details of all three of these processes will be explored in subsequent chapters. Although the enzymes of the citric acid cycle and β-oxidation are either contained in the outer membrane or dissolved in the mitochondrial matrix, the enzymes and other factors participating in the process of oxidative phosphorylation are known to be compartmentalized within the inner membrane, particularly within the cristae. Although it is not depicted in Figure 9–5, the ultrastructure of the cristae themselves is developed to an exquisite degree. This aspect of mitochondrial structure is discussed elsewhere (see page 359, Chapter 13).

It was just a few years ago that considerable controversy was generated by reports that mitochondria contained DNA. Initial findings have been confirmed; the controversy has since subsided; and the existence of mitochondrial DNA is now generally accepted. A current controversy exists concerning the function of the mitochondrial DNA (approximately 2–4% of the total DNA in the cell). One proposal is that the DNA in the mitochondrion contains all of the necessary genetic information required for the development and replication of this organelle. In other words, the mitochondrion may be a secondary, miniaturized cell within the primary cell. This intriguing suggestion has received support by recent reports that mitochondria also possess their own ribosomes. Thus, mitochondria may contain not only a genetic apparatus (DNA) but also the necessary machinery to transcribe the genetic program (DNA → RNA), to replicate the genetic program (DNA → DNA), and to translate the genetic program (RNA → proteins). Assuming that this is so, it has been argued further that mitochondria may have evolved from primitive bacteria. Their presence in eucaryotic cells may have occurred via an infection of a developing eucaryotic organism early in its evolution by a parasitic, mitochondrion-like bacterial cell. At this stage, the primitive eucaryotic cell may have acquired a natural selective advantage in that the activities of the host cell and the invading bacterial cell proved to be complementary, and the two may then have continued to evolve as a unit cell. Obviously, the hypothesis is an impossible one to prove, but an interesting one, nevertheless.

ENDOPLASMIC RETICULUM

Whereas the nucleus and the mitochondrion were first observed with light microscopy, the discovery of the endoplasmic reticulum had to await the development of electron microscopy. First observed in 1953, it is now recognized as an organelle that occurs in nearly all types of higher plant and animal eucaryotic cells. What is it? Well, the simplest description is that it is a *netlike system* (reticulum) of *flattened membrane-bound regions* that are localized within the cytoplasm (endoplasmic) of the cell. Thus, the endoplasmic reticulum is not a singular, highly ordered entity such as the nucleus and mitochondrion, but rather an irregular and interconnected array of membranous vesicles. In many cells it is quite profuse, occupying much of the available intracellular space. Two types of endoplasmic reticulum are known. One is called *rough endoplasmic reticulum* (RER) due to the presence of small dense granules that appear to be attached to the outer surface of the membrane vesicle. The granules are now known to be *ribosome* particles. The second type is termed *smooth endoplasmic reticulum* (SER) and is characterized by the absence of attached ribosomes. In schematic cross-section, each type would appear as already shown in Figure 9–3, with solid lines representing the membranous system and the black dots on the RER representing the ribosomes. The appearance of the reticulum, particularly the rough type, under the electron microscope is represented in Figure 9–4 (surrounding the nucleus) and in Figure 9–5 (to the left and lower right of the mitochondrion).

The specialized functions of the reticulum are in protein biosynthesis and protein transport through the cell. Proteins are synthesized at the surface of the ribosomes adhering to the RER, pass into the inner compartment (the *cisternal space*) of the reticulum, and are then transported through a catacomb complex of the cisternal spacings to the surface of the cell. Another route is a channeling of the proteins from the RER to the SER and then to the Golgi apparatus (see below), which segregates and concentrates several molecules of one particular type of protein or of different but functionally related proteins into a dense granule that is ultimately secreted from the cell. A fact consistent with these roles of the reticulum is that the reticulum, especially the rough variety, is most abundant in those cells which are known to be specialized sites for the synthesis of various proteins. For example, the partial views in Figures 9–4 and 9–5 (both of which show a high RER content) are of a pancreas cell which daily produces and secretes rather large amounts of several enzymes that participate in the digestion of ingested foodstuffs by mammals. It does not appear, however, that the RER is the cellular site for the biosynthesis of all protein. The bulk of the proteins produced by the cell for use within the cell itself are believed to be assembled at ribosomal clusters found free in the cytoplasm. A region of unbound ribosomes is seen at the top right of the micrograph shown in Figure 9–5. In support of this is the observation that significantly smaller levels of RER are found in those cells where little protein is produced for secretion and then used elsewhere.

GOLGI APPARATUS

The Golgi apparatus (sometimes simply called the *Golgi body*) is likewise a network of flattened, membrane-bound vesicles found in the cytoplasm. The membrane surface is of the smooth type. Unlike the endoplasmic reticulum, however, the Golgi apparatus is not an extensive system permeating large regions of the cytoplasm. Rather, it is more restricted in size. Moreover, the vesicles of the apparatus are frequently

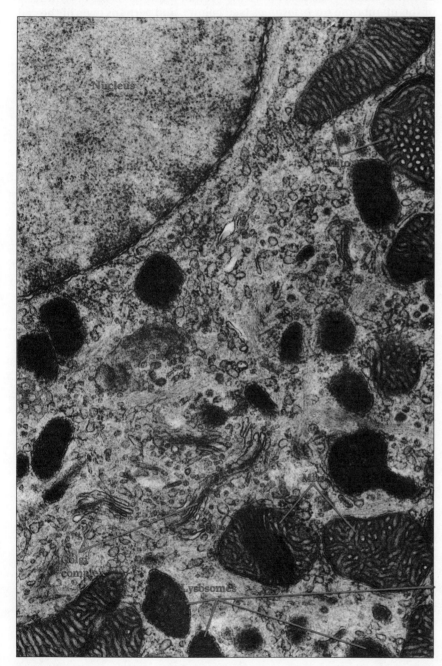

Figure 9–6 An electron micrograph of a cell interior showing several organelles. Clearly visible are: lysosomes (LYS), two distinct Golgi complexes, several mitochondria (MITO), and a portion of the nucleus. The specimen was obtained from the suprarenal cortex of a hamster. Magnification: 25,000 ×. (Taken with permission from *An Atlas of Fine Structure: The Cell,* Fawcett, D. W., Philadelphia: W. B. Saunders Company, 1966. Photograph generously supplied by D. W. Fawcett.)

stacked in a small cluster and are usually localized near the nucleus or near the apex of specialized secreting cells. Its electron microscopic appearance in cross-section is shown in Figure 9–6. (Refer to Figure 9–3 for an idealized representation.) As stated earlier, one of the known functions of the Golgi apparatus is that it accepts proteins from the RER-SER system for concentration and packaging into dense granules which are then secreted into the extracellular fluid. Another function is that it collects and assembles the protein required in the biosynthesis of the membrane for *lysosomes* (see below), and perhaps even of the cell membrane itself. Among other specialized roles that have been proposed for the Golgi apparatus is that it serves as the cellular site for the bio-synthesis of complex heteropolysaccharides which are ultimately secreted from the cell and then deposited in the mucopolysaccharide coating of the cell. Considerable research is in progress to clarify these roles and to investigate others. Since the Golgi apparatus is present in cells that do not specialize in secreting protein as well as in those that do, it may have a general and essential function in the biochemistry and physiology of the cell.

LYSOSOME

Lysosomes are irregular-shaped, single-membrane-bound bodies of variable occurrence in the cell. Under the electron microscope (Figure 9–6), they appear as areas having a more or less homogeneous electron density. Presumably, the lysosomes are concentrated bodies of protein consisting of one or more types of hydrolytic enzymes (ribonucleases, phosphatases, hydrolases, glucosidases). In other words, these enzymes are segregated, stored, and then used in the intracellular degradation of proteins, nucleic acids, and carbohydrates brought into the cell in unhydrolyzed form, or in the degradation of similar materials within the cell during their metabolic turnover (degradation followed by syn-thesis).

CELL MEMBRANE, CELL WALL, CELL SURFACE COAT

The surface cell membrane of a eucaryotic cell is not visible in any of the electron micrographs in Figures 9–4 through 9–6, simply because these photos are high-magnification partial views of the intracellular environment. A whole-cell view, however, would reveal that the pe-ripheral cell membrane has an appearance just like that of any other smooth-surfaced, single-membrane system such as that seen with the endoplasmic reticulum. In fact, as we stated earlier, it has been hy-pothesized that the endoplasmic reticulum is actually a cytoplasmic continuation of the surface membrane (see Figure 9–3). Since the endoplasmic reticulum in turn is believed to be continuous with the nuclear envelope, all of these membranous particulates may be part of one massive membrane system that not only surrounds the cell but also folds within the cell and permeates throughout the cytoplasm, even-tually enveloping the nucleus. In addition to partitioning the cell into individual units and providing it with some protection, the cell membrane also plays an important role in regulating the passage of materials into and out of the cell. This is true, of course, for the membranes of both eucaryotic and procaryotic cells. In many instances, the transport mechanism may be rather specialized, involving specific proteins localized in the membrane and often requiring an expenditure of energy. Such a process is called *active transport*. In recent years, the list of other functions attributed to the membrane has been growing. These functions vary from species to species, from cell to cell, and from one physiological state to another. The biochemistry and physiology of membranes are now very active and specialized areas of modern biological research.

In addition to the cell membrane, many eucaryotic cells, particularly plant cells, also contain additional protection in the form of a *cell wall* external to the surface membrane. Similar to that found in bacteria, the wall of the higher eucaryotic cells is a rigid covalent network composed largely of polysaccharide material. In plants the major components are closely packed cellulose fibers, cemented together by interaction with a viscous fluid containing other homo- and heteropolysaccharide substances. Animal cells generally do not have a cell wall.

In most cells (eucaryotes and procaryotes alike), the surface cell membrane and cell wall are frequently covered with a viscous substance called a *cell coat*. The composition of this substance is quite variable from one cell to another, but usually is known to contain complex heteropolysaccharides in conjugation with minor constituents such as proteins and lipids. In a multicellular tissue, adjacent cells make an irregular contact through their respective coats across the intracellular space (see Figure 9–3). It has been proposed that this cellular contact serves as a form of communication among neighboring cells, resulting in a control of their growth and division. The phenomenon is frequently termed *contact inhibition*. This property of normal cells is a logical one, since uncontrolled cell division—that is, cancer—is known to be associated with many harmful effects. Shortly before this book went into production, a significant discovery was made in this regard. A few years ago it had been demonstrated that a virus-induced conversion of normal fibroplast cells having growth control into tumor cells lacking growth control could be mimicked by replacing the virus with a specific protein known to react with and modify the composition of the cell coat. Thus, the formation of tumor cells was suggested to be linked to an alteration of the cell coat material in normal cells. The recent discovery was that the viral-transformed tumor cells could be reconverted to normal cells by treatment with a substance that, in effect, repaired the damage done to the cell coat. In other words, the process was reversible. What does this mean? Well, for one thing these results confirm the proposal that the types of tumor cells under study did indeed possess a unique biochemical characteristic, namely, an alteration in the cell coat substance. Moreover, the data further suggest that this alteration, induced in some way by the virus, is the very reason why the normal cells were transformed in the first place. In other words, the alteration may be the immediate cause of the transformation. The effect of the transformation is the loss of growth control. Whether or not this phenomenon applies to the formation of other types of tumor cells, and whether it has any clinical potential, are areas now under investigation.

CHLOROPLAST

Although eucaryotic cells of higher animals and plants share most of the structural organization described above, many plant cells, particularly photosynthesizing cells, do contain a unique organelle, namely, the *chloroplast* (Greek: *chloros*—green; *plast*—formed mass). Chloroplasts contain the green *chlorophyll* molecules and are the specialized membrane-bound bodies that function in the crucial processes of harnessing and converting the energy of the sun into useful metabolic energy as ATP, which is then used in the fixation and conversion of atmospheric CO_2 into carbohydrate material (Chapter 15). The shape and size of the chloroplast are quite variable. In some cells, the chloroplast is similar in both respects to the nucleus—somewhat spherical and very large. In other cells, it is more cylindrical in shape but significantly larger (2–5 times) than a typical mitochondrion. As indicated in Figure 9–7, the chloroplast displays a considerable amount of fine inner structure. The most prominent feature is the presence of several electron-dense stackings. These are called *grana* and represent ordered pilings of flattened membranous systems that presumably originate from the main membrane surrounding the periphery of the chloroplast. The white bodies in the interior of the chloroplast represent large storage

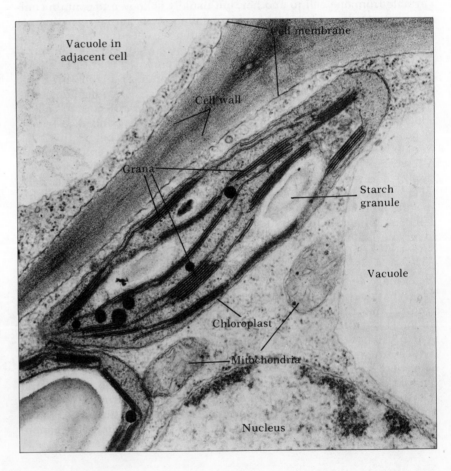

Figure 9–7 An electron micrograph showing, in cross-sectional view, pieces of adjacent cells in tomato stem tissue. An intact chloroplast containing several grana can be seen in the lower cell, situated very close to the cell membrane. The thick, cellulose-containing cell wall of each cell is also visible. Other organelles visible in the lower cell are two mitochondria and a portion of the cell nucleus. The large clear region at the right is a portion of a vacuole surrounded by a membrane. Vacuoles are present in most plant cells, particularly in older cells, functioning as storage compartments for dissolved sugars, proteins, oxygen, carbon dioxide, and other substances. See Figures 14–2 and 14–3 for more detail of chloroplast ultrastructure. (Photograph generously supplied by Hilton H. Mollenhauer, Charles F. Kettering Research Laboratory, Yellow Springs, Ohio.)

vacuoles of the carbohydrate end products of photosynthesis. They are not common to all chloroplasts. The small darkened bodies are granules of unknown composition and function. The structural and functional characteristics of the chloroplast will be discussed in greater detail in Chapter 15.

CELLULAR FRACTIONATION

In regard to cellular organization, the objective of the biochemist is to unravel the secrets of each subcellular region as they pertain to questions such as: (a) what type of biomolecules are found in each compartment? (b) what are the chemical properties and the biological role of these substances? (c) specifically, what enzymes are localized in the various compartments? (d) what are the metabolic functions of these enzymes and hence of the compartment itself? (e) what are the metabolic interrelationships of one compartment to another? (f) what is the relationship of the ultrastructure of each compartment to its function in the cell? (g) what is the characteristic structure and function of the membrane of each particulate body and of the cell itself? To pursue any of these areas initially requires the capability of isolating and studying each subcellular system *in vitro* in as pure a state as possible. Currently, this requirement is achieved by well-established and, for the most part, generally routine procedures. First, whole cells are disrupted (broken) to yield a *cell-free system,* frequently termed a *homogenate.* Individual systems are then separated from each other by *differential centrifugation* (see page 22, Chapter 2).

CELL DISRUPTION

A variety of methods are available to break open (lyse) cells. The most common techniques are (a) blending, (b) grinding, (c) exposure to ultrasonic frequencies, (d) osmotic shock, (e) high-pressure extrusion, and (f) treatment with lysozyme. The first three (a,b,c) are generally used in the processing of animal and plant tissue, while the latter four (c,d,e,f) are employed in the lysis of the smaller bacterial cells. Whatever the case, the decision to choose one procedure over another is based on the particular type of cell, the objective of the experimenter, and the mass of the material to be processed. In the absence of published guidelines in the literature, the choice is essentially based on trial and error. What procedure will give the best results? The desired objectives are *maximum disruption of whole cells* and *minimum damage to subcellular components,* particularly the organelles to be studied.

Blending is generally accomplished with electrical devices of various construction, each offering different advantages and disadvantages. The basis of rupture is quite simple, namely, a shearing of cellular tissue by rotating blades. In grinding methods, the cells are merely rubbed against an abrasive and hence against each other. The simplest tools are a mortar and pestle. Typical abrasives are ground-glass beads, sand, or alumina. For the routine processing of small samples, specially constructed glass *homogenizers* are often used.

These consist of a ground-glass barrel with a fitted ground-glass piston to provide a clearance of 0.005 inch. On moving the piston up and down the barrel containing the sample, the tissue is forced through this small clearance. The use of ultrasonic vibrations is a relatively recent development and is widely used. Two reasons for its popularity are that (a) in most cases the subcellular organelles can be recovered in a reasonably intact, undamaged state, and (b) the severity of the treatment can be finely controlled. One of the mildest techniques is that of osmotic shock. Here the cells are first suspended in a solution of high solute concentration, causing the migration of water out of the cell. Then they are transferred to pure water, whereupon the water rushes into the cell and it bursts open. With the high-pressure extrusion method, small cells such as bacteria are efficiently and gently broken by forcing a concentrated suspension through a small opening under several thousand pounds of pressure. The most delicate of all disruption procedures is with lysozyme (see page 121), but unfortunately its use is confined to lysing bacterial cells. Regardless of the method utilized, all operations are normally conducted in the presence of a defined buffer solution and at reduced temperature to minimize denaturation of soluble proteins and of the particulate organelles themselves.

SEPARATION OF ORGANELLES

The separation of the soluble cell fluid from the particulate matter, as well as the further fractionation of the latter by differential centrifugation, is based on a simple principle. Since virtually all of the components in the cell-free system have a different mass-to-volume ratio—that is, a different density—heavier bodies will sediment under low speeds and low gravitational forces, while lighter substances will require higher speeds and higher gravitational forces. Particles of intermediate density will obviously require intermediate conditions. Consequently, an efficient fractionation can be achieved by starting on the low side and performing a series of separate and successive centrifugations toward the high side. Such a scheme is diagrammed below.

Outline of a Typical Fractionation Procedure

low-speed centrifugation | high-speed centrifugation

$1000 \times g$ 5–15 min → $10,000 \times g$ 15 min → $100,000 \times g$ 1–2 hr → $>100,000 \times g$

soluble components in supernatant

pellet

tissue homogenate — nuclei — mitochondria lysosomes — reticular systems, ribosomes — differential sedimentation of heavy solubles

The specified steps and their conditions approximate only a general and simplified situation. The precise conditions are generally more numerous and complex.

Having examined in this chapter the structural characteristics of the cell and its component parts, and having previously examined in earlier chapters the nature of the biomolecules that are found therein, our emphasis in the remaining chapters will be directed to a study of how these materials participate in the chemical dynamics of the living process. This is the subject of metabolism.

LITERATURE

ALLISON, A., "Lysosomes and Disease," *Scientific American,* 217, 62–72 (1967). Description of the structure of lysosomes and their function in normal and pathological cells.

BRACHET, J., and A. E. MIRSKY (eds.), *The Cell.* New York: Academic Press. A collection of six volumes on the biochemistry, physiology, and morphology of cells. Volume 2 is devoted to the component parts of cells. Although published in 1960, this is still a valuable reference work.

BURGER, M. M., and K. D. NOONAN, "Restoration of Normal Growth by Covering of Agglutinin Sites on Tumor Cell Surfaces," *Nature,* 228, 512–515 (1970). The original article describing the restoration of tumor cells to normal cells by modification of the cell coat substance.

CAROTHERS, Z. B., "Membrane Continuity Between Plasmalemma and Nuclear Envelope in Spermatogenic Cells of *Blasia,*" *Science,* 175, 652–654 (1972). Electron microscopic evidence that in a eucaryotic plant cell the outer membrane of the nuclear envelope is an intracellular extension of the main cell membrane which continues uninterrupted around the cell periphery.

FAWCETT, D. W., *An Atlas of Fine Structure: The Cell—Its Organelles and Inclusions,* Philadelphia: W. B. Saunders Company, 1966. A collection of illustrations obtained from electron microscopy of various types of cells. Emphasis given to the major subcellular components of mammalian cells. Text descriptions of the illustrations are also included.

LEHNINGER, A. L., *The Mitochondrion.* New York: W. A. Benjamin, Inc., 1965. An authoritative monograph providing a comprehensive review of the molecular basis of the structure and function of the mitochondrion.

The Living Cell and *From Cell to Organism.* San Francisco: W. H. Freeman Company, 1965 and 1967. Two books containing a collection of articles from *Scientific American* on cell biology. Excellent introductory material on a variety of topics dealing with cellular and subcellular ultrastructure and biological function.

MARGULIS, M., "Symbiosis and Evolution," *Scientific American,* 225, 48–57 (1971). A discussion of the origin and symbiotic evolution of specialized organelles (chloroplasts and mitochondria) of the cells of higher plants and animals.

NEUTRA, M., and C. P. LEBLOND, "The Golgi Apparatus," *Scientific American,* 220, 100–107 (1969). A well-illustrated article describing the ultrastructure and cellular function of this organelle.

UMBREIT, W. W., R. H. BURRIS, and J. F. STAUFFER, *Manometric and Biochemical Techniques,* Fifth Edition. Minneapolis: Burgess Publishing Company, 1972. Contains an excellent coverage of the many techniques available for the preparation of animal, plant, and bacterial cell-free extracts.

10

Energetics and High-Energy Compounds

The first half of this book was primarily devoted to an analysis of the chemistry of the four main classes of biomolecules—proteins, nucleic acids, carbohydrates, and lipids. With this task complete, it might seem that we are now prepared to explore the subject of metabolism and to investigate how all of these materials participate in the dynamics of the living state. However, such a conclusion would be premature. The deficiency in our preparation is singular—namely, we have yet *to establish a solid foundation for understanding the energetics of a living cell.* This chapter is designed to satisfy just such a deficiency.

In a text of this type, the inclusion of a chapter devoted to the physical concepts and principles of energetics is not intended to provide the student with an exercise in abstract thought. On the contrary, the justification is more substantive; without this knowledge, the subject of metabolism would largely appear as an incomprehensible mess. Only with it can one understand and appreciate that there is, indeed, a design—a pattern—a logic—to metabolism. In a previous chapter, we have already, in a rather broad sense, made reference to one important aspect of this design. That is, *on a net basis, degradative reactions are energy yielding, and synthetic reactions are energy requiring; hence, the two phases of metabolism are complementary.*

The qualitative and/or quantitative description of the energetics of any system—living or non-living; organic or inorganic; chemical, physical, or biological—is the domain of a specialized field called *thermodynamics* where emphasis is placed on *energy changes* as the system undergoes a transformation from one state to another. In the language of thermodynamics, energy changes can be described in a variety of ways, but by far the most useful is given in terms of the *change in free energy.* For chemical systems, the free-energy change is extremely useful, because under the commonly encountered conditions of constant temperature and constant pressure, it provides a valid method of predicting the feasibility of a reaction, as well as being representative of the maximum amount of chemical energy that is potentially available for doing useful work.

In the following pages we will examine the basic principles of thermodynamics and their significance, with particular attention to the free-energy concept. For some this may be a brief review of material covered in other courses, while for others it possibly represents a first exposure. In either case, but especially for the latter group, it is advised that you study these principles carefully and not proceed further until their meaning and significance are assimilated. Following that, we will apply these principles to an analysis of a limited number of naturally occurring materials that are intimately involved in the energetics of metabolism. Pre-eminent in this group is *adenosine triphosphate (ATP)*. Finally, special attention will be given to the so-called *coupling phenomenon* which explains the metabolic relationships between energy-yielding and energy-requiring reactions.

PRINCIPLES OF THERMODYNAMICS

ENERGETICS OF STATE TRANSITIONS

Any physical or chemical transformation is most directly and most simply described by contrasting the physical and/or chemical properties of the *initial* and *final states* of the system. Included among these properties are pressure, temperature, volume, the physical states of the materials, the concentration of each material, and the chemical composition of each material. Two simple exercises are given below. One process represents a physical transformation, the other a chemical transformation. (For both we will impose conditions of constant temperature and pressure and, for reasons of simplicity, neglect any changes in volume.) In the former, the nature of the initial and final states is obvious—water is converted from a liquid to a vapor state. Although more involved, a description of the chemical process is similarly made—the inorganic substances, CO_2 and H_2O (initial), are converted into an organic carbohydrate substance plus oxygen (final) in respective reacting proportions of $6 + 6 \rightarrow 1 + 6$. This latter process, of course, represents the net reaction of the assimilation of atmospheric carbon dioxide during photosynthesis.

$$H_2O(l) \longrightarrow H_2O(v)$$

Initial state　　　Final state

P and T are constant

$$6CO_2 + 6H_2O \longrightarrow C_6H_{12}O_6 + 6O_2$$

Initial state　　　　　Final state

P and T are constant

Although both descriptions are valid, common experience tells us they are incomplete. The major shortcoming is that we have neglected to indicate that each transformation requires an input of energy from the surroundings—heat energy and radiant energy, respectively. That is to say, we have not included a comparison of the energy levels of the initial and final states. Since energy is required in both processes, it logically follows that, in each instance, the initial state is at a lower energy level than the final state, and that the energy put into the system is converted to some other form. In the vaporization of water, the difference in energy levels is primarily due to a greater amount of molecular motion in water molecules in the vapor versus the liquid state. Thus, in the course of this physical change, the heat energy is converted to kinetic energy of molecular motion. In the photosynthetic fixation of carbon dioxide, the variance in energy levels is primarily due to a greater chemical bonding energy in the carbohydrate product than in the inorganic reactants. Thus, in the course of this chemical change, the radiant energy is converted into chemical energy needed for the formation of several covalent bonds within an organic molecule.

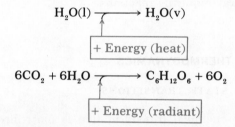

The point of these introductory remarks is really quite simple— *a complete physicochemical description of any change in state necessarily includes an analysis of the energetics of the process, which provides a deeper insight into the nature of the transformation and the participating substances.* While this principle applies to all systems, it is particularly appropriate to the study of biochemical transformations in the living state. Indeed, as stated previously, without such an approach our understanding of cellular metabolism would be obscured.

To describe the transition from one state to another in thermodynamic terms can become somewhat abstract unless a proper foundation is established. Accordingly, we will continue our analysis of the principles of bioenergetics only after a brief excursion into the discipline of classical thermodynamics. Since this is not a course in thermodynamics, per se, our approach will not encompass all facets nor will it be highly technical. Our major intent is to understand the basic principles of thermodynamics and in particular the free-energy principle. To reiterate some of the introductory remarks, the free-energy principle has special significance, because it allows one to give a meaningful description of the energetics of a transformation and to predict whether the transformation could occur spontaneously. As we will shortly discover, the ability to do both is quite advantageous in understanding any given reaction or any set of consecutive reactions. The free-energy principle will be developed after first considering two relationships— both based on man's observation of the material world—that govern all energy changes and are profoundly called the *First Law* and the *Second Law of Thermodynamics.*

FIRST LAW OF THERMODYNAMICS

The First Law of Thermodynamics can be stated in many ways, but perhaps the most useful is as follows: *The total energy of a system in any given state in relation to its surroundings is constant, although during a change in state of the system the energy may change from one form to another.* In effect, this is a somewhat technical statement of the conservation of energy axiom which states that, *although all forms of energy are interconvertible, energy can neither be created nor destroyed.*

A less abstract mathematical statement of the First Law is given by the relationship

$$\Delta E = E_f - E_i = Q - W$$

where Q is the heat absorbed *by* the system from the surroundings, W is the work done *by* the system on the surroundings, and ΔE is the change in *internal energy* (E) of the system between the initial (E_i) and final (E_f) states. This is a valid statement for all state changes, be they chemical, physical, mechanical, electrical, and so on, or any combination thereof. The internal energy of the system is a thermodynamic property and by definition is simply the total energy of a specific system in a specific state. Furthermore, it is dependent *only* on the state of the system and, as such, it is most accurately called a thermodynamic *state function.* Although it is not possible to determine the actual value of the internal energy of the system in any state, the equation above does state rather clearly that the difference in the internal energy between any two states of the system can be calculated from a knowledge of the exchange of heat and work between the system and the surroundings during the course of a transformation.

The basic utility of the First Law should be quite evident. It allows for a relative comparison of any two states of a system in terms of the difference between their total energy content. Aside from this, however, the First Law has little functional significance, particularly with regard to predicting the potential of any process to occur spontaneously. The reason is simple enough—there is no consistent pattern between spontaneity and the value of the change in the internal energy. Intuitively, one might arrive at a different conclusion by arguing that any system would spontaneously change to a state of lower total energy, that is, with E_f smaller than E_i. In other words, a spontaneous change would have a negative ΔE. However, such is not the case; on the contrary, we could list several spontaneous transformations of different types, some of which would have a positive ΔE, others with a negative ΔE, and still others a ΔE equal to zero.

Aside from the theme of energy conservation, the First Law of Thermodynamics and the concept of internal energy have no practical application to bioenergetics. Nevertheless, our discussion of same has touched upon other principles that will be helpful in our development of more useful thermodynamic properties such as entropy and free energy. Most important are two points: (a) unless the system is totally isolated, a change in a thermodynamic property must necessarily consider the interaction of the system and its surroundings; and (b) thermodynamic properties are dependent only on the state of a system, thus permitting a net overall description of the energetics of the system undergoing a change from one state to another.

SECOND LAW OF THERMODYNAMICS

The Second Law of Thermodynamics is without question one of the most troublesome relationships of the physical sciences. Yet the meaning of the Second Law in terms of man's experience with the material universe is rather simple; namely, *all systems spontaneously tend to undergo a change that decreases their capacity for further change.* In other words, *all systems spontaneously tend to approach a state of equilibrium.* For example, heat spontaneously flows from a hot to a cold body, water spontaneously flows downhill, a gas will spontaneously expand against a decreasing external pressure, upon dissolution a solute will spontaneously distribute itself uniformly throughout the solution, and an adult living organism spontaneously tends to undergo a degenerative aging process.

The difficulty with the Second Law is due to its operational definition in terms of the thermodynamic function called *entropy (S)*. What is entropy? In the context of the statement given above, the entropy of a system is a *measure of the extent to which the system is displaced from an equilibrium position, but in an inverse relationship.* That is, a low entropy value corresponds to a large displacement from equilibrium. Since equilibrium states, relative to non-equilibrium states, represent a more randomized state, the entropy is also a useful measure of the molecular order of the system, again in an inverse sense, with a low entropy value corresponding to a large degree of molecular orderliness. For example, a globular protein in its native conformation (high molecular order; non-random conformation) would have a low entropy value, whereas the denatured protein (low molecular order; random conformation) would have a high entropy value. Regardless of the interpretation given to entropy, it is, like the internal energy, a thermodynamic state function dependent only on the initial and final states.

Mathematically, the Second Law states that a finite change in entropy (ΔS) is given by

$$\Delta S = S_f - S_i = \frac{Q}{T}$$

where Q = heat absorbed
         T = temperature

Recognizing that we must necessarily speak of the entropy change of both the system and its surroundings, we can write

$$\Delta S_{\text{system}} = \left(\frac{Q}{T}\right)_{\text{system}} \quad \text{and} \quad \Delta S_{\text{surroundings}} = \left(\frac{Q}{T}\right)_{\text{surroundings}}$$

and

$$\Delta S_{\text{total}} = \Delta S_{\text{system}} + \Delta S_{\text{surroundings}}$$

One of the truly remarkable characteristics of our universe is that *for any spontaneous transformation, the total entropy change is a positive number.* An equally valid corollary is that a negative ΔS_{total} corresponds to a non-spontaneous process. Given these empirical observations and the principles stated previously, it logically follows that if the entropy change is zero, the system is at equilibrium.

$$\left(\frac{Q}{T}\right)_{sys} + \left(\frac{Q}{T}\right)_{sur} > 0 \qquad \text{spontaneous process } (\Delta S_{total} \text{ is } +)$$

$$\left(\frac{Q}{T}\right)_{sys} + \left(\frac{Q}{T}\right)_{sur} < 0 \qquad \text{non-spontaneous process } (\Delta S_{total} \text{ is } -)$$

$$\left(\frac{Q}{T}\right)_{sys} + \left(\frac{Q}{T}\right)_{sur} = 0 \qquad \text{equilibrium condition } (\Delta S_{total} \text{ is } 0)$$

Since there are *no known exceptions* to these relationships, we conclude that ΔS is a useful criterion of predicting the capacity of a transformation to occur spontaneously. Although such a conclusion is valid, the practical application is limited because of the difficulty in making precise and accurate measurements of $\Delta S_{surroundings}$.

FREE ENERGY

The inadequacy of the First Law and the non-feasibility of the Second Law as useful tools in predicting spontaneity were circumvented by Gibbs and Helmholtz who, by merging the First and Second Laws, created a new thermodynamic state function called the *free energy*. A simplified version of how the free energy concept was created is as follows.

The Second Law states that at constant temperature

$$\Delta S_{sur} + \Delta S_{sys} \geqq 0$$

(> for spontaneous process; equality for equilibrium condition)

However, the First Law states that energy must be conserved and, since the entropy is a function of energy, we can write a *separate* relationship as follows:

$$\Delta S_{sur} = -\Delta S_{sys} = -\left(\frac{Q}{T}\right)_{sys}$$

The minus sign is used to merely signify that there is loss of entropy. Its appearance with ΔS_{sys} is purely arbitrary, and an equivalent expression would be

$$-\Delta S_{sur} = \Delta S_{sys} = \left(\frac{Q}{T}\right)_{sys}$$

In either case, this subtle maneuver permits a substitution for ΔS_{sur} in the first equation to yield an expression *applicable only to a system at constant temperature*:

$$-\left(\frac{Q}{T}\right)_{sys} + \Delta S_{sys} \geqq 0 \quad \text{(constant temperature)}$$

or

$$\left(\frac{Q}{T}\right)_{sys} - \Delta S_{sys} \leqq 0$$

or

$$Q_{sys} - T\Delta S_{sys} \leqq 0$$

At *constant pressure* and, assuming that only pressure-volume work ($W = P\Delta V$) is done by the system, the First Law states

$$Q_{sys} = \Delta E_{sys} + P\Delta V_{sys} \qquad \text{(constant pressure)}$$

Substituting this for Q_{sys} in the previous equation gives the following relationship which now applies *at constant temperature and pressure*

$$\Delta E_{sys} + P\Delta V_{sys} - T\Delta S_{sys} \leqq 0$$

where the total quantity on the left is *defined* as equal to the change in the free energy (ΔG_{sys}) of the system

$$\Delta E_{sys} + P\Delta V_{sys} - T\Delta S_{sys} \equiv \Delta G_{sys} \leqq 0 \quad \text{(constant } T \text{ and } P)$$

According to the original interpretation of the equation symbols in the mathematical statement of the Second Law, a *zero value for* ΔG should still correspond to a *system at equilibrium*, but now a *minus value* (<0) should specify a *spontaneous process* and a *positive value* should specify a *non-spontaneous process*.

$$\Delta G_{sys} < 0 \qquad \text{spontaneous process } (\Delta G \text{ is } -)$$

$$\Delta G_{sys} > 0 \qquad \text{non-spontaneous process } (\Delta G \text{ is } +)$$

$$\Delta G_{sys} = 0 \qquad \text{equilibrium condition}$$

These theoretical conclusions have been validated through physical measurements, and indeed there are no known exceptions. Hence, we conclude that ΔG is—like ΔS—an unequivocal criterion of spontaneity. Moreover, the specifications that these relationships apply under the conditions of constant temperature and pressure make the free energy change a most suitable criterion, since these conditions apply to most laboratory studies as well as to the environment of the living cell. In addition, the free energy change can be readily measured.

Without our deriving a conceptual proof, suffice it to say that the new function (G) was appropriately termed free energy, because a finite change in its value from one state to another ($G_f - G_i$) is a measure of the maximum amount of energy in the system that is potentially available for useful work under the conditions of constant T and P. In the technical language of thermodynamics, there are several other interpretations of the free energy function, but in a discussion of this type, they are relatively unimportant. Most important, however, is a less technical interpretation, namely, that the *free energy of a chemical system is a thermodynamic property directly related to the total energy (chemical energy) and hence to the chemical stability of the individual components of the system.* In this context, a high free energy value is representative of a potentially unstable system which would spontaneously tend to a lower level of free energy under the appropriate conditions. In other words, a *negative value* for the change in free energy ($-\Delta G$) corresponds to an *energy-yielding reaction* resulting in a change from an unstable state of high chemical energy content to a more stable state of lower chemical energy content. Such a reaction is termed an *exergonic reaction* and is said to be *thermodynamically favorable*. If such a transition were to occur by itself, the output of chemical energy would be lost, primarily as heat energy. However, if it were to occur in the presence of a *thermodynamically unfavorable process* ($+\Delta G$)—that is, an *energy-requiring* or *endergonic reaction*—the output of chemical energy from the exergonic reaction could serve as an input of chemical energy to drive the endergonic process. This type of behavior is termed

If the chemical energy of reactants (G_i) is less than that of products (G_f), the reaction would be endergonic, that is, energy-requiring, and the value of ΔG would be positive.

$$\begin{array}{ccc} \text{reactants} & \longrightarrow & \text{products} \\ \text{(initial state)} & & \text{(final state)} \\ G_i & & G_f \\ & \Delta G = G_f - G_i & \end{array}$$

If the chemical energy of reactants (G_i) is greater than that of products (G_f), the reaction would be exergonic, that is, energy-yielding, and the value of ΔG would be negative.

coupling and represents the basis of energy flow in a living organism including both the conservation and utilization of chemical energy within the living cell. To understand this point further, it is necessary that we first examine some of the biomolecules that participate in cellular energetics. We will begin such an analysis shortly.

A complete treatment of thermodynamics and free energy would demand much more space than is allowed here. The objective of our brief analysis was much more restricted in scope. To summarize, our intentions were: (1) to establish the fundamental principles describing the energetics of material transformations; (2) to establish that a description of same is solely dependent on the difference between the energy levels of the system in the initial and final states; (3) to establish that an analysis of energetics can provide a criterion for predicting the capacity of a system to undergo a spontaneous change; (4) to establish that the most useful measure of predicting spontaneity under conditions of constant temperature and pressure is the change in free energy; and finally (5) to establish that the latter is also a relative measure of the chemical stability of the system in the initial and final states.

MEANING AND MEASUREMENT OF THE STANDARD FREE ENERGY CHANGE ($\Delta G°$)

Under conditions of constant temperature and pressure, for the general chemical transformation involving reactants A and B and products C and D

$$aA + bB \rightleftarrows cC + dD \qquad \text{(constant } T, P\text{)}$$

it can be shown that the free energy change is given by the classical relationship

$$\Delta G = \Delta G^0 + RT \ln \left(\frac{[C]^c [D]^d}{[A]^a [B]^b} \right)$$

where

$$[\ ] = \text{molar concentration}$$
$$R = 1.98 \text{ calories/degree/mole}$$
$$T = \text{absolute temperature (degrees Kelvin)}$$

Here ΔG represents the free energy change at any point in the course of the transformation, and $\Delta G°$ corresponds to the *standard free energy change* which applies only to a particular set of conditions, namely, when all participants are in their *standard states*. (Although the conditions of the standard state are purely arbitrary, there is universal agreement, and for solutes dissolved in solution, the accepted criterion is unit activity ($a = 1.0$) or approximately 1 M for most materials.) Thus, at a specific temperature and pressure, the value of ΔG will vary with changes in the existing concentrations of all participants, whereas $\Delta G°$ is constant and will change only if the temperature and/or pressure is altered. For these reasons and because the use of the standard state condition creates a common denominator for all systems, the standard free energy change is a much more desirable measurement, permitting a *direct comparison of the chemical energetics of different systems* at the same temperature and pressure.

A direct method of determining $\Delta G°$ is possible by recognizing that, when the system is at equilibrium, $\Delta G = 0$ and hence

$$\Delta G^\circ = -RT \ln \left(\frac{[C]^c[D]^d}{[A]^a[B]^b} \right)$$

But now since the system is at equilibrium, the concentration ratio is actually the equilibrium constant (K_{eq}) of the system, and we can write

$$\Delta G^\circ = -RT \ln (K_{eq}) = -2.3RT \log (K_{eq})$$

This last equation is one of the most useful relationships of thermodynamics. Its utility is obvious: at any temperature, the ΔG° can be calculated directly from the equilibrium constant, which in most cases can be determined in the laboratory. Some problems based on the use of this equation are provided at the end of the chapter.

Many reactions—especially those that occur in nature—involve H^+ as a product or reactant, and hence, a quotation of their ΔG° would necessarily mean that the concentration of H^+ is approximately 1 M (standard condition of unit activity). Since this means that the value would apply to pH = 0, it would certainly be unrealistic to quote the ΔG° of H^+-dependent reactions in a cell where the pH is approximately 7. Accordingly, when the equilibrium constants of pH-dependent reactions are measured, the system is studied at a pH of 7 and the resultant standard free energy changes are specified as being so calculated. To avoid confusion with a true ΔG°, the standard free energy changes of H^+-dependent reactions calculated under a non-standard–state condition of $[H^+]$ are symbolized differently, with a $\Delta G^{\circ\prime}$ notation being most common.

The meaning of ΔG° ($\Delta G^{\circ\prime}$) values is slightly different from that given previously for ΔG. Most different is the interpretation given to a zero value. When $\Delta G^\circ(\Delta G^{\circ\prime}) = 0$, this means that there is no appreciable difference between the chemical stability of initial and final states, and under standard conditions the reaction is neither appreciably endergonic nor exergonic. The system is not necessarily at equilibrium. When $\Delta G = 0$, the system is at equilibrium. The important point, however, is that the interpretation given to negative and positive values of ΔG° ($\Delta G^{\circ\prime}$) is basically the same as for ΔG, with minus (negative) values corresponding to a thermodynamically favorable process (exergonic and potentially spontaneous) and plus (positive) values corresponding to a thermodynamically unfavorable process (endergonic and non-spontaneous).

Endergonic (*requires energy for completion*)	$A + B \longleftarrow C + D$ equilibrium favors reactants $K'_{eq} <<< 1$ $\Delta G^{\circ\prime} = \oplus$ value Stability$_{reactants}$ > Stability$_{products}$
Exergonic (*yields energy*)	$A + B \rightleftharpoons C + D$ equilibrium favors products $K'_{eq} >>> 1$ $\Delta G^{\circ\prime} = \ominus$ value Stability$_{reactants}$ < Stability$_{products}$

Although the equation, $\Delta G^\circ = -RT \ln (K_{eq})$, has a general utility for all chemical reactions, it is possible to prove that for *oxidation-reduction reactions* the standard free energy change is given by

$$\Delta G^\circ = -n\mathscr{F}\mathscr{E}^\circ \quad \text{or} \quad \Delta G^{\circ\prime} = -n\mathscr{F}\mathscr{E}^{\circ\prime}$$

where

n = number of moles of electrons transferred

$\mathscr{F}$ = Faraday's Constant (~23,000 calories/volt)

$\mathscr{E}^\circ$ = net standard *oxidation–reduction potential* (volt)

$\mathscr{E}^{\circ\prime} = \mathscr{E}^\circ$ at pH 7

The basis of this relationship is that an oxidation–reduction system is capable of doing useful work due to the transfer of electrons from that part of the system undergoing oxidation (loss of electrons) to that undergoing reduction (gain of electrons). Such a system is called an *electrochemical cell*, and the net potential ($\mathscr{E}^\circ$) is merely a measure of the difference between each part of the system to undergo oxidation and reduction. Although we could continue here with an analysis of the basic principles and thermodynamics of electrochemical cells, the subject is more logically discussed in conjunction with the phenomena of respiratory electron transfer and the cellular production of useful metabolic energy in the form of ATP. Accordingly, we will defer further discussion until we consider these subjects in Chapter 13. Although the relationship has already been exposed on several occasions, our later development of these topics will serve as a striking example of why biological phenomena cannot be separated from physicochemical phenomena.

HIGH-ENERGY BIOMOLECULES

Our discussion of the principles of thermodynamics constitutes the first of two phases in developing the groundwork necessary for a meaningful study of cellular energetics. The rest of the chapter will be devoted to the second phase wherein we will consider the thermodynamic characteristics of a unique and exclusive group of molecules that participate in the flow of chemical energy within a cell. In so doing, be advised that we will be developing some extremely basic and important principles regarding the energetics of the living state. To dismiss them lightly or to label them as being irrelevant to your study of the living state would be—to put it mildly—very unwise.

After completing the next several chapters, you will discover that without question the single most important substance of cellular energetics is *adenosine triphosphate (ATP)*. At this point, however, you must only identify with the general message of the diagram below.

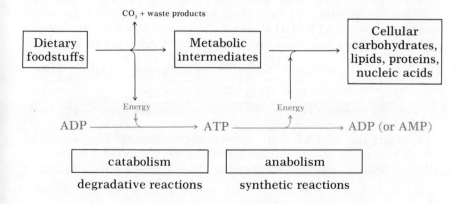

The diagram states that, on an overall basis, chemical energy is conserved in the degradative reactions of *catabolism* via the formation of ATP from ADP and P_i and utilized in the synthetic reactions of *anabolism* where ATP is hydrolyzed to ADP and P_i or to AMP and PP_i.

In this section our objective will be to establish why ATP is so well suited for this central role. Our approach will be based on the principles of classical thermodynamics. In addition to ATP, we will also consider other compounds that fulfill supplementary but equally important roles in cellular energetics. All have one thing in common; namely, a large amount of energy is released when they undergo a chemical transformation. Accordingly, they are called high-energy compounds. It is generally accepted that the term "high-energy" implies that the amount of energy released is 7,000 calories per mole or greater.

ADENOSINE TRIPHOSPHATE

Rather than proceed with a direct description of ATP energetics, let us develop the subject by analyzing a single reaction system which is representative of ATP participation in metabolism, namely, the enzymatic conversion of glutamate to glutamine. This reaction is particularly important in nitrogen metabolism (page 418), but for the moment its metabolic function is not of interest. At this time we are primarily interested in analyzing the net reaction as a *model* system to learn something about ATP.

$$-OCCH_2CH_2CHCO^- + NH_4^+ + ATP \underset{\substack{\text{glutamine} \\ \text{synthetase}}}{\overset{Mg^{++}}{\rightleftharpoons}} H_2NCCH_2CH_2CHCO^- + ADP + P_i$$

glutamate   glutamine

Mg^{++} required for optimal activity

at pH 7, 37°C: $\Delta G^{\circ\prime} = -3670$ calories

Conclusion: Forward reaction is thermodynamically favorable.

The specification of the standard free energy change for the complete reaction is vital to our analysis for we conclude that the net process is exergonic. Hence, the formation of glutamine from glutamate in the presence of ATP hydrolysis is thermodynamically favorable. However, this conclusion does not in any way suggest what purpose is served by the conversion of ATP to ADP and P_i. To resolve this question, we can look upon the net process as being composed of two separate reactions:

(1) $\text{glutamate} + NH_4^+ \xrightarrow{\text{synthetase}} \text{glutamine} + H_2O$ (10-1)

(2) $ATP + H_2O \xrightarrow{Mg^{++}} ADP + P_i$ (10-2)

(1) + (2) $\text{glutamate} + NH_4^+ + ATP \longrightarrow \text{glutamine} + ADP + P_i$ (10-3)

This maneuver, which is both conceptually permissible and practically possible, permits one to consider the enzyme-catalyzed glutamate + $NH_4^+ \rightarrow$ glutamine system independent of ATP involvement. In fact, a study of this type has been made, and on the basis of equilibrium measurements, the following result was reported.

$$\text{glutamate} + NH_4^+ \xrightarrow{\text{synthetase}} \text{glutamine} + H_2O$$
$$\text{at pH 7, 37°C: } \Delta G^{\circ\prime} = +3750 \text{ calories}$$

Yes, the sign of the free energy change is correct, and the formation of the amide from the free acid is actually an endergonic reaction. In the presence of ATP, however, we have already established that the same reaction is exergonic. With a little thought, a conclusion as to the participation of ATP is inescapable—the hydrolysis of ATP to ADP and P_i must be sufficiently exergonic to provide the chemical energy needed to mediate the endergonic formation of glutamine. In other words, the

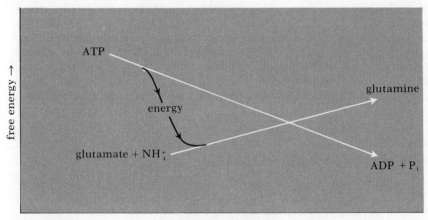

progress of reaction →

complete reaction involving glutamate, NH_4^+, and ATP can be considered as a coupling of a thermodynamically unfavorable reaction to a thermodynamically favorable reaction, with the latter acting as an energetic driving force of the former. In this particular case, it has been empirically established that the whole process is mediated by the actual transfer of energy due to the formation of *phosphoglutamate,* an activated (unstable) reaction intermediate, which reacts further to complete the process as shown below.

Proposed Mechanism of Glutamine Formation

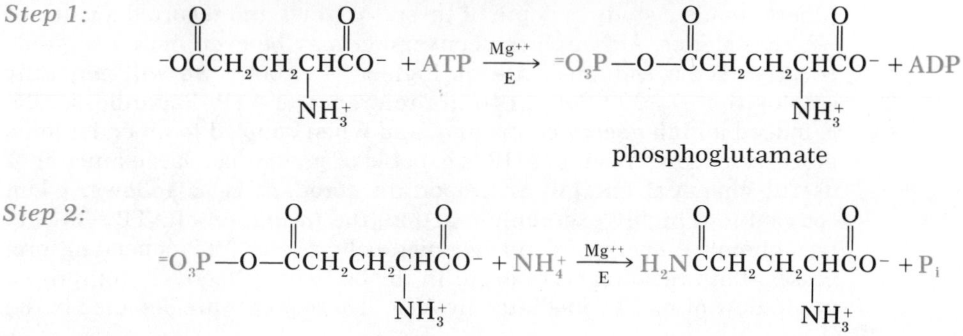

Step 1:

$$^-OCCH_2CH_2CHCO^- + ATP \xrightarrow[E]{Mg^{++}} {}^=O_3P{-}O{-}CCH_2CH_2CHCO^- + ADP$$
with NH_3^+ substituents

phosphoglutamate

Step 2:

$$^=O_3P{-}O{-}CCH_2CH_2CHCO^- + NH_4^+ \xrightarrow[E]{Mg^{++}} H_2NCCH_2CH_2CHCO^- + P_i$$
with NH_3^+ substituents

where $\quad$ ${}^=O_3POCCH_2CH_2CHCO^-$ $\quad$ is a reaction intermediate

$$
\begin{array}{ccc}
& O & \quad O \\
& \parallel & \quad \parallel \\
{}^=O_3POC & CH_2CH_2CH & CO^- \\
& & | \\
& & NH_3^+
\end{array}
$$

To summarize: in our model system we have established that the ATP → ADP conversion is a thermodynamic driving force of an otherwise unfavorable process. Although we have considered a specific chemical transformation of the living state distinguished by specific thermodynamic values and a specific mechanism, the *theme of ATP participation applies to all ATP-dependent processes*. Many different examples will be encountered in subsequent chapters.

A more precise analysis of ATP energetics necessitates that we establish the value of the free energy change for ATP hydrolysis under physiological conditions. To make this calculation, we need look no further than the glutamate–glutamine reaction system for which the $\Delta G^{\circ\prime}$ values for glutamine formation were given in the presence and absence of ATP. Since changes in thermodynamic functions are dependent solely on the initial and final states, we can express the net standard free energy change as equal to the sum of the free energy changes corresponding to any component parts. Hence,

$$\Delta G^{\circ\prime}_{net} = \Delta G^{\circ\prime}_1 + \Delta G^{\circ\prime}_2$$

where
$$\Delta G^{\circ\prime}_{net} = -3670 \text{ calories} \quad \text{(reaction 10–3)}$$
$$\Delta G^{\circ\prime}_1 = +3750 \text{ calories} \quad \text{(reaction 10–1)}$$
$$\Delta G^{\circ\prime}_2 = ? \quad \text{(reaction 10–2)}$$

Solving for $\Delta G^{\circ\prime}_2$:

$$\Delta G^{\circ\prime}_2 = \Delta G^{\circ\prime}_{net} - \Delta G^{\circ\prime}_1 = -7420 \text{ calories}$$

that is, for

$$\text{ATP} + H_2O \xrightleftharpoons{\text{Mg}^{++}} \text{ADP} + P_i$$

at pH 7, 37°C:

$$\Delta G^{\circ\prime} = -7420 \text{ calories}$$

Until recently there has been considerable debate as to the most accurate value of $\Delta G^{\circ\prime}$ for ATP hydrolysis, with reported values ranging from −7,000 to −9,000 calories. The chief difficulty is that the hydrolysis of ATP is quite sensitive to pH and Mg^{++} concentration. In 1968 R. A. Alberty made a study in depth of these variables and reported a value of −7,300 calories. Although the conversion may be even more exergonic *in vivo* (some estimates are as high as −11,000), we will generally employ the −7,300 figure in future reference to ATP. Regardless, ATP is indeed a high-energy compound, and when coupled to an endergonic process, its conversion to ADP is capable of providing a large amount of useful chemical energy. An important corollary is as follows: when coupled to a highly exergonic reaction, the formation of ATP serves to trap chemical energy for further metabolic use in ATP-dependent processes. Both reaction types occur in the cell and collectively comprise a cyclic flow of energy mediated by ATP. These points are depicted in the

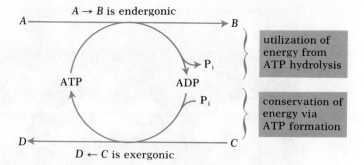

$A \rightarrow B$ is endergonic

utilization of
energy from
ATP hydrolysis

conservation of
energy via
ATP formation

$D \leftarrow C$ is exergonic

diagram above. Note that the principles expressed by this diagram are the same as those contained in the diagram on page 245.

To conclude our analysis of ATP, we can ask one final question— *why* is ATP such a thermodynamically unstable compound? Or the same question asked differently—why is a large amount of energy required for the formation of ATP from ADP and P_i? In general terms, the answer to each is that the ATP molecule must contain sufficient chemical energy to alleviate structural features which tend to act as destabilizing forces. In particular, two such forces can be identified: (1) *electrostatic repulsion* and (2) *opposing resonance*. The potential for electrostatic repulsion is readily apparent by recognizing that, at physiological pH, ATP probably exists as a tetra-anion due to the ionization of the four —P—O—H bonds. The result is a spatial localization of like negative charges that have a natural tendency to repel each other. This repulsion constitutes a structural strain on the whole molecule, but the —P—O—P— bonds are most affected. The principle of opposing resonance argues that a potential competition will exist between successive phosphorus atoms for an unshared pair of electrons from the sandwiched oxygen atoms. The competition is established due to the presence of a partial positive charge on each P atom resulting from the polarization of each P=O bond. Although the electrostatic stress is probably more significant, the important point to realize is that, under physiological conditions, the very existence of ATP is dependent on the presence of sufficient chemical energy within the molecule to overcome these physicochemical stresses. The energy is not confined to any one particular bond in ATP, but is distributed among several. When ATP is converted to ADP, the stresses are minimized and energy is released. Finally, it should be noted that the energetics of ATP hydrolysis are not significantly dependent on the presence of adenine grouping. That is to say, all of the purine and pyrimidine triphosphonucleotides are similarly characterized.

Although the arbitrary restriction that the $\Delta G^{\circ\prime}$ of hydrolysis be equal to or more negative than −7,000 calories limits the number of substances to be classified as high-energy compounds, the list is not confined to nucleoside triphosphates alone. Other naturally occurring substances that meet this specification are *acyl phosphates, enoyl phosphates, thioesters, phosphoguanidines,* and the *nicotinamide adenine dinucleotides.* An example of each type, along with a reference to illustrate its participation in metabolism, is given in Table 10–1. Of the substances listed, those with a more general importance are the thioesters and the nicotinamide dinucleotides.

Adenosine triphosphate (ATP) pH 7

opposing resonance

ATP (unstable)

electrostatic repulsion

ADP (more stable)

both factors
minimized

THIOESTERS

Thioesters, particularly those involving *coenzyme A* (symbolized HSCoA), play a very important role in metabolism; namely, they serve as the *metabolically active form of acyl* (R—C—) *groups*. Indeed, the bulk of enzyme reactions involving the transfer of acyl groups, in addition to many involving the chemical modification of acyl groups, require the acyl group to be in the form of an acyl-SCoA ester. As shown below for *acetyl-SCoA,* the single most important thioester, acyl-SCoA derivatives are generally formed from the free acid and coenzyme A in an ATP-dependent reaction catalyzed by a thiokinase (see page 250). Reactions of this type typify the coenzyme role of HSCoA (refer back to page 109). As with most coenzymes, HSCoA is actually incorporated into the reaction product, with the original form being regenerated in a later step.

Although the structure of HSCoA is obviously complex, note that the reactive functional group is a terminal, free *sulfhydryl group.* Also

Table 10–1 A summary of high-energy compounds of biological importance.

System	$\Delta G°'$(pH 7) calories/mole
Hydrolysis of Triphosphonucleotides:	
$ATP \xrightarrow[H_2O]{} ADP + P_i$ (see text, this chapter)	$-7,300$
Hydrolysis of Acyl Phosphates:	

$$R-\overset{\overset{\textstyle O}{\|}}{C}-OPO_3^= \xrightarrow[H_2O]{} R-COO^- + P_i$$

| 1,3-diphosphoglycerate $\xrightarrow[H_2O]{}$ 3-phosphoglycerate (see page 267) | $-11,800$ |
| **Hydrolysis of Enoyl Phosphates:** | |

$$RCH=\underset{\underset{\textstyle PO_3^=}{\overset{\textstyle |}{O}}}{\overset{\textstyle |}{C}}-COO^- \xrightarrow[H_2O]{} RCH_2-\overset{\overset{\textstyle }{C}}{\underset{\underset{\textstyle O}{\|}}{}}-COO^- + P$$

| phosphoenolpyruvate $\xrightarrow[H_2O]{}$ pyruvate $+ P_i$ (see page 267) | $-14,800$ |
| **Hydrolysis of Acyl Thioesters of Coenzyme A:** | |

$$R-\overset{\overset{\textstyle O}{\|}}{C}-SCoA \xrightarrow[H_2O]{} R-\overset{\overset{\textstyle O}{\|}}{C}-O^- + HSCoA$$

| acetyl-SCoA $\xrightarrow[H_2O]{}$ acetate $+ HSCoA$ (see text, this chapter) | $-7,370$ |
| **Hydrolysis of Guanidinium Phosphates:** | |

$$R-CH_2N\underset{\underset{\textstyle +NH_2}{\|}}{H}CNHPO_3^= \xrightarrow[H_2O]{} RCH_2N\underset{\underset{\textstyle +NH_2}{\|}}{H}CNH_2 + P_i$$

creatine phosphate $\xrightarrow[H_2O]{}$ creatine $+ P_i$ (see page 290)	$-10,300$
Oxidation of Nicotinamide Adenine Nucleotides:	
$NADH(NADPH) + H^+ \xrightarrow[\frac{1}{2}O_2]{} NAD^+(NADP^+) + H_2O$	$-52,600*$
reduced forms oxidized forms	
* with O_2 as oxidizing agent (see text, this chapter)	

noteworthy is that part of the HSCoA molecule is composed of *β-alanine* and *pantothenic acid,* the latter being an essential vitamin for mammals. Consequently, it is generally believed that HSCoA represents the metabolically active form of pantothenic acid. Since this type of terminology is often improperly interpreted by beginning students, let us put it another way: when pantothenic acid is ingested, the bulk of it is utilized in the biosynthesis of coenzyme A, which of course is required for normal metabolism. With a prolonged dietary deficiency of pantothenic acid, the body levels of HSCoA become subnormal. The latter condition obviously impairs normal metabolism, since many reactions are HSCoA dependent. A deficiency of pantothenic acid (HSCoA) is manifested in many forms depending on the species of animal. However, there is yet no report of a clear association between a particular physio-

$$^-OOCCH_2CH_2NH_3^+$$
β-alanine

$$^-OOCCH_2CH_2\overset{\overset{\textstyle H}{|}}{N}-\overset{\overset{\textstyle }{|}}{\underset{\underset{\textstyle O}{\|}}{C}}-\overset{\overset{\textstyle OH}{|}}{\underset{\underset{\textstyle H}{|}}{C}}-\overset{\overset{\textstyle CH_3}{|}}{\underset{\underset{\textstyle CH_3}{|}}{C}}-CH_2OH$$

pantothenic acid

logical abnormality and a specific set of HSCoA-dependent reactions. To review a point we made in Chapter 5: the general theme of this brief discussion applies to most vitamins; that is, the physiological function of a vitamin is described in terms of its participation as a coenzyme or its conversion to a coenzyme form. (See Table 5-3 on page 109.)

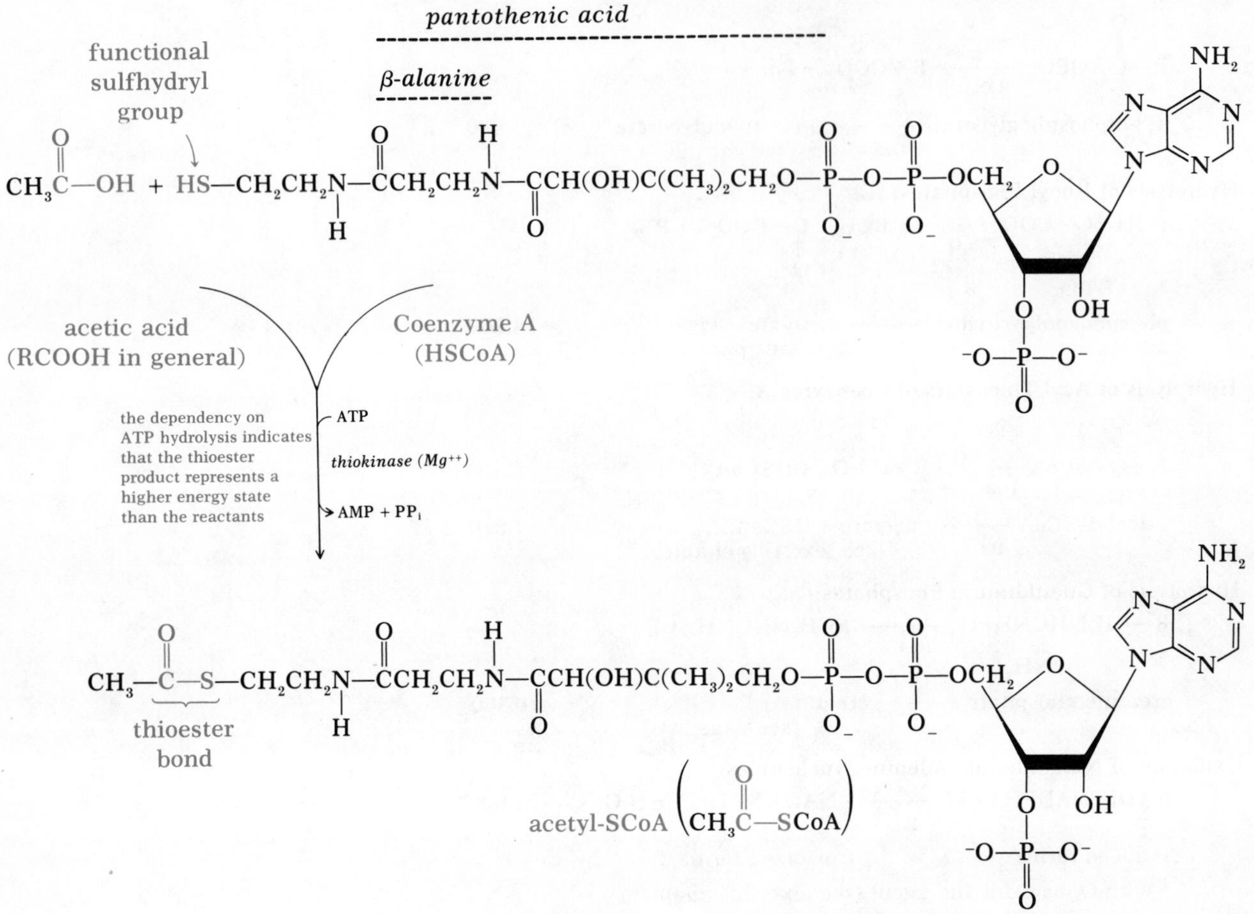

The tip-off to the significant thermodynamic characteristic of acyl-SCoA compounds is given in the reaction above for the formation of acetyl-SCoA. The clue is the dependency on ATP, which indicates that the formation of the thioester from the acid and HSCoA is highly endergonic. Accordingly, the thioester represents a high-energy state of the acyl group. That is to say, the acyl group of the thioester is more susceptible to participating in chemical reactions than the free acid. The natural selection of thioesters as the metabolically active form of acyl groups is a logical one, simply because thioesters are more chemically reactive than oxyesters. The sites in the acyl grouping most susceptible to reaction are the *carbonyl carbon* and its *alpha carbon* atom. Two of the important cellular reactions of acyl-SCoA compounds in general, and acetyl-SCoA in particular, are shown below. For simplicity the enzymes that catalyze each reaction are not shown. The formation of citrate from acetyl-SCoA and oxaloacetate is the first reaction of an extremely vital metabolic pathway, the citric acid cycle (see Chapter 12). The biological significance of N-acetyl-D-glucosamine formation should be apparent by thinking in terms of our discussion of the carbohydrates. Additional examples will be encountered in other chapters but most notably in Chapter 15 dealing with the metabolism of fatty acids.

NICOTINAMIDE DINUCLEOTIDES

The nicotinamide dinucleotides represent another class of high-energy compounds of special biochemical importance. To understand why they are so classified, let us first examine their structure and metabolic function. Two distinct types exist in nature—*nicotinamide adenine dinucleotide (symbolized NAD)* and *nicotinamide adenine dinucleotide phosphate (symbolized NADP)*. (According to an older and now less used convention, they were termed pyridine nucleotides and called diphosphopyridine nucleotide (DPN) and triphosphopyridine nucleotide (TPN), respectively.) As shown on page 252, the structural difference between NAD and NADP is rather subtle, to say the least, with NADP containing an extra phosphate group at C_2' of the ribose unit attached to adenine.

Although the line drawings of these materials tend to convey a complex structure, they are not complex at all. Actually, there is only one part of the structure that we haven't yet encountered, namely, the *nicotinamide* moiety, a substituted *pyridine*. The remainder is composed of adenine, β-D-ribose, and phosphate. Moreover, the linkages are familiar. In fact, as the name implies, the molecules can be considered as composed of two nucleotide units linked together by a phosphodiester

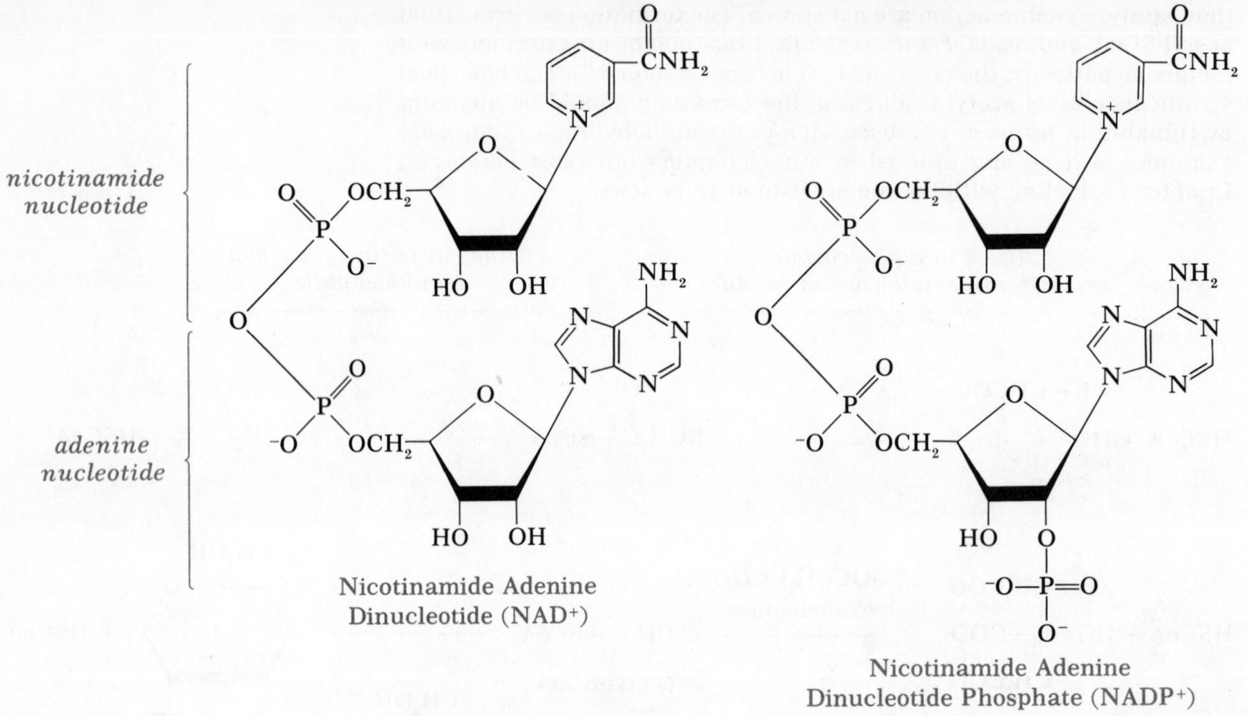

nicotinamide nucleotide

adenine nucleotide

CNH_2

OCH_2

HO OH

NH_2

O

OCH_2

HO OH

Nicotinamide Adenine
Dinucleotide (NAD⁺)

CNH_2

OCH_2

HO OH

NH_2

O

OCH_2

HO O

$-O-P=O$

O^-

Nicotinamide Adenine
Dinucleotide Phosphate (NADP⁺)

bridge. The nicotinamide component is especially important for two reasons. First, nicotinamide is a derivative of the vitamin, *nicotinic acid*, sometimes called *niacin*. Since nicotinamide does not generally occur in the free state but largely in glycosidic linkage with ribose in NAD and NADP, the latter are assumed to be the metabolically active forms of the vitamin. Secondly, and more important, is the fact that the pyridine ring of nicotinamide comprises the active site of NAD and NADP (see

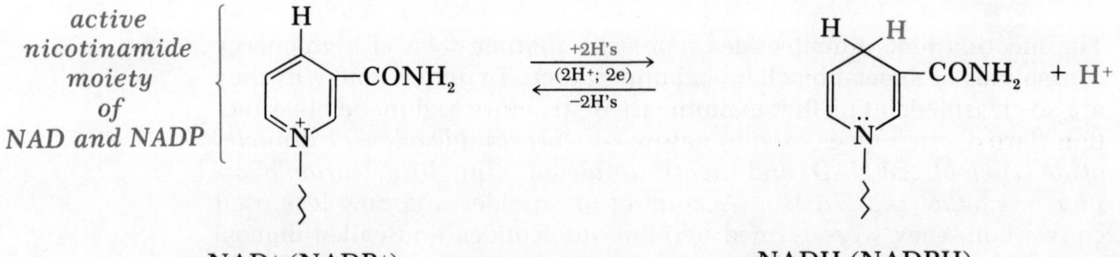

active nicotinamide moiety of NAD and NADP

H

$-CONH_2$

N^+

$\{$

NAD⁺ (NADP⁺)
oxidized form

$\xrightarrow[\text{−2H's}]{\substack{\text{+2H's} \\ \text{(2H⁺; 2e)}}}$

H   H

$-CONH_2 \quad + \text{H}^+$

N

$\{$

NADH (NADPH)
reduced form

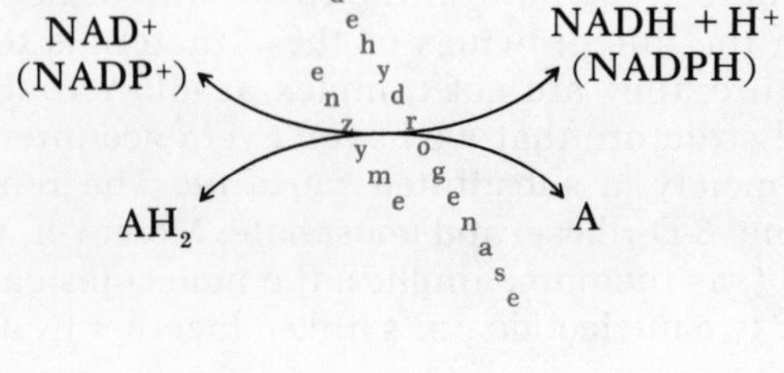

NAD⁺
(NADP⁺)

AH₂

NADH + H⁺
(NADPH)

A

dehydrogenase

below). That is to say, it is the pyridine ring that actually functions in the reversible transfer of electrons and a proton.

On a functional basis, both NAD and NADP are classified as co-enzymes for a large number of dehydrogenases (see page 108), with the sole function of acting as agents in the transfer of hydrogen atoms in oxidation–reduction reactions. Accordingly, two forms of each coenzyme exist—an *oxidized form* and a *reduced form*. The structures given above are of the oxidized species and normally symbolized as NAD^+ and $NADP^+$ due to the positive charge on the pyridine N atom. In the presence of a reduced substrate (hydrogen donor) and an appropriate dehydrogenase, the *pyridine ring is reduced* by accepting the equivalent of one proton (H^+) and two electrons, with the second proton yielded to the medium. The reduced form is symbolized as NADH or NADPH. The process is reversible; indeed, most dehydrogenase-catalyzed reactions occur reversibly.

No doubt you are wondering what all this has to do with bio-energetics and high-energy compounds. Well, the explanation is that, once they are produced in the cell, the primary metabolic fate of the reduced forms—especially NADH—is to be reoxidized as the first step in a series of consecutive oxidation–reduction reactions that terminate with the reduction of molecular oxygen. Although this also applies to NADPH, its primary metabolic fate is to serve as a hydrogen donor in many biosynthetic reactions (see page 261, Chapter 11). The complete process, termed *electron transport,* is most important for a very good reason—the great majority of organisms in the biosphere utilize this operation or a variation of it (a terminal electron acceptor other than molecular oxygen) as the main source of energy needed for the intra-cellular formation of ATP. In other words, it constitutes the means by which a cell converts the chemical energy of exogenously supplied food-stuffs to useful metabolic energy. Still, why are NADH and NADPH to be considered as high-energy compounds? Because we are deferring discussion of oxidation–reduction potentials until Chapter 13, our approach to this question will necessarily be limited at this point. For now, suffice it to say that whenever an oxidation–reduction reaction is composed of a reducing system and an oxidizing system that are sep-arated by a positive potential difference, the reaction will be exergonic with the amount of released energy dependent on the magnitude of the potential difference. As a statement of fact—to be discussed later in Chapter 13—under physiological conditions (pH 7; 37°C), the overall potential difference between the initial reducing half-reaction (NADH → NAD^+) or (NADPH → $NADP^+$) and the terminal oxidizing half-reaction ($\frac{1}{2}$ O_2 → H_2O) is +1.14 volts. We can appreciate the significance of this number by using the equation on page 243 of this chapter which yields $\Delta G^{o\prime} \approx -53,000$ calories ($n = 2$ for the transfer of two electrons). Hence, the process is extremely exergonic and we conclude that the *reduced* nicotinamide dinucleotides represent high-energy compounds. The component steps of electron transfer and the means by which the re-leased energy is conserved by a cell through the coupled formation of ATP comprise one of the most fascinating biochemical processes in nature. The complete coupled process is termed *oxidative phosphoryl-ation.* Many of the details have been established and will be discussed in Chapter 13.

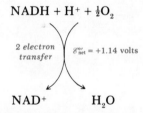

$$NADH + H^+ + \tfrac{1}{2}O_2$$

2 electron transfer $\mathscr{E}^{o\prime}_{net} = +1.14$ volts

$$NAD^+ \qquad H_2O$$

$$\Delta G^{o\prime}_{net} = -(2)(23,063)(1.14)$$
$$\Delta G^{o\prime}_{net} = -52,584 \text{ calories}$$

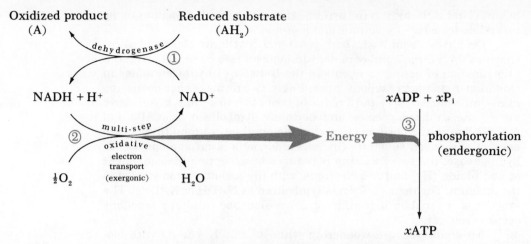

① formation of NADH by dehydrogenation of reduced substrate

② oxidation of NADH by electron transport, with oxygen as the terminal electron acceptor

③ phosphorylation of ADP to yield ATP

② + ③ oxidative phosphorylation

COUPLING PHENOMENON

The coupling of endergonic and exergonic reactions is a theme through all of metabolism, resulting in (a) an efficient conservation and utilization of metabolic chemical energy, and (b) an efficient flow of metabolic intermediates through a pathway composed of several consecutive reactions. Throughout the next few chapters, we will encounter many specific examples of both points, but in order to recognize and appreciate their metabolic significance, one must have a prerequisite understanding of the nature of coupled reactions. Accordingly, we conclude this chapter by focusing on same. In so doing, we will briefly reiterate some of the previous material, but will also develop other aspects yet to be mentioned.

Reduced to the simplest and most functional of terms, the *coupling principle means that a thermodynamically (energetically) unfavorable reaction is driven to completion by a thermodynamically favorable reaction.* This effect is realized in either of two ways which differ in terms of whether or not there is an actual transfer of energy. Reactions involving an actual transfer of energy occur by one of two mechanisms (Case I and Case II below). In Case I—a single reaction catalyzed by a single enzyme—the energy transfer is effected through the formation of an intermediate during the course of the conversion of the primary reactant to the primary product. This typifies many ATP-dependent reactions such as the formation of glutamine and acetyl-SCoA (pages 245 and 250 of this chapter). Related to this type of reaction, but not in the strict sense a coupled system, is the direct enzymatic formation of organic phosphates mediated by ATP-dependent kinases. A variation of this theme is shown in Case II where the net reaction results from the consecutive occurrence of two distinct reactions catalyzed by two separate enzymes. Here the common intermediate is, in fact, the primary product of one reaction and the primary reactant of the second. The biosynthesis of sucrose is representative of this form of coupling. In reactions where an actual energy transfer does not occur (Case III), the coupling is explained purely in terms of equilibrium considerations. Here one of the characteristic differences from the previous two types is that ATP is not involved. However, as in Case II, we are dealing with consecutive reactions catalyzed by different enzymes. As indicated, the unfavorable equilibrium of one reaction can be displaced if the product of that reactant then serves as a substrate (reactant) with a strong tendency to be converted to another material in a subsequent reaction.

COUPLED SYSTEMS: A SUMMARY

CASE I (ATP dependent)

Energy transfer during a single reaction catalyzed by a single enzyme

$$X + Y + ATP \xrightarrow{E} X\text{-}Y + AMP + PP_i$$

or

$$X + Y + ATP \xrightarrow{E} X\text{-}Y + ADP + P_i$$

where the thermodynamically unfavorable process of $X + Y \rightarrow X\text{-}Y$ with a $+\Delta G^{\circ\prime}$ is coupled to the thermodynamically favorable process of ATP hydrolysis (to AMP and PP_i or ADP and P_i) with a $-\Delta G^{\circ\prime}$ according to a two-step mechanism such as

Step 1: $\qquad\qquad X + ATP \xrightarrow{E_1} [X \sim AMP] + PP_i$

Step 2: $\qquad\qquad [X \sim AMP] + Y \xrightarrow{E_1} X\text{-}Y + AMP$

$\qquad$ (where $X \sim AMP$ is a reaction intermediate)

Net: $\qquad\qquad X + Y + ATP \xrightarrow{E_1} X\text{-}Y + AMP + PP_i$

Example: $\quad$ acetate + CoASH + ATP $\longrightarrow$ acetyl-SCoA + AMP + PP_i

or

Step 1: $\qquad\qquad X + ATP \xrightarrow{E_1} [X \sim P] + ADP$

Step 2: $\qquad\qquad [X \sim P] + Y \xrightarrow{E_1} X\text{-}Y + P_i$

$\qquad$ (where $X \sim P$ is a reaction intermediate)

Net: $\qquad\qquad X + Y + ATP \xrightarrow{E_1} X\text{-}Y + ADP + P_i$

Example: $\quad$ glutamate + NH_4^+ + ATP $\longrightarrow$ glutamine + ADP + P_i

This type of coupling is also related to the kinase-catalyzed formation of sugar phosphates as shown below:

$$X + ATP \xrightarrow{\text{kinase}} X\text{-}PO_3^= + ADP$$

Example: $\quad$ glucose + ATP $\xrightarrow{\text{glucokinase}}$ glucose-6-phosphate + ADP

CASE II (ATP dependent)

Energy transfer accompanying two or more separate reactions catalyzed by separate enzymes

$$X + Y + ATP \xrightarrow{E_1} \xrightarrow{E_2} X\text{-}Y + ADP + P_i$$

where the thermodynamically unfavorable process of $X + Y \rightarrow X\text{-}Y$ with a $+\Delta G^{\circ\prime}$ is coupled to the thermodynamically favorable process of

ATP hydrolysis (to AMP and PP_i or ADP and P_i) with a $-\Delta G^{\circ\prime}$ via two separate reactions such as

Reaction 1: $\qquad X + ATP \xrightarrow{E_1} X\text{–}P + ADP$

Reaction 2: $\qquad X\text{–}P + Y \xrightarrow{E_2} X\text{–}Y + P_i$

Net: $\qquad X + Y + ATP \xrightarrow{E_1} \xrightarrow{E_2} X\text{–}Y + ADP + P_i$

Example: $\qquad$ glucose + ATP $\xrightarrow{E_1}$ glucose-1-phosphate + ADP

glucose-1-phosphate + fructose $\xrightarrow{E_2}$ sucrose + P_i

---

glucose + fructose + ATP $\xrightarrow{E_1} \xrightarrow{E_1}$ sucrose + ADP + P_i

CASE III (ATP independent)

No actual transfer of energy in two or more separate reactions catalyzed by separate enzymes

$$X \xrightarrow{E_1} Y \xrightarrow{E_2} Z$$

where a thermodynamically unfavorable process of $X \to Y$ with a $+\Delta G^{\circ\prime}$ is driven to completion by being coupled to the thermodynamically favorable process of $Y \to Z$ with a $-\Delta G^{\circ\prime}$ according to the following:

Reaction 1: $\qquad X \xleftarrow{E_1} Y \qquad K_{eq_1} <<< 1 \quad \Delta G^{\circ\prime}_1 = +$

Reaction 2: $\qquad Y \xrightarrow{E_2} Z \qquad K_{eq_2} >>> 1 \quad \Delta G^{\circ\prime}_2 = -$

Net: $\qquad X \xrightarrow{E_1} \xrightarrow{E_2} Z \quad K_{eq_{net}} > 1 \qquad \Delta G^{\circ\prime}_{net} = -$

Example: $\qquad$ malate $\xrightarrow{E_1}$ oxaloacetate $\qquad \Delta G^{\circ\prime} = +6.7$ Kcal

oxaloacetate + acetyl-SCoA $\xrightarrow{E_2}$ citrate + HSCoA $\qquad \Delta G^{\circ\prime} = -9$ Kcal

---

malate + acetyl-SCoA $\xrightarrow{E_1} \xrightarrow{E_2}$ citrate + HSCoA $\Delta G^{\circ\prime}_{net} = -2.3$ Kcal

LITERATURE

KLOTZ, I. M., *Energy Changes in Biochemical Reactions*. New York: Academic Press, 1967. A small monograph (available in paperback) on the fundamental concepts of thermodynamics as they apply to biological systems. Written by a chemist for the biologist.

LEHNINGER, A. L., *Bioenergetics,* Second Edition. New York: W. A. Benjamin, Inc., 1971. A superb introductory book (available in paperback) emphasizing the energy relationships in living cells at the metabolic level. Allosteric regulation and recent advances in the molecular organization of membranes, mitochondria, and chloroplasts are also included.

MONTGOMERY, R., and C. A. SWENSON, *Quantitative Problems in the Biochemical Sciences.* San Francisco: W. H. Freeman and Company, 1969. Chapter 10 summarizes basic principles of biochemical energetics and applies them in problem solving.

MORRIS, J. G., *A Biologist's Physical Chemistry.* Reading: Addison-Wesley Publishing Company, 1968. Chapters 7, 8, and 9 contain a lucid discussion into the basic principles of classical thermodynamics and their application to biochemical systems.

WILLIAMS, V. R., and H. B. WILLIAMS, *Basic Physical Chemistry for the Life Sciences*. San Francisco: W. H. Freeman and Company, 1967. Chapters 2 and 3 contain thorough presentations of the principles of thermodynamics and the free energy concept as they apply to biochemical and biological systems.

EXERCISES

10-1 The standard free energy change for the hydrolysis of glucose-1-phosphate at pH 7 and 37°C has been measured as −5,000 calories/mole. Calculate the equilibrium constant for this reaction.

$$\text{glucose-1-phosphate} \rightarrow \text{glucose} + P_i$$

10-2 On the basis of material presented in this chapter and the principle of the relationship between structure and function, would you predict the $\Delta G^{\circ\prime}$ for the reaction below to be approximately (a) +3,600 calories/mole, (b) −3,600 calories/mole, (c) +6,800 calories/mole, (d) −6,800 calories/mole, or (e) +1,875 calories/mole?

$$\text{asparagine} \rightarrow \text{aspartate} + NH_3$$

10-3 The standard free energy change for the hydrolysis of glucose-6-phosphate at pH 7 and 25°C has been measured as −3,300 calories/mole. Given this and the information in Exercise 10–1, calculate the $\Delta G^{\circ\prime}$ for the following reaction at pH 7 and 37°C.

$$\text{glucose-1-phosphate} \rightarrow \text{glucose-6-phosphate}$$

10-4 Which of the reactions given below would be likely candidates to be coupled to the formation of ATP from ADP and P_i? (Assume that pH 7 and 37°C apply to both $\Delta G^{\circ\prime}$ and K_{eq}).

	$\Delta G^{\circ\prime}$ (cal.)	K_{eq}
a) phosphoenolpyruvate → pyruvate + P_i	—	2.5×10^{10}
b) 3-phosphoglycerate → 2-phosphoglycerate	—	1.8×10^{-1}
c) fructose-6-phosphate → fructose + P_i	− 3,200	—
d) succinyl-SCoA → succinate + HSCoA	−11,000	—

10-5 The overall standard free energy change for the reaction

$$\text{pyruvate} + \text{ATP} + CO_2 \rightarrow \text{oxaloacetate} + P_i + \text{ADP}$$

is 1,100 calories/mole. From this, calculate the $\Delta G^{\circ\prime}$ for

$$\text{pyruvate} + CO_2 \rightarrow \text{oxaloacetate}$$

(Assume pH 7 and 37°C for all $\Delta G^{\circ\prime}$ values). Classify the coupled reaction involving ATP as Case I, Case II, or Case III.

10-6 Dihydroxyacetone phosphate (DHAP) is one of the principal intermediates produced during the degradation of hexoses such as glucose. Under anaerobic conditions, certain bacteria can produce glycerol from glucose due to the action of two enzymes which catalyze the reduction of dihydroxyacetone phosphate to glycerol-1-phosphate and then the hydrolysis of glycerol phosphate to yield free glycerol and inorganic phosphate.

	$\Delta G^{\circ\prime}$ (cal.)
dihydroxyacetone phosphate + 2H's → glycerol-1-phosphate	+8,750
glycerol-1-phosphate → glycerol + P_i	−2,400

Calculate whether the overall sequence from DHAP to glycerol is endergonic or exergonic. Is the overall sequence an example of coupling according to Case I, Case II, or Case III?

10-7 In the cell, the enzyme (a dehydrogenase) that catalyzes the reduction of DHAP to glycerol-1-phosphate utilizes NADH as the source of reducing power. The NADH is in turn oxidized to NAD^+. The complete reaction is

$$DHAP + NADH + H^+ \rightarrow glycerol\text{-}1\text{-}phosphate + NAD^+$$

Given that the $\Delta G^{\circ\prime}$ for the oxidation of NADH to NAD^+ is −14,760 calories, calculate the $\Delta G^{\circ\prime}$ for the formation of glycerol phosphate according to this reaction. Compare this value to that given in the preceding exercise and explain the difference. What effect does the NADH-dependent reduction of DHAP have on the energetics of the overall conversion of DHAP to glycerol as it occurs in the cell?

10-8 The steady state concentration of ATP in a red blood cell has been estimated to be approximately 13 times greater than that of ADP. In addition, the concentration of inorganic phosphate has been estimated to be approximately 8 times greater than that of ADP. Given this information calculate the value of the free energy change ($\Delta G'$) that would apply to ATP hydrolysis in the red blood cell.

10-9 A buffered (pH 7) solution containing phosphoenolpyruvate (30 millimoles), glucose (20 millimoles), and small amounts of adenosine diphosphate, pyruvate kinase, and hexokinase was incubated at 37°C. Given the information below: (a) explain what will occur during the incubation process, particularly in the early stages; (b) write the net reaction that would occur; and (c) predict whether or not the net reaction would proceed to completion in that there would be little or none of the original substrates remaining.

$$phosphoenolpyruvate + ADP \xrightarrow{\text{pyruvate kinase}} pyruvate + ATP$$
$$glucose + ATP \xrightarrow{\text{hexokinase}} glucose\text{-}6\text{-}phosphate + ADP$$

10-10 Given the thermodynamic information in this chapter, calculate the theoretical yield of ATP from the oxidation of $NADH(H^+)$ during the coupled process of oxidative phosphorylation.

11

Carbohydrate Metabolism

PRINCIPLES OF METABOLISM

Metabolism can be defined as the *sum of all the reactions that occur in a living organism.* This definition suggests that this is a vast subject, and indeed it is. The number of reactions alone is staggering, with different organisms, depending on their complexity, characterized by several hundred to several thousand. However, the study of metabolism is anything but a numbers game. Of utmost importance is that the collective reactions of any organism constitute the biochemical and physiological reality of that organism. In other words, an organism—be it man or microbe—does what it does because, biochemically speaking, it is capable of performing a specific set of reactions (most of which are enzyme catalyzed) responsible for such things as cellular differentiation, specific cellular functions, cellular adaptation to a changing environment, and growth in general. In summary, they are responsible for sustaining the very viability of the organism. In this context, although each reaction can be considered as a separate entity of individual importance, it is imperative to realize that the *metabolic expression of the whole organism is due to the integration of each individual reaction into a dynamic reaction circuitry of intricate design controlled by a host of sensitive regulatory checks and balances.* In general, it can be said that the maintenance and control of this design sustain normal metabolism, whereas its disruption contributes to abnormal metabolism.

These opening remarks suggest that the subject of metabolism is not only massive but complex as well, and again, indeed it is. Yet, despite the nature of the beast, great strides have been made in unraveling many of the details concerning the metabolic dynamics of the living state. This success is due to many factors such as the development of biochemical methodologies (Chapter 2) and the scientific genius and talent of many workers. However, the real key to the growth of our knowledge has been provided by nature herself, for despite the tremendous metabolic diversity represented by all living forms, there is a very definite theme of *metabolic unity*. This should not be so surprising, since we have already emphasized in previous chapters that all cells contain the same classes of biomolecules—proteins, nucleic acids, lipids and carbohydrates. At this point we are saying that, on the whole, the collective participation of these molecules is in principle basically the same from one organism to another. In other words, all of the organisms of our biosphere appear to possess a common metabolic design or pattern. Two particular observations—of many—represent the theme of this principle. First, all living forms depend on enzymes as biocatalysts. Although structurally identical enzymes are not found in all organisms, in many cases functionally identical enzymes are commonplace. Despite the absence of a complete structural equivalency, however, enzymes having the same or similar functions in different organisms generally possess similar structures. Secondly, the main reaction pathways are widely distributed, with little variation in the chemical details from one organism to another. In Chapter 6 we mentioned the process of protein biosynthesis as one example. Another is the very important reaction sequence of the citric acid cycle for which there is abundant evidence to suggest that it is probably found in all organisms. In this cyclic pathway, the number (8) and nature of the constituent reactions do not vary. Rather than wander any further into specific examples, let us return to a more cohesive analysis by first considering the general principles that define the overall design of metabolism.

All of the reactions that comprise the total metabolism of any cell can be broadly segregated into two types—*degradative* and *synthetic*. As mentioned on occasion in previous chapters, the degradative reactions are collectively referred to as *catabolism* and the sum of synthetic reactions as *anabolism*. This concept of degradation versus synthesis is not, however, the only manner in which we can differentiate the reactions occurring in a living cell. Additional comparisons in terms of whether the reactions involve oxidation or reduction, of the energetics of the reaction sequences, and of the nature of the starting materials and end products are listed below. The logical and correct conclusion from this chart is that anabolism and catabolism are unlike in all respects.

Catabolism		Anabolism
degradative	(1)	synthetic
oxidative in nature	(2)	reductive in nature
energy yielding	(3)	energy requiring
a variety of starting materials with well-defined end products	(4)	well-defined starting materials with a variety of end products

However, if the principle of biochemical unity is valid, it suggests that there ought to be some similarities between catabolism and anabolism. Similarities do exist, and it is interesting to note that they are defined in terms of the very characteristics that constitute the differences given above.

(a) *On the level of oxidation versus reduction:* Although catabolism is oxidative in nature and anabolism is reductive in nature, in each case most of the oxidative or reductive steps utilize the nicotinamide adenine dinucleotides as chemical instruments to generate or utilize reducing power. More specifically, catabolism utilizes the oxidized forms (NAD^+ and $NADP^+$) and produces the reduced forms (NADH and NADPH), whereas anabolism requires the reduced forms and produces the oxidized forms. Generally speaking, however, NADH is produced in catabolism whereas NADPH is utilized in anabolism. Nevertheless, while different forms (diphospho- versus triphospho-) are involved, the general participation of nicotinamide adenine dinucleotides in both processes is a distinct common denominator.

(b) *On the level of energetics:* Catabolism is exergonic (energy yielding) with a net requirement for ADP and a net production of ATP. The ATP then serves as the source of energy for the endergonic reactions (energy requiring) of anabolism and ADP is produced.

(c) *On the level of starting materials, end products, and intermediary metabolites:* The end products and intermediary metabolites that are generated in catabolism generally serve as the starting materials in anabolism. The reverse is also true.

Thus, though the two types of metabolic activity obviously possess different characteristics, we can conclude that they are *integrated, complementary processes in that what is produced by catabolism is required by anabolism and vice versa.* This integration of metabolism provides for an optimal level of metabolic efficiency in nature and will serve to unify our analysis throughout the next several chapters.

Our first consideration will be in the area of carbohydrate metabolism, with specific emphasis given to the reaction pathways termed *glycolysis* (sugar degradation) and the *hexose-monophosphate shunt.* The glycolytic pathway is particularly appropriate for initial study, because it represents a universally occurring reaction sequence and thus exemplifies the aforementioned theme of biochemical unity.

Depending on the organism and/or its growth conditions, the glycolytic pathway fulfills many functions. In many microbes growing under *anaerobic conditions* (absence of oxygen), it serves as the main energy-yielding catabolic route for carbohydrate substrates, resulting in the production of specific metabolic end products such as ethanol. This type of process is specifically referred to as alcohol *fermentation* rather than glycolysis. Most of the microbial fermentative processes are, however, variations of the basic chemical theme of glycolysis. Fermentation is a much more general term, implying only that the initial substrate is degraded anaerobically. Glycolysis specifically refers to the anaerobic degradation of carbohydrate substrates, forming *lactate* as a metabolic end product. Although specific and genetically characteristic fermentations are associated largely with certain species of the microbial kingdom, the reactions of glycolysis also occur in all types of *aerobic* (dependent on oxygen) organisms including higher animals, plants, and bacteria. In some instances, the pathway fulfills a definite role such as supplying most of the energy needed for muscle contraction in the cells of skeletal muscle tissue under anaerobic conditions. In a broader sense, however, the reactions of glycolysis have a greater

significance, for they comprise the initial anaerobic phase of carbohydrate metabolism that is then linked to the important aerobic phase
composed primarily of the set of reactions called the *citric acid cycle.*
In this case, glycolysis does not result in the terminal production of
lactate, but rather stops at the level of *pyruvate,* which is the immediate
precursor of lactate (see below). The aerobic phase results in the complete oxidative degradation of the pyruvate produced in glycolysis to
CO_2, with an accompanying release of large amounts of potentially
useful metabolic energy largely in the form of reduced nicotinamide
adenine dinucleotides (NADH). The NADH is then reoxidized via the
oxygen-dependent process of *oxidative phosphorylation* resulting in the
production of ATP. This aerobic phase of metabolism is commonly
termed *respiration,* and is the main process whereby oxygen-dependent
cells produce most of their needed metabolic energy as ATP. Since
most cells depend on carbohydrates, specifically glucose, as the primary
source of chemical energy, it should be apparent that the glycolytic
production of pyruvate does, indeed, have a special importance.

$C_6H_{12}O_6$
glucose
(glycogen)

glycolysis

ATP

anaerobic

$2CH_3CHCOO^-$ ⟵ $2CH_3CCOO^-$ ⟶ $2CH_3CH_2OH + 2CO_2$
| ‖
OH   O   ethanol
lactate   pyruvate

*citric
acid
cycle*

ADP + P_i

NADH → NAD$^+$ + H_2O + ATP

O_2

aerobic

Chapter 12 $6CO_2$ *oxidative phosphorylation*

Chapter 13

Although most of this chapter deals with the glycolytic pathway
(the citric acid cycle and oxidative phosphorylation will be considered
in the next two chapters), we will also analyze the events of an *alternate
pathway of carbohydrate* (glucose) *metabolism,* namely, the *hexose-
monophosphate shunt.* Like glycolysis, the shunt pathway occurs in
all types of cells, but generally to a lesser degree. Most interesting,
however, is the fact that in many cells the glycolytic pathway and the
shunt pathway do not exclude each other. That is, both pathways exist
in the same cell. This is not to be interpreted as a measure of metabolic
repetition or inefficiency, for, as we shall see, the shunt pathway does
have the potential to serve specific metabolic functions which glycolysis
cannot.

As a final introductory note, be advised that our approach to metabolism will not merely consist of enumerating the specific events of

the primary metabolic pathways. Accordingly, your study of the subject should not be characterized by rote memorization. Though some memorization will be required, little will be accomplished if this is all you do. To counteract this tendency, we will complement the description of chemical events with an analysis intended to explain the intricate design and balance of biochemical dynamics. In many cases, such an analysis is now possible due to the explosion of biochemical knowledge in the past ten to fifteen years. One of the most important developments in this regard has been the discovery that the chemical events of metabolism do not proceed in a random or haphazard fashion, but instead are highly regulated and controlled by the cell itself. Consequently, the spirit of our analysis will be to investigate the primary pathways in terms of both their metabolic function and the phenomena regulating the fulfillment of that function. Basically, the control mechanisms are of two types, both of which involve the *regulation of enzymes*. It has become customary to refer to these processes as (1) the *fine control mechanisms*, which regulate the *activities* of enzymes after they are synthesized, and (2) the *coarse control mechanisms*, which regulate the *synthesis* of enzymes. The fine control mode is explained in terms of the allosteric properties of the enzymes, whereas the coarse control mode is a consequence of gene regulation explained by the modern theory of *induction and repression* originally proposed by Jacob and Monod in 1963. Whereas the theory of allosterism has already been examined in Chapter 5, the principles of gene control by induction and repression will be discussed later in Chapter 18.

In this rather lengthy introduction, we have attempted to survey the general principles of metabolism, and of carbohydrate metabolism in particular. Do not be concerned if you feel somewhat confused. This state is a natural characteristic of one's initial exposure to metabolism. The many principles will become more coherent chapter by chapter. In other words, there is no such thing as an instant appreciation of metabolism. On the contrary, it develops gradually.

EXPERIMENTAL HISTORY OF GLYCOLYSIS

A historical survey of the experimental events which led to the complete elucidation of the glycolytic pathway is given below. The time period involved—that is, the late nineteenth century through the early 1940's—covers the early growth of biochemistry as a science and illustrates the slow progress compared to contemporary standards. However, to equate this slow pace with inept workers would be incorrect and indeed unjust. One must keep in mind that biochemistry was in its infancy, and that specific knowledge concerning the chemical events of the living state was quite limited. In fact, the glycolytic pathway was the first metabolic sequence to be established. Equally significant was the primitive state of biochemical methodology. Delicate techniques for cell fractionation had not been developed; radioisotopes were not available for use as metabolic tracers; and refined chromatographic and electrophoretic techniques had not yet evolved. In this context, the accomplishments of the many participants were nothing short of exceptional.

Chronological Development of Glycolysis

1. In 1897 the Buchner brothers accidentally discovered that a cell-free extract of yeast was capable of fermenting sugar to alcohol. This represented the first observation that chemical events associated with life forms were not dependent on intact cells. At the time this must have been a rather startling finding. However, the Buchners did not pursue it further, and the significance of their discovery, namely, that the biochemistry of living cells could be studied without using whole cells, was not recognized for several years.

2. In the early part of the twentieth century (1905–1910), A. Harden and W. J. Young were the first to exploit the discovery of the Buchners. In a systematic study of alcohol production from glucose with cell-free yeast extracts under anaerobic conditions, Harden and Young made four important observations: (a) the process was absolutely dependent on inorganic phosphate; (b) a hexose diphosphate accumulated, which they subsequently identified as fructose-1,6-diphosphate; (c) the extract could be separated by dialysis into a heat-sensitive component and a heat-stable component, neither of which was individually capable of fermenting glucose; and (d) the production of alcohol could be restored by merely combining the heat-sensitive and heat-stable fractions.

3. Glucose-6-phosphate was isolated (1914) and identified (1931) by A. Harden and R. Robinson.

4. Fructose-6-phosphate was isolated and identified by C. Neuberg in 1932.

5. Glucose-1-phosphate was isolated and identified by C. F. Cori, S. P. Colowick, and G. T. Cori in 1936. (For this and other studies that established the pattern of glycogen degradation through glucose-1-phosphate, Carl and Gerty Cori, who were husband and wife, were jointly awarded the Nobel Prize in 1947. While this has nothing to do with biochemistry, it is interesting to note that the only other husband and wife to receive the Nobel Prize were Pierre and Marie Curie in 1903 for their investigations of radioactive phenomena. Anything in a name?)

6. In 1928 O. Warburg and W. Christian established a linkage between oxidation–reduction and phosphorylation. In 1935 these same workers also identified the nature of the heat-stable component observed by Harden and Young as consisting of adenine nucleotides and the oxidized form of nicotinamide adenine dinucleotide (NAD^+).

7. For about fifteen years (1925–1940) Meyerhof, Embden, Parnas, and Warburg studied the interrelationships among the various intermediates and isolated and characterized many of the enzymes involved. One of the most significant discoveries was the isolation and characterization of the enzyme, aldolase, by Meyerhof in 1936.

To immortalize their contributions in discovering the complete reaction sequence, the glycolytic pathway is sometimes referred to as the *Embden-Meyerhof-Parnas* (EMP) pathway. The humanistic and professional spirit of this traditional name association is quite appropriate, but the omission of Warburg's name is unjust. His contributions in this area were of prime value. In fact, Warburg has been acclaimed as this century's most talented biochemist because of his pioneering discoveries and theories which played a large part in the development and progress of modern biochemical science. He died at the age of 87 in 1970.

GLYCOLYSIS—AN OVERALL VIEW

INTRODUCTION

The entire reaction sequence of glycolysis is shown in Figure 11–1. If your immediate reaction to the many details of the diagram is one of bewilderment, consider this a normal response. Thousands of other students of biochemistry have reacted similarly. For the moment, it is not the details of glycolysis that are important. Rather, the purpose of the diagram is to provide you with an overall perspective by illustrating that the degradation of the initial substrates (glucose or glycogen) proceeds through a sequence of defined intermediates via several consecutive enzyme-catalyzed reactions resulting in the formation of specific products—lactate or alcohol and CO_2. In the next several pages, we will examine many facets of this pathway with the intent of establishing its metabolic design. When we have finished, the maze of structures and arrows in Figure 11–1 will be better understood. One of the most rational approaches to deciphering a metabolic pathway of this type is to begin with an analysis of *net effects*.

NET CHEMISTRY

Under anaerobic conditions, the reactions of glycolysis account for the formation of lactate from glucose or glycogen in some cells, and for the production of alcohol from glucose in others. To review some points of the Introduction: the formation of lactate is the primary anaerobic pathway of carbohydrate degradation in skeletal muscle and in a few select microbes, whereas alcohol fermentation occurs exclusively in the microbial world. Regardless, as Figure 11–1 clearly illustrates, the majority of the reactions are *identical, with the only difference being the fate of pyruvate*.

    The net reactions of glycolysis are given on p. 268 for each metabolic route. Although the equations are limiting in that they do not indicate the participation of all intermediates, they do clearly specify the essential reactants and the characteristic end products. For each process a family of equations are given, with each successive equation intended to be more descriptive than the previous ones. The first equation merely defines the overall transformation in terms of the carbon skeletons of the reactants and products. From these it is obvious what is meant by degradative reactions of catabolism. Most obvious is the cleavage of carbon–carbon bonds. The second equation includes the participation of inorganic phosphate (P_i) and the adenine nucleotides, and by so doing, provides a net analysis of the bioenergetics of glycolysis. The appearance of ATP on both sides of the equation indicates that *ATP is both required and produced* in the overall process. Note, however, that in each case the *amount of ATP produced exceeds the amount required*. Hence, the overall process is *energy yielding* (see next section). The third equation, which is the most descriptive, includes the participation of the nicotinamide nucleotides. As with ATP, the involvement of NAD^+ is twofold—it is both *required and produced*. In this case, however, note that there is neither a net requirement nor a net gain. Before we probe deeper into the participation of ATP, ADP, P_i, and NAD^+, you should

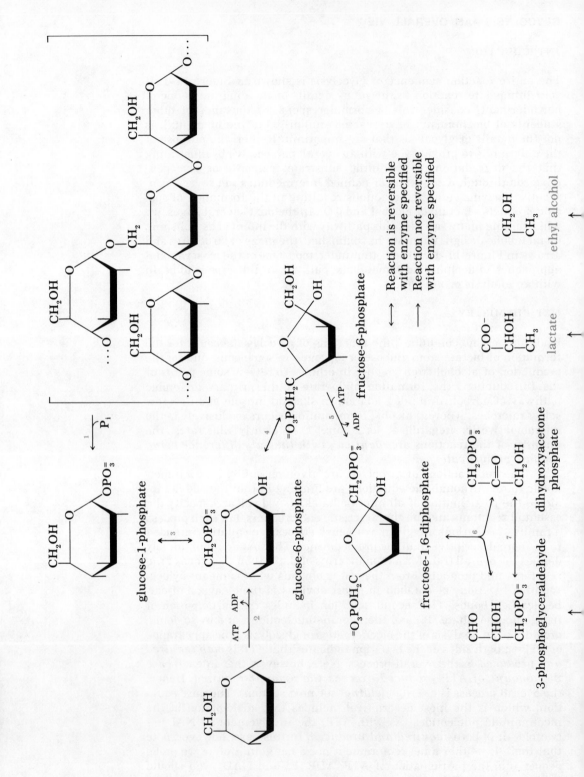

Figure 11–1 A scheme for glycolysis
and alcoholic fermentation.

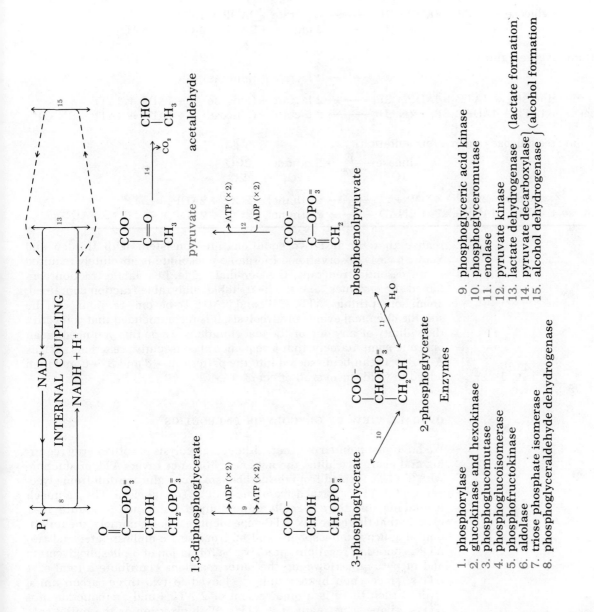

Enzymes

1. phosphorylase
2. glucokinase and hexokinase
3. phosphoglucomutase
4. phosphoglucoisomerase
5. phosphofructokinase
6. aldolase
7. triose phosphate isomerase
8. phosphoglyceraldehyde dehydrogenase
9. phosphoglyceric acid kinase
10. phosphoglyceromutase
11. enolase
12. pyruvate kinase
13. lactate dehydrogenase (lactate formation)
14. pyruvate decarboxylase } (alcohol formation)
15. alcohol dehydrogenase

A Reaction Summary of Glycolysis

Lactate from free glucose:

$$\text{glucose} \xrightarrow[\text{enzymes}]{11} 2 \text{ lactate}$$
$$1C_6 \qquad\qquad 2C_3$$

$$\text{glucose} + 2\text{ATP} + 4\text{ADP} + 2P_i \longrightarrow 2 \text{ lactate} + 2\text{ADP} + 4\text{ATP}$$
$$\text{glucose} + 2\text{ATP} + 4\text{ADP} + 2P_i + 2\text{NAD}^+ \longrightarrow 2 \text{ lactate} + 2\text{ADP} + 4\text{ATP} + 2\text{NAD}^+$$

Lactate from glycogen glucose:

$$(\text{glucose})_n \xrightarrow[\text{enzymes}]{12} 2 \text{ lactate} + (\text{glucose})_{n-1}$$

$$(\text{glucose})_n + 1\text{ATP} + 4\text{ADP} + 3P_i \longrightarrow 2 \text{ lactate} + (\text{glucose})_{n-1} + 1\text{ADP} + 4\text{ATP}$$
$$(\text{glucose})_n + 1\text{ATP} + 4\text{ADP} + 3P_i + 2\text{NAD}^+ \longrightarrow 2 \text{ lactate} + (\text{glucose})_{n-1} + 1\text{ADP} + 4\text{ATP} + 2\text{NAD}^+$$

Ethanol from free glucose (alcohol fermentation):

$$\text{glucose} \xrightarrow[\text{enzymes}]{12} 2 \text{ ethanol} + 2CO_2$$
$$1C_6 \qquad\qquad 2C_1 \qquad 2C_2$$

$$\text{glucose} + 2\text{ATP} + 4\text{ADP} + 2P_i \longrightarrow 2 \text{ ethanol} + 2CO_2 + 2\text{ADP} + 4\text{ATP}$$
$$\text{glucose} + 2\text{ATP} + 4\text{ADP} + 2P_i + 2\text{NAD}^+ \longrightarrow 2 \text{ ethanol} + 2CO_2 + 2\text{ADP} + 4\text{ATP} + 2\text{NAD}^+$$

---

realize that the last two equations are consistent with Harden and Young's early observations. Inorganic phosphate is absolutely required as an essential reactant; the non-dialyzable, heat-labile fraction contained the enzymes; and the heat-stable, dialyzable fraction contained, among other things, ATP, ADP, and NAD^+. To become familiar with the specific chemical events of glycolysis, it is recommended that you verify the validity of any one of the last equations. To do this you need recall only one point, namely, that a sequence of consecutive reactions such as $A \rightarrow B \rightarrow C$ can be dissected into the pattern $A \rightarrow B$ and $B \rightarrow C$ and then added to yield the overall effect of $A \rightarrow C$.

OVERALL VIEW OF GLYCOLYSIS ENERGETICS

We have just pointed out that, although glycolysis is both energy requiring and energy yielding, the net energy balance favors ATP production, with 3 ATP's formed from the catabolism of one glucose unit from glycogen and 2 ATP's formed from one unit of free glucose. The approach in making this tally is really quite simple. Reference to Figure 11–1 reveals that there are two ATP-dependent reactions, namely, the formation of glucose-6-phosphate and of fructose-1,6-diphosphate; and two ATP-generating reactions, namely, the formation of 3-phosphoglycerate and of pyruvate. However, the latter reactions contribute a total of 4 ATP's, since each hexose unit is cleaved to two three-carbon units. Overall then there is a requirement of 2 ATP's and a production of 4 ATP's, giving a net gain of 2 ATP's. With glycogen as the initial substrate, ATP is required only in the formation of fructose diphosphate, and thus a net gain of 3 ATP's is realized. This type of analysis is relatively straightforward and there should be no difficulty in understanding its significance, namely, glycolysis, resulting in partial degradation of carbohydrate substrates, provides a net gain of useful metabolic energy as ATP. In skeletal muscle tissue where glycogen is the primary substrate, this pathway serves as the major source of energy needed for muscle contraction under anaerobic conditions (see page 289). In fermenting microbes, it serves as the primary source of energy needed to sustain virtually all of the energy-requiring processes.

Although the preceding analysis is valid—and granted it is significant—it is rather superficial because there is more to the energetics of glycolysis than merely counting ATP's. To appreciate that this is so, let us now concentrate on the energetics of each reaction rather than the net effect. Our approach will be purely thermodynamic. To be more specific: it will be based on a comparison of the known free energy changes ($\Delta G^{\circ\prime}$) of each reaction (see Figure 11–2). Before using these data, it should be noted that the free energy changes given in Figure 11–2 are for the reactions involving only the glycolytic intermediates and do not consider any coupling to ATP hydrolysis or ADP phosphorylation. For example, the value of +3.3 kcal corresponds to GLU $\xrightarrow{P_i}$ G6P and not GLU + ATP → G1P + ADP, and the value of −13.1 kcal corresponds to PEP → PYR + G6P and not to PEP + ADP → PYR + ATP.

GLU	glucose
G1P	glucose-1-phosphate
G6P	glucose-6-phosphate
F6P	fructose-6-phosphate
F16DP	fructose-1,6-diphosphate
DHAP	dihydroxyacetone phosphate
GAP	glyceraldehyde phosphate
13DPGA	1,3-diphosphoglycerate
3PGA	3-phosphoglycerate
2PGA	2-phosphoglycerate
PEP	phosphoenolpyruvate
PYR	pyruvate
LAC	lactate

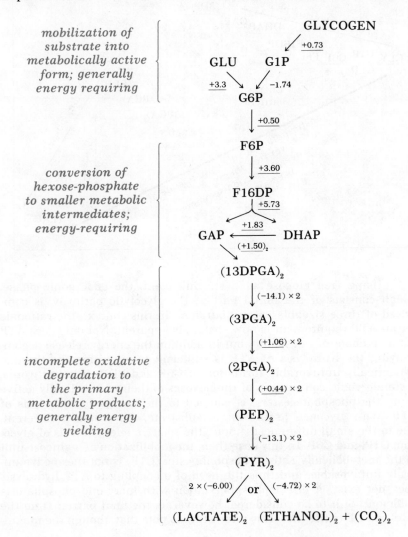

mobilization of substrate into metabolically active form; generally energy requiring

conversion of hexose-phosphate to smaller metabolic intermediates; energy-requiring

incomplete oxidative degradation to the primary metabolic products; generally energy yielding

Figure 11–2 Free energy changes (kilocalories) of the constituent reactions of the glycolytic pathway. Endergonic reactions are underlined.

An obvious question at this point is: What value do these data have in understanding glycolysis? Well, given the free energy change of each reaction, we can construct an *energy profile diagram* of the complete pathway which should depict the relative differences in free energy among all of the primary metabolic intermediates. Such a diagram is shown in Figure 11–3. A close study reveals that the tactic in constructing the diagram is really quite simple. Each intermediate, which is involved in at least two consecutive reactions, has been positioned on a free energy scale in terms of its free energy content relative to those of both its immediate precursor and its immediate product. When this is done, note that there emerges a pattern to the composite energetics of glycolysis in that we can *clearly distinguish two different phases—* one *endergonic* and the other *exergonic*. We will now examine each phase more closely.

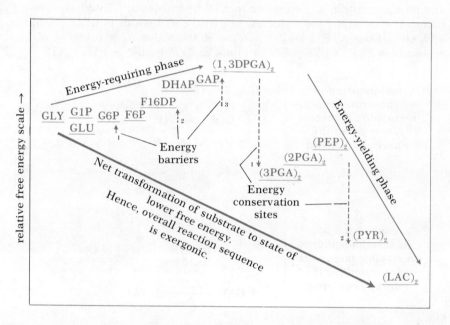

Figure 11–3 A skeleton view of the thermodynamic (free energy) relationships among the metabolic intermediates of the glycolytic pathway. Horizontal lines indicate relative energy state of each intermediate.

Using free glucose as a starting point, the endergonic phase, which consists of the initial part of the glycolytic pathway, is comprised of three sizeable *energy barriers*. In this context, the rationale for an ATP requirement is now strikingly apparent. Not only does ATP act as a donor of phosphate, but in addition the energy release accompanying the hydrolysis of ATP is sufficient to overcome the thermodynamically unfavorable formation of G6P and FDP. In other words, the endergonic conversions of the hexoses to their metabolically active form, the phosphate esters, is coupled to the exergonic hydrolysis of ATP. With glycogen as the initial substrate, the profile is different, due to the small differences among the relative energy levels of glycogen, G1P, and G6P. In this case then, the mobilization of a glucose unit to the metabolically active phosphate ester (G1P) is not thermodynamically unfavorable, and thus the need of a coupling to ATP hydrolysis does not exist. A direct phosphorylation with inorganic phosphate is sufficient. Still to be considered, however, is the final barrier from the level of FDP to $(DPGA)_2$. It is interesting to note that, though the magnitude of this barrier is rather considerable—being roughly equivalent to the first two combined—it is not coupled to ATP hydrolysis. Nevertheless, when the glycolytic pathway operates, this barrier does not contribute to a metabolic blockage resulting in the accumulation of FDP. The key to understanding why this does not occur is provided by the thermodynamics of the very next reaction consisting of the extremely favorable (exergonic) conversion of DPGA to 3PGA. (Recall that 1,3-diphosphoglycerate, an acyl phosphate, is a high-energy compound—see page 249.) Thus, since the reactions are consecutive, the endergonic sequence of FDP through DPGA is driven to completion by being *coupled* to the thermodynamically favorable removal of DPGA as it is formed. Notice that the coupling in this case occurs without an actual transfer of energy (Case III, page 255).

The conversion of $(DPGA)_2$ to $(3PGA)_2$ is especially important, because it is not only coupled to the degradation of FDP but also to the phosphorylation of 2ADP to yield 2ATP. Thus, one exergonic reaction (DPGA → 3PGA) is coupled to two endergonic reactions (FDP → DPGA and ADP → ATP). Finally, note that the exergonic phase consists of two additional energy-yielding steps. One of these involving the high-energy enol phosphate (PEP) is similarly coupled to the formation of ATP. It is of interest to note that, although the last reaction of glycolysis (PYR → LAC) has the capacity to be coupled to ATP formation, such does not occur and the energy is not conserved. One might argue that, in view of the thermodynamic design already discussed, this non-conservation site is not consistent with metabolic efficiency. However, one can argue that just the opposite may be true. One suggestion is that the appearance of this type of reaction occurring independently of an energy-requiring process and positioned at the end of a multi-step sequence may represent a tactic used by nature as added insurance that preceding intermediates will be efficiently converted to the final product. The fact that other metabolic pathways display a similar pattern supports such a suggestion. In so doing, the cell pays a price—energy is not conserved as ATP.

The merit of this analytical exercise is not justified simply because it gives a meaningful perspective to the whole of glycolysis energetics. Equally important is the fact that it introduces many principles that apply to all reaction pathways—whether catabolic or anabolic—principles which, if mastered and understood at this point, will benefit your comprehension of metabolism in general. Of prime significance is the operational pattern of coupling which effects (a) the formation of metabolically active intermediates such as the hexose phosphates in ATP-dependent reactions; (b) the conservation and conversion of chemical energy into useful metabolic energy via the formation of ATP, with the ATP then available for use elsewhere in energy-dependent processes; and (c) the maintenance of an efficient flow of metabolic intermediates through a chain of several consecutive reactions.

NAD$^+$ IN GLYCOLYSIS

A second characteristic of glycolysis which reflects the remarkable molecular design of metabolism is evident by the participation of nicotinamide adenine dinucleotide. The point becomes rather clear by inspecting Figure 11–1 and observing that glycolysis—be it lactate or ethanol formation—consists of *two NAD-dependent dehydrogenases*. One *requires NAD+* and *produces NADH* whereas the other *requires NADH* and *produces NAD+*. In light of the preceding discussion, there is no reason for a lengthy description of what this means. Simply, the two reactions are coupled. The metabolic significance of this *internal coupling* is great. Under anaerobic conditions, the glycolytic pathway will not become sluggish due to an unfavorably high ratio of NADH/NAD+. In other words, the oxidative phosphorylation of phosphoglyceraldehyde to diphosphoglycerate and the accompanying formation of NADH that is then utilized in the reduction of pyruvate to lactate renders the whole pathway *autocatalytic* and self-sustaining on the level of the nicotinamide nucleotides.

SOME INDIVIDUAL REACTIONS OF GLYCOLYSIS

A considerable part of biochemical research—both past and present—is characterized by the detailed investigation of individual reactions. This type of research involves the isolation and purification of the enzyme, followed by extensive studies of its structure and catalytic properties. Easier said than done. Nevertheless, all the enzymes of glycolysis have been so studied, and accordingly our current knowledge about this pathway is extensive and detailed. Despite the scope of this knowledge, it is not our purpose to treat the subject in its entirety. This is more appropriate to advanced courses. Alternatively, we will confine our attention to a few select reactions which are (a) unique to glycolysis and (b) representative of principles such as enzyme specificity, coenzyme participation, and metabolic regulation. Recall that each of these areas was treated separately in earlier chapters. In this section we will now investigate the operational significance of these principles in terms of specific enzymes. The material will center on *glycogen phosphorylase, hexokinase, phosphofructokinase, aldolase, phosphoglyceraldehyde dehydrogenase,* and *lactate dehydrogenase*. The emphasis on the enzymes themselves should be appreciated. If it is not, you will shortly discover why it should be.

GLYCOGEN PHOSPHORYLASE

The first reaction in the catabolism of glycogen is the sequential removal of glucose residues catalyzed by the widely distributed enzyme, *glycogen phosphorylase*. On the surface the reaction seems to be relatively straightforward (see below). In the presence of the enzyme, inorganic phosphate attacks an $\alpha(1 \rightarrow 4)$ glycosidic bond at the non-reducing end of the polysaccharide chain, resulting in the formation of G1P and the shortening of the chain by one hexose unit. This proceeds along the chain until an $\alpha(1 \rightarrow 6)$ branch is reached, at which point a different enzyme will participate (an $\alpha(1 \rightarrow 6)$ glucosidase). After cleavage of the $\alpha(1 \rightarrow 6)$ bond, the phosphorylase action resumes. Thus, glucose is converted from its storage form to a metabolically active form. While these brief statements describe the net effect, they tell us very little about the nature of the reaction. This can be done only by a more detailed description of the enzyme itself.

(glucose)$_n$

$$P_i \xrightarrow{\text{glycogen phosphorylase}}$$

glucose-1-P + (glucose)$_{n-1}$

sequential phosphorolysis of $\alpha(1 \to 4)$ glucoside bonds

A tip-off to the general nature of both the structure and the catalytic properties of phosphorylase is given in the Michaelis-Menten plot of Figure 11–4a. Observe the *sigmoid* nature of the curve and recall the generalization given in Chapter 5 (page 132) as to its significance, namely, that this kinetic pattern typifies *allosteric properties* of the enzyme. By way of review: according to the modern theory of allosterism, the data suggest that the enzyme possesses two distinct characteristics—one structural and one functional. Structurally, the active enzyme is a protein probably consisting of more than one polypeptide chain. It is oligomeric. Functionally, the enzyme contains more than one active site and may also contain one or more regulatory sites. The former would account for homotropic effects (as observed for phosphorylase with inorganic phosphate—Figure 11–4a), while the latter would explain heterotropic effects (as observed for phosphorylase with inorganic phosphate in the presence of AMP acting as an activator—Figure 11–4b). So what?—you ask. Well, if the catalytic activity of phosphorylase is so characterized, it is quite probable that the cellular formation of glucose-1-phosphate is regulated. To be more specific, we can argue that *appreciable levels of phosphorylase activity will result when the cellular levels of P_i and AMP are high. When they are low, the rate of formation of glucose-1-phosphate is considerably diminished.* Hence, these two variables can act as *metabolic signals which modulate carbohydrate metabolism in general, and the action of phosphorylase in particular.* We are not yet in a position to explain how these signals—varying levels of P_i and AMP—are generated in the cell. At this time, suffice it to say that they will change as the overall metabolism of the cell changes. For now we are interested only in es-

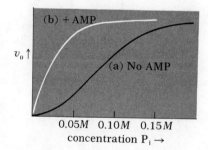

$v_0 \uparrow$

(b) + AMP

(a) No AMP

0.05M 0.10M 0.15M
concentration $P_i \to$

Figure 11–4 Michaelis-Menten kinetics of glycogen phosphorylase (*b* form; see text): (a) effect of varying levels of inorganic phosphate concentration in the absence of AMP; (b) as in (a), with $10^{-5}M$ AMP present. Constant glycogen concentration (0.25%); temperature of 28°C. (Data obtained with permission from *Regulation of Enzyme Activity and Allosteric Interactions*, M. H. Buc and H. Buc, New York: Academic Press, 1968, p. 118.)

tablishing that the phosphorylase step *is a kinetic control point* explainable in terms of allosteric effects. The integration of this control with the whole of metabolism will be developed later.

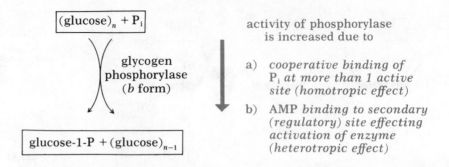

activity of phosphorylase is increased due to

a) *cooperative binding of* P_i *at more than 1 active site (homotropic effect)*

b) AMP *binding to secondary (regulatory) site effecting activation of enzyme (heterotropic effect)*

Intriguing as this control mechanism may appear, it accounts for only a small part of phosphorylase regulation. To understand other facets of phosphorylase control, we must consider the enzyme in greater detail.

During the past five years, phosphorylase preparations have been obtained from a variety of organisms and tissues. The most clearly understood is muscle phosphorylase, which is known to be a tetramer (MW ~ 370,000) of identical subunits. Among other things, each protomer contains a phosphorylated serine residue ($-CH_2OPO_3^=$) which is essential for catalytic activity. (Each protomer also contains free sulfhydryl groups ($-SH$) and one unit of pyridoxal phosphate (page 419) covalently attached to a lysine residue.) This phosphorylated tetrameric form, called *phosphorylase a,* is fully active and is not subject to extensive allosteric activation by AMP. However, it can be converted to another form, called *phosphorylase b,* which is inactive. The *b* form (MW ~ 185,000) consists of dimeric molecules and is further characterized by the absence of the serine phosphate (see below). This conversion occurs naturally due to the presence of a *phosphatase enzyme* found in muscle. The conversion is reversible but involves a different enzyme—namely an ATP-dependent *kinase* (also found in muscle), resulting in the phosphorylation of four serine residues. In contrast to that of the *a* form, the activity of the *b* form is appreciably stimulated by AMP. Thus, the kinetics of Figure 11–4 apply primarily to the *b* form.

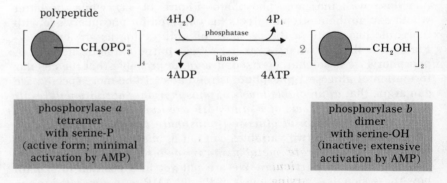

If you are not yet impressed by the concept of metabolic regulation at the level of enzymes, consider the following. The kinase which catalyzes the conversion of the inactive *b* form to the active *a* form itself exists in both an active and inactive state with the formation of the active species being stimulated by *cyclic-AMP* (see page 148). In turn adenyl cyclase, the enzyme which catalyzes the formation of cyclic-AMP from ATP also exists in active and inactive states. In this case the formation of the active species of adenyl cyclase is strongly stimulated by *epinephrine* (sometimes called *adrenalin*), a mammalian hormone (see page 431, Chaper 16). Thus, the formation of active phosphorylase *a* from phosphorylase *b* is under a set of three distinct but cooperative mechanisms. There is substantial evidence to indicate that both the cyclic-AMP action on the kinase and the epinephrine action on the cyclase are mediated via allosteric, secondary-site effects. All of these relationships, including the AMP allosteric activation of phosphorylase *b*, are diagrammed below.

The existence of hormones and their ability to regulate metabolism have been known for many years. However, it wasn't until the past decade that we began to understand how they perform that function. This phase of modern endocrinology was born with the discovery of cyclic-AMP and the development of the theory of allosterism. The efforts of recent research are exemplified in part by the elucidation of the control of glycolysis by epinephrine and permit the following generalization. *Many hormones function as allosteric effectors capable of modulating metabolism by stimulating and/or depressing the activities of key enzymes in primary metabolic pathways.* Frequently the hormonal effect is indirect, meaning that the hormone itself does not actively interact with the enzyme(s) which is ultimately the target of its control. Rather the regulation is mediated by another effector and it is the formation of this other effector that is actually under direct hormonal control. In other words, the control process can be envisaged as a molecular relay system. This explanation for the hormonal control of metabolism was first proposed by E. Sutherland in the early 1960s. In fact Sutherland's suggestion resulted from his studies to explain the known stimulation of glycolysis by epinephrine. The key to his theory,

$3' \rightarrow 5'$-cyclic AMP

epinephrine

which he termed the *secondary-messenger theory,* was his discovery of cyclic-AMP. For his unique contributions, which have revolutionized modern thinking of hormonal control and metabolic regulation by cyclic-AMP, Sutherland was awarded the Nobel Prize in 1971.

The control of glycolysis by epinephrine is even more remarkable in view of the fact that epinephrine doesn't actually enter the cell. How can this be? Well, the answer to this riddle is that the cyclase enzyme which is directly activated by epinephrine is localized in the cell membrane. Thus, epinephrine binds to the *outside* of the membrane, presumably at specific sites, causing the formation of the active form of the cyclase in the membrane, which in turn results in the increased rate of production of cyclic-AMP *inside* the cell. Whatever the precise details of this type of membrane-mediated process, the pattern of hormone → cyclic-AMP → enzyme is now established as a major regulatory relationship, especially in higher multicellular organisms. In the lower unicellular organisms, such as bacteria, where metabolism is not under the influence of various hormones, the primary regulator appears to be cyclic-AMP itself. Thus, the emergence of cyclic-AMP as a secondary messenger probably represents an evolutionary development advantageous to the higher and more metabolically complex living forms.

Despite the apparently advanced state of knowledge in this area, much work still needs to be done. In mammals especially, there are many unanswered questions where both physiological variables and different cell types are numerous. For example, depending on the source of the enzyme, the mechanism of glycogen phosphorylase activation is quite diverse. Muscle phosphorylase is activated by epinephrine. Liver phosphorylase, however, is activated by *glucagon* (a polypeptide hormone produced by the pancreas) as well as by epinephrine. Glucagon has little effect on muscle phosphorylase. The effect of glucagon is identical to that of epinephrine—it activates adenyl cyclase in the cell membrane of liver cells. On the other hand, brain phosphorylase does not seem to be affected by either glucagon or epinephrine. Furthermore, the hormone → cyclic-AMP → enzyme pattern does not apply to all hormones. The regulatory effects of other hormones such as steroids result from their actual entry into the cell. They control metabolism from within, so to speak, by regulating protein activity (not just of enzymes either) and possibly by directing the biosynthesis of specific proteins.

HEXOKINASE

Glucose is by far the most abundant monosaccharide in nature, being utilized by all types of organisms as the primary source of both carbon and energy. In serving this role, glucose participates in many different enzyme-catalyzed reactions, but without question the most important is its initial conversion to a phosphate ester by an ATP-dependent *kinase.* Recall our earlier mention of the phosphorylated form as the metabolically active form (page 177). In other words, unless glucose is first converted to a phosphate ester, it will not be metabolized. The importance of the hexokinase enzyme is that simple. Remember also the difference in the permeability of the cell membrane with respect to the free sugars and the sugar phosphates (page 178, Chapter 7).

Hexokinase activity is common to all types of organisms from man to microbe, with each cellular source typified by a unique enzyme possessing a specific set of structural and functional properties. Despite the differences, which vary in degree, all of the enzymes are collectively classified as hexokinases, because they all catalyze the same kind of reaction. (These comments really apply to all enzymes of major metabolic pathways. In the previous section, for example, we made reference to different glycogen phosphorylases.) The repetition we give to this concept is to emphasize the principle of biochemical unity at the level of biocatalysis. (From this point on, unless we specifically state that an enzyme is unique to a certain type of organism, you can assume that the enzyme in question is widely distributed.) As the name implies, hexokinases display a broad range of substrate specificity. However, most show a strong affinity ($K_m \sim 10^{-5}\ M$) for glucose. In some organisms more than one hexokinase is present. Mammals, for example, contain at least three hexokinases, and in some tissues all are present in the same cell. Although their presence appears to be characteristic of the tissue, the physiological significance is not clear. As further evidence of the biochemical diversity in our biosphere, note that some organisms also possess a *glucokinase*. Operationally, glucokinase fulfills the same role as a hexokinase, but is characterized by a much more restricted specificity, favoring glucose as a substrate. In mammals it has been proposed that glucokinase serves as a metabolic safety valve in that it operates only when blood glucose levels are high. By preventing the latter situation, many physiological disorders are circumvented.

Hexokinases are oligomeric, but it is uncertain whether the native form is a dimer or a trimer. In general, they are completely inhibited by iodoacetate and *p*-chloromercurobenzoate (page 118), indicating that free sulfhydryl groups are essential for activity. (Optimum catalytic activity is generally also dependent on the presence of a divalent metal cation, M^{++}, such as Mg^{++}.) They are also typified by allosteric effects, with a high concentration of glucose-6-phosphate having an inhibitory effect on many hexokinases. This is not surprising, since metabolic control at this critical point would be an effective way of controlling carbohydrate metabolism, particularly glycolysis. Notice that in this case the enzyme inhibitor is actually the product of the reaction. In other words, the reaction is capable of self-control by a feedback inhibition. Thus, when the cellular level of glucose-6-phosphate builds up due to the lack of a need for extensive carbohydrate degradation (that is, when the organism is in a resting state with a low energy demand), the rate of mobilization of glucose for catabolism is diminished. A remarkable feature, yet it is only a part of the control existing in the glycolytic pathway. The major control point involves the interconversion of fructose-6-phosphate and fructose-1,6-diphosphate (see below and pages 287 and 330).

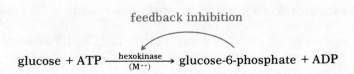

feedback inhibition

$$\text{glucose} + \text{ATP} \xrightarrow[\text{(M}^{++})]{\text{hexokinase}} \text{glucose-6-phosphate} + \text{ADP}$$

When the concentration of G6P in the cell is high, its binding to the enzyme causes allosteric effects resulting in a decrease of its catalytic activity and thus a reduced rate of glucose utilization.

PHOSPHOFRUCTOKINASE

As stated earlier, the first truly *unique* reaction of the glycolytic pathway is the formation of the hexose diphosphate. Overall, the reaction is typical of other ATP-dependent kinases. Now that you are conditioned to

$$\text{fructose-6-phosphate} + \text{ATP} \xrightarrow[\text{kinase}]{\text{phosphofructo-}} \text{fructose-1,6-diphosphate} + \text{ADP}$$

unique reaction of glycolytic pathway

the theme of metabolic control, you might expect that, since this is the first unique chemical event of glycolysis, in the spirit of efficiency this reaction would be a likely candidate as a major control point. There is a considerable amount of data that supports exactly this type of reasoning. To be specific: ADP, AMP, citrate, and isocitrate are known allosteric activators. The metabolic significance of this is discussed in a later section (see page 287).

ALDOLASE

Aldolase catalyzes the first degradative step of the glycolytic pathway resulting in the cleavage of a C_6 unit into two C_3 units. In conjunction with the next reaction catalyzed by *trioseisomerase,* the overall effect is specifically the conversion of 1 unit of FDP to 2 units of GPA (see Figure 11–1). It should be obvious to you that this isomerization is a key step in glycolysis, since it provides for the complete catabolism of the whole hexose unit and not just half of it.

The enzyme has been isolated from a wide variety of sources, and many variant forms are known. As represented by muscle aldolase, the active form from higher organisms appears to be a tetramer (MW = 160,000) composed of four identical subunits. Yeast aldolase, however, appears to be a dimer (MW = 80,000) of two identical subunits. The numbers would seem to indicate that the active enzyme of lower organisms is only one-half the size of that found in more advanced life forms. The formation of a *Schiff base* between the carbonyl group of the substrate and the ϵ-amino group of a lysine residue has been suggested as the active form of the enzyme-substrate complex (see p. 279). Although the enzyme exhibits a broad range of substrate specificity, it does have a strong preference for sugars with a *trans* orientation of the C-3 and C-4 hydroxyls.

It is not clear whether the activity of aldolase is subject to any cellular control. This is due to the fact that meaningful kinetic studies require a highly purified preparation and aldolase is difficult to purify. Recent isolation efforts have been successful and a report of any regulatory properties should be forthcoming.

GLYCERALDEHYDE-3-PHOSPHATE DEHYDROGENASE

The conversion of glyceraldehyde-3-phosphate to 1,3-diphosphoglycerate represents the distinct oxidative step of glycolysis. As we have

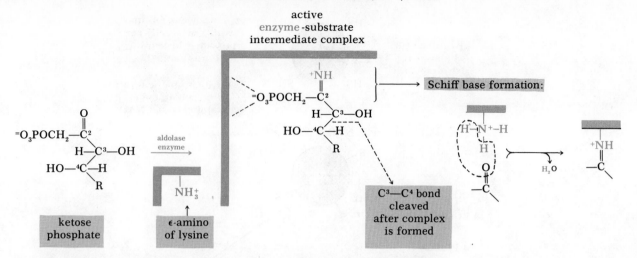

already learned, the reaction is particularly important, because DPGA is a high-energy compound whose hydrolysis to 3PGA in the very next reaction is coupled to the formation of ATP—one of only two such sites in glycolysis. More generally, this reaction is representative of an important and widespread group of biological oxidation—reduction reactions, namely, those catalyzed by dehydrogenases having an absolute requirement for the nicotinamide nucleotides as coenzymes.

Within the past decade much has been learned about GPA-dehydrogenase as both a protein and an enzyme. As a protein, it is believed to be an oligomeric molecule consisting of four identical chains. The protomer of both pig muscle and lobster has been sequenced completely and shown to contain 333 amino acid residues (MW = 37,000) in each case. Moreover, of the total 333 residues, 240 are identical in each preparation. The extent of homology in amino acid sequence is surprising, because the pig and lobster are widely separated on a phylogenetic scale. This suggests then that a great majority of amino acid residues are essential for catalytic activity. Regardless of specific differences in the enzyme from various sources, all preparations studied possess several sulfhydryl groups which are absolutely required for activity. Although the number of SH groups per chain is known to vary, it appears that at least one is part of the active site of each protomer. The active form of the enzyme is also proposed to contain bound NAD at each active site. Some of the details for the proposed mechanism of action are diagrammed on p. 280. The mechanism is extremely interesting in that it depicts the principle, previously stated in Chapter 5, that the progress of an enzyme-catalyzed reaction may proceed through several intermediate stages. The particulars, of course, apply only to GPA-dehydrogenase and should not be assumed to be representative of all dehydrogenases.

LACTATE DEHYDROGENASE

The last reaction of the glycolytic sequence has been discussed earlier relative to its operational significance in terms of internal coupling

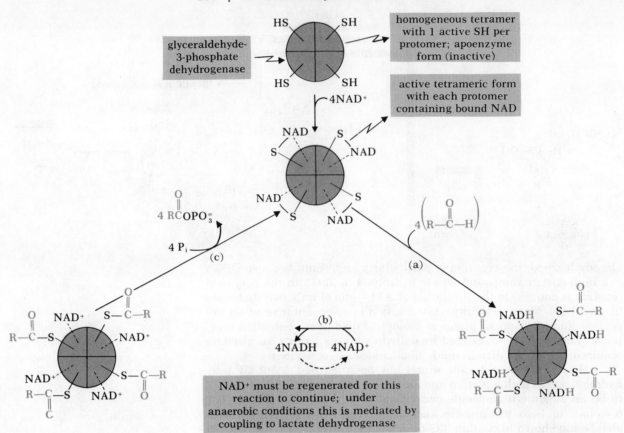

via NAD to GPA-dehydrogenase. However, this is not the only metabolic function of lactate dehydrogenase (LDH). Another operational characteristic of importance is that the enzyme also catalyzes the reverse reaction, that is, the formation of pyruvate from lactate. In animals the significance of this is that the lactate generated in the anaerobic metabolism of certain tissues such as skeletal muscle can be transported to other more aerobic tissues such as the liver where it is reconverted to pyruvate. The pyruvate can then be metabolized further via the citric acid cycle or be reconverted to carbohydrate material as free glucose or stored as glycogen. The latter process, involving still other reversible steps of the glycolytic pathway, will be discussed shortly.

Like many of the glycolytic enzymes, LDH is an oligomer and specifically a tetramer. The most unique aspect of LDH is that it exists in multiple *hybrid* molecular forms, each of which is a tetramer consisting of different proportions of two polypeptide chains. The chains are generally referred to as the H and M chains due to their preponderance in either heart or muscle tissue. The five possible combinations—H_4, HM_3, H_2M_2, H_3M, M_4—are collectively referred to as a family of *isoenzymes* or *isozymes* (see page 95). In man, LDH is widely distributed in various tissues and body fluids. Furthermore, for reasons which are not yet clear, each source apparently possesses different but characteristically normal levels of each hybrid form. Nevertheless, the phenomenon has been exploited as a sensitive clinical tool, since both the serum level of LDH activity and the isoenzyme pattern are modified in various disease states. The clinical value is due to the fact that the changes are often characteristic of a particular disease and of the stage of the disease (see margin).

CATABOLISM OF OTHER SUGARS

The operation of the glycolytic pathway is not solely confined to the degradation of glucose or glycogen. On the contrary, the same overall sequence is responsible for the catabolism of most other simple sugars as well. All that is required is a port of entry by conversion of the sugar into one of the three phosphorylated intermediates—G1P, G6P, or F6P—which lead to the formation of fructose-1,6-diphosphate. The simplest example is the hexokinase-catalyzed conversion of *fructose* to fructose-6-phosphate. *Mannose* can enter at the same level via a two-step process. The first involves a kinase-catalyzed conversion to mannose-6-phosphate followed by an isomerase-catalyzed conversion to F6P. The formations of F6P and M6P are identical to the glucose → glucose-6-phosphate conversion, and in fact all are catalyzed by the same hexokinase.

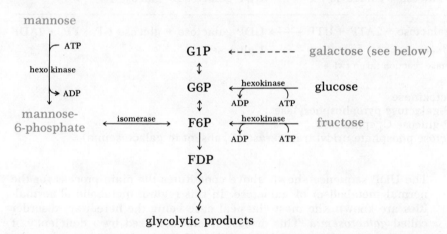

In view of the entrance mechanism for mannose, you might expect *galactose* to be processed in a similar fashion, but such is not the case. Rather, a completely different process operates here, with galactose being converted to glucose through the combined action of four different enzymes (see below). First (step a), galactose is converted to galactose-1-phosphate. Gal-1-P and UTP then act as substrates for the formation of *UDP-galactose* (step b). The latter is representative of a group of special carbohydrate derivatives, called *nucleoside diphosphate sugars* (*NuDP-sugars*), that are of considerable importance in carbohydrate metabolism. Note that the linkage between the hexose unit and UDP is covalent and involves the anomeric carbon. In the key reaction of this process (step c), catalyzed by UDP-galactose-C_4-epimerase, the C_4 position of the galactose moiety is epimerized to yield

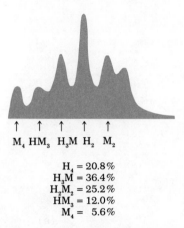

LDH Isoenzyme Patterns on Electrophoresis (pH 8.8)

normal serum

H_4 = 20.8%
H_3M = 36.4%
H_2M_2 = 25.2%
HM_3 = 12.0%
M_4 = 5.6%

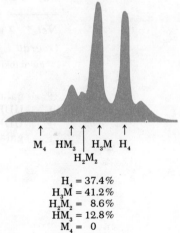

serum after coronary embolism

H_4 = 37.4%
H_3M = 41.2%
H_2M_2 = 8.6%
HM_3 = 12.8%
M_4 = 0

UDP-glucose. In other words, this is the step where the conversion of galactose to glucose actually occurs. In the last step (d), the glucose unit is released as glucose-1-phosphate in a transfer reaction between UDP-glucose and a second unit of galactose-1-phosphate. The overall process is summarized by the net reaction given.

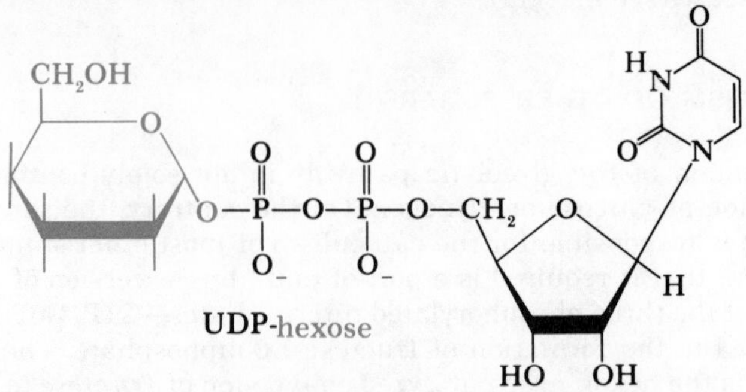

UDP-hexose

(a)	galactose + ATP $\xrightarrow{E_1}$ galactose-1-P + ADP	
(b)	galactose-1-P + UTP $\xrightarrow{E_2}$ UDP-galactose + PP$_i$	
(c)	UDP-galactose $\xrightarrow{E_3}$ UDP-glucose	
(d)	UDP-glucose + galactose-1-P $\xrightarrow{E_4}$ UDP-galactose + glucose-1-P	

---

*Net:** 2 galactose + 2ATP + UTP $\xrightarrow{4E's}$ UDP-galactose + glucose-1-P + PP$_i$ + 2ADP

Overall Effect: 1 galactose $\longrightarrow$ 1 glucose

*galactokinase reaction taken twice

E$_1$: galactokinase
E$_2$: UDP-galactose pyrophosphorylase
E$_3$: UDP-glucose C$_4$ epimerase
E$_4$: galactose phosphate uridyl transferase (E$_4$ absent in galactosemia)

The UDP sequence shown above constitutes the main process for the normal metabolism of galactose. In this regard, metabolic abnormalities are known, the most classical case being the hereditary disorder called *galactosemia*. This disease is characterized by a deficiency of galactose phosphate uridyl transferase (E$_4$), creating a blockage in the metabolism of galactose. The immediate result is an abnormally high cellular level of galactose-1-phosphate. The situation is quite serious in infants where the major natural source of dietary carbohydrate is milk lactose, which of course contains galactose (page 182, Chapter 7). Severe cases of infant galactosemia are characterized by cataract formation, cirrhosis of the liver and spleen, and in some cases mental retardation. Generally, however, all of these clinical manifestations can be avoided by simply eliminating galactose and all galactose-containing substances from the diet. As the infant ages, less dietary control is required, since the adult galactosemic is capable of metabolizing galactose-1-phosphate by alternate routes. In view of modern developments in biochemical genetics and molecular biology, there is a possibility that man may ultimately possess the capacity to correct or replace the defective gene that underlies this disease and other genetic abnormalities. If and when this comes to pass, it will represent one of man's greatest achievements—if not the greatest—and will provide him with a power certain to cause a moral and ethical dilemma of astounding proportions as to how such knowledge should be used.

The biochemical significance of UDP-sugars far exceeds the galactose → glucose conversion. To prove the point, we could cite a multitude of individual reactions. However, this is not within the scope of this book; suffice it to say that the bulk of carbohydrate reactions involving the monosaccharides, including the important biosynthetic reactions of oligosaccharides and polysaccharides, are dependent on nucleoside diphosphate derivatives (NuDP—sugar) of the monosaccharides. Most are UDP-derivatives. Some examples are given below.

UDP-Sugars in Carbohydrate Metabolism

$$UTP + sugar_A\text{-}1\text{-}P \rightarrow UDP\text{-}sugar_A + PP_i$$

$$UDP\text{-}sugar_A + sugar_B \xrightarrow{E} sugar_A\text{—}sugar_B + UDP$$

a variety of reactions occur involving
different sugars and enzymes

Examples:

UDP-galactose + glucose → lactose + UDP

UDP-glucose + fructose → sucrose + UDP

UDP-glucose + $(glycogen)_n$ → $(glycogen)_{n+1}$ + UDP

UDP-N-acetylglucosamine ⎫

UDP-N-acetylgalactosamine ⎬ → glycolipids and
heteropolysaccharides

UDP-glucuronic acid ⎭

GLYCOGENESIS AND AN OVERALL VIEW OF THE REGULATION OF CARBOHYDRATE METABOLISM

In the preceding pages we have seen how the reactions of glycolysis effect the degradation of carbohydrates. With this analysis now complete, the next obvious question to consider concerns the biosynthesis of carbohydrates (termed *glycogenesis*) from smaller carbon fragments such as pyruvate and lactate. (*Note:* For the moment we are focusing attention on the formation of carbohydrates in non-photosynthetic organisms. The photosynthetic assimilation of CO_2 into carbohydrate material will be discussed separately in Chapter 14.) Since lactate dehydrogenase is capable of reversibly catalyzing a conversion of pyruvate and lactate, the question is reduced to how pyruvate is converted to glucose or glycogen. In addressing ourselves to this question, the immediate tendency would be to suggest that glycogenesis proceeds by a complete reversal of glycolysis. However, this would be incorrect. In that case, then, a logical counter-suggestion would be that a completely different pathway is involved. However, once again this would be incorrect. What then, you ask, is the mechanism of glycogenesis? Well, a little thought would lead you to conclude that, if neither of these possibilities was correct, then the pathway of glycogenesis probably consists of a blend of both. In this case you would be correct. Although valid, the conclusion generates a logical uncertainty; namely, to what extent is the glycolytic pathway reversible? That is, which of the reactions are reversible and which are irreversible?

Departing from this *a priori* approach, suffice it to say that the biosynthesis of the metabolically active forms of glucose (G1P and G6P) from smaller carbon units proceeds by a direct reversal of the same reactions of glycolysis, with only *two exceptions*. The two irreversible reactions are those catalyzed by *pyruvate kinase* and *phosphofructokinase*. If we consider the biosynthesis of free glucose and free glycogen, then two other reactions are to be included as well, namely, those catalyzed by *hexokinase* and *phosphorylase*. In other words, the four sites of enzyme irreversibility in the pathway of glycolysis are: PYR → PEP; FDP → F6P; G6P → GLU; and G1P → glycogen. The reason why all these reactions are not biologically reversible is quite simple—the *glycolytic enzymes in question are specific only for the catabolic substrates and do not form an active complex with the product*. Therefore, they don't work in reverse.

These sites of enzyme irreversibility are logically circumvented, however. Each conversion involves enzymes different than those that operate in glycolysis. The most complicated bypass is for PYR → PEP because it occurs in different ways in different cells. In some bacteria, for example, the reaction is catalyzed by a single, ATP-dependent enzyme (*phosphoenolpyruvate synthetase*) resulting in the direct formation of PEP from PYR (route 1 on the facing page). In other bacteria and also in the higher plant and animal organisms the conversion is indirect and involves the participation of two enzymes, namely, *pyruvate carboxylase* and *phosphoenolpyruvate carboxykinase* (route 2). The carboxylase catalyzes the ATP-dependent carboxylation of pyruvate (C_1 plus C_3) to yield oxaloacetate (C_4). This reaction requires the participation of *biotin* as an essential coenzyme as do several other CO_2 fixation reactions. (The role played by biotin in this type of reaction will be examined further in Chapter 15, see page 398.) In addition, the activity of the carboxylase is strongly activated by high concentrations of acetyl-SCoA. As we will see in the next chapter this fits into the overall pattern of metabolic control resulting in increased rates of glycogenesis under certain conditions. The carboxykinase then catalyzes a decarboxylation of oxaloacetate accompanied by phosphorylation to yield phosphoenolpyruvate. Depending on the cell-type, the carboxykinase shows a distinct preference to utilize either GTP (guanosine triphosphate) or ITP (inosine triphosphate) as the phosphate donor rather than ATP. In the eucaryotic cells of higher organisms the pyruvate carboxylase seems to be localized exclusively in the mitochondrion regardless of cell-type. This creates no problem since pyruvate can enter the mitochondrion by direct passage across the membrane. Phosphoenolpyruvate carboxykinase, however, has been found in either the mitochondrion or in the cytoplasm depending on the source. When it occurs in the mitochondrion, this means that PEP is formed within the mitochondria (route 2). Although the subsequent utilization of PEP in glycogenesis must occur in the cytoplasm (that's where the enzymes are), there is no problem because the phosphoenolpyruvate like pyruvate can readily cross the mitochondrial membrane.

When the carboxykinase occurs in the cytoplasm, however, a problem does exist because oxaloacetate, the substrate of the carboxy-

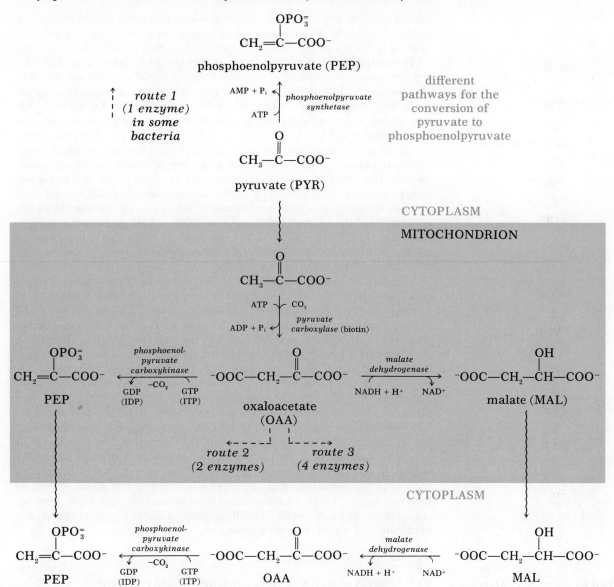

kinom, is generated in the mitochondrion and it does not readily cross the mitochondrial membrane. Thus, if the oxaloacetate is formed within the mitochondrion, the question is how can it be converted to PEP when the necessary enzyme is located outside the mitochondrion? Well, it is proposed that this apparent short-circuit is circumvented by the participation of two additional enzymes, namely, *malate dehydrogenase* and *malate dehydrogenase*. No, this is not an error, the enzymes have the same name and they do catalyze the same reaction, namely, a reversible oxidation-reduction reaction between malate (an alpha hydroxy dicarboxylic acid) and oxaloacetate (an alpha keto dicarboxylic acid). Both enzymes are also NAD-dependent. The enzymes differ, however, in terms of their cellular localization in that one occurs *inside* the mitochondrion and the other occurs *outside* the mitochondrion, that is, in the cytoplasm. Their proposed participation in the PYR → PEP conversion is shown in the diagram as route 3. In this case the link between what occurs in the mitochondrion and in the cytoplasm is provided by the movement of malate across the mitochondrial membrane. We will discuss the malate dehydrogenase enzymes again in the next chapter.

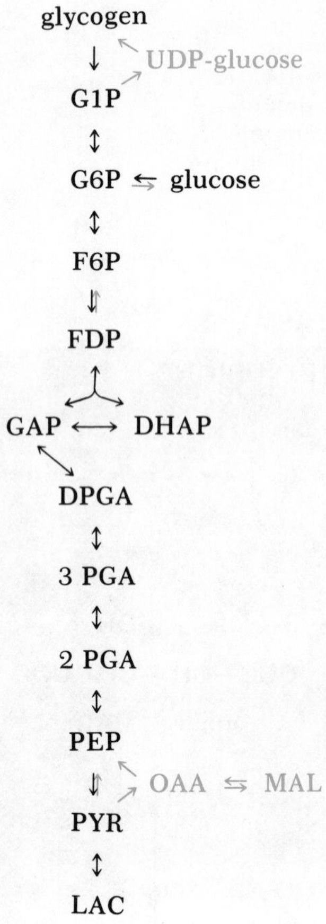

The considerable attention we have given to the PYR → PEP conversion is not to imply any special preeminence for it. Certainly it is an important and key step but so are several other reactions. The point is that it serves as an excellent example of both the biochemical diversity that exists in nature and the principle of compartmentalization. Despite the diversity, however, note that in each route the same net effect is realized. Pyruvate is converted to phosphoenolpyruvate in a process that requires the expenditure of what can be considered as the equivalent of 2 ATP molecules: ATP → ADP → AMP in bacteria; ATP → ADP and GTP(ITP) → GDP(IDP) in eucaryotic cells. The expenditure of energy is to be expected since phosphoenolpyruvate is a high-energy chemical species relative to pyruvate.

After its formation from PYR by either of these routes, PEP is then converted to FDP by a direct reversal of glycolysis. Once FDP is formed the three remaining irreversible sites of glycolysis are bypassed by processes involving still other enzymes. The first bypass utilizes *fructose diphosphatase* to convert FDP to F6P (see below). The F6P is then converted to G6P by the same isomerase that functions in glycolysis. *Glucophosphatase* then converts G6P to free glucose. Alternatively, the G6P can be converted to G1P by the same mutase that functions in glycolysis. Finally, the glucose moiety of G1P is incorporated into glycogen via a two-enzyme sequence. First, G1P is converted to UDP-glucose by the action of a specific *pyrophosphorylase* and then the glucose moiety of UDP-glucose is incorporated into glycogen via *glycogen synthetase.* (Recall our earlier mention of the role of NuDP-sugars in polysaccharide biosynthesis.) Thus, we see that although the pathways of glycolysis and glycogenesis involve the same chemical intermediates (the two exceptions are oxaloacetate and UDP-glucose) specialized sites do exist which require different enzymes for the catabolic and anabolic conversions.

glycogen
↓ ↖ UDP-glucose
G1P
↕
G6P ⇆ glucose
↕
F6P
↓↑
FDP
↑
GAP ⟷ DHAP
↙
DPGA
↕
3 PGA
↕
2 PGA
↕
PEP
↕↗ OAA ⇆ MAL
PYR
↕
LAC

PYR → → PEP   (see page 284)

then by reversal of glycolysis: PEP → 2PGA → 3PGA → DPGA → GAP → DHAP ⟶ FDP

then: FDP $\xrightarrow[\text{H}_2\text{O}]{\text{diphosphatase}}$ F6P + P_i (inhibited by AMP, ADP)

then by reversal of glycolysis: F6P → G6P

then: G6P $\xrightarrow[\text{H}_2\text{O}]{\text{monophosphatase}}$ glucose + P_i

or by reversal of glycolysis: F6P → G6P → G1P

then: G1P $\xrightarrow[\text{UTP} \quad \text{PP}_i]{\substack{\text{UDP-glucose} \\ \text{pyrophosphorylase}}}$ UDP-glucose $\xrightarrow[\text{(glucose)}_n \quad \text{UDP}]{\substack{\text{glycogen} \\ \text{synthetase}}}$ $(glucose)_{n+1}$

(Synthetase inhibited by cyclic-AMP)

On the basis of studies with purified preparations of the enzymes identified above, it turns out that their operation in glycogenesis confers a definite advantage on the organism in the maintenance of metabolic economy. To be more specific, it has been shown that the activity of each enzyme is subject to regulation in a pattern that is totally consistent with the control on its catalytic counterpart in glycolysis. The clearest example of this remarkable phenomenon is provided by the data for phosphofructokinase and fructose diphosphatase. The former is activated by AMP and ADP whereas the latter is inhibited by AMP and ADP. In other words, here is a situation where identical effector substances cause different effects. By itself, this isn't too startling, since the two effectors are acting on two different enzymes. What is remarkable is that these effects are exerted at the same metabolic step in a perfectly complementary fashion. Thus, whenever the physiological state of the organism results in high cellular levels of AMP or ADP—a condition which can be interpreted generally as an energy-consuming state, that

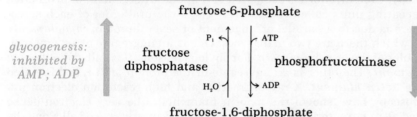

Complementary Allosteric Control at Site of F6P ⇌ FDP

fructose-6-phosphate

glycogenesis: inhibited by AMP; ADP

fructose diphosphatase

P_i ← | ⌐ ATP

H_2O ⌐ | → ADP

phosphofructokinase

glycolysis: activated by AMP; ADP; cyclic AMP (also inhibited by ATP)

fructose-1,6-diphosphate

is, *ATP is being utilized at a high rate*—a signal is received by the enzymes of carbohydrate metabolism resulting in the *stimulation* of carbohydrate degradation and *depression* of carbohydrate biosynthesis to satisfy the increased demand for metabolic energy. On return to a less active metabolic state in which the *ATP utilization is low,* the increase in ATP and the reduction in the levels of AMP and ADP then act as metabolic signals that *depress* glycolysis by allosterically inhibiting the activity of the pyruvate kinase and phosphofructokinase enzymes. Other control sites of glycolysis and glycogenesis exhibit the same general pattern. Another example is that cyclic-AMP not only activates glycogen phosphorylase but also inhibits glycogen synthetase. Thus, the enzymes of the main pathways of carbohydrate metabolism are efficiently programmed to the needs of an organism in the most economic way possible. It will become evident that this principle applies to the whole of biochemical dynamics.

The point of our constant referral to allosteric properties and their operational significance to enzyme systems is quite simple: they constitute an intricate mechanism of natural checks and balances which regulate the flow of matter and energy within the cell. It is understandable if at this point you are experiencing some difficulty in appreciating this concept. The difficulty, however, is not due to the complexity of the concept as much as to the fact that we have yet to illustrate how the major metabolic pathways are *integrated* with each other. As your knowledge of metabolism grows, so will your understanding of these catalytic control mechanisms. When appropriate (Chapter 12), we will review some of the details covered in this chapter.

CARBOHYDRATE CATABOLISM AND MUSCLE CONTRACTION

The fascinating phenomenon of muscle contraction has long interested many workers. Originally it was thought to be purely a physical process due to the mechanical shortening of muscle fibers. This idea was laid to rest in 1954 when A. F. Huxley and H. E. Huxley independently proposed a molecular mechanism for contraction involving the relative *sliding movement* of protein filaments within muscle tissue. (One of the oddities of modern science is that the two Huxleys are not related.) Since then the sliding filament model has been supported and refined by extensive research and is now accepted as the nucleus of our current theory of the contractile process. To understand the proposed mechanism and ultimately the function of ATP generated by glycolysis and other energy-yielding processes, it is necessary to first examine some of the details of the ultrastructure of muscle tissue.

As shown in Figure 11-5, the cells of muscle tissue are bundles of longitudinal fibers called *myofibrils*. As revealed by electron microscopy, each myofibril is composed of a linear arrangement of distinctive repeating units called *sarcomeres*. The structural order of each sarcomere is due to a parallel arrangement of several protein *myofilaments* of which there are two main types. One is an aggregate of several molecules of the protein, *myosin*. For obvious reasons, it is called the *myosin filament*. The other is an aggregate of the protein, *actin,* and is called the *actin filament*. X-ray diffraction and high-resolution electron microscopy have shown the myosin filaments to be very electron dense and also characterized by short projections regularly spaced all along the surface of the filament. The projections are believed to arise from the globular regions of individual myosin molecules which protrude away from the filament proper. In the filament itself, the myosin molecules are complexed with each other via interactions among the non-globular (that is, fibrillous) regions of individual molecules.

By comparison, the actin filament is smaller in diameter (less electron dense) and contains no surface protrusions. It does contain several binding sites along its length that interact with the myosin filament. In the context of these structural characteristics of each myofilament, the electron micrographs of muscle tissue are interpreted as shown in the drawings of Figure 11-5. In each sarcomere, myosin filaments are located only in a region called the *A band*, whereas the actin filaments traverse the region called the *I band* and protrude longitudinally into the A band. The protrusion contributes to an overlapping of actin and myosin filaments in the A band. See the legend of Figure 11-5 for additional features.

Now, the sliding filament model proposes that muscle changes length as the overlapping arrays of actin and myosin filaments slide past each other in each sarcomere, with the actin filament drawn further into the A band when the muscle is contracted and further out of the A band when the muscle is stretched. The controversy exists regarding the molecular events which mediate the relative movement of filaments. Huxley proposes that the key to the movement is the shifting of binding sites in an active *actomyosin complex formed by the contact of the myosin protrusions with the smooth actin filaments.* One possible suggestion is that the globular myosin projections undergo a con-

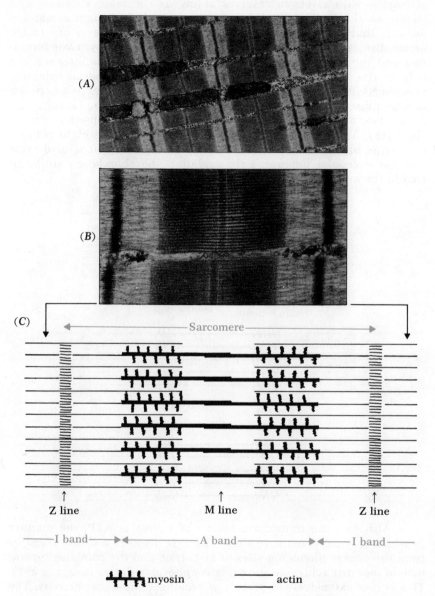

(A)

(B)

(C)

←———————————— Sarcomere ————————————→

↑ Z line   ↑ M line   ↑ Z line

←——I band——→ ←———— A band ————→ ←— I band ——→

⊣⊢⊣⊢ myosin   ——— actin

Figure 11–5 Ultrastructure of muscle.
(A) Electron micrograph of myofibrils
in a fiber of papillary muscle tissue of cat
heart. The myofibrils run horizontally and
are separated by the sarcoplasm containing mitochondria and glycogen
granules. The latter appear as black dots.
Magnification: 8,000 ×. (B) Electron
micrograph of sarcomere unit in two
adjacent myofibrils. Magnification:
24,960 ×. (C) Diagrammatic representation of sarcomere unit depicting the
parallel arrangement of myosin and actin
filaments. Actin filaments occupy the
light I band and penetrate some distance
into the A band where they interact with
projections of myosin filaments. The Z
line corresponds to the joining of actin
filaments from two adjacent sarcomeres.
The M line corresponds to the joining of
myosin filaments within the A band.
(Reproduced with permission from An
Atlas of Fine Structure, Fawcett, D. W.,
Philadelphia: W. B. Saunders Company,
1966. Photographs in A and B generously
supplied by D. W. Fawcett.)

formational change causing a shift to a new binding site on the actin
filaments. The effect would be a relative movement or sliding of the two
filaments via a longitudinally directed displacement. The explanation
is consistent with experimental observations that neither the myosin-
filament nor the actin-filament undergoes a change in axial length.
Only their relative positions are changed. It is the repeating sarcomere
unit that changes in length. (Refer to the diagram on page 290.)

Regardless of the molecular details of the sliding phenomenon,
the process is definitely known to be energy dependent, with the direct
energy source, ATP, being supplied almost exclusively by the breakdown
of carbohydrate. In skeletal muscle where the oxygen tension is low and
the bulk of metabolism is therefore anaerobic, the primary pathway is

glycolysis, with glycogen reserves acting as the main substrate and lactate as the final product. In other muscle tissues, such as cardiac muscle, that are capable of a considerably greater level of aerobic metabolism, the combined action of glycolysis through pyruvate formation and the citric acid cycle is more prevalent. In this instance, the bulk of the needed ATP will be supplied by mitochondrial oxidative phosphorylation. Consistent with this operational distinction between aerobic muscle tissue and anaerobic muscle tissue is the fact that the former type of cells generally contains a much larger proportion of mitochondria than the latter. Approximately 40% of the dry weight of heart represents mitochondria. (*Note:* The enzymes of the citric acid cycle and the molecular apparatus for oxidative phosphorylation are localized in the mitochondria. See page 225.)

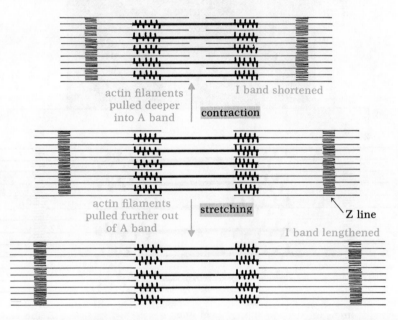

actin filaments pulled deeper into A band

I band shortened

contraction

actin filaments pulled further out of A band

stretching

Z line

I band lengthened

Diagrammatic representation of sliding movement within a sarcomere

Although the immediate source of energy is ATP, the manner in which it is delivered is twofold. The first involves a *direct transfer* from the energy-producing sites of glycolysis and the combined operations of the citric acid cycle and oxidative phosphorylation (see page 291). This occurs extensively in periods of prolonged muscular activity. The second involves the formation of ATP coupled to the hydrolysis of *creatine phosphate*, a *high-energy phosphoguanidine compound* (see page 249 and below), which is the molecular form in which energy is stored when the muscle is at rest. The source of energy for the formation of creatine phosphate is, of course, the ATP produced in the degradation of carbohydrate. On demand (a condition known to be signaled by the elevation of the concentration of Ca^{++} in the sarcoplasm), the hydrolysis of creatine phosphate is sufficiently exergonic to mediate the phosphorylation of ADP. This mode of ATP delivery would typify brief periods of activity and the initial phase of a prolonged stress as stored energy is utilized. As the muscle returns to rest (controlled by a drop in the level of Ca^{++}), the ATP generated by carbohydrate metabolism is then stored again as creatine phosphate.

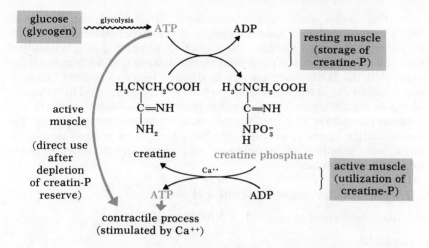

In the contractile process proper, there appear to be two ATP-requiring systems. One involves the conversion of actin from an inactive form to an active form, designated *G-actin* and *F-actin,* respectively. F-actin is the form that binds with myosin. In all likelihood, this is not the primary ATP-dependent system, because F-actin normally predominates. The second and probably most important ATP-dependent system is the actomyosin complex itself, where it has been shown that the exergonic *hydrolysis of ATP is a prerequisite for sliding to occur.* Although the specific events of this energy transfer are largely unknown, recent studies have shown that the myosin projections which bridge the actin and myosin filaments in the actomyosin complex do possess ATPase activity.

HEXOSE-MONOPHOSPHATE SHUNT

Although the combined reactions of glycolysis and the citric acid cycle serve as the main catabolic route for the complete oxidation of carbohydrates to CO_2 in most aerobic organisms, many possess alternate pathways. This is particularly common in the bacterial world. It is not our intent to investigate all such pathways. Rather, we will consider only one, namely, the *hexose-monophosphate shunt* (HMS). The HMS sequence is widely distributed in animals, plants, and bacteria. Hence, it is the most common alternate pathway of carbohydrate metabolism. However, you will quickly discover that it merits our attention for much more significant reasons. An indicator of its importance is provided by extensive observations that many cells possess enzymes of the HMS sequence in addition to glycolysis and the citric acid cycle, all of which operate simultaneously but usually to varying degrees. The metabolic logic of this phenomenon can be appreciated only after an examination of the chemical events that characterize the shunt pathway. For the moment, suffice it to say that the operation of the hexose-monophosphate shunt is not merely a metabolic redundancy of the combined pathways of glycolysis and the citric acid cycle. Rather, it is a reaction sequence which has the potential to fulfill certain vital functions not common to either of the latter pathways. Let us now analyze the reaction sequence.

The seven distinctive reactions of the hexose-monophosphate shunt are given below (see Figure 11–6 for structural formulae). Although it is difficult to deduce the metabolic effect due to this family of reactions when they are presented in this manner, close inspection reveals that the HMS reactions can be divided into two distinct phases—one *oxidative* and the other *non-oxidative* (Figure 11–6). The oxidative phase is characterized by the conversion of a hexose phosphate to a pentose phosphate and CO_2 via two $NADP^+$-dependent reactions. The non-oxidative phase is exclusively characterized by pentose isomerizations and transfers of two-carbon and three-carbon units between ketoses and aldoses.

(1) $NADP^+$ + glucose-6-phosphate → 6-phosphogluconate + NADPH + H^+

(2) $NADP^+$ + 6-phosphogluconate → ribulose-5-phosphate + CO_2 + NADPH + H^+

(3) ribulose-5-phosphate → ribose-5-phosphate

(4) ribulose-5-phosphate → xylulose-5-phosphate

(5) ribose-5-phosphate + xylulose-5-phosphate →
$$\text{glyceraldehyde-3-phosphate} + \text{sedoheptulose-7-phosphate}$$

(6) sedoheptulose-7-phosphate + glyceraldehyde-3-phosphate →
$$\text{fructose-6-phosphate} + \text{erythrose-4-phosphate}$$

(7) xylulose-5-phosphate + erythrose-4-phosphate → fructose-6-phosphate + glyceraldehyde-3-phosphate

To understand the potential overall chemical effect, it is necessary only to consider the above reactions occurring in conjunction with other cellular reactions. In this instance, the most appropriate candidates are some of the enzymes of glycolysis (hexose isomerase, triose phosphate isomerase, aldolase) and of glycogenesis (diphosphatase). There is nothing invalid in this approach, because the specificity of an enzyme is typified by its action on a certain substrate rather than by its participation in a particular set of reactions in which the substrate is metabolized. Furthermore, in this instance all of the pathways in question occur in the same subcellular compartment, namely, the cytoplasm. In other words, an enzyme is not necessarily confined to functioning only in one specific pathway. When this is done, it is possible to assemble the reactions in the fashion illustrated in Figure 11–6. (Note that the enzymes of glycolysis and glycogenesis would function in the conversion of the two units of glyceraldehyde-3-phosphate to glucose-6-phosphate.) Because of the divergence after ribulose-5-phosphate formation, it is advantageous to start with a non-unit stoichiometry. The convenience of starting with 3 units of G6P will emerge as you study the various interactions.

Although the diagram appears to be a complicated maze, it does neatly illustrate the metabolic function of the HMS sequence. However, as shown to the right, the latter is revealed most directly through an analysis of the net chemical effect by considering each reaction to interact as diagrammed. Our conclusion as to the metabolic function of the HMS pathway is now quite direct: Given the theoretical operation of the shunt pathway for 6 units of G6P as illustrated, the *net chemical effect is the same as the combined operation of glycolysis and the citric acid cycle, namely, the equivalent of one hexose unit is oxidatively degraded to* $6CO_2$. Also note that the pathway is equally effective in conserving chemical energy, since the 12 units of NADPH can theoretically be reoxidized to $NADP^+$ via the same mitochondrial or particulate system for NADH with the coupled formation of several ATP molecules. The hexose-monophosphate shunt is indeed an effective alternate pathway for glucose catabolism.

Despite the theoretical validity of these observations, they probably do not represent the true *in vivo* functions of the HMS sequence. Most evidence suggests that the *more significant* metabolic functions of the shunt reactions are, first, to serve as a major cellular *source of reduced NADP* needed for the reductive reactions of anabolism, and second, to *supply ribose* needed for the biosynthesis of nucleotides and nucleic acids. In addition, in plants and microbes, erythrose-4-phosphate is a biosynthetic precursor of the aromatic amino acids, phenylalanine, tyrosine, and tryptophan (see page 430). All of these possibilities are consistent with the cellular localization of all the enzymes that would be involved. That is, the bulk of biosynthetic reactions (NADPH dependent) occur in the cytoplasm which, as we stated before, is also where the enzymes of the shunt pathway are localized.

In man, the shunt pathway is not found in all tissues. In fact, it is relatively unimportant in skeletal muscle where the main reaction sequence is glycolysis. It is more significant in aerobic tissues characterized by considerable biosynthetic activity, such as the liver. In a few cases, such as corneal tissue, it has been implicated as the major metabolic pathway. In no case, however, has a strict quantitative analysis of the relative contributions of the HMS reactions and the combined pathways of glycolysis and citric acid cycle been reported. In plants, a variation of the shunt pathway functions in the photosynthetic fixation of atmospheric CO_2 and its subsequent conversion into carbohydrate (see Chapter 14).

Although these generalizations are interesting and once again illustrate the complexity of metabolism, it would be undesirable to close discussion at this point. Generalities have their place, but they can also cause confusion. One specific function of the HMS pathway has been documented, specifically in red blood cells (RBC) where the production of NADPH plays a particularly important role in sustaining the normal metabolism of these cells. Indeed, many conditions of anemia can be traced to impaired RBC metabolism of glucose, and specifically to an impaired operation of the shunt pathway. The most studied situation is that characterized by cells having a low activity of glucose-6-phosphate dehydrogenase. To understand the details of this dehydrogenase-deficient syndrome, let us first describe something of the function of NADPH in red blood cells. In normal cells, there is substantial evidence to indicate that one of the key functions of NADPH is to maintain a cellular pool of *reduced glutathione* (GSH; see page 73). This is especially important because reduced glutathione is considered to be the main substrate protecting other molecules in the cells from oxidation. The most notable compound affected by oxidation is hemoglobin. When it is converted to its oxidized form, called *methemoglobin,* it is rendered inactive. Reduced glutathione, by a process not yet clear, prevents this from occurring.

It is clear, however, that the maintenance of high concentrations of reduced glutathione in the red blood cells is due to the operation of the HMS pathway. Unfortunately, there is proof of this relationship in the form of the above-mentioned metabolic disorder typified by an in-

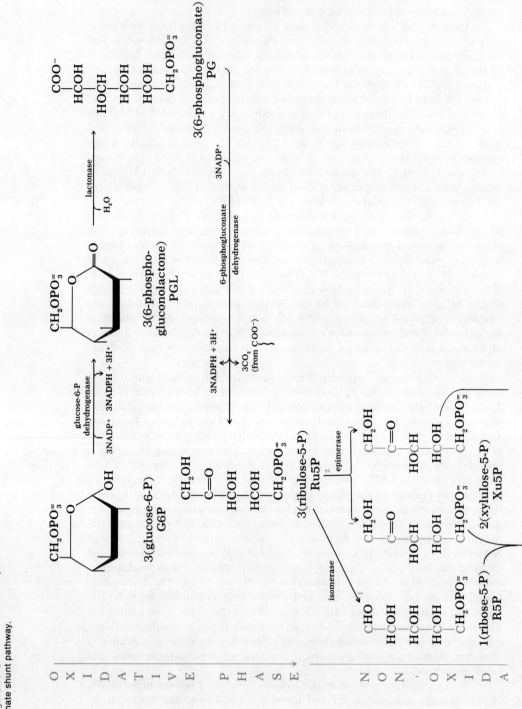

Figure 11-6 The hexose-monophosphate shunt pathway.

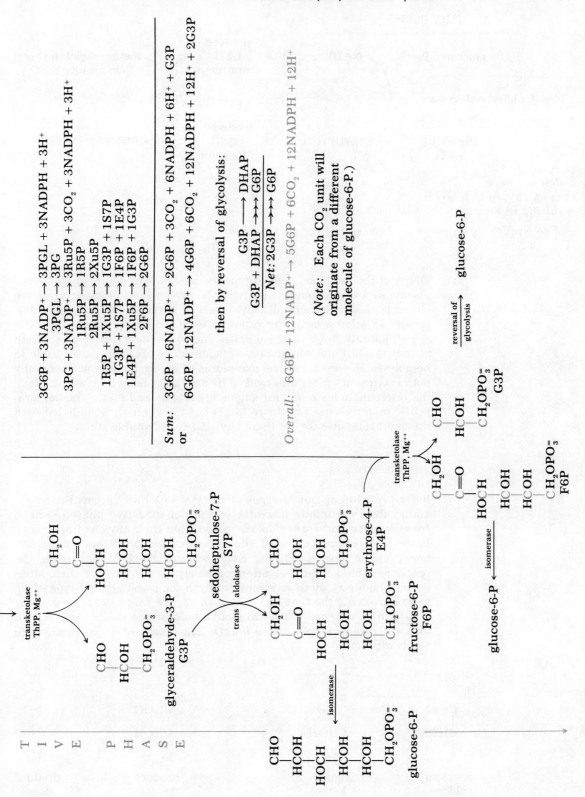

$$3G6P + 3NADP^+ \rightarrow 3PGL + 3NADPH + 3H^+$$
$$3PGL \rightarrow 3PG$$
$$3PG + 3NADP^+ \rightarrow 3Ru5P + 3CO_2 + 3NADPH + 3H^+$$
$$1Ru5P \rightarrow 1R5P$$
$$2Ru5P \rightarrow 2Xu5P$$
$$1R5P + 1Xu5P \rightarrow 1G3P + 1S7P$$
$$1G3P + 1S7P \rightarrow 1F6P + 1E4P$$
$$1E4P + 1Xu5P \rightarrow 1F6P + 1G3P$$
$$2F6P \rightarrow 2G6P$$

Sum: $3G6P + 6NADP^+ \rightarrow 2G6P + 3CO_2 + 6NADPH + 6H^+ + G3P$

or $6G6P + 12NADP^+ \rightarrow 4G6P + 6CO_2 + 12NADPH + 12H^+ + 2G3P$

then by reversal of glycolysis:

$$G3P \longrightarrow DHAP$$
$$\underline{G3P + DHAP \ggg G6P}$$
Net: $2G3P \ggg G6P$

Overall: $6G6P + 12NADP^+ \rightarrow 5G6P + 6CO_2 + 12NADPH + 12H^+$

(*Note:* Each CO_2 unit will originate from a different molecule of glucose-6-P.)

HMS Pathway

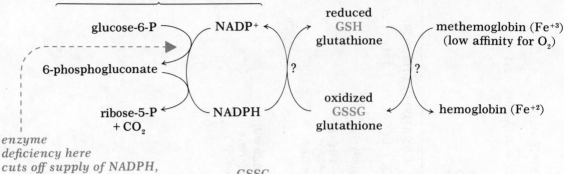

enzyme deficiency here cuts off supply of NADPH, resulting in an increase in the ratio of $\dfrac{GSSG}{GSH}$ and consequently an increased amount of methemoglobin

ability of the red blood cells to produce adequate amounts of glucose-6-phosphate dehydrogenase. Individuals carrying this genetic trait are characterized by abnormally low levels of NADPH and reduced gluta-thione. In other words, the ratios of GSSG/GSH and NADP$^+$/NADPH are abnormally high in these cells. The consequence of this condition is that the G6P-dehydrogenase–deficient cells are more susceptible to hemolysis. However, clinical symptoms of severe anemia are generally not manifested unless first evoked by a primary hemolytic agent. Since the latter includes many infectious organisms and many chemothera-peutic materials used in the treatment of infection, those afflicted with this metabolic disease are in an obviously unfavorable state.

TRANSKETOLASE

Before concluding our analysis of the HMS pathway, let us briefly ex-amine the two unique enzymes of the non-oxidative phase, namely, *transketolase* and *transaldolase*. Aside from their obvious importance in the HMS sequence proper, the same enzymes participate in the car-bon cycle of photosynthesis. Even without these justifications, the reactions would merit our attention solely on the basis of their inter-esting chemistry. Both enzymes catalyze the same general type of re-action involving the *transfer of a small carbon fragment from a donor ketose to an acceptor aldose* to yield an *aldose of shorter chain length and a ketose of longer chain length*. The details of each reaction are vastly different.

Transketolase catalyzes the transfer of a two-carbon *glycoalde-hyde* unit [HOH$_2$C—$\overset{\overset{\displaystyle O}{\|}}{C}$—]. Note also (Figure 11–6) that the ketolase reaction involves Mg^{++} and a substance designated ThPP. They are more than merely involved, since both are absolutely required for transketolase activity. The ThPP notation refers to *thiamine pyrophosphate* (see below), which represents the metabolically active *coenzyme form of thiamine* (vitamin B$_1$). Although ThPP is not firmly bound to the enzyme, it is required for the formation of the active enzyme complex and actually undergoes chemical modification during the course of the reaction. The active complexes are stabilized by inter-

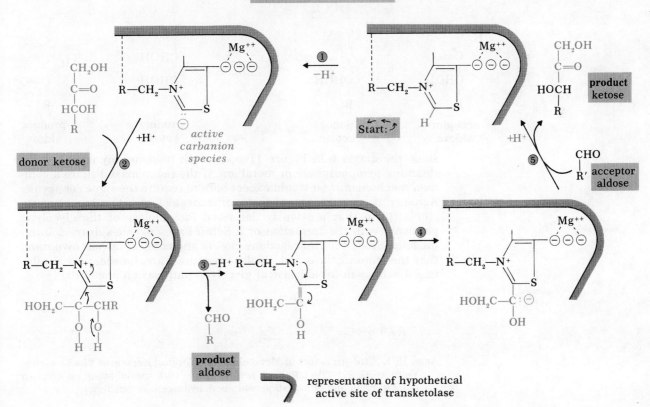

Thiamine pyrophosphate

Transketolase Mechanism

representation of hypothetical active site of transketolase

action with magnesium ion. The active site of ThPP resides in the C_2 position of the *thiazole ring,* which has a strong tendency to lose its hydrogen as a proton. This results in the formation of an active carbanion species of ThPP that is very susceptible to condensation with carbon atoms of a carbonyl grouping. Depending on the nature of the carbonyl-containing compound and the specificity of the enzyme, the fate of the resultant adduct is variable. In the transketolase reaction, the adduct undergoes a rearrangement characterized by the cleavage of a C—C bond, resulting in the formation of the product aldose and an anion form of an alkylated ThPP intermediate. The latter then undergoes a condensation with the carbonyl carbon of the acceptor aldose, generating the product ketose and the original form of ThPP. The net effect is the transfer of a glycoaldehyde unit. An intriguing reaction representative of coenzyme function.

TRANSALDOLASE

The mechanism of transaldolase catalysis involving the transfer of a three-carbon *dihydroxyacetone* unit (HOH_2C—$\overset{\overset{\displaystyle O}{\|}}{C}$—$\underset{\underset{\displaystyle OH}{|}}{CH}$—) is wholly unlike that of transketolase. You shouldn't find this too surprising,

since the diagram in Figure 11–6 does not indicate any necessity for thiamine pyrophosphate or metal ion. If the reactions did share a common mechanism, you would expect both to require the same coenzyme. Actually, the proposed mechanism of transaldolase action has a greater similarity to that previously described for aldolase of the glycolytic pathway, with the formation of a Schiff-base enzyme-substrate intermediate. Study the two reactions closely and confirm in your own mind that the transaldolase and aldolase reactions are, indeed, very similar (see mechanism for aldolase of glycolytic pathway on page 279).

LITERATURE

AEBI, H. E., "Inborn Errors of Metabolism," in *Annual Review of Biochemistry,* Volume 36, 271–306 (1967). A review article with special attention given to galactosemia and glucose-6-phosphate dehydrogenase deficiency.

AXELROD, B., "Glycolysis" and "Other Pathways of Carbohydrate Metabolism," in Volume 1 of *Metabolic Pathways,* Third Edition, D. Greenberg (ed.). New York: Academic Press, 1967. Two review articles giving a thorough analysis of reaction pathways.

BALDWIN, E., *Dynamic Aspects of Biochemistry,* Fifth Edition. London and New York: Cambridge University Press, 1967. For twenty years, which have included five editions and printings in several foreign languages, this uniquely organized textbook has drawn praise from teacher and student alike. The major emphasis of the book is metabolism, specifically the metabolism of mammalian systems. Chapters 17 and 18 are devoted to the anaerobic metabolism of carbohydrates (glycolysis) as it applies to alcoholic fermentation and muscle contraction.

BYGRAVE, F. L., "The Ionic Environment and Metabolic Control," *Nature,* **214,** 667–671 (1967). An article summarizing the possible control of glycolysis by enzyme regulation mediated by metal ions.

DAVIS, R. E., "On the Mechanism of Muscular Contraction," in Volume 1 of *Essays in Biochemistry,* P. N. Campbell and G. D. Greville, (eds.), 29–56. New York: Academic Press, 1965. A review article focusing primarily on the role of ATP and phosphocreatine in the contractile process.

FISCHER, E. H., A. POCKER, and J. C. SAARI, "The Structure, Function, and Control of Glycogen Phosphorylase," in Volume 6 of *Essays in Biochemistry,* P. N. Campbell and F. Dickens (eds.), 23–68. New York: Academic Press, 1970. A superb review article on this allosteric enzyme.

GINSBURG, V., "Sugar Nucleotides and the Synthesis of Carbohydrates," in Volume 26 of *Advances in Enzymology.* New York: John Wiley, 1964. A review article dealing with nucleoside diphosphate sugars.

HALES, C. N., "Some Actions of Hormones in the Regulation of Glucose Metabolism," in Volume 3 of *Essays in Biochemistry,* P. N. Campbell and G. D. Greville (eds.), 73–104. New York: Academic Press, 1967. An excellent review article on an important subject treated only briefly in this chapter.

HORECKER, B. L., "Transaldolase and Transketolase," in Volume 15 of *Comprehensive Biochemistry,* M. Florkin and E. H. Stotz (eds.). Amsterdam-New York: Elsevier Publishing Company. A review article on the mechanism of action of these two important enzymes in carbohydrate metabolism.

HOYLE, G., "How is Muscle Turned On and Off?" *Scientific American,* **222,** 84–93 (1970). An article describing the role of calcium ion in the contraction and relaxation of muscle tissue.

HUXLEY, H. E., "The Mechanism of Muscular Contraction," *Science,* **164,** 1356–1365 (1969). An authoritative review describing the possible mechanism of action at the molecular level for the sliding of actin and myosin filaments during contraction.

WOOD, W. A. (ed.), *Carbohydrate Metabolism.* Volume 9 of *Methods in Enzymology,* S. P. Colowick and N. O. Kaplan, (eds.). New York: Academic Press, 1966. A reference source for procedures in the isolation and assay of enzymes associated with carbohydrate metabolism, including summaries of catalytic properties.

EXERCISES

11-1 What is meant by the statement that the reduced forms of nicotinamide adenine dinucleotides have complementary roles in catabolism and anabolism?

11-2 What is the biological significance of catabolic reactions that result in the formation of ATP?

11-3 If radioactive glucose, labeled in positions 3 and 4 with C^{14}, were incubated with a cell-free liver homogenate under anaerobic conditions, what positions in the lactate produced would be labeled with C^{14}?

11-4 The metabolism of sucrose first involves the action of sucrose phosphorylase to yield glucose-1-phosphate and fructose. Assuming that both glucose-1-phosphate and fructose are further metabolized to lactate (a) how many ATP's would be required? and (b) how many ATP's would be produced?

11-5 Under a growth condition resulting in the production of ethyl alcohol via the glycolytic pathway in fermenting bacteria, what internal coupling mechanism involving NAD would parallel that in muscle cells actively degrading carbohydrate under the same condition? What type of condition is in effect?

11-6 If 0.001 mole of 3-phosphoglyceraldehyde were incubated with 0.005 mole of P_i, 0.0001 mole of NAD^+, and 3-phosphoglyceraldehyde dehydrogenase, a reaction would occur which would reach equilibrium rather quickly. This equilibrium would be characterized by the presence of a considerable amount of the 3-phosphoglyceraldehyde originally added. Predict what would happen to this equilibrium mixture if 0.005 mole of pyruvate and lactate dehydrogenase were added.

11-7 Write a complete balanced equation that would best describe the net catabolism of mannose to pyruvate.

11-8 Is the net requirement of metabolic energy as ATP for the production of glucose-1-phosphate from lactate greater than, less than, or the same as the net production of ATP from the catabolism of glucose-1-phosphate to lactate. (In solving this problem, remember that all of the purine and pyrimidine nucleotides are thermodynamically equivalent. In addition assume that the reactions are those that would occur in eucaryotic cells.)

11-9 In thermodynamic terms, what would be the significance of the reactions between 1,3-diphosphoglycerate and fructose-6-phosphate during *glycogenesis*?

11-10 If ribose-5-phosphate, uniformly labeled with radioactive carbon, were incubated in a suitably buffered solution containing xylulose-5-phosphate (no C^{14}), thiamine pyrophosphate, Mg^{++}, and transketolase, what two new carbohydrates would be produced, and what would be the labeling pattern of carbon-14 in each one?

12

Citric Acid Cycle

On several occasions in the preceding chapter, we referred to the citric acid cycle as the set of reactions responsible for the complete, energy-yielding, oxidative degradation to carbon dioxide of the pyruvate produced in glycolysis. In that context the citric acid cycle can be considered as a pathway common to carbohydrate metabolism. However, to exclusively identify the citric acid cycle as a pathway that fulfills *only* this metabolic role would be incorrect. On the contrary, its metabolic significance is much broader in scope. Indeed, *in nearly all organisms it serves as a central pathway in the metabolism of all the main classes of biomolecules.* Furthermore, this relationship is on the level of *both degradation* (catabolism) *and synthesis* (anabolism). The most important consequence of this operational characteristic is that the many separate facets of cellular metabolism are *integrated into a dynamic unit.*

The details as to how these functions are fulfilled are many and varied. Nevertheless, one important generalization can be made: Regardless of how they mediate the metabolic flow of carbon, the oxidative reactions of the citric acid cycle, in conjunction with the process of oxidative phosphorylation, serve as the *principal source of metabolic energy in the form of ATP.*

The diagram below attempts to summarize these principles by illustrating that metabolic intermediates of the citric acid cycle can be both *diverted into biosynthetic reactions* and *formed from degradative reactions* of carbohydrates, lipids, proteins, and nucleic acids. Also depicted is the production of energy which accompanies the cyclical interconversions involving these intermediates. It is impossible to describe and understand these relationships without first analyzing the reaction sequence of the cycle in greater detail. These are the objectives of this chapter.

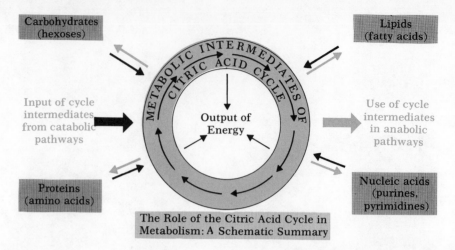

The Role of the Citric Acid Cycle in Metabolism: A Schematic Summary

REACTIONS OF THE CITRIC ACID CYCLE

EXPERIMENTAL HISTORY

In the development of any scientific discipline, there are what can be called key discoveries. In the biochemical area one such discovery was made in the late 1930s by Hans Krebs, a German-born English biochemist, in his experiments on the utilization of simple organic acids by pigeon breast muscle, which is characterized by a high level of aerobic metabolism. The experimental design was simple and straightforward. The rate of oxygen consumption (respiration) by muscle homogenates was determined when the muscle was incubated in the presence of glycogen, glucose, or pyruvate as a primary carbon and energy source, and then compared to that of the same system supplemented with small amounts of various organic acids. In summary form, the important findings were (a) that regardless of carbon source, the presence of certain dicarboxylic acids such as fumaric acid, succinic acid, malic acid, oxaloacetic acid, α-ketoglutaric acid, and certain tricarboxylic acids such as citric acid, *cis*-aconitic acid, and isocitric acid *stimulated* respiration, that is, increased oxygen consumption and carbon dioxide production, and (b) that *in each case* the stimulation could be *inhibited* by malonic acid—at the time a known inhibitor of succinate → fumarate—resulting in an accumulation of succinate *in each case*.

These data suggested that all of the acids were intermediates of a common pathway which was capable of degrading pyruvate completely to carbon dioxide. Krebs discovered the key in another experiment wherein he incubated the same homogenate in the presence of pyruvate supplemented only with oxaloacetate, but under *anaerobic* conditions. In this system he found that *citrate* accumulated. Based on these findings, Krebs proposed that when the formation of citrate from oxaloacetate and pyruvate was interpreted in combination with other reactions (some of which were known at that time), the metabolic scheme most consistent with all data was a *cyclic* sequence (see below). Without lengthy documentation, suffice it to say that Kreb's hypothesis proved correct.

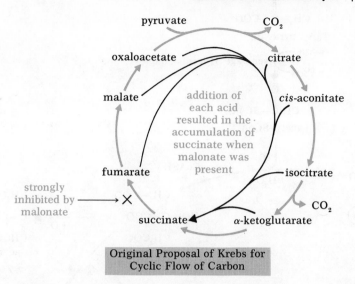

pyruvate CO_2

oxaloacetate   citrate

malate   cis-aconitate

addition of
each acid
resulted in the
accumulation of
succinate when
malonate was
present

fumarate   isocitrate

strongly
inhibited by ⟶ ✕ CO_2
malonate

succinate   α-ketoglutarate

Original Proposal of Krebs for
Cyclic Flow of Carbon

The discovery by Krebs (Nobel Prize—1953) was to have a monumental significance to classical biochemistry comparable to the impact of the Watson and Crick proposal for DNA structure on modern biology. The first recognized metabolic function of the *citric acid cycle*—frequently called the *tricarboxylic acid cycle* (TCA cycle) or the *Krebs cycle*—was that it accounted for the aerobic link between glycolysis and the complete degradation of carbohydrates. In short order, however, it was quickly recognized as a pathway which was the nucleus of the whole of metabolism, including the cellular production of energy. Since then both of these important roles have been unequivocally documented by abundant evidence. Moreover, this importance is not confined to any one select group of cells. On the contrary, as stated earlier, the citric acid cycle is probably the most widespread metabolic sequence in our biosphere, being found in all animals, most plants, and many microorganisms.

OVERALL VIEW

A modern version of the citric acid cycle (with structures of the intermediates) is shown in Figure 12–1. Note that the flow of carbon differs from the initial proposal of Krebs in two important respects: (1) in what can be considered the *priming step* of the cycle, the carbon unit that condenses with oxaloacetate is *acetyl-SCoA*; and (2) the conversion of α-ketoglutarate to succinate involves the intermediate formation of succinyl-SCoA. Both modifications were made during the late 1940s and early 1950s, accompanying the isolation and characterization of coenzyme A.

Beginning with the formation of citrate, the characteristic chemistry of the eight reactions of the cycle can be descriptively summarized as follows: (1) the formation of a carbon–carbon bond between a thioester-activated acetyl group (C_2 unit) and a C_4 α-keto dicarboxylic acid to yield a C_6 tricarboxylic acid; (2) a positional isomerization of the C_6 tricarboxylic acid; (3) the first of two successive NAD^+-dependent oxida-

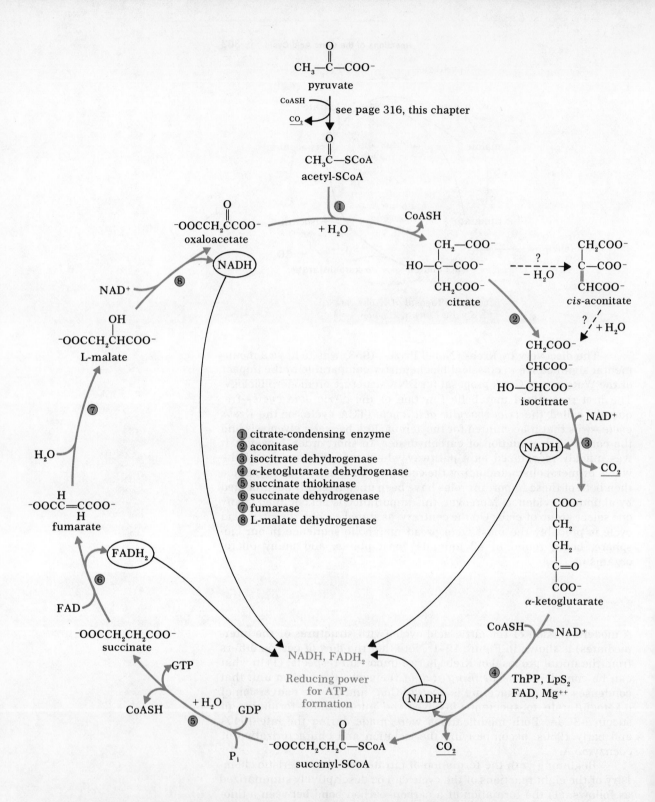

Figure 12–1 A modern representation of the citric acid cycle. Each enzyme is coded by a number, with the traditional names given in the center of the diagram. Wherever appropriate, the participation of coenzymes in a reaction is indicated symbolically. The mechanics of ATP formation coupled to the utilization of the reducing power generated by the cycle are discussed in Chapter 13. General principles of this coupling are discussed in this chapter.

tive decarboxylations, resulting in the conversion of the C_6 isomeric tricarboxylic acid to a C_5 α-keto dicarboxylic acid; (4) the second NAD^+-dependent oxidative decarboxylation, resulting in the formation of a thioester of a C_4 dicarboxylic acid; (5) the exergonic hydrolysis of the C_4 thioester to yield a free C_4 dicarboxylic acid in its fully saturated form; (6) an FAD-dependent dehydrogenation to yield a C_4 unsaturated dicarboxylic acid; (7) the hydration of the unsaturated acid to yield a C_4 α-hydroxy dicarboxylic acid; and (8) an NAD^+-dependent dehydrogenation to form the original C_4 α-keto dicarboxylic acid. Symbolic representations of each reaction are shown below along with a listing of the free energy changes (pH 7) for each reaction.

Transformations of the Citric Acid Cycle $\qquad$ $\Delta G^{\circ\prime}$ (kcal)

(1)	C_2—SCoA(acetyl—SCoA) + C_4(OAA) + H_2O	$\xrightarrow{E_1}$	C_6(CIT) + CoASH	−9.08
(2)	C_6(CIT)	$\xrightarrow{E_2}$	C_6'(ISOCIT)	+1.59
(3)	C_6'(ISOCIT) + NAD^+	$\xrightarrow{E_3}$	C_5(αKG) + CO_2 + NADH + H^+	−1.70
(4)	C_5(αKG) + NAD^+ + CoASH	$\xrightarrow{E_4}$	C_4(SUC—SCoA) + CO_2 + NADH + H^+	−9.32
(5)	C_4(SUC—SCoA) + GDP + P_i + H_2O	$\xrightarrow{E_5}$	C_4(SUC) + GTP + CoASH	−2.12
(6)	C_4(SUC) + FAD	$\xrightarrow{E_6}$	C_4'(FUM) + $FADH_2$	0
(7)	C_4'(FUM) + H_2O	$\xrightarrow{E_7}$	C_4''(MAL)	−0.88
(8)	C_4''(MAL) + NAD^+	$\xrightarrow{E_8}$	C_4(OAA) + NADH + H^+	+6.69

$Net:$ (1 + 8) $\quad$ CH$_3$CSCoA + 3NAD$^+$ + FAD + 3H$_2$O + GDP + P$_i$ $\xrightarrow[\text{Enzymes}]{8}$ 2CO$_2$ + 3NADH + 3H$^+$ + FADH$_2$ + GTP + CoASH $\qquad$ −14.82

The overall chemical effect is clearly summarized by the net equation: the operation of the cycle through one complete turn results in the complete oxidation of the initial two-carbon acetyl unit to two units of CO_2. The oxidation of the acetyl substrate is accompanied by the formation of 3 units of reduced NAD and 1 unit of reduced FAD. Details of the metabolic fate of the NADH and $FADH_2$ are discussed in the next chapter. Recall from the previous chapter that their reoxidation to NAD^+ and FAD via the respiratory electron transport provides the necessary energy for the formation of most of the ATP in the cell (see bottom of page 306). Finally, note that, although many of the individual reactions in the cycle are exergonic, there is only one unit of metabolically useful energy produced directly by the cycle reactions. Furthermore, it is produced as GTP rather than as ATP.

Examination of the $\Delta G^{\circ\prime}$'s shows that the composite pathway is exergonic and thus thermodynamically favorable. Yet not every individual reaction is exergonic. Note, however, that, as was the case with the glycolytic pathway, there is a thermodynamic design to the cycle consistent with the maintenance of an efficient flow of all intermediates. For example, the malate → oxaloacetate conversion is strongly endergonic and by itself would serve as a natural thermodynamic barrier that would favor an accumulation of malate and thus impede the operation of the cycle. A closer analysis, however, reveals that the probability of this occurrence is minimized considerably—indeed, it is eliminated—since the malate → oxaloacetate conversion is *followed in the cycle* by two highly exergonic reactions, namely, the formation of citrate (reaction 1) and the formation of succinyl-SCoA (reaction 4). Reaction 1 is quite significant since it is directly coupled to the malate → oxaloacetate reaction. Hence, in the presence of acetyl-SCoA, reactions 1 and 4 will contribute to the efficient removal of oxaloacetate, preventing both a sluggish flow and a gradual buildup of other intermediates.

The citric acid cycle bears another resemblance to our previous discussion of glycolysis on the basis of internal coupling. In the citric acid cycle, the internal coupling is on two levels. The first and most obvious one is due to the unique position of oxaloacetate. In the first reaction (1) it is a reactant, whereas in the last reaction (8) it is a product. Of course, this is the key feature that confers a cyclic pattern on the overall reaction sequence. The second is the coupling between reactions 4 and 5 involving coenzyme A. In reaction 4 CoASH is an essential reactant, whereas in reaction 5 it is produced. The significance of these factors should be recognized; namely, the cycle is autocatalytic and thus self-efficient as long as catalytic quantities of all intermediates are present.

Of course, the continued operation of the cycle is also dependent on the availability of catalytic levels of NAD^+, FAD, and GDP. A close inspection of the reaction sequence reveals that the cycle itself is not autocatalytic with regard to any of these substances. Rather, the need is satisfied by the regeneration of these materials in other processes. NAD^+ and FAD are regenerated almost solely by the electron transport chain, with oxygen as the terminal electron and hydrogen acceptor. It is this participation of oxygen which renders the citric acid cycle an aerobic pathway (see below). As we will see later, the cellular localization of the citric acid cycle enzymes and the components of the electron transport chain is consistent with this metabolic link—all are compartmentalized in the mitochondrion.

It is difficult to pinpoint specific processes for the regeneration of GDP. Two likely candidates are given below. One involves the exchange of phosphate between GTP and a nucleoside diphosphate catalyzed by a *nucleoside diphosphate kinase,* an enzyme widely distributed in nature. The second involves a GTP-dependent decarboxylation of oxaloacetate to phosphoenolpyruvate catalyzed by *phosphoenolpyruvate carboxykinase.* The probability that one or both of these enzymes functions in this capacity is supported by the fact that both are found in the mitochondria and are thus compartmentalized with the enzymes of the citric acid cycle. The contribution of each will vary from organism to organism and will also be controlled by growth conditions. You will recall that PEP carboxykinase has been proposed to operate in the reversal of glycolysis (see page 284, Chapter 11, and page 323, this chapter).

Regeneration of NAD^+ and FAD: (see Chapter 13)

$$NADH + H^+ + \tfrac{1}{2}O_2 \xrightarrow[\text{transport}]{\text{electron}} NAD^+ + H_2O + Energy \quad \textit{for ATP}$$

$$FADH_2 + \tfrac{1}{2}O_2 \xrightarrow[\text{transport}]{\text{electron}} FAD + H_2O + Energy \quad \textit{formation}$$

Regeneration of GDP:

$$GTP + ADP \xrightarrow[\text{diphosphate kinase}]{\text{nucleoside}} GDP + ATP$$

$$oxaloacetate + GTP \xrightarrow[\text{carboxykinase}]{\text{PEP}} phosphoenolpyruvate + GDP + CO_2$$

INDIVIDUAL REACTIONS OF THE CITRIC ACID CYCLE

In this section our attention turns to the individual reactions of the cycle, some of which are very remarkable. As previously explained in describing the enzymes of the glycolytic and hexose shunt pathways, the rationale for this approach is twofold. Although the details unique to each reaction will serve as a basis for gaining a deeper insight of the citric acid cycle as a reaction pathway, at the same time they represent general principles of enzyme action. Once again it is worth noting that such an analysis is quite possible since each enzyme has been isolated and studied in pure form. The items we will emphasize are (a) enzyme specificity, (b) coenzyme participation, (c) regulatory properties, and (d) the existence and operation of multi-enzyme complexes.

CITRATE SYNTHETASE

The reaction catalyzed by *citrate synthetase* (sometimes called the *citrate-condensing enzyme* or *citrogenase*) is unique to the cycle, because it represents the only reaction involving the formation of a C—C bond. Moreover, when we consider it as a separate reaction, a little reflection suggests that it is also an unusual component of the cycle that is basically a degradative pathway. However, when viewed in the context of one reaction integrated into the complete sequence, the logic and efficiency of this chemistry become clear.

Another noteworthy point is that, although the reaction involves the condensation of two carbon compounds—a chemical event that requires an input of energy—the overall reaction is *not* ATP dependent. Even then the overall reaction is still very energy yielding ($\Delta G^{\circ\prime}$ = -9 kcal). The reason for this becomes clear by recalling that acetyl-SCoA is a high-energy compound (page 248). This then is our first encounter with a reaction system that involves a thioester as substrate. In addition to the fact that the thioester (acetyl-SCoA) is more reactive than the free acid (acetate), its hydrolysis during the course of the reaction supplies chemical energy, some of which is utilized for the formation of a carbon-carbon bond in the accompanying production of citrate. In a later chapter we will discover that this same principle is utilized in the metabolism of lipids, particularly the fatty acids.

Like all of the enzymes of the citric acid cycle, citrate synthetase has been detected in all aerobic organisms so far examined. In a few cases crystalline preparations have been obtained. The enzyme from pig heart has a molecular weight of approximately 90,000 as determined by ultracentrifugation, and is believed to be oligomeric. Catalytically, the enzyme is rather specific for acetyl-SCoA and oxaloacetate, with fluoroacetyl-SCoA and fluoro-oxaloacetate being the only known alternative substrates. However, neither of these fluorine-containing substances occurs naturally. Recent kinetic studies suggest that the enzyme is a key regulatory site of aerobic metabolism. In particular, ATP is a strong competitive inhibitor of acetyl-SCoA. Another inhibitor is palmityl-SCoA (thioester of a C_{16} fatty acid) which is believed to function allosterically. The significance of these kinetic observations relative to intracellular metabolic control will be explored later on page 331.

$$\overset{O}{\overset{\|}{^-OOCCH_2CCOO^-}}$$

oxaloacetate

$$CH_3\overset{O}{\overset{\|}{C}}-SCoA \quad \text{acetyl-SCoA}$$

CoASH

$$\begin{array}{c} CH_2COO^- \\ | \\ HO-C-COO^- \\ | \\ CH_2COO^- \end{array}$$

citrate

ACONITASE

The reversible conversion of citrate to isocitrate is a most remarkable reaction. However, this is not due to the overall chemical event, which is merely a positional isomerization. The remarkable feature is the catalytic mode of action of aconitase. Prior to describing this, let us first examine some data which typify this reaction.

Incubation of radioactive acetyl-SCoA containing a uniformly labeled (C^{14}) acetyl group and non-labeled oxaloacetate in the presence of citrate synthetase results in the formation of citrate with a labeling pattern as shown below. No other pattern will occur. Now, when this material is incubated in the presence of aconitase, it is observed that the isocitrate that is formed likewise exhibits a specific labeling pattern (see below). No other compound is formed. In this case, however, you would not expect this, because citrate is a symmetrical molecule containing two chemically identical —CH_2COO^- groupings. (*Note:* The presence of C^{14} only renders the —CH_2COO^- groups physically different and not chemically different. Furthermore, the presence of radioactive carbon atoms does not interfere with the overall reaction.) What you would expect then is a 50–50 mixture of two radioactive compounds. Because only one is produced, we conclude that the enzymatic conversion of the symmetrical citrate molecule to isocitrate occurs *asymmetrically*. In other words, the *enzyme has the ability to distinguish between identical chemical groups.*

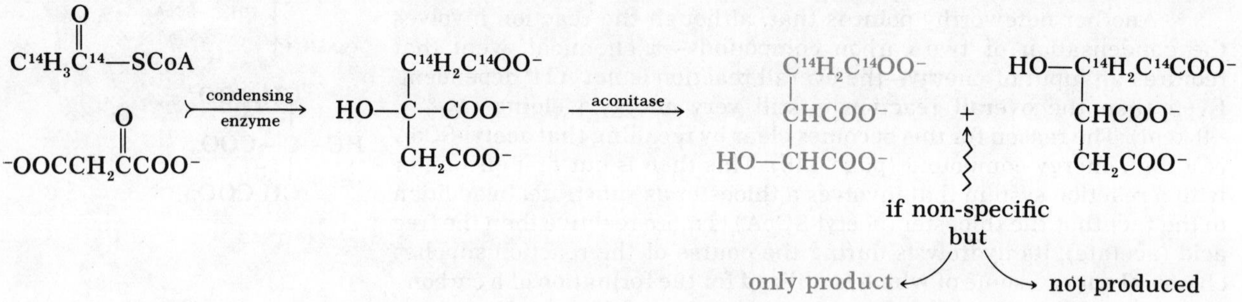

When you think about it, this is a rather profound characteristic. To explain it, however, there is no need to evoke a mystical or supernatural argument. The key resides in the enzyme. One explanation was proposed several years ago by Ogston, who suggested a three-point attachment of substrate to the enzyme at an *asymmetric active site* resulting in a specific three-dimensional binding of the substrate in the active enzyme-substrate complex, followed by a specific and directional chemical transformation (see below). In other words, the deterministic role in the asymmetric modification of a symmetrical substrate is fulfilled by the structural asymmetry of the active site of the enzyme. Although the exact details of this type of catalysis are not known for aconitase nor for any of the few other enzymes that display the same type of specificity, the proposal of active site asymmetry is well documented and wholly consistent with the principles of protein structure.

Hypothetical Representation of Asymmetrical Binding and Catalysis by Aconitase

A, B, C correspond to specific binding residues at enzyme surface, with the chemical event specifically mediated by the catalytic residues, D and E

The precise mechanism of aconitase action is unknown, but the process is dependent on Fe^{++}. Disagreement also exists as to whether the isomerization proceeds directly to isocitrate or whether it is mediated via a pattern of dehydration and hydration involving the intermediate formation of the unsaturated tricarboxylic acid, *cis*-aconitate (see Figure 12–1). There are no known allosteric activators or inhibitors, suggesting that aconitase is not a regulatory enzyme.

ISOCITRATE DEHYDROGENASE

Though the oxidative decarboxylation of isocitrate to α-ketoglutarate has been known for several years, much of our current understanding of this reaction is due to fairly recent studies. One of the more intriguing results has been the discovery that cells contain two different types of isocitrate dehydrogenase. One is NAD^+ dependent, the other $NADP^+$ dependent. Moreover, the former is a particulate enzyme (localized in the mitochondrion) and the latter is a soluble enzyme (localized in the cytoplasm). Although both have a similar mode of action—for example, each has an absolute requirement for Mn^{++} or Mg^{++} for optimal activity and each exhibits the same substrate specificity (see below)—it is now believed that the NAD^+-dependent enzyme is the catalyst that operates in the citric acid cycle, whereas the $NADP^+$-dependent enzyme is thought to function primarily in generating α-ketoglutarate in the cytoplasm for use in anabolic reactions (see page 326).

Although precise physicochemical data concerning the structure of NAD^+-isocitrate dehydrogenase are not available, the molecule does appear to be very large (MW $\sim 10^5$) and the native conformation is proposed to be oligomeric. Our knowledge of its catalytic properties is more extensive and refined. In this regard, there are two important characteristics. First, the enzyme displays a high degree of stereospecificity. In fact, the specificity of action may be absolute, since the only effective substrate appears to be *threo*-D_s-isocitrate (see below). All other stereoisomers are inactive. It is noteworthy that this specificity is

$$
\begin{array}{c}
CH_2COO^- \\
| \\
CHCOO^- \\
| \\
HO{-}CHCOO^-
\end{array}
$$

isocitrate

NAD$^+$

CO_2 ⇄ NADH + H$^+$

$$
\begin{array}{c}
CH_2COO^- \\
| \\
CH_2 \\
| \\
O{=}C{-}COO^-
\end{array}
$$

α-ketoglutarate

completely consistent with the aconitase enzyme which produces only the *threo*-D_s isomer in the previous step. (*Note:* the *threo* and *erythro* designations refer to the relative orientation of the —OH and the —COO⁻ groups, using the structures of the sugars, threose and erythrose, as frames of reference. The D_s notation refers specifically to the spatial orientation of the —OH, using the structure of D-serine as a frame of reference.)

$$\text{isocitrate} \xrightarrow[\substack{\text{NAD}^+ \\ (\text{NADP}^+)}]{\overset{\text{isocitrate}}{\underset{\text{·NADH + H}^+}{\text{dehydrogenase}}}} \alpha\text{-ketoglutarate} + CO_2$$

$$\text{NAD}^+ \quad \text{·NADH + H}^+$$
$$(\text{NADP}^+) \quad (\text{NADPH + H}^+)$$

```
      COO⁻              COO⁻               COO⁻                COO⁻
       |                 |                  |                   |
   H—C—OH            H—C—OH             HO—C—H              HO—C—H
       |                 |                  |                   |
  ⁻OOC—C—H           H—C—COO⁻           H—C—COO⁻            ⁻OOC—C—H
       |                 |                  |                   |
    CH₂COO⁻           CH₂COO⁻            CH₂COO⁻             CH₂COO⁻
```

threo-D_s-isocitrate   *erythro*-D_s-isocitrate   *threo*-L_s-isocitrate   *erythro*-L_s-isocitrate

"preferred" substrate   *"inactive"*   *"inactive"*   *"inactive"*

Secondly, the enzyme—particularly the NAD⁺-dependent form—is typified by second-site (allosteric) kinetics effecting both the stimulation and the inhibition of activity. ADP and NAD⁺ are activators. In the case of ADP, recent experimentation has correlated the activation with a change in conformation of the molecule, which tends to support the structural arguments of the theory of allosterism. On the other hand, ATP and NADH are inhibitors. The effect of ATP is also believed to be allosteric, but the mode of action of NADH is believed to be competitive inhibition with NAD⁺. In any event, isocitrate dehydrogenase is a potential regulatory enzyme of the citric acid cycle. Indeed, current thinking is that the isocitrate dehydrogenase reaction is the *key metabolic control point* of the cycle. Further discussion of this point is deferred until later in the chapter (page 330).

α-KETOGLUTARATE DEHYDROGENASE

The oxidative decarboxylation of α-ketoglutarate to succinyl-SCoA is similar to the previous reaction only in that both require an NAD⁺-dependent dehydrogenase. Furthermore, not only are the two enzymes different proteins, but the reaction catalyzed by α-ketoglutarate dehydrogenase is much more complex. The tip-off to each of these points is given in Figure 12–1, which indicates that the activity of α-ketoglutarate dehydrogenase not only requires NAD⁺ as a coenzyme and a metal ion as a cofactor, but also requires *coenzyme A, thiamine pyrophosphate* (ThPP), *flavin adenine dinucleotide* (FAD), and *lipoic acid* (LpS₂). The latter four substances also function as obligatory *coenzymes*. The general biochemistry of coenzyme A and thiamine pyrophosphate have been discussed in earlier chapters, and hence their role as coenzymes is not being encountered for the first time. Flavin adenine dinucleotide and lipoic acid will be considered shortly.

$$-OOCCH_2CH_2\overset{\overset{\displaystyle O}{\|}}{C}COO^- \xrightarrow[\substack{NAD^+ \\ \quad}]{\substack{CoASH \quad \text{α-ketoglutarate} \\ \text{dehydrogenase} \\ ThPP, FAD, LpS_2 \\ Mg^{++} \qquad NADH}} -OOCCH_2CH_2\overset{\overset{\displaystyle O}{\|}}{C}\!-\!SCoA + CO_2$$

$$\quad\quad\text{α-ketoglutarate} \qquad\qquad\qquad\qquad\qquad\qquad\qquad\quad \text{succinyl-SCoA}$$

$$CH_3\overset{\overset{\displaystyle O}{\|}}{C}COO^- \xrightarrow[\substack{NAD^+ \\ \quad}]{\substack{CoASH \quad \text{pyruvate} \\ \text{dehydrogenase} \\ ThPP, FAD, LpS_2 \\ Mg^{++} \qquad NADH}} CH_3\overset{\overset{\displaystyle O}{\|}}{C}\!-\!SCoA + CO_2$$

$$\quad\quad\text{pyruvate} \qquad\qquad\qquad\qquad\qquad\qquad\qquad\quad \text{acetyl-SCoA}$$

An obvious question is why one enzyme requires such a large number of different coenzymes. Well, the fact is that α-ketoglutarate dehydrogenase is not a single enzyme, but rather a *multi-enzyme complex* composed of an aggregate of three different enzymes with each individual enzyme participating in part of the overall reaction. The remarkable property of this system is that, though each enzyme is functionally and structurally distinct, they do not exist separate from each other in the native state. Rather, they exist as an *ordered aggregate*, that is, as a massive *polyprotein complex*.

We will defer further analysis to a later discussion of the *pyruvate dehydrogenase* system, which is likewise a multi-enzyme complex and very similar in structure *and* mode of action to α-ketoglutarate dehydrogenase. This similarity is not surprising, since both enzyme systems catalyze the same general type of reaction—the oxidative decarboxylation of an α-keto acid to an acyl thioester. The reason for deferring analysis to pyruvate dehydrogenase is simple—we know more about it.

SUCCINYL THIOKINASE

The immediate fate of the succinyl-SCoA generated from α-ketoglutarate is hydrolysis to the free acid, with the energy released being conserved through the coupled formation of a nucleoside triphosphate. Reactions of this type are generally referred to as *substrate level phosphorylations* to distinguish them from the production of nucleoside triphosphates (mostly ATP) coupled to electron transport. Other examples of substrate level phosphorylation are represented by the conversions of 1,3-diphosphoglycerate to 3-phosphoglycerate and of phosphoenolpyruvate to pyruvate in the glycolytic pathway (see page 271, Chapter 11).

The unique feature of succinyl thiokinase is that it is rather specific for *guanine nucleotides*. Nevertheless, due to the known facility of phosphate transfer between different nucleoside triphosphates and diphosphates (page 454), the formation of GTP is metabolically equivalent to the production of ATP. Because both GTP and ATP are high-energy compounds, the operational significance of this reaction is that it contributes directly to the production of useful metabolic energy.

This particular site of GTP formation is not to be interpreted, how-

$$-OOCCH_2CH_2\overset{\overset{\displaystyle O}{\|}}{C}\!-\!SCoA$$

$$\text{succinyl-SCoA}$$

$$\Big\downarrow \quad \overset{GDP + P_i}{\underset{GTP}{\rightthreetimes}}$$

$$CoASH$$

$$-OOCCH_2CH_2COO^-$$

$$\text{succinate}$$

ever, as the primary base of energy production by the citric acid cycle. It is only a small part of this role. As stated repeatedly, the bulk of energy production (ATP) via the citric acid cycle occurs in conjunction with the oxygen-dependent reoxidation of NADH and $FADH_2$ in the process of oxidative phosphorylation.

SUCCINATE DEHYDROGENASE

The conversion of succinate to fumarate is the third of four dehydrogenations in the cycle. However, succinate dehydrogenase is unique in that the coenzyme hydrogen acceptor is *flavin adenine dinucleotide* (FAD), whereas the other three dehydrogenases are NAD^+ dependent. Since the FAD is firmly bound to the protein portion, succinate dehydrogenase is frequently referred to as a *flavoprotein*.

FAD represents the metabolically active form of *riboflavin* (vitamin B_2). As shown below, the active portion of FAD is localized in the fused *isoalloxazine* ring system. The unsaturated species represents the oxidized form of FAD, which, upon acceptance of two hydrogen atoms ($2H^+$'s and 2 electrons), is converted to the reduced form, symbolized $FADH_2$. Participation in this type of hydrogen transfer is the sole metabolic function of FAD. The process is readily reversible. Although succinate dehydrogenase is not the only FAD-dependent protein found in nature, it is the best known, the most studied, and perhaps the most important.

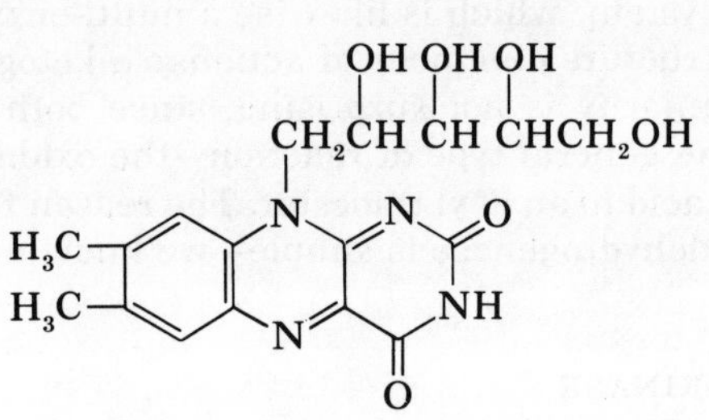

Riboflavin (Vitamin B_2)

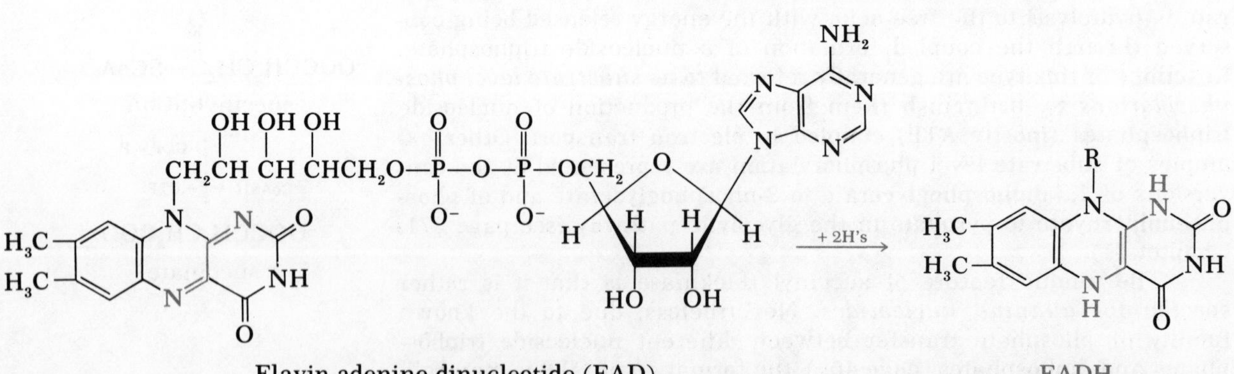

Flavin adenine dinucleotide (FAD)
Oxidized form

$FADH_2$
Reduced form

On a structural level, succinate dehydrogenase is distinguished by (a) a large molecular weight ($\sim 2 \times 10^5$), suggesting that it is oligomeric;

(b) the presence of 4 to 8 tightly bound iron atoms per molecule, whose function is unknown; and (c) a covalent attachment of the FAD co-enzyme to the protein portion. The enzyme is very difficult to isolate in soluble form since it is tightly embedded in the mitochondrial membrane. Moreover, its integration with all other membrane proteins—both structural and functional—is thought to be highly ordered (see page 359).

On a functional level, the most remarkable catalytic property of the enzyme is its stereochemical specificity of hydrogen elimination. Despite the fact that the four hydrogens of the two methylene groupings in succinate are chemically identical, the dehydrogenation is exclusively *trans*. If this specificity did not exist, a 50–50 mixture of two isomeric unsaturated decarboxylic acids would be formed—maleate (*cis*) and fumarate (*trans*). Only the latter is formed, however. The ability of succinate dehydrogenase to discriminate between structurally equivalent hydrogen pairs is another example of asymmetric catalysis of a symmetrical substrate.

The high level of substrate specificity is also typified by the previously discussed potent competitive inhibition of malonate. Although recent studies have shown that the activity of the dehydrogenase is subject to positive and negative allosteric effects, it is uncertain whether the enzyme is a main metabolic control point such as isocitrate dehydrogenase.

FUMARASE

The hydration of fumarate to malate, catalyzed by fumarase, is still another example of enzyme specificity. In fact, the enzyme displays absolute specificity with fumarate as the only active substrate and L-malate as the only product. The isomer, D-malate, is not formed. Extremely pure preparations of fumarase have been obtained, thus permitting detailed physicochemical studies. The enzyme isolated from pig heart appears to be a homogeneous tetramer with each protomer having a molecular weight of 48,500 (MW of tetramer ~ 194,000). The native enzyme contains no disulfide bonds, but does possess twelve free sulfhydryl groups. Although the —SH groups are not part of the active site, their presence is absolutely required for activity.

MALATE DEHYDROGENASE

⁻OOCCH₂CHCOO⁻
|
OH

L-malate

NAD⁺
NADH + H⁺

⁻OOCCH₂CCOO⁻
||
O

oxaloacetate

The NAD⁺-dependent conversion of L-malate (α-hydroxy acid) to oxalo-acetate (α-keto acid) is the closing reaction and the fourth oxidative dehydrogenation of the cycle. Typical of all the cycle enzymes, malate dehydrogenase is highly specific. In fact, absolute specificity is once again proposed.

The biochemistry of L-malate dehydrogenase is similar to that of two other enzymes we have already discussed. The enzyme is similar to isocitrate dehydrogenase in that it exists in two structurally and catalytically distinct forms in the cells of higher organisms. One form is located in the mitochondrion and the other in the cytoplasm. However, the isocitrate dehydrogenases require either NAD⁺ or NADP⁺, whereas both malate dehydrogenases are NAD⁺-dependent. The proposed metabolic function of the cytoplasmic, NAD⁺-dependent malate dehydrogenase is similar to that proposed for the cytoplasmic, NADP⁺-dependent isocitrate dehydrogenase, namely, it participates in anabolic processes involving intermediates of the citric acid cycle. In this regard you may recall from the previous chapter that we have already discussed one possible participation of the cytoplasmic malate dehydrogenase in the biosynthesis of carbohydrate from pyruvate via oxaloacetate (see page 285). Malate dehydrogenase is also similar to lactate dehydrogenase since it is known to exist in hybrid (isoenzyme) forms. The biological significance of malate dehydrogenase isoenzymes is unknown.

Since L-malate dehydrogenase has been isolated in pure form from a variety of sources, a lot of information is available for making a comparative biochemical analysis among different cell species. Some of this information is summarized in Table 12–1 for the enzyme isolated from two bacteria and from the mitochondria and cytoplasm of heart tissue from two animal species. The point of these data is to illustrate the principles of biochemical unity and biochemical diversity at the molecular level. The fact that all sources contain an enzyme with similar kinetic properties (K_m's) for the malate $\rightleftarrows$ oxaloacetate interconver-

Table 12–1 A comparative analysis of L-malate dehydrogenase isolated from various natural sources.

Source	Localization	K_m^1	Molecular Weight	Number of Polypeptide Chains per Molecule[2]	Number of —SH Groups per Molecule[2]
Escherichia coli	—	50	61,000	2	6
Bacillus subtilis	—	61	150,000	4	0
Beef heart	Mitochondria	34	62,000	2	12
Beef heart	Cytoplasm	42	52,000	2	6
Chicken heart	Mitochondria	38	67,000	2	6 (?)
Chicken heart	Cytoplasm	50	67,000	2	6 (?)

1. Michaelis-Menten constant measured for the reverse reaction using oxaloacetate as a substrate, with units in micromoles/liter. Although the values are numerically different, they do not represent large variations in the catalytic properties of each enzyme, because they are all of the same order of magnitude. Rather, they are similar in this regard.
2. A comparison of these characteristics with the molecular weights provides a basis for examining structural similarities and differences. Although categorical conclusions are not possible, some general observations can be made. Most interesting are (a) the similarity of the bacterial and animal enzymes—the *Bacillus* enzyme is a distinct exception; (b) the differences between the two enzymes isolated from beef heart; and (c) the similarities between the two enzymes isolated from chicken heart.

sion and in some instances with similar structural features (chicken heart mitochondria and cytoplasm) illustrates the biochemical unity. The variations in structure, expressed here by size and the number of polypeptide chains and sulfhydryl groups per molecule, illustrate the biochemical diversity. Although the principles of biochemical unity and diversity are made in Table 12-1 with specific reference to L-malate dehydrogenase, they have a general application to most other enzymes that are present in two or more different sources.

POSTSCRIPT

Having completed our analysis of individual reactions of the citric acid cycle, a recapitulation of our purpose for doing so seems in order. That objective can be stated quite simply, namely, to illustrate principles of biocatalysis that apply to enzymes in general and to the operation of the citric acid cycle in particular. Relative to the former, we analyzed the principles of coenzyme participation, substrate specificity, modulation of kinetic activity, and protein structure, with each enzyme of the cycle being uniquely characterized in each respect. The important thing to realize is that, as a consequence of these descriptions, the second part of our objective was fulfilled. In other words, the biochemical essence of the citric acid cycle is due to the individual properties of its constitutive enzymes. This, of course, is true of any metabolic pathway and, indeed, of the whole metabolism of any organism.

ROLE OF THE CITRIC ACID CYCLE IN METABOLISM

Our analysis of the net chemical effect and the individual reactions of the citric acid cycle provides a base of understanding so that we may now consider how the cycle functions in metabolism. The material in this section is divided into two parts to consider the role of the cycle in both catabolism and anabolism in that order. In each case the material is subclassified into areas dealing with the role of the cycle in the metabolism of the four main classes of biomolecules. It must be emphasized, however, that the cycle is not a pathway common to either phase of metabolism or to the metabolism of any one specific class of molecules, but rather a central pathway which integrates and unifies the whole of metabolism. It is unfortunate that we must fragment this subject in order to discuss it.

PART A: ROLE OF THE CITRIC ACID CYCLE IN CATABOLISM

CARBOHYDRATE CATABOLISM

Under normal conditions, most aerobic organisms utilize carbohydrate materials as their major supplies of carbon and energy. Thus, though the citric acid cycle is not to be considered unique to the catabolism of any one class of compounds, in most organisms it is of great importance in the catabolism of carbohydrates. Recall from the previous chapter, however, that the citric acid cycle itself is not solely responsible for the degradation of carbohydrate, but operates in concert with glycolysis. The latter effects the anaerobic conversion of hexose phosphates to pyruvate, which under aerobic conditions is then completely degraded to carbon dioxide via the citric acid cycle.

A question that may occur to you is: How can pyruvate be degraded by the citric acid cycle if it isn't one of the metabolic intermediates of the cycle? Although the question is very basic, it is a good one to raise, because it points to the fact that, in order for two or more separate pathways to be integrated, there must exist a metabolic *link*. In this instance the link is provided by the enzyme *pyruvate dehydrogenase*, which catalyzes the oxidative decarboxylation of pyruvate to acetyl-SCoA. The latter can then condense with oxaloacetate and the cycle is primed, with one complete turn thus resulting in the complete degradation of the C_2 acetyl unit to $2CO_2$.

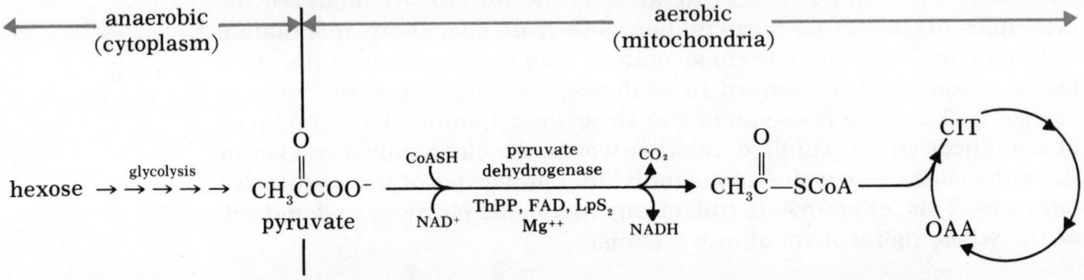

The metabolic significance of pyruvate dehydrogenase should be obvious. Without this step, the pyruvate produced during glycolysis would not be catabolized further by the citric acid cycle. Not so obvious, however, is the manner in which the enzyme operates. From the above diagram, the only deduction one can make is that the overall reaction, which is absolutely dependent on the participation of several coenzymes (NAD+, CoASH, ThPP, FAD, and LpS_2), is undoubtedly characterized by a complex mechanism. Such is the case. The key to appreciating the mode of action of pyruvate dehydrogenase is in its structure. A hint as to the nature of its structure is provided by the term *pyruvate dehydrogenase complex*, which is a more correct basis of referring to this enzyme system, since it is known to be a *multi-enzyme complex* consisting of an aggregate of more than one enzyme. Specifically, the pyruvate dehydrogenase complex (PDC) is composed of three different enzymes: (a) *pyruvate dehydrogenase*, sometimes called *pyruvate decarboxylase*; (b) *dihydrolipoyl transacetylase*, and (c) *dihydrolipoyl dehydrogenase*. Furthermore, the complex contains different amounts of each. The PDC isolated from *E. coli*, which is structurally representative of other preparations including those from mammals, contains 12 dimeric molecules (24 polypeptide chains) of pyruvate dehydrogenase; 1 molecular aggregate (60 polypeptide chain subunits) of transacetylase; and 6 monomeric molecules (6 polypeptide chains) of dihydrolipoyl dehydrogenase. The entire complex is obviously quite large. Its particle weight is approximately 4×10^6.

Each component enzyme is believed to act in concert, catalyzing a certain part of the overall reaction. The pyruvate dehydrogenase (E_{PDH}), which is dependent on ThPP, catalyzes the decarboxylation of the

α-keto acid with the C_2 alkyl unit transferred to ThPP (reaction A). The transacetylase (E_{TA}) then catalyzes the transfer of the C_2 unit to lipoic acid, which is an obligatory coenzyme believed to be covalently attached to E_{TA} via the ϵ-amino group of a lysine residue (reaction B). The reactive grouping of lipoic acid is a disulfide linkage capable of undergoing a reversible reduction to the sulfhydryl form. In this case the oxidized form of lipoic acid (LpS_2) acts as an acceptor of the acyl grouping from

$$CH_2CH_2CHCH_2CH_2CH_2CH_2COO^-$$

the E_{PDH}-ThPP—CHCH$_3$ intermediate. The acylated transacetylase is
              |
             OH
then attacked by CoASH, generating the reduced form of the trans-acetylase-lipoate enzyme and acetyl-SCoA (reaction C). Thus, reactions A through C account for the complete conversion of substrate (pyruvate)

Rx A: $CH_3CCOO^- + E_{PDH} - ThPP \xrightarrow{Mg^{++}} E_{PDH} - ThPP - CHCH_3 + CO_2$

Rx B: $E_{PDH} - ThPP - CHCH_3 + E_{TA} - NHC(CH_2)_4 - CH \quad CH_2 \longrightarrow E_{PDH} - ThPP + E_{TA} - NHC$

Rx C: $E_{TA} - NHC \cdots + CoASH \longrightarrow E_{TA} - NHC \cdots + CH_3C - SCoA$

Rx D: $E_{TA} - NHC \cdots + E_{LDH} - FAD \longrightarrow E_{TA} - NHC(CH_2)_4 - CH \quad CH_2 + E_{LDH} - FADH_2$

Rx E: $E_{LDH} - FADH_2 + NAD^+ \longrightarrow E_{LDH} - FAD + NADH + H^+$

Net Rx: $CH_3CCOO^- + NAD^+ + CoASH \longrightarrow CH_3C - SCoA + CO_2 + NADH + H^+$

to products (CO_2 + acetyl-SCoA). The last two steps are required to regenerate all catalytic components of the complex in their original form. The oxidized form of the transacetylase is regenerated by dihydrolipoyl dehydrogenase (E_{LDH}), a flavoprotein (reaction D). Finally, the oxidized form of the flavoprotein is regenerated through the participation of NAD^+ as a hydrogen acceptor (reaction E). The net reaction (sum of reactions A through E) is the oxidative (NAD^+-dependent) decarboxylation of pyruvate to the metabolically active, high-energy compound, acetyl-SCoA without the expenditure of metabolic energy as ATP.

Despite the inherent complexity of this reaction, the most remarkable properties of the PD complex are its ultrastructural order and its capacity for self-assembly from its constituent subunits. All of the component parts are known to be arranged in a certain spatial and geometric pattern which, for reasons unknown, is necessary for optimal activity. Proof of this non-random arrangement is given by recent studies wherein the complex was first dissociated into its separate parts, which can be isolated, and then mixed together to yield a fully active complex with the same structure. Presumably, the latter process occurs in the cell as the polypeptides are synthesized. In review of the important principle of structure and function, it is worth noting that the molecular information that probably controls this ordered self-assembly is the amino acid sequence of each polypeptide.

The PD complex, which itself is localized in the mitochondrial membrane of higher organisms and thus appropriately compartmentalized to serve as a link with the citric acid cycle, is but one of several multi-enzyme complexes known to exist in nature. Mention has already been made of the α-ketoglutarate dehydrogenase system, which is a close relative of the PD complex on both a structural and a functional level (page 311). Additional examples such as the *fatty acid synthetase complex* in the biosynthesis of fatty acids and the *electron transport chain* will be encountered in subsequent chapters.

Although the precise operational advantage of a multi-enzyme aggregate remains debatable, it is reasonable to suggest that it would be an extremely efficient metabolic system, since all of the required participants are localized in one position, thus eliminating the need for all to diffuse to a common site. In fact, this may be the prime asset. Of course one definite metabolic advantage is that the acetyl unit is mobilized into a highly reactive chemical species as a thioester. The reaction not only proceeds without requiring ATP but it also produces NADH which can be reoxidized via the electron transport chain to produce ATP. This is an excellent example of metabolic efficiency. Whatever the advantage, recent studies have shown that multienzyme systems such as this are subject to strict regulatory controls. The PD complex, for example, is strongly inhibited by ATP and strongly activated by ADP. As stated earlier, both effectors are metabolic signals of modulations in cellular metabolism. In a later section, this regulation of the PD complex will be integrated with other regulatory enzymes in carbohydrate metabolism.

Our discussion of the metabolic fitness of the pyruvate → acetyl-SCoA + CO_2 conversion should not close without taking note that the overall reaction is quite thermodynamically favorable ($\Delta G^{\circ\prime}$ is approximately $-8,000$ calories/mole) and that it is an irreversible reaction. Both characteristics contribute to a unidirectional flow of carbon from pyruvate to acetyl-SCoA. Moreover, when one considers the pyruvate as originating from phosphoenolpyruvate and the acetyl-SCoA then entering the citric acid cycle, the net thermodynamics is even more one-sided. That is, all three of the reactions are exergonic (see below) and thus strongly favor the flow of carbon from glycolysis into the citric acid cycle.

phosphoenol-
pyruvate
$\xrightarrow[\text{ADP} \quad \text{ATP}]{P_i}$ pyruvate $\xrightarrow[\text{NAD}^+ \quad \text{NADH} + \text{H}^+]{\text{CoASH} \quad \text{CO}_2}$ acetyl-SCoA $\xrightarrow[\text{oxaloacetate}]{\text{CoASH}}$ citrate

$\Delta G^{\circ\prime} = -5,800$ $\Delta G^{\circ\prime} = -8,000$ $\Delta G^{\circ\prime} = -9,080$

$$\Delta G^{\circ\prime}_{net} = -22,880 \text{ calories/mole}$$

thus, $K_{eq_{net}} \approx 10^{19}$

In the event that our discussion of the details of the PD complex may have detracted from its metabolic significance, let us summarize briefly. This complex is the major metabolic link between glycolysis and the citric acid cycle, which together effect the complete degradation of a hexose unit to CO_2. The overall chemistry involving a total of 19 distinct reactions is summarized in the following equations.

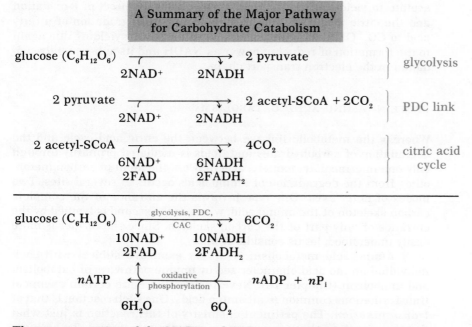

A Summary of the Major Pathway
for Carbohydrate Catabolism

glucose ($C_6H_{12}O_6$) $\xrightarrow[\text{2NAD}^+ \quad \text{2NADH}]{}$ 2 pyruvate $\qquad$ glycolysis

2 pyruvate $\xrightarrow[\text{2NAD}^+ \quad \text{2NADH}]{}$ 2 acetyl-SCoA + $2CO_2$ $\qquad$ PDC link

2 acetyl-SCoA $\xrightarrow[\substack{\text{6NAD}^+ \quad \text{6NADH} \\ \text{2FAD} \quad \text{2FADH}_2}]{}$ $4CO_2$ $\qquad$ citric acid cycle

glucose ($C_6H_{12}O_6$) $\xrightarrow[\substack{\text{10NAD}^+ \quad \text{10NADH} \\ \text{2FAD} \quad \text{2FADH}_2}]{\text{glycolysis, PDC,} \\ \text{CAC}}$ $6CO_2$

nATP $\xleftarrow[\substack{\text{6H}_2\text{O} \qquad \text{6O}_2}]{\text{oxidative} \\ \text{phosphorylation}}$ nADP + nP$_i$

The representation of the NAD$^+$ and FAD acting as hydrogen acceptors is most relevant, because the oxygen-dependent reoxidation of the reduced species coupled to the phosphorylation of ADP constitutes the distinguishing feature of aerobic catabolism. The details of oxidative phosphorylation, as well as the value of n, will be treated in the next chapter. For now it is important only to realize that the bulk of the reducing power (largely as NADH) produced in the degradation of carbohydrates, and hence the bulk of the ATP production, is provided by the enzymes of the citric acid cycle and of the PD complex.

LIPID CATABOLISM

Since we have not yet explored the metabolic pathways common to the catabolism of lipids, our treatment of this subject will be necessarily limited. Yet it will not be incomprehensible, because the pertinent facts are few in number and rather easy to understand. In our previous discussion of lipid structure (Chapter 8) it was pointed out that the principle constituents of neutral and compound lipids were the fatty acids. Well, when these lipids are degraded, the respective hydrolysis products can be catabolized further. In the case of the fatty acids, further catabolism proceeds in virtually all organisms by the process of β-oxidation (Chapter 15). The net result of this process is the successive removal of C_2 units from the fatty acid molecule as acetyl-SCoA.

$$CH_3(CH_2)_nCOO^- \xrightarrow[\text{CoASH}]{\substack{\text{enzymes of} \\ \beta\text{-oxidation}}} CH_3\overset{\overset{\displaystyle O}{\|}}{C}-SCoA \xrightarrow{\substack{\text{enzymes of} \\ \text{citric acid} \\ \text{cycle}}} CO_2 + \text{Energy}$$

This then is the link of lipid catabolism to the citric acid cycle, namely, the acetyl-SCoA originating from fatty acids can condense with oxaloacetate to yield citrate. Potentially, the combined effect of β-oxidation and the citric acid cycle would be the complete degradation of a fatty acid to CO_2. Of course, the process would be energy yielding due again to the formation of reducing power as NADH and its subsequent reoxidation in the electron transport chain.

PROTEIN (AMINO ACID) CATABOLISM

Whereas the metabolic linkage between the citric acid cycle and the degradation of carbohydrates and lipids is mediated primarily through only one intermediate, namely, acetyl-SCoA, the input of carbon metabolites from the degradation of amino acids occurs at several sites. Two modes of entry exist. One type involves the entrance of the complete carbon skeleton of the amino acid, whereas the second is typified by the entrance of only part of the carbon skeleton. Since the former is more easily understood, let us consider it first.

Amino acid metabolism is a very extensive subject with each individual amino acid characterized by unique pathways of catabolism and anabolism (Chapter 16). Nevertheless, there are certain chemical transformations common to all amino acids. One such reaction is that of *transamination.* The pertinent chemistry of this reaction is just what the term implies, that is, an amino group is transferred. To be more specific, the *amino group of a donor amino acid is transferred to an acceptor α-keto acid,* resulting in the conversion of the original amino acid into an α-keto acid (below). Enzymes that catalyze this conversion are called *transaminases* (see page 417) and require the participation of pyridoxal phosphate as an essential coenzyme (pages 109 and 419). They are indispensable for normal metabolism.

$$\underset{\text{amino acid } A}{\overset{\overset{\displaystyle NH_3^+}{|}}{R_A\!-\!CH\!-\!COO^-}} + \underset{\alpha\text{-keto acid } B}{\overset{\overset{\displaystyle O}{\|}}{R_B\!-\!C\!-\!COO^-}} \underset{\text{phosphate)}}{\overset{\text{transaminase}}{\underset{\text{(pyridoxal}}{\rightleftharpoons}}} \underset{\alpha\text{-keto acid } A}{\overset{\overset{\displaystyle O}{\|}}{R_A\!-\!C\!-\!COO^-}} + \underset{\text{amino acid } B}{\overset{\overset{\displaystyle NH_3^+}{|}}{R_B\!-\!CH\!-\!COO^-}}$$

While all amino acids can participate in transamination reactions, those involving glutamate or aspartate are most important. One particular reason for this, which is relevant to our current discussion, is illustrated by the reactions given below. You will note that when either glutamate or aspartate is involved, the product keto acids are α-ketoglutarate and oxaloacetate, respectively, both of which are intermediates of the citric acid cycle. Consequently, each can enter the cycle for further

$$\underset{\text{aspartate}}{\overset{\overset{\displaystyle NH_3^+}{|}}{^-OOCCH_2CHCOO^-}} + \underset{}{\overset{\overset{\displaystyle O}{\|}}{R\!-\!C\!-\!COO^-}} \underset{\text{phosphate)}}{\overset{\text{transaminase}}{\underset{\text{(pyridoxal}}{\rightleftharpoons}}} \underset{\text{oxaloacetate}}{\overset{\overset{\displaystyle O}{\|}}{^-OOCCH_2CCOO^-}} + \underset{}{\overset{\overset{\displaystyle NH_3^+}{|}}{R\!-\!CH\!-\!COO^-}}$$

$$\underset{\text{glutamate}}{\overset{\overset{\displaystyle NH_3^+}{|}}{^-OOCCH_2CH_2CHCOO^-}} + \underset{}{\overset{\overset{\displaystyle O}{\|}}{R\!-\!C\!-\!COO^-}} \underset{\text{phosphate)}}{\overset{\text{transaminase}}{\underset{\text{(pyridoxal}}{\rightleftharpoons}}} \underset{\alpha\text{-ketoglutarate}}{\overset{\overset{\displaystyle O}{\|}}{^-OOCCH_2CH_2CCOO^-}} + \underset{}{\overset{\overset{\displaystyle NH_3^+}{|}}{R\!-\!CH\!-\!COO^-}}$$

catabolism. Note, however, that when the cycle is primed at either point, its continued operation will depend on the availability of sufficient acetyl-SCoA to form citrate. The latter can be supplied by the degradation of carbohydrates, fatty acids, or other amino acids.

The fact that many amino acids can furnish acetyl-SCoA also accounts for the integration of their degradation with the citric acid cycle. Among those amino acids which have *part* of their carbon skeleton converted to acetyl-SCoA are alanine, serine, cysteine, lysine, tryptophan, phenylalanine, and tyrosine. The first three enter via pyruvate and the others via multi-step catabolic pathways that yield acetyl-SCoA as one product. Although the details of each conversion are not important at this point, some can be found in Chapter 16.

Rather than continue with a written description of how the carbon skeletons of other amino acids can enter the cycle at other sites, I direct your attention to Figure 12–2, which diagrammatically summarizes the main catabolic relationships of the citric acid cycle. By careful inspection of the diagram coupled with our discussion of the role of the cycle in catabolism, you should appreciate why the cycle is considered a central pathway of catabolism in general, rather than a pathway specific to the degradation of any one compound or class of compounds.

PART B: ROLE OF THE CITRIC ACID CYCLE IN ANABOLISM

In the preceding section we have described how various metabolites originating from different sources can be shunted into the cycle for further degradation resulting in the production of ATP. By the same token, the cycle intermediates can be bled off at various points for use

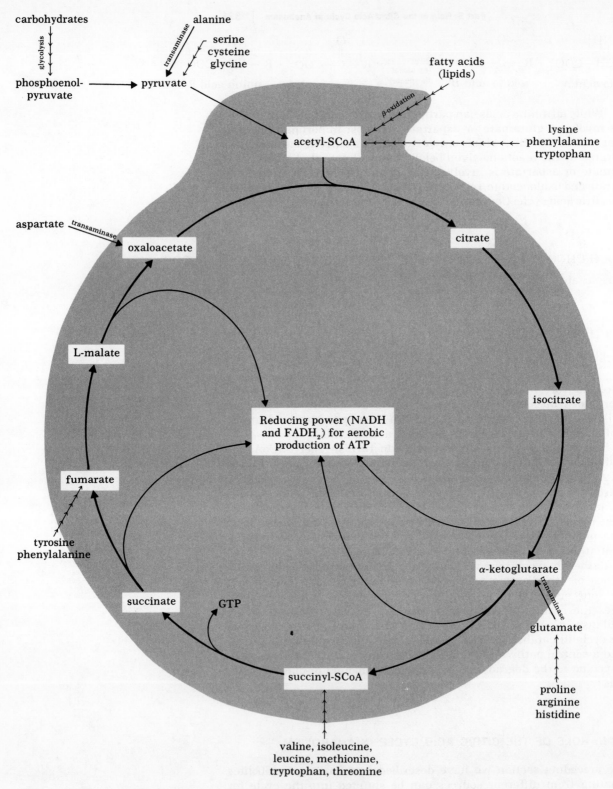

Figure 12-2 The citric acid cycle in catabolism. Degradative pathways involving more than one enzymatic step are indicated by multiple arrows (→→→→→). Shaded area corresponds to intramitochondrial processes.

as precursors in the biosynthesis of different materials. The unique aspect of this function of the cycle is that the removal of intermediates must occur simultaneously with the *continued* catabolic operation of the cycle for the purpose of supplying the ATP that is also needed for anabolism. In other words, the cycle must simultaneously fulfill two roles for one process.

Such is not the case when the cycle is linked to catabolic reactions, because here the production of energy is, in fact, a natural consequence of the exergonic and oxidative operation of the cycle and its coupling to oxidative phosphorylation. The linkage to anabolic reactions requires then that there always be sufficient catalytic levels of all intermediates—even as they are being bled off into other pathways—to maintain a certain flow of carbon through the reactions of the cycle for energy production. The material below is addressed to these anabolic relationships.

CARBOHYDRATE ANABOLISM

The relationship of the cycle to the biosynthesis of carbohydrates is primarily due to the operation of one enzyme, *phosphoenolpyruvate carboxykinase*. The enzyme, which is localized in mitochondria, catalyzes the energy-dependent conversion of oxaloacetate to phosphoenolpyruvate. This reaction is not new to us, since it was previously discussed (page 284) as one of two enzymes responsible for effecting the conversion of pyruvate to phosphoenolpyruvate, which is then utilized in the biosynthesis of carbohydrate by the reversal of glycolysis. Our current discussion does not change any of that. But now we are seeing exactly how the enzyme is integrated into the whole of metabolism. The difference from our previous discussion is that, in this integrated framework, it is clear that the oxaloacetate, which is used as the precursor for phosphoenolpyruvate, is not necessarily formed only from pyruvate. Rather, the oxaloacetate can originate from pyruvate *or any* metabolite that can be converted to one of the intermediates of the citric acid cycle, each of which can then be converted to oxaloacetate.

The removal of OAA for carbohydrate biosynthesis represents a serious problem to the continued operation of the cycle, which is inherently dependent on the maintenance of catalytic amounts of all intermediates. The maintenance of catalytic levels of the cycle intermediates is in turn primarily dependent on the condensation of acetyl-SCoA with OAA to form citrate. In other words, if OAA is continually bled off without being regenerated by some other reaction, the activity of the citric acid cycle will eventually become very sluggish. Moreover, since the cycle is at the center of all metabolism, the entire metabolic activity of the cell will become sluggish. The same principle applies to the continued drain of any cycle intermediate.

To counteract this eventuality, nature has evolved a rather remarkable set of safety valves called *anaplerotic reactions*. The basic function of these reactions is to maintain an adequate supply of a crucial intermediate which participates in a central pathway such as the citric acid cycle, when that intermediate is bled off into other metabolic pathways. Relative to our current discussion, the most important reaction of this type—particularly in mammals—is the conversion of pyruvate to oxaloacetate catalyzed by *pyruvate carboxylase*. Recall that this enzyme was also discussed earlier as the first step in glycogenesis from pyruvate (page 284). Thus we see how one enzyme can have different metabolic roles. In this case, the anaplerotic function of pyruvate carboxylase is believed to be primary.

$$\underset{\text{pyruvate}}{CH_3\overset{\displaystyle O}{\overset{\|}{C}}COO^- + CO_2} \xrightarrow[\text{ATP}]{\overset{\text{ADP}+P_i}{\underset{\text{carboxylase}}{\text{pyruvate}}}} \underset{\text{oxaloacetate (OAA)}}{^-OOCCH_2\overset{\displaystyle O}{\overset{\|}{C}}COO^-}$$

Being such a crucial enzyme, you might suspect—in view of our previous discussions—that the catalytic activity of pyruvate carboxylase would be under strict intracellular control. Indeed, this has been confirmed through recent kinetic studies on the purified enzyme which have shown that acetyl-SCoA is a strong allosteric activator. The activation by acetyl-SCoA fits a pattern of metabolic logic. As OAA is bled off, the catabolic input of acetyl-SCoA from other sources begins to accumulate, since it requires OAA to form citrate. This buildup thus serves as

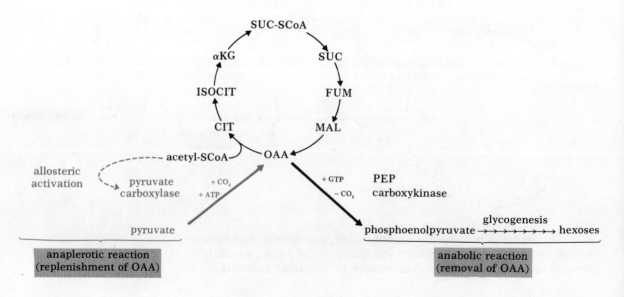

a metabolic signal which acts as an allosteric activator of the anaplerotic enzyme. More OAA is produced, insuring the formation of citrate and the flow of carbon through the cycle. The whole pattern is diagrammed on page 324.

LIPID ANABOLISM

In Chapter 15 we will discover that the biosynthesis of most lipids originates primarily from acetyl-SCoA. In fact, acetyl-SCoA is the metabolic source of *all* the carbon atoms in the synthesis of fatty acids, carotenoids, and steroids. The anabolic utilization of acetyl-SCoA does not, however, create an operational strain on the normal functioning of the citric acid cycle as does the removal of one of the internal intermediates such as oxaloacetate. The cellular sources of acetyl-SCoA are many, and as long as an adequate amount of OAA exists to keep the cycle primed, the operation of the latter to provide the necessary ATP will not be impeded.

The anabolic utilization of acetyl-SCoA does create one problem, since most of the biosynthetic reactions, including those for lipids, occur in the cytoplasm, whereas the bulk of acetyl-SCoA production occurs within the mitochondria. While it was once thought that acetyl-SCoA simply diffuses out of the mitochondrion, recent studies have implicated another route mediated by a special enzyme found in the cytoplasm. The enzyme, called *ATP:citrate lyase* or *citrate cleavage enzyme,* catalyzes the breakdown of citrate to acetyl-SCoA and oxaloacetate. Thus, it is proposed that citrate diffuses across the mitochondrial membrane and is cleaved in the cytoplasm. In other words, the utilization of mitochondrial acetyl-SCoA proceeds via an indirect mechanism. Note, however, that a small amount of citrate will still proceed through the cycle to maintain the catalytic level of OAA required for continued operation. It is worth repeating that normal operation is needed not just to process acetyl-SCoA but to supply ATP necessary for the anabolic utilization of acetyl-SCoA in the cytoplasm.

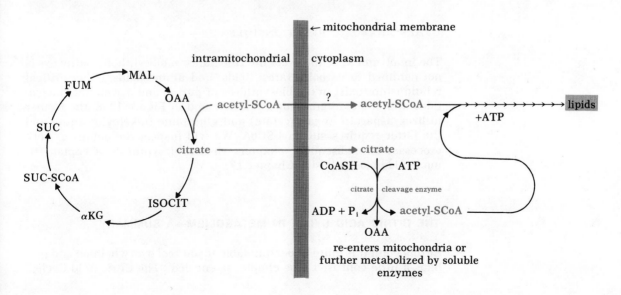

oxaloacetate   fumarate

OH

$^-OOCCH_2CHCOO^-$

malate
(mitochondria)

membrane

malate
(cytoplasm)

malate
dehydrogenase
- NAD$^+$
- NADH + H$^+$

O
‖
$^-OOCCH_2CCOO^-$

oxaloacetate

transaminase
- NH$_3^+$
- RCHCOO$^-$
- O ‖ RCCOO$^-$

NH$_3^+$

$^-OOCCH_2CHCOO^-$

aspartate

PROTEIN (AMINO ACID) ANABOLISM

Virtually all organisms are capable of synthesizing amino acids. Although differences exist in the number of acids synthesized by any one type of organism (most plants and bacteria, for example, can synthesize all of the twenty amino acids required for proteins, whereas animals including man are capable of synthesizing only certain ones, relying on an exogenous dietary supply for the rest), the intermediates of the citric acid cycle are crucial carbon precursors in most cases. The key compounds are the α-keto acids—oxaloacetate and α-ketoglutarate. A third precursor is pyruvate, also an α-keto acid and of course closely linked to the citric acid cycle. The biosynthetic relationship of each keto acid to the amino acids is diagrammatically summarized in Figure 12–3. The reaction details of some of these conversions are given in Chapter 16. Note that the utilization of oxaloacetate and α-ketoglutarate involves the diffusion out of the mitochondria into the cytoplasm of their respective citric acid cycle precursors, namely, malate and isocitrate. In the cytoplasm malate and isocitrate would then be converted to oxaloacetate and α-ketoglutarate by the respective cytoplasmic dehydrogenases (dashed arrows in Figure 12–3). The events involved in the formation of aspartate are shown in the margin. Although this represents an indirect removal of oxaloacetate and α-ketoglutarate, the effect is the same as a direct removal because their immediate precursors in the cycle are removed. Finally, with the utilization of these intermediates for amino acid biosynthesis, you should recognize the need for an anaplerotic reaction. It is likely that pyruvate carboxylase performs this role just as previously explained in regard to the utilization of OAA in carbohydrate biosynthesis. It doesn't make any difference that we are now discussing the removal of cycle intermediates for amino acid biosynthesis. In other words, the anaplerotic role of the carboxylase is independent of the *reason* for the removal of the cycle intermediates; it acts simply because they *are* removed.

OTHER ANABOLIC RELATIONSHIPS

The involvement of the cycle intermediates in biosynthetic pathways is not confined to carbohydrates, lipids, and amino acids. Other critical relationships exist in the biosynthesis of purine and pyrimidine nucleotides and of heme groupings. As indicated in Figure 12–3, the former utilizes aspartate (oxaloacetate) and glutamine (α-ketoglutarate), and the latter requires succinyl-SCoA. We will inspect the details of both processes in subsequent chapters (heme biosynthesis—Chapter 16; nucleotide biosynthesis—Chapter 17).

THE CITRIC ACID CYCLE IN METABOLISM—A SUMMARY

At this point it is quite understandable if you feel overwhelmed and perhaps a little confused. The chapter is entitled "The Citric Acid Cycle,"

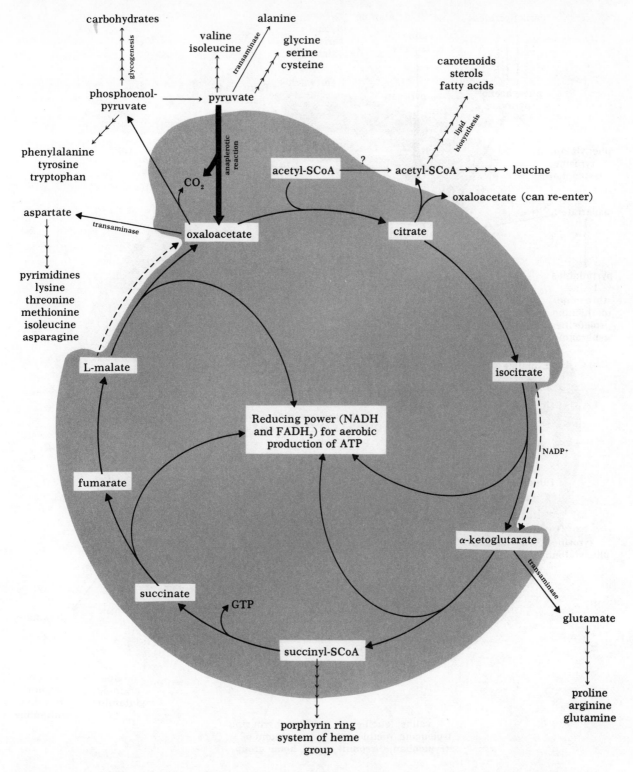

Figure 12–3 The citric acid cycle in anabolism. Synthetic pathways involving more than one enzymatic step are indicated by multiple arrows
(→→→→). Shaded area corresponds to intramitochondrial processes. For an indication of which amino acids are not synthesized in higher
animals, see page 444. The heavy arrow (→) indicates the key anaplerotic reaction of the cycle. Soluble dehydrogenases are coded by (-----→).

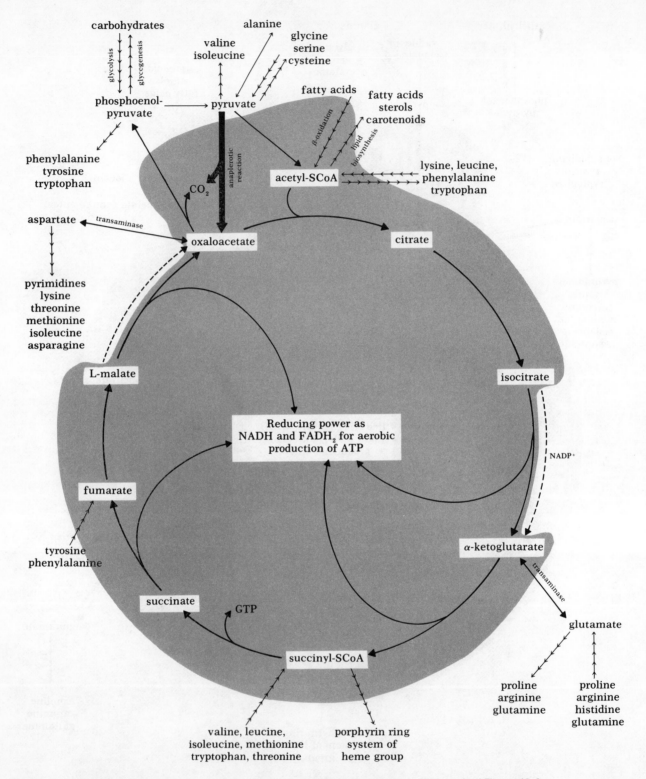

Figure 12–4 A summary of the role of the citric acid cycle in the major areas of metabolism. See legends of Figures 12–2 and 12–3 for explanations of arrows and shading.

but yet we have digressed into many other areas. You can take solace in one respect, however; our digressions could have been even more extensive. Regardless, any uncertainty in your mind as to what the metabolic role of the cycle is can now be removed by thinking back over the last several pages and *recognizing that all of our separate digressions were analyzed in terms of the participation of the citric acid cycle. Thus, we have not fragmented and separated metabolism; rather, we have unified and integrated it. Therein lies the most important function of the cycle.* The whole of cellular metabolism is thus interconnected, and hence interrelated and interdependent.

Figure 12–4 attempts to summarize this principle. The diagram, of course, is nothing more than a combination of Figures 12–2 and 12–3. A direct experimental proof of this principle would be to supply an organism—either man or microbe—with tracer levels of radioactive glucose (C^{14}) and then determine the occurrence of the label in other compounds. If you understand the role of the citric acid cycle, you should be able to predict what the outcome would be and also to recognize that the same would be true if the original labeled material were glutamate, aspartate, pyruvate, acetate, and so on.

Finally, it is important for us to note (a) that the multitude of reactions can occur *simultaneously* in a steady state of dynamic equilibrium, and (b) that one or two sets of reactions may predominate, due to the intracellular control of key regulatory enzymes triggered by a changing cellular environment and numerous physiological stimuli.

METABOLIC CONTROL OF CARBOHYDRATE METABOLISM—A SUMMARY

Throughout this and the previous chapter, we have described the catalytic properties of individual enzymes of glycolysis, glycogenesis, and the citric acid cycle. Included were many references to naturally occurring materials that serve as modulators of the activity of certain enzymes by acting as inhibitors or activators. Having done this, we are now prepared to piece together all these separate characteristics and analyze how their collective participation serves as a balanced and integrated network of metabolic control. Although our analysis will be in the particular area of carbohydrate metabolism, the general principle applies to all other areas of metabolism.

In order to do this, it will be useful to briefly recapitulate that most metabolic shifts stem from *alterations in the energy demands* of an organism. Hence, for obvious reasons of efficiency, it is very desirable that a cell be capable of adjusting its production of energy to its utilization of energy. As we will discover, this balance is mediated by regulation of energy (ATP) production in particular. Finally, since most aerobic organisms rely on the catabolism of carbohydrate material as the major source of useful metabolic energy, the target pathways of this regulation are glycolysis, glycogenesis, and the citric acid cycle.

The theme of this control is summarized in Figure 12–5, which symbolically illustrates the flow of carbon in the main pathways of carbohydrate metabolism in mammalian systems. (The same principle applies to lower organisms such as bacteria. In these instances, however, the control sites are more numerous, probably because of the lack of defined subcellular organelles such as mitochondria, which in higher organisms also contribute somewhat to metabolic control via compartmentalization effects.) Seven major control points (heavy arrows) are shown in Figure 12–5: two in the anaerobic phase (glycolysis), two in the aerobic phase (citric acid cycle), one in the pyruvate dehydrogenase reaction linking the anaerobic and aerobic phases, and two involved in the conversion of pyruvate to phosphoenolpyruvate. Positioned at each control point are those substances which act as *inhibitors* (–) or *activators* (+) of the enzymes involved. Most of the effects are allosteric. To analyze the pattern of control requires a clear understanding of the basic principles of bioenergetics so often referred to in this and previous chapters. As an aid in review, the significant principles are summarized below.

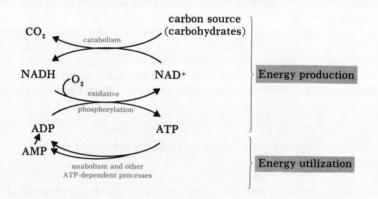

The basic strategy of metabolic control that nature has selected is quite remarkable. Most evidence indicates that there are two major control signals: (a) the cellular ratio of ATP/ADP(AMP), and (b) the cellular ratio of NADH/NAD⁺. The logic of the strategy is apparent by recognizing that each ratio reflects the energy needs—that is, the metabolic state—of the organism. When the cell is very active, and hence the demand for and utilization of energy is high, both ratios will *decrease*. More specifically, the levels of ADP(AMP) and NAD⁺ will increase and the levels of ATP and NADH will decrease. By close study of Figure 12–5, you will observe that the increased level of ADP(AMP) is a key *stimulatory* signal throughout all phases of carbohydrate catabolism. At one point, namely, the interconversion of F6P → FDP, the signal is twofold, since the anabolic reaction is also inhibited (see page 287). The elevated level of NAD⁺ also has a positive effect by stimulating the activity of the citric acid cycle at the point of isocitrate dehydrogenase. Recall that the isocitrate → α-ketoglutarate step was referred to earlier as the key regulatory site within the cycle. Note here that the same enzyme is likewise activated by ADP. The combined effect of these activations will be an increased rate of production of NADH, which will then enter oxidative phosphorylation, resulting in the necessary increased production of ATP. In other words, the "turning on" of a few key

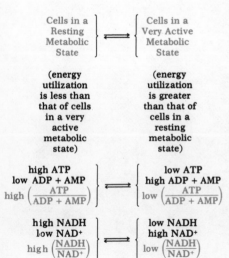

enzymes of carbohydrate catabolism results in the "turning on" of ATP production. It is important to note that the term "turning on" does not mean that these reactions were not occurring prior to activation. The point is that after activation the catabolism of carbohydrates and ATP production occur at a greater rate to keep pace with the demand.

On a shift to a condition requiring less ATP utilization—for example, contracted muscle returning to a relaxed or resting state—the control on metabolism operates in the same fashion, but in reverse. Since the need for energy is decreased, the production of ATP will be in excess of what is needed. Because ATP formation is coupled to NADH oxidation, the reduced turnover of ATP hydrolysis to ADP(AMP) will also

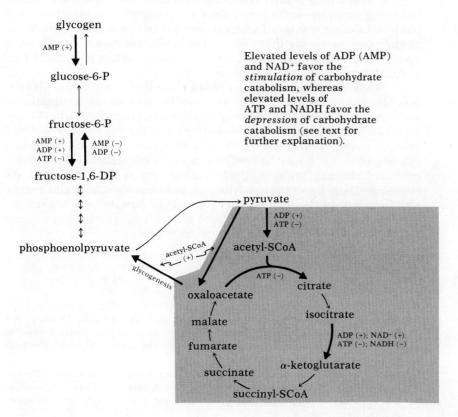

Elevated levels of ADP (AMP) and NAD$^+$ favor the *stimulation* of carbohydrate catabolism, whereas elevated levels of ATP and NADH favor the *depression* of carbohydrate catabolism (see text for further explanation).

be accompanied by cellular levels of NADH likewise in excess of requirements. Consequently, the ratios of ATP/ADP(AMP) and NADH/NAD$^+$ will *increase*. In other words, (a) levels of ATP begin to increase while levels of ADP and AMP decrease and (b) levels of NADH begin to increase while the level of NAD$^+$ decreases. Inspection of Figure 12–5 reveals that these changes serve as metabolic signals effecting the *reduction* of the rate of carbohydrate catabolism. In other words, the "turning off" of a few key enzymes results in the "turning off" of ATP production. Do you understand now why the isocitrate → α-ketoglutarate conversion is said to be a major regulatory site of metabolism?

The controls exerted by ATP, ADP, AMP, NAD$^+$, and NADH are complemented by still other metabolic signals. For example, the conver-

Figure 12–5 A partial summary of the metabolic control in carbohydrate metabolism by higher organisms. Control sites are symbolized by heavy arrows, with a (+) representing enzyme activation and a (−) representing enzyme inhibition. The majority of the effects are allosteric in nature. Regulation due to compartmentalization effects is implied by shading. The diagram is only partial, because those sites also subject to control by hormones, cyclic-AMP, and by other allosteric effectors are not indicated.

sions of pyruvate → oxaloacetate → phosphoenolpyruvate are stimulated by increases in the cellular level of acetyl-SCoA. Although a buildup of acetyl-SCoA would occur when other substances such as fatty acids are catabolized, it would also occur when the energy demands of the cell are diminished and the activity of the citric acid cycle is reduced by the regulatory effects of ATP and NADH on isocitrate dehydrogenase and the condensing enzyme. In other words, the effect of ATP and NADH signals in diminishing the rate of aerobic carbohydrate catabolism results in the generation of another signal which in turn would then stimulate the anabolism of carbohydrate from pyruvate—that is, glycogenesis.

It takes only a brief reflection to realize the significance of the foregoing analysis—*cells are indeed programmed for metabolic self-control*. In other words, a living organism is not merely a conglomerate of chemical processes that operate randomly, but rather an efficiently coordinated symphony of integrated reactions subject to a distinct set of regulatory checks and balances.

While these last few pages climax much of the material given in preceding chapters, one point—often overlooked—merits recapitulation and emphasis. *All of the events of metabolism, including both the specificity of the chemical transformations and the control exerted on a select few, are occurring at the level of enzymes.* That is to say, the very essence of cellular metabolism and of its characteristic self-control is mediated through proteins. Each has its own specific structure and consequentially a specific catalytic and, in some cases, a specific regulatory function. In the final chapter we will see how, in most organisms, this fine control at the level of enzyme activity is augmented by a coarse control exerted at the level of enzyme biosynthesis.

LITERATURE

BALDWIN, E., *Dynamic Aspects of Biochemistry*, Fifth Edition. London–New York: Cambridge University Press, 1967. Chapters 19 and 20 are devoted to the aerobic metabolism of carbohydrates and the citric acid cycle. See page 299 for a description of the book.

GINSBURG, A., and E. R. STADTMAN, "Multienzyme Systems," in *Annual Review of Biochemistry*, Volume 39, 431–472 (1970). A current review article on the biochemistry of multi-enzyme complexes including α-keto acid dehydrogenase complexes.

KORNBERG, H. L., "Anaplerotic Sequences and Their Role in Metabolism," in Volume 2 of *Essays in Biochemistry*, P. N. Campbell and G. D. Greville (eds.), 1–32. New York: Academic Press, 1966. A good review article of this important phenomenon.

LOWENSTEIN, J. M. (ed.), *Citric Acid Cycle*. Volume 13 of *Methods in Enzymology*, S. P. Colowick and N. O. Kaplan (eds.). New York: Academic Press, 1969. A reference source for procedures in the isolation and assay of enzymes of the citric acid cycle including summaries of catalytic properties.

LOWENSTEIN, J. M., "The Tricarboxylic Acid Cycle," in Volume 1 of *Metabolic Pathways*, Third Edition, D. Greenberg (ed.). New York: Academic Press, 1967. A review article giving a thorough analysis of this reaction pathway.

MAHLER, H. R., and E. H. CORDES, *Biological Chemistry*, Second Edition. New York: Harper & Row, Publishers, 1971. Chapter 14 of this textbook contains an excellent discussion of the individual enzymes of the cycle, the stereospecificity of the cycle, and the integration of the cycle with other areas of metabolism.

EXERCISES

12-1 Write all of the reactions in the citric acid cycle that comprise the oxidative transformations of the pathway.

12-2 Relative to the other reactions of the citric acid cycle, what is unique about the transformations catalyzed by
a) succinyl thiokinase
b) α-ketoglutarate dehydrogenase

12-3 If a molecule of uniformly labeled (C^{14}) pyruvate were oxidatively degraded to acetyl-SCoA and the latter then entered the citric acid cycle, which of the label patterns below would correspond to the α-ketoglutarate that would be produced in the first turn of the cycle?

$$^-OOC^{14}C^{14}H_2CH_2\overset{O}{\overset{\|}{C}}COO^- \quad \text{or} \quad {}^-OOCCH_2CH_2\overset{O}{\overset{\|}{C}}{}^{14}C^{14}OO^-$$

12-4 The citric acid cycle is frequently described as the major pathway of aerobic metabolism, which means that it is an oxygen-dependent, degradative process. Yet none of the reactions of the cycle directly involve oxygen as a reactant. Why then is the pathway oxygen dependent (aerobic) rather than oxygen independent (anaerobic)?

12-5 Which of the following equations would best describe the net aerobic catabolism of one molecule of pyruvate to α-ketoglutarate?
a) $PYR + OAA + 2NAD^+ + HSCoA \rightarrow \alpha KG + 2CO_2 + 2NADH + 2H^+$
b) $PYR + 2NAD^+ + HSCoA \rightarrow \alpha KG + 2CO_2 + 2NADH + 2H^+$
c) $PYR + OAA + 2NAD^+ \rightarrow \alpha KG + 2CO_2 + 2NADH + 2H^+$
d) $PYR + OAA + O_2 \rightarrow \alpha KG + 2CO_2 + 2H_2O$
e) $PYR + 2\ acetyl\text{-}SCoA + O_2 \rightarrow \alpha KG + 2CO_2 + 2H_2O$
f) $PYR + OAA + \frac{1}{2}O_2 \rightarrow \alpha KG + 2CO_2 + H_2O$

12-6 If uniformly labeled tyrosine (C^{14}) were incubated with a cell-free liver extract, some of the tyrosine molecules would be metabolized in the following manner.

$$HO-\underset{}{\bigcirc}-CH_2\overset{NH_3^+}{\underset{|}{C}}HCOO^- \rightarrow \rightarrow \rightarrow \rightarrow \rightarrow {}^-OOC^{14}C^{14}\overset{H}{\underset{H}{\overset{|}{=}}}{}^{14}C^{14}OO^-$$

(all C's are C^{14})

Show all of the necessary reactions that would account for the subsequent appearance in fructose-1,6-diphosphate of the carbons arising from fumarate. Indicate the distribution of radioactive carbons—and nonradioactive carbons, if there will be any—in the hexose.

12-7 If the citric acid cycle were being primed with intermediates originating from aspartate (oxaloacetate) and glutamate (α-ketoglutarate), what compound would have to be generated by some other source in order for the enzymes of the cycle to continually and efficiently process these intermediates? Explain.

12-8 Write a net equation for the conversion of a molecule of isocitrate to oxaloacetate via the enzymes of the citric acid cycle. Write the equation for the same conversion when it is linked to the mitochondrial electron transport chain.

12–9 If purified mitochondria were separately incubated under each of the conditions listed below, predict which of the conditions would result in (a) the least and (b) the greatest amount of oxygen uptake.

a) in the presence of succinate and malonate combined

b) in the presence of succinate alone, followed after two minutes by the addition of malonate

c) in the presence of fumarate and malonate combined

d) in the presence of fumarate alone, followed after two minutes by the addition of a malonate

12–10 How would you compare the ratios of both NADH/NAD$^+$ and ATP/ADP in smooth heart muscle during periods of sleep and handball playing?

12–11 Summarize your understanding of the central role of the citric acid cycle in metabolism.

13

Oxidative Phosphorylation

All living organisms depend on a supply of energy from the surrounding environment for their existence. Photosynthetic organisms depend on an input of *radiant (solar) energy*. Non-photosynthetic organisms—with the exception of a few microbes that can utilize inorganic substances, such as ammonia (NH_3) and nitrites (NO_2^-)—depend on an input of *carbon-containing, organic substances*. Although carbohydrate (monosaccharides) is the primary energy source, lipid (fatty acids) and protein (amino acids) can also be utilized. Photosynthetic and non-photosynthetic organisms also differ in regard to the harnessing of the input energy. In photosynthetic cells there is *first a conversion process* with the input radiant energy being transformed to chemical energy. This then is *followed by a conservation process* with the chemical energy being salvaged in a readily utilizable metabolic form. In photosynthetic cells, there is *first a conversion* of the input radiant energy to chemical energy *followed by a conservation* of same. In non-photosynthetic cells, there is *only a conservation* of the input chemical energy as it is released in the oxidation of organic substrates to CO_2. Despite these differences, a distinct common denominator does exist, namely, that *the input energy is ultimately harnessed and conserved by both types of cells through the production of ATP from ADP and P_i, and subsequently utilized through* the *reverse process of ATP hydrolysis*. Indeed, this role of ATP in the flow of energy in metabolism is common to all living organisms and is a major *unifying biochemical principle* of our biosphere. This chapter deals with the process of *oxidative phosphorylation*—the primary process of ATP formation in non-photosynthetic organisms. A similar process in photosynthesizing cells,

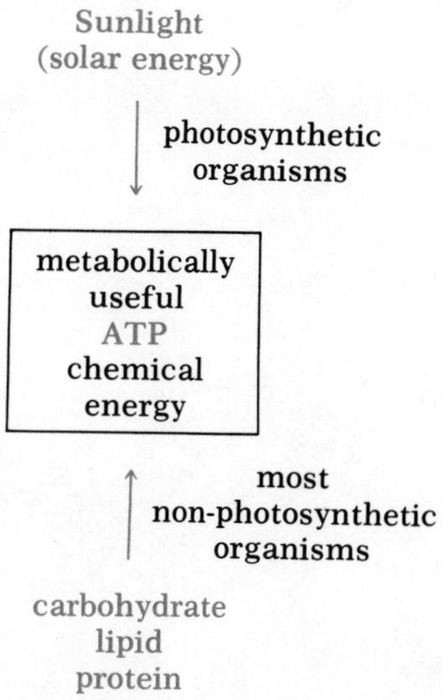

Sunlight
(solar energy)

$\downarrow$ photosynthetic
organisms

metabolically
useful
ATP
chemical
energy

$\uparrow$ most
non-photosynthetic
organisms

carbohydrate
lipid
protein

namely, *photophosphorylation,* will be considered in the following chapter.

The general principles of oxidative phosphorylation are well known and universally accepted. *Electrons originating from the oxidation of high-energy reduced substrates are ultimately transferred to a low-energy terminal electron acceptor* (such as molecular oxygen in aerobes), *accompanied by the release of chemical energy coupled to and sufficient for the phosphorylation of ADP to yield ATP.* Although the complete details are not yet resolved despite a period of about 30 years of study by hundreds of researchers, our current state of knowledge is rather extensive and sophisticated. Our purpose here will be to investigate some of the basic and, indeed, fascinating characteristics of this important process.

ELECTRON TRANSFER SYSTEMS—SOME BASIC PRINCIPLES

Biological oxidative phosphorylation is a term which collectively refers to two processes: (1) the *exergonic oxidation of reduced species such as NADH and FADH₂ via a concerted sequence of electron transport reactions with oxygen frequently acting as the final electron acceptor;* and (2) the *endergonic phosphorylation of ADP.* Both processes are membrane localized, with the intracellular site in higher organisms being specifically the inner mitochondrial membrane. Although each is distinct, they are *coupled processes,* and the energy released in electron transport is used for ATP formation. In other words, the former process acts as an energetic driving force of the latter. With the pertinent chemistry of the $ADP + P_i \rightarrow ATP$ system already having been explored in Chapter 10, it should be obvious that our understanding of the basis for this coupled relationship now requires an analysis of the exergonic phase of oxidative electron transport.

The process of biological electron transport consists of a set of several chemical systems, each of which is a distinct component capable of undergoing a reversible oxidation–reduction [*redox*] reaction. All components act in sequence to mediate the *transport of electrons from an initial high-energy donor in the reduced state to a terminal low-energy acceptor in an oxidized state.* Because of this molecular architecture, the process is frequently termed the *electron transport chain.* When oxygen is the terminal acceptor, as it is in all aerobes, the process is termed the *respiratory chain.* A coherent discussion and a meaningful understanding of electron transport demand as prerequisite a brief digression into certain general physicochemical principles which underlie the very essence of electron transfer systems. Depending on your own previous training, such material may or may not be largely a review. Whatever the case, it is extremely important that these principles be understood.

REDUCTION POTENTIALS

One of the most basic concepts learned in any general chemistry course is that all oxidation–reduction reactions involve the reversible transfer of electrons, with electrons being lost from the component undergoing oxidation and gained by the component undergoing reduction. The theme of this type of process is summarized in the following equations, particularly in the representation of the two *half-reactions* which together comprise the complete system. Half-reactions are frequently called *couples*, signifying the oxidized and reduced forms of the same substance as a pair. Two principles are implicit in this type of reaction: (1) the reacting participants differ in terms of their affinity for electrons;

Net Reaction

Oxidized A + Reduced B $\rightleftarrows$ Reduced A + Oxidized B

from left to right [→]:
A undergoes reduction (electrons gained are donated by B)
B undergoes oxidation (electrons lost are donated to A)

composed of two half-reactions [couples]:
Reduced B $\rightleftarrows$ Oxidized B + ne
Oxidized A + ne $\rightleftarrows$ Reduced A

and (2) an event of oxidation must be accompanied by an event of reduction. Our major concern below will be addressed to the first principle. Finally, we should note that, like any other chemical transformation, an oxidation–reduction reaction can be described in terms of its overall energetics and of whether it can occur spontaneously or not. The point we wish to establish in this section is that both factors will be controlled by the relative differences in the tendency of the reduced reactant of one couple to lose electrons and be oxidized, and of the oxidized reactant of the other couple to gain electrons and be reduced.

To develop our understanding of these concepts, let us begin by considering the system illustrated in Figure 13–1. The diagram is a

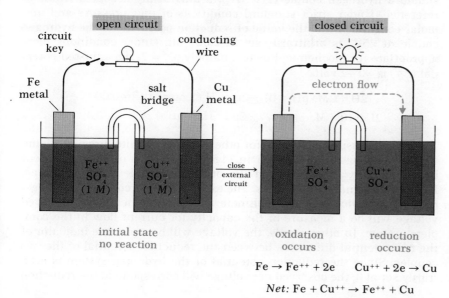

initial state
no reaction

oxidation
occurs

reduction
occurs

$$\text{Fe} \rightarrow \text{Fe}^{++} + 2e \qquad \text{Cu}^{++} + 2e \rightarrow \text{Cu}$$

$$\textit{Net: } \text{Fe} + \text{Cu}^{++} \rightarrow \text{Fe}^{++} + \text{Cu}$$

Figure 13–1 An electrochemical cell. *Left:* circuit open; no reaction. *Right:* circuit closed; electrons will spontaneously flow from iron couple to copper couple.

conventional representation of a simple *electrochemical cell,* which by definition is a chemical system capable of generating a flow of current, that is, electricity. The assembly consists of four parts: (a) two containers consisting of a slab of pure metal in contact with a unit molar solution of its ions—for example, Fe with $Fe^{++}SO_4^{=}$ and Cu with $Cu^{++}SO_4^{=}$; (b) a salt bridge which acts as an essential internal circuit connecting the two systems without permitting mixing; and (c) an external circuit consisting of a conducting wire. After assembly and before the circuit key is closed, the bulb will be off, indicating the absence of any current flow. In chemical terms, this means that neither chemical couple is undergoing reaction and no equations are appropriate. When the key is closed, however, the bulb will light, signifying a spontaneous generation of current flow through the external circuit. Putting it another way, the system is generating useful energy. It is a simple matter to demonstrate that accompanying this physical change— in fact, the very reason for the current flow—is a net oxidation–reduction reaction involving each compartment, with the iron couple undergoing oxidation and the copper couple undergoing reduction. Thus, the concentration of Cu^{++} in the right compartment will decrease, whereas the concentration of Fe^{++} in the left compartment will increase. Reflecting on the spontaneity of the process, we can conclude that on a relative basis the copper couple (Cu^{++}, Cu) has a greater tendency to accept electrons and undergo reduction than does the iron couple (Fe^{++}, Fe). Consequently, the iron couple undergoes an oxidation in this system. Although comparisons of redox couples are customarily made in terms of their different ability to undergo reduction, an alternative but equally valid statement of the same conclusion is that on a relative basis the iron couple has a greater tendency to donate electrons and undergo oxidation than does the copper couple.

In physicochemical terms, the capacity of any couple to undergo reduction is expressed in terms of *standard reduction potentials* (symbolized as $\mathscr{E}°$ with volts as units), all of which are measured against the standard hydrogen couple ($2H^+$, H_2), a universally accepted frame of reference. Under strict standard conditions of unit pressure and unit molar concentrations, the value of reduction potential for the hydrogen couple at 25°C is arbitrarily set at 0.00 volt. Under conditions more appropriate for biochemical usage, namely pH = 7, the adjusted potential ($\mathscr{E}°'$) is −0.42 volt.

$$2H^+(1\ M;\ pH = 0) + 2e \rightleftarrows H_2(1\ atm) \quad \mathscr{E}° = 0.00$$

$$2H^+(10^{-7}\ M;\ pH = 7) + 2e \rightleftarrows H_2(1\ atm) \quad \mathscr{E}°' = -0.42$$

The measurement of $\mathscr{E}°$ for other couples is quite direct, utilizing a setup similar to that shown in Figure 13–1 with one compartment being the $2H^+$, H_2 couple and the other the couple to be measured. Both are at standard conditions. The external circuit contains a voltage-measuring device such as a voltmeter or a potentiometer. The observed voltage will be a measure of the capacity for current flow in the complete system. In other words, the voltage will be a positive indicator of the net potential difference between the reduction potential of the two couples. Since the reduction potential of the hydrogen system is arbitrarily set at 0, the observed net voltage will correspond to the reduction potential of the other couple.

net potential of complete system = positive difference between reduction potentials of each couple

that is:

$$\mathscr{E}^{\circ}{}_{net} = \mathscr{E}^{\circ}{}_{\substack{couple \\ undergoing \\ reduction}} - \mathscr{E}^{\circ}{}_{\substack{couple \\ undergoing \\ oxidation}}$$

By convention, a positive [+] sign accompanies the reduction potential of any couple which in fact has a greater tendency to undergo reduction relative to the hydrogen system; a negative [−] sign accompanies the reduction potential of any couple that has a lesser tendency to undergo reduction relative to the hydrogen system and in fact undergoes an oxidation instead. If the couple is pH dependent, appropriate calculations are made to adjust the $\mathscr{E}^{\circ}$ value to a condition applicable to pH 7($\mathscr{E}^{\circ\prime}$). The reduction potentials of certain couples including some of biological importance are listed in Table 13–1.

Half-reaction couple	$\mathscr{E}^{\circ}$	$\mathscr{E}^{\circ\prime}$
$\frac{1}{2}O_2 + 2H^+ + 2e \rightleftarrows H_2O$	—	+0.82
$Fe^{+++} + 1e \rightleftarrows Fe^{++}$	+0.77	—
$Cu^+ + 1e \rightleftarrows Cu$	+0.52	—
$Cu^{++} + 2e \rightleftarrows Cu$	+0.34	—
$2H^+ + 2e \rightleftarrows H_2$	0.00	−0.42
$Fe^{++} + 2e \rightleftarrows Fe$	−0.44	—
Cytochrome $a_3 \cdot Fe^{+++} + 1e \rightleftarrows$ Cytochrome $a_3 \cdot Fe^{++}$	—	$+0.3 \rightarrow 0.5$*
Cytochrome $f \cdot Fe^{+++} + 1e \rightleftarrows$ Cytochrome $f \cdot Fe^{++}$	—	+0.37
Cytochrome $a \cdot Fe^{+++} + 1e \rightleftarrows$ Cytochrome $a \cdot Fe^{++}$	—	+0.29
Cytochrome $c \cdot Fe^{+++} + 1e \rightleftarrows$ Cytochrome $c \cdot Fe^{++}$	—	+0.25
Cytochrome $c_1 \cdot Fe^{+++} + 1e \rightleftarrows$ Cytochrome $c_1 \cdot Fe^{++}$	—	+0.22
Coenzyme $Q + 2H^+ + 2e \rightleftarrows$ Coenzyme QH_2 (in ethanol)	—	+0.10
Cytochrome $b \cdot Fe^{+++} + 1e \rightleftarrows$ Cytochrome $b \cdot Fe^{++}$	—	+0.04
$FAD + 2H^+ + 2e \rightleftarrows FADH_2$	—	−0.06
$NADP^+ + 2H^+ + 2e \rightleftarrows NADPH[H^+]$	—	−0.34
$NAD^+ + 2H^+ + 2e \rightleftarrows NADH[H^+]$	—	−0.32
Oxidized ferredoxin $+ 1e \rightleftarrows$ reduced ferredoxin	—	−0.43

Table 13–1 A listing of some standard reduction potentials in volts (for $\mathscr{E}^{\circ\prime}$: pH 7; T of 20–30°C).

* Very doubtful value; *in vivo* cyt a_3 is complexed with cyt a; the $\mathscr{E}^{\circ\prime}$ of the a, a_3 complex, called *cytochrome oxidase*, is approximately +0.29.

Since all reduction potentials are determined in the same fashion —that is, against the same reference system—it follows that the relative tendency of any two couples to participate in an electron transfer reaction can be readily predicted. As implied in the above material, the guideline that is used is as follows: *given any two couples, under appropriate conditions the system with the more positive reduction potential will spontaneously tend to gain electrons and undergo reduction.* Consider, for example, the system of Figure 13–1 consisting of an Fe^{++}, Fe couple with $\mathscr{E}^{\circ} = -0.44$ volt and a Cu^{++}, Cu couple with $\mathscr{E}^{\circ} = +0.34$ volt.

Reduction Half-Reactions   *Reduction Potentials*

$$Fe^{++} + 2e \rightleftarrows Fe \qquad\qquad \mathscr{E}° = -0.44 \text{ volt}$$
$$Cu^{++} + 2e \rightleftarrows Cu \qquad\qquad \mathscr{E}° = +0.34 \text{ volt}$$

A comparison of $\mathscr{E}°$'s predicts that Cu^{++} will be reduced, that Fe will be oxidized, and that

$$\mathscr{E}°_{net} = \mathscr{E}°_{Cu^{++},\, Cu} - \mathscr{E}°_{Fe^{++},\, Fe} = +0.78 \text{ volt.}$$

Note that this prediction is consistent with our earlier description of what, indeed, occurs with an iron-copper electrochemical cell. Finally, let us consider an example of biological importance, namely, a reaction involving the NAD and oxygen couples. Applying the same principle reveals that the oxidative transfer of electrons from NADH to molecular oxygen will be the favored process.

Reduction Half-Reactions   *Reduction Potentials (pH 7)*

$$NAD^+ + 2H^+ + 2e \rightleftarrows NADH + H^+ \qquad\qquad \mathscr{E}°' = -0.32 \text{ volt}$$
$$\tfrac{1}{2}O_2 + 2H^+ + 2e \rightleftarrows H_2O \qquad\qquad \mathscr{E}°' = +0.82 \text{ volt}$$

A comparison of $\mathscr{E}°'$'s predicts that O_2 will be reduced and NADH will be oxidized, and that

$$\mathscr{E}°'_{net} = \mathscr{E}°'_{O_2,\, H_2O} - \mathscr{E}°'_{NAD+,\, NADH} = +1.14 \text{ volts}$$

ENERGETICS OF ELECTRON TRANSFER

In our development of electron transfer systems, reference was made to the fact that the difference in reduction potentials is linked to the spontaneity of such processes. By recalling the principles of Chapter 10, you should recognize that the overall chemical energetics of electron transfer reactions, embodied by $\Delta G°'$, ought to be related to the net potential difference ($\mathscr{E}°'_{net}$). Neglecting any detailed development of this, suffice it to say that such is the case. The exact form of the mathematical relationship has already been given in Chapter 10, but is briefly reviewed here. That equation is

$$\Delta G°' = -n\mathscr{F}\mathscr{E}°'_{net}$$

where n is the number of electrons transferred in the overall process, $\mathscr{F}$ is a proportionality constant equal to 23,060 calories per volt, and of course $\mathscr{E}°'_{net}$ is the net potential difference between the two couples. The point to note is that, whenever the potential difference has a positive value, the $\Delta G°'$ will be negative, signifying that the process not only is capable of occurring spontaneously but also is exergonic. Applying this equation to the reduction of NADH via molecular O_2 reveals, for example, that the potential output of energy is −52,580—a sizeable energy yield indeed. Shortly you will discover that this relationship, when applied in this context, will serve to greatly clarify the basis of the coupling of ATP formation to biological electron transport.

$$NADH + H^+ + \tfrac{1}{2}O_2 \rightleftarrows NAD^+ + H_2O \qquad \mathscr{E}°' = +1.14 \text{ volts}$$

Where $n = 2$ electrons

$$\Delta G°' = -(2)(23,060)(1.14) = -52,580 \text{ calories}$$

RESPIRATORY CHAIN OF ELECTRON TRANSPORT

ROLE OF OXYGEN IN METABOLISM

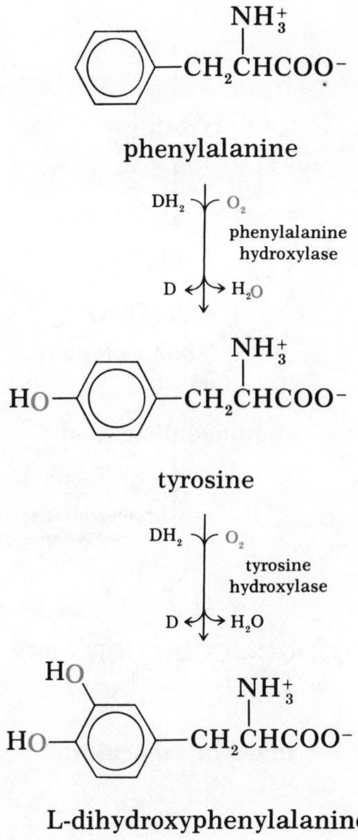

After more than 50 years of investigation, our current understanding of how molecular oxygen participates in biological oxidations can be summarized by the following reactions. In two cases (1 and 2), the

phenylalanine

Molecular Oxygen in Biological Oxidations

1. $SH_2 + O_2 \xrightarrow[\underset{DH_2 \quad D}{}]{hydroxylases} SH{O}H + H_2O$

2. $SH_2 + O_2 \xrightarrow{oxygenases} S({O}H)_2$

3. $SH_2 + \frac{1}{2}O_2 \xrightarrow{oxidases} S + H_2O$

oxygen is incorporated directly into the substrate. Depending on the nature of the reaction, the enzymes that catalyze these reactions are called *hydroxylases* (reaction 1) and *oxygenases* (reaction 2). Hydroxylases, sometimes called monooxygenases, catalyze the insertion of but one of the atoms of molecular oxygen into the substrate (SH_2) as part of a hydroxyl group (—OH). The hydroxylase-catalyzed reactions have a strict requirement for the participation of a second reduced substrate (DH_2), which also undergoes an oxidation—specifically, a dehydrogenation. Although the complete mechanism of a hydroxylase-catalyzed reaction varies from one hydroxylase to another, in most instances the hydrogen donor (DH_2) is usually NADH or NADPH. Some examples of hydroxylase-catalyzed reactions will be encountered in Chapter 16 in our discussion of amino acid metabolism. Three very important reactions in mammalian systems are the conversions of (a) phenylalanine to tyrosine; (b) tyrosine to L-dihydroxyphenylalanine; and (c) tryptophan to 5-hydroxytryptophan. (See margin and Chapter 16, pages 425 and 428–29).

Oxygenases, sometimes called dioxygenases, catalyze the insertion of both atoms of molecular oxygen into the substrate. As indicated in the above general equation (2), the product may be a dihydroxy derivative of the substrate. In other instances stable dihydroxy derivatives are not produced. Rather the oxygen atoms are incorporated as part of a

carbonyl ($\overset{\diagdown}{\underset{\diagup}{C}}$=O) or carboxyl (—COO⁻) grouping. An example of the

latter reaction type, illustrating the oxidation of homogentisic acid to maleylacetoacetate, is given in the margin. This reaction is an important step in the catabolism of the aromatic amino acids, phenylalanine and tyrosine (see Chapter 16, pages 427–28).

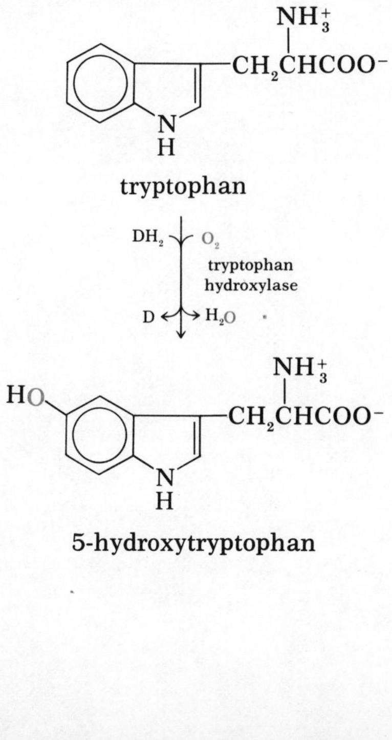

In the third type of biological oxidation involving oxygen (reaction 3), the oxygen molecule is not actually incorporated into the substrate. Rather, the oxygen molecule functions as a *hydrogen acceptor*. Because the hydrogen atom is composed of a proton (H^+) and an electron, the role of oxygen in this type of oxidation is generally described as that of an *electron acceptor*. Enzymes catalyzing this type of reaction are called *oxidases*. Since the oxidase-catalyzed reaction is representative of the

tyrosine

L-dihydroxyphenylalanine

tryptophan

5-hydroxytryptophan

phenylalanine

↓

tyrosine

↓

bond cleavage

homogentisic acid

O₂
homogentisic acid
oxygenase

$$^-OOCC\!\!=\!\!CCCH_2CCH_2COO^-$$

maleylacetoacetate

role of oxygen in biological electron transport, let us study it further.

The generalized form of the oxidase reaction given above is somewhat deceptive regarding the role of oxygen in respiration, because it suggests that the oxidation of a reduced substrate proceeds via a direct dehydrogenation, with oxygen serving as an immediate electron acceptor. Although there are a few examples of this type of reaction in nature, the participation of oxygen in electron transport is of a completely different nature, with more than one catalyst involved. The pioneering work in this area was done independently by H. Wieland, T. Thunberg, O. Warbug, and D. Keilin in the 1920s and 1930s. From the studies of Wieland, Thunberg, and Keilin it became clear that biological oxidations did involve dehydrogenation and that oxygen probably served as an electron acceptor. Wieland made a particularly important discovery in his studies with non-biological systems involving a catalyzed dehydrogenation, which he proposed would simulate the nature of biological oxidations. He discovered that during the course of the reaction the catalyst itself was hydrogenated and that the hydrogen could then be transferred to oxygen or a number of other non-biological (artificial) acceptor molecules. He then suggested that oxygen-dependent dehydrogenations in biological systems involved one or more *intermediate electron carriers* which intervened between the initial electron donor (SH_2) and the final electron acceptor (O_2 or some artificial acceptor). These intermediate carriers would first intervene in their oxidized state and be converted to their reduced state. The reduced state would then transfer its electrons to another carrier in the oxidized state or to the terminal electron acceptor, and in so doing would be reconverted back to the original oxidized state. Thus, the carriers were proposed to undergo a cyclic set of conversions between their reduced and oxidized states.

Thunberg demonstrated that dehydrogenations of metabolic intermediates such as glucose, succinate, malate, fumarate, and lactate in biological (cellular) systems also occurred with the reduction of molecular oxygen or artificial acceptors. These studies resulted in the origin of the term dehydrogenases, which he proposed were the agents that catalyzed the transfer of the hydrogen from donor substrate to the acceptor molecule. In this early period it was proposed that the primary function of the catalysts involved was that of *hydrogen activation*. That is to say, the catalyst activated the reduced substrate donor and thus, participated in the initial electron transfer between substrate and the first carrier.

Warburg's contribution was his suggestion that iron-containing compounds played a crucial role in the utilization of molecular oxygen by aerobic organisms. The basis of this proposal was his observation of an extensive inhibition of oxygen consumption by yeast cells incubated in the presence of low concentrations of cyanide ion, then known to be a potent inhibitor of reactions catalyzed by iron-containing compounds. Warburg theorized that the inhibited compound functioned as a catalyst. He called this catalyst *Atmungsferment* ("respiratory enzyme") and later demonstrated that it was a heme-containing protein. Although he accepted the notion of intermediary electron carriers between initial substrate and oxygen as the final acceptor, Warburg suggested that the crucial role of the catalyst which he had demonstrated was that of *oxygen activation* rather than hydrogen activation. In other words, this heme-containing protein activated oxygen in the last step of electron transport.

With the efforts of several other workers, the pattern that eventually evolved for oxygen-dependent dehydrogenations reflected both the principles of hydrogen activation and oxygen activation. Indeed, all of the electron transfer reactions involve catalysts. As shown in the diagram below, the pattern is one of a successive series of oxidation-reduction reactions involving several intermediate carriers with the net effect being $SH_2 + \frac{1}{2}O_2 \rightarrow S + H_2O$. The reason for terming this process an *electron transport chain* is clearly evident, since each constituent step is linked to another. Warburg was largely responsible for validating the

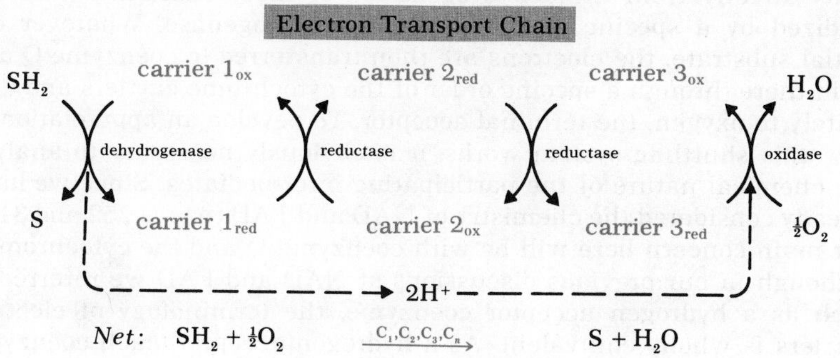

Electron Transport Chain

$$Net: \quad SH_2 + \tfrac{1}{2}O_2 \xrightarrow{C_1,C_2,C_3,C_n} S + H_2O$$

carrier model by his isolation of the NAD and FAD coenzymes acting as intermediate carriers at the beginning of the chain. Warburg also supported part of his own hypothesis with his isolation of a cell-free preparation from yeast containing the proposed "respiratory enzyme." Later studies suggest that Warburg's preparation contained *cytochrome oxidase* which is now accepted as the active component in the last step of the respiratory chain.

Still another key contribution in the development of this model was made at this time by Keilin, who rediscovered the cytochromes (evidence for their existence was first suggested 40 years earlier in 1886 by C. MacMunn, but his data were not accepted by the scientific community) and demonstrated their heme-containing character and their involvement in oxygen uptake by aerobic organisms. Eventually the cytochromes were assigned the role of electron carriers between NAD(FAD) at one end of the chain and oxygen at the other.

ELECTRON CARRIERS

The principal intermediate carriers of the respiratory chain are now fairly well established. In higher organisms they are: *nicotinamide adenine dinucleotides* (NAD); *flavin adenine dinucleotides* (FAD); *coenzyme Q* (CoQ); and a family of *cytochromes* (designated *b, c₁, c, a, a₃*). Recent studies have implicated the participation of additional substances such as *non-heme iron* (NHI)-containing proteins (see below), but decisive proof of their role is not yet available. Although the exact sequence in which these and other possible carriers operate is not unequivocally known at present, the pattern most consistent with experimental studies and most widely supported is as follows.

$$SH_2 \xrightarrow[\text{dehydrogenase}]{NAD^+} NAD \rightarrow FAD \searrow$$
$$CoQ \rightarrow cyt\ b \rightarrow cyt\ c_1 \rightarrow cyt\ c \rightarrow cyt\ a, a_3 \rightarrow O_2$$
$$S'H_2 \xrightarrow[\text{dehydrogenase}]{FAD} FAD \nearrow$$

The process begins with a transfer of electrons from a reduced substrate (SH_2 or $S'H_2$) to either NAD or FAD, depending on whether the particular dehydrogenase involved is NAD^+-dependent or FAD-dependent. When the process is initiated at the level of NAD, note that the next carrier is also FAD. The FAD molecule accepting electrons from NADH, however, is not the same FAD molecule which accepts electrons directly from the dehydrogenation of those substrates that are oxidized by a specific FAD-dependent dehydrogenase. Whatever the initial substrate, the electrons are then transferred to coenzyme Q and from there through a specific order of the cytochrome carriers and ultimately to oxygen, the terminal acceptor. To develop an appreciation of how this shuttling system works, it is obviously necessary to analyze the chemical nature of the participating intermediates. Since we have already considered the chemistry of NAD and FAD (pages 252 and 312), our main concern here will be with coenzyme Q and the cytochromes. Although in our previous discussions of NAD and FAD we referred to each as a hydrogen acceptor coenzyme, the terminology of electron carriers is wholly equivalent. As a hydrogen acceptor, each coenzyme gains the equivalent of 2 electrons. (*Note:* Two hydrogen atoms are equivalent to two protons plus two electrons.) With NADH only one proton is incorporated and the other is gained by the medium (see page 253), whereas in $FADH_2$ both protons are accepted (see page 312).

$$SH_2 + NAD^+ \longrightarrow S + NADH + H^+$$
$$S'H_2 + FAD \longrightarrow S' + FADH_2$$
$$\overrightarrow{}$$
$$-2\ H's\ [2H^+, 2e]$$

In referring to the reduced state of NAD throughout this chapter, the NADH and NADH + H^+ designations are used interchangeably. Dropping the proton is merely a matter of convenience.

Coenzyme Q Among the more recent developments in the continuing study of the respiratory chain has been the demonstration that one of the intermediary electron carriers is a lipid material called *coenzyme Q* (see structure below). The coenzyme Q designation, concocted for biochemical usage, refers to a family of *quinone* compounds some-times called *ubiquinones* because of their ubiquitous occurrence in nature. Coenzyme Q molecules differ from source to source in the length of the hydrocarbon side chain, with the value of n ranging from 6 (microbes) to 10 (mammals). The structure of coenzyme Q is quite consistent with its proposed function as an electron carrier, since the quinone grouping is capable of undergoing a reversible conversion to the hydroquinone. In support of its participation in the respiratory chain is the fact that the bulk of cellular coenzyme Q is found in the mito-chondrial membrane (the subcellular site of electron transport), from which it can be readily extracted by chloroform and other lipid solvents. Whether or not the *in vivo* activity of CoQ is cooperatively dependent on its being complexed to a protein within the membrane is unknown.

oxidized coenzyme Q (CoQ)
(quinone form)

reduced coenzyme Q (CoQH$_2$)
(hydroquinone form)

Cytochromes First detected in the late nineteenth century in various mammalian tissues, *cytochromes* ("cellular pigments") are now known to be common biomolecules of all types of organisms. They are localized primarily in membranes and in eucaryotic cells, specifically in the mitochondrial membrane. All cytochromes are *hemoproteins,* and hence are structural and possibly evolutionary relatives of myoglobin and the monomeric unit of hemoglobin. Unlike that of the latter two proteins, however, the function of the cytochromes is not to bind with and transport oxygen, but rather to participate in electron transfer reactions. This functional characteristic is conferred on the cytochromes through the fact that the *iron atom of the heme grouping can readily undergo a reversible oxidation–reduction.* Recall that the oxygen-binding ability of myoglobin and hemoglobin requires the heme to con-tain iron in the reduced Fe^{++} form. In the oxidized Fe^{+++} form, myoglobin and hemoglobin are inactive.

The cytochrome family is a numerous and heterogeneous lot with approximately 25–30 different species now known to exist throughout nature. All types are classified on the basis of distinctive spectrophoto-metric properties, with those of similar spectroscopic behavior segre-gated into groups designated by lower case letters (a, b, c, etc.). Within each group, individual cytochromes with unique spectral properties are then designated by numerical subscripts such as b, b_1, b_2, b_3, etc. The two factors accounting for the multiplicity of cytochromes are (a) varia-tions in the side chain substituents of the tetrapyrrole moiety of the heme group (see page 346), and (b) variations in the protein component and in the way it is complexed to the heme unit. The former distinguishes one cytochrome class from another, that is, cytochrome a from cytochrome b from cytochrome c; the latter distinguishes among members of the same class, that is, cytochrome b from cytochrome b_1 from cytochrome b_2 and so on.

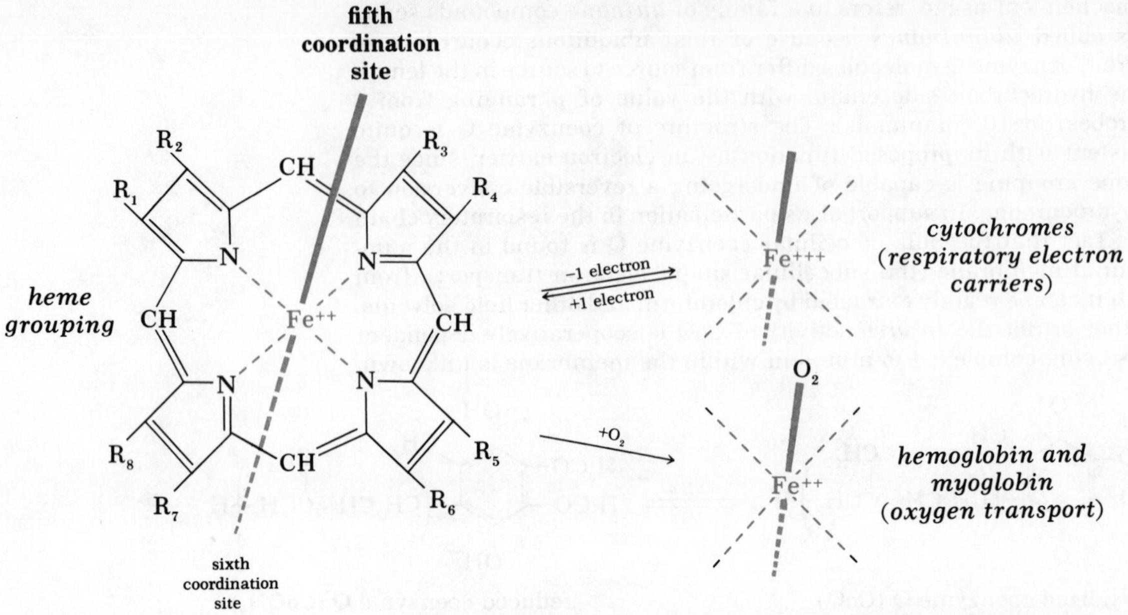
fifth coordination site
R₂
R₃
R₁
CH
R₄
N
N
Fe⁺⁺
CH
CH
heme grouping
N
N
R₈
CH
R₅
R₇
R₆
sixth coordination site
−1 electron
+1 electron
Fe⁺⁺⁺
cytochromes (respiratory electron carriers)
+O₂
O₂
Fe⁺⁺
hemoglobin and myoglobin (oxygen transport)

A more thorough discussion of the structural variations among the cytochromes is beyond the scope of this book. The important thing to realize is that *each cytochrome is structurally unique*. Given this fact and our previous discussion of the structure–function relationship, you should appreciate the validity of the corollary that the *functional properties of each cytochrome are also unique*. In other words, variations in cytochrome structure produce variations in the capacity of each cytochrome to participate in electron transfer reaction. The truth of this premise is evidenced by the characteristic $\mathscr{E}^{\circ\prime}$ values of the major

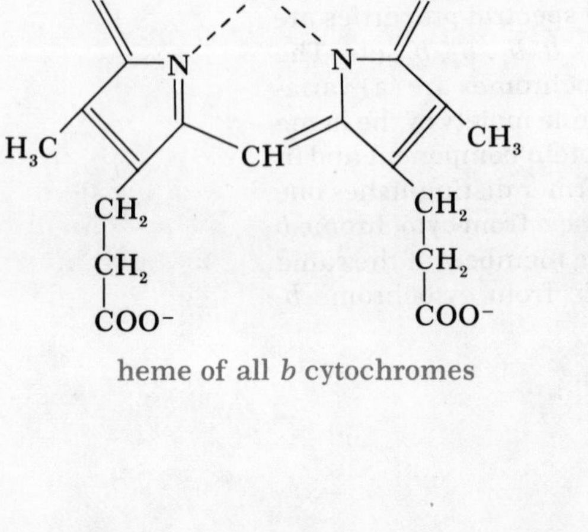

heme of all *b* cytochromes

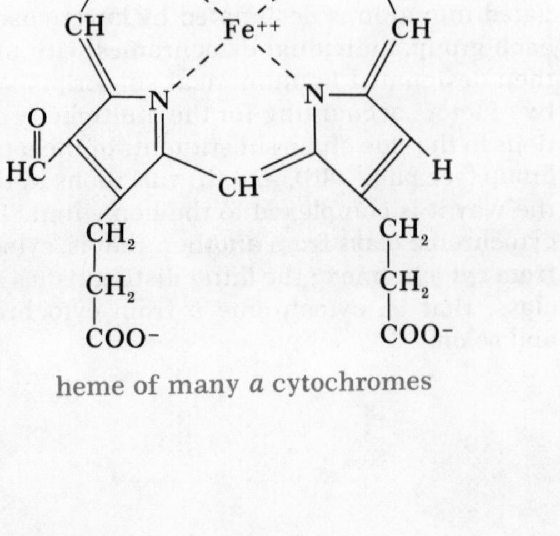

heme of many *a* cytochromes

cytochromes of the respiratory chain (Table 13–1). The significance of the respective $\mathscr{E}°'$ values to the linear sequence of cytochromes in the respiratory chain will be discussed shortly.

Of the major respiratory cytochromes found in higher organisms—namely, b, c_1, c, a, and a_3—the first three can be isolated separately, with cytochrome c being the easiest to obtain in pure form. On the other hand, cytochromes a and a_3 appear to exist and to function as an aggregate. The a, a_3 complex is further distinguished by the presence of copper (Cu) presumably bound to the a_3 species. The unique functional feature of the a, a_3 complex is that it is the only cytochrome system that will act directly with oxygen. Accordingly, the a, a_3 complex is frequently called *cytochrome oxidase*. This is presumably the oxygen-activating respiratory enzyme isolated 40 years ago by Warburg.

The complete three-dimensional structure of cytochrome c was recently determined by R. E. Dickerson and coworkers. This now paves the way for a detailed study of the mechanism of action of cytochromes. The spatial orientation of the heme grouping relative to the polypeptide chain of cytochrome c is shown in Figure 13–2. Note the extensive set of interactions between the heme grouping and the polypeptide chain. The diagram is a good review of the principles of protein structure discussed earlier in Chapter 4.

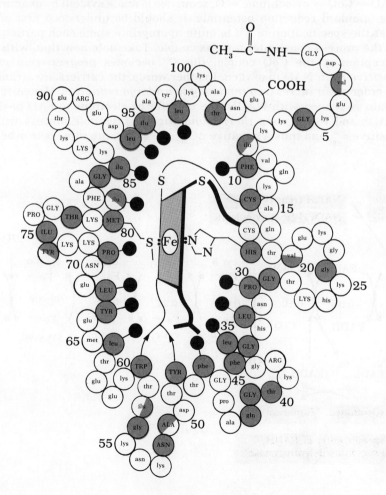

Figure 13–2 Heme-packing diagram of the cytochrome *c* molecule. *Heavy circles* indicate side chains that are buried on the interior of the molecule, and attached *black dots* mark residues whose side chains pack against the heme. *Light circles* indicate side chains on the outside of the molecule, and *dark half-circles* show groups that are half-buried at the surface. *Arrows* from tryptophan 59 and tyrosine 48 to the buried propionic acid group represent hydrogen bonds. Residues designated by *capital letters* are totally invariant among the proteins of 29 different species. (Reprinted with permission from R. E. Dickerson, et al., Ferricytochrome *c*: General Features of the Horse and Bonito Proteins at 2.8 Å Resolution, *J. Biol. Chem.*, **246**, 1511–1535 (1971).)

Other Carriers In recent years much evidence has been collected implicating materials other than those mentioned above as active participants in the respiratory chain. Included here are a group of substances called *non-heme iron* (NHI) *proteins,* designating the complexing of iron to protein but without a heme grouping. Although NHI-proteins are not extensively characterized, significant amounts are found in the mitochondrial membrane. Likewise undetermined as yet is their possible mode of action in electron transport.

Certain bacteria utilize *Vitamin K naphthoquinones* (page 211) as intermediate carriers acting between FAD and coenzyme Q. Since they are quinones, it is likely that their mode of action is similar to that proposed for coenzyme Q. It remains unresolved whether Vitamin K-type compounds play a corresponding role in higher organisms.

DESIGN FOR RESPIRATORY CHAIN

Having described the general nature of the respiratory chain and its major participants, let us now consider the process in greater detail. A modern version of what is proposed to occur is diagrammed in Figure 13–3. The key to understanding why nature has selected the NAD $\rightarrow$ FAD $\rightarrow$ CoQ $\rightarrow$ cytochrome $\rightarrow$ O_2 sequence is made evident by examining the standard reduction potentials. It should be understood first of all that the specification of $\mathscr{E}°'$ is quite appropriate since each participant in the process constitutes a redox couple. Take note now that, with the exception of the CoQ couple, the $\mathscr{E}°'$ becomes *progressively more positive* from NAD to oxygen. In other words, the carriers are arranged in order of an *increasing tendency to undergo reduction.* Hence, if the chain is primed with NADH, the transfer of electrons to FAD to yield NAD$^+$ and FADH$_2$ is a *thermodynamically favorable* process with a positive $\mathscr{E}°'_{net}$ and thus a negative $\Delta G°'_{net}$. Likewise, the same is true of the

Figure 13–3 A diagrammatic representation of the respiratory chain. ($\mathscr{E}°'$ values of each half-reaction couple are reduction potentials in volts.)

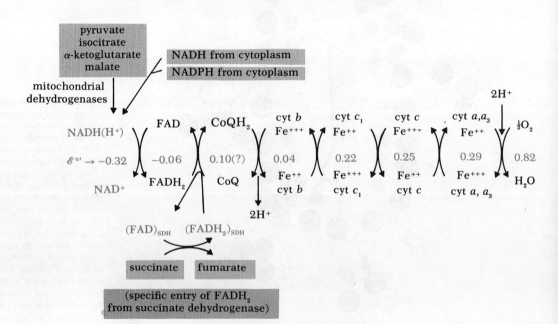

$$NADH + H^+ \rightarrow NAD^+ + 2H^+ + 2e \qquad \mathscr{E}^{o\prime}_{ox} = -(-0.32)$$
$$FAD + 2H^+ + 2e \rightarrow FADH_2 \qquad \mathscr{E}^{o\prime}_{red} = -0.06$$

$$NADH + H^+ + FAD \rightarrow NAD^+ + FADH_2 \qquad \mathscr{E}^{o\prime}_{net} = +0.26$$

$$\Delta G^{o\prime}_{net} = -n\,\mathscr{F}\mathscr{E}^{o\prime}_{net} = -(2)(23{,}060)(0.26) = -12{,}000 \text{ calories}$$

next step involving $FADH_2$ and CoQ (ox). Since this type of pattern is *continuous*, the thermodynamic design is clearly evident: the electron carriers are arranged so that each transfer has the capacity to proceed *spontaneously* and *exergonically*. (*Note:* The non-fit of the coenzyme Q couple should be considered in the context of the conditions under which the $\mathscr{E}^{o\prime}$ has been calculated, namely, in 95% ethanol, a condition not exactly representative of the natural environment of a biological membrane. It has been suggested that the true ability of CoQ to function as an electron carrier *in vivo* is more closely approximated by a value of 0.0 volts for $\mathscr{E}^{o\prime}$.)

The overall chemical and thermodynamic design of the respiratory chain is summarized below with each event of electron transfer represented as a complete oxidation–reduction reaction. Indeed, this is what happens *in vivo*. Although two electrons are transferred in the overall process, it is not known whether the cytochrome sequence in particular involves one cytochrome molecule functioning twice or two separate molecules transferring one electron each. The $(cyt)_2$ designation is employed here only for bookkeeping purposes to account for the *net* transfer of two electrons.

Respiratory Chain Reactions	$\Delta\mathscr{E}^{o\prime}$ (v)	$\Delta G^{o\prime}$ (cal)
$NADH(H^+) + FAD \rightarrow NAD^+ + FADH_2$	+0.26	−12,000
$FADH_2 + CoQ(ox) \rightarrow FAD + CoQH_2(red)$	+0.16	− 7,380
$CoQH_2 + (cyt\ b\cdot Fe^{+++})_2 \rightarrow CoQ + (cyt\ b\cdot Fe^{++})_2 + 2H^+$	−0.06	+ 2,770
$(cyt\ b\cdot Fe^{++})_2 + (cyt\ c_1\cdot Fe^{+++})_2 \rightarrow (cyt\ b\cdot Fe^{+++})_2 + (cyt\ c_1\cdot Fe^{++})_2$	+0.18	− 8,300
$(cyt\ c_1\cdot Fe^{++})_2 + (cyt\ c\cdot Fe^{+++})_2 \rightarrow (cyt\ c_1\cdot Fe^{+++})_2 + (cyt\ c\cdot Fe^{++})_2$	+0.03	− 1,380
$(cyt\ c\cdot Fe^{++})_2 + (cyt\ a, a_3\cdot Fe^{+++})_2 \rightarrow (cyt\ c\cdot Fe^{+++})_2 + (cyt\ a, a_3\cdot Fe^{++})_2$	+0.04	− 1,840
$(cyt\ a, a_3\cdot Fe^{++})_2 + \frac{1}{2}O_2 + 2H^+ \rightarrow (cyt\ a, a_3\cdot Fe^{+++})_2 + H_2O$	+0.53	−24,440
Net: $NADH(H^+) + \frac{1}{2}O_2 \rightarrow NAD^+ + H_2O$	+1.14	−52,580

In comparing the net reaction with the multi-step pathway, two features are clearly evident. First, the intervention of the intermediate carriers results in the *production of energy in increments* rather than the whole amount being liberated in one direct step. It can be argued that, relative to a massive release of energy, a stepwise yield is a much more efficient route if the energy is to be conserved. However, despite the availability of useful chemical free energy at several points, the number of conservation sites for ATP formation is significantly smaller. We will shortly pursue this matter further. The second feature is that the complete sequence is *autocatalytic*. Thus, in the presence of a high rate of catabolism, the participating NAD^+- and FAD-dependent dehydrogenases are assured of being efficiently supplied with the oxidized form of each coenzyme required for the continued operation of these enzymes.

FORMULATION OF THE SEQUENCE OF ELECTRON CARRIERS

Up to now no mention has been made as to how the electron carriers were eventually sequenced. Well, part of the rationale was a presumption that each carrier would be most efficiently arranged in order of an increasing ability to accept electrons and undergo reduction. Hence, knowledge of the $\mathscr{E}°'$ values was a useful guideline. Another key discovery was that cytochrome oxidase (cyt a, a_3 couple) was the last carrier. A further tactic was the use of *artificial* (non-biological) *redox acceptors* with known $\mathscr{E}°'$ values to shunt electrons from the chain at points of specific respiratory carriers. Of immeasurable importance were the discovery, characterization, and subsequent use of *respiratory inhibitors* which act at specific sites along the chain (see page 353). For example, *amytal* and other *barbiturates* are potent inhibitors of electron transfer in the FAD → CoQ (cyt b) region. The antibiotic, *antimycin* A, specifically inhibits electron transfer at the cyt b → cyt c_1 site. *Cyanides* (CN⁻), *azides* (N₃⁻), and *carbon monoxide* (CO) are potent inhibitors of cytochrome oxidase. In each instance, it was possible by the use of sensitive spectrophotometric techniques to measure the amount of the various carriers that existed in the reduced state and to compare these with the levels of reduced carriers in the control system when neither artificial acceptor nor respiratory inhibitor was present. Both the occurrence of divergent electron flow in the presence of artificial acceptors and the inhibition of electron flow in the presence of respiratory inhibitors would be characterized by decreased levels of the carriers in their reduced state *after* the site of divergence or inhibition. Only the inhibition of electron flow by a respiratory inhibitor would result in increased levels of the reduced state of the carriers existing prior to the site of inhibition. This increase would not occur in the presence of an artificial acceptor, since electrons would not build up in this case prior to the site of action by the acceptor, but would instead be removed by the acceptor. For example, in the presence of antimycin A one would observe that the amounts of cytochromes c_1, c, a, and a_3 in the reduced state would decrease. It is possible to detect and measure these changes with refined spectroscopic techniques because each of the carriers displays a different absorption spectrum in its oxidized and reduced states. For example, reduced cytochrome c displays a strong absorption spectrum at approximately 550nm whereas oxidized cytochrome c displays a weak absorption at the same wavelength. Thus a measure of the decrease in absorption at 550nm would indicate the decrease in the amount of reduced cytochrome c and the increase in the amount of oxidized cytochrome c.

COUPLING OF RESPIRATORY CHAIN TO ATP FORMATION

PHOSPHORYLATION SITES

Our discussion of electron transport in the respiratory chain accounts for the oxidative, exergonic phase of oxidative phosphorylation. Now we are prepared to consider the endergonic phase of phosphorylation of ADP to yield ATP. Although it is a point to which we have referred on

reduced substrate (SH₂)

e ↓

ox. carrier

red. carrier

e ⌐ --- e --→ artificial acceptor (a diversion of electrons at any site would diminish the amount of carriers in the reduced state after the site of diversion)

ox. carrier

red. carrier

e ↓

ox. carrier

red. carrier

e ■ ---→ respiratory inhibitor (a blockage of electron flow at any site would diminish the amount of carriers in the reduced state after the site of inhibition and increase the amount of carriers in the reduced state prior to the site of inhibition)

ox. carrier

red. carrier

e ↓

ox. carrier

red. carrier

e ↓

O₂

several occasions, it merits recapitulation that these *two distinct processes are indeed coupled through an energy transfer from the process of electron transport to that of phosphorylation.* The evidence for this coupling is threefold. The first and obvious proof is that the mitochondrial oxidation of NADH or $FADH_2$ is in fact accompanied by the simultaneous formation of ATP (see below). A second proof is the fact that mitochondrial ATP formation can be blocked without any inhibition of electron transport by the addition of chemical agents called *uncouplers*. The most classical uncoupler is *2,4-dinitrophenol* (DNP). Moreover, the removal or deactivation of the uncoupler results in a restoration of ATP formation linked to the respiratory chain. Exactly how the uncouplers short-circuit the transfer of energy is not known. The third and perhaps most convincing proof is that the extent of mitochondrial ATP formation is significantly reduced in the presence of respiratory chain inhibitors such as antimycin A and the others mentioned above. Experimental examples of these points will be illustrated in the following material.

In accounting for ATP formation, the basic factor which must be taken into consideration is the amount of energy needed for the formation of ATP from ADP and P_i. Using the value of $-7,300$ calories for the $\Delta G^{\circ\prime}$ of ATP hydrolysis given in Chapter 10, this means that, at the very least, 7,300 calories must be made available for ATP production.

$$ADP + P_i \rightarrow ATP \qquad \Delta G^{\circ\prime} = +7,300 \text{ calories}$$

Now, by inspecting the thermodynamic data given earlier (page 349) in the skeletonized summary of the respiratory chain, one would conclude that four sites ideally meet this requirement: the NAD-FAD system ($\Delta G^{\circ\prime} = -12,000$ calories); the FAD-CoQ system ($\Delta G^{\circ\prime} = -7,380$ calories); the cytochrome *b*-cytochrome c_1 system ($\Delta G^{\circ\prime} = -8,300$ calories); and the cytochrome *a*, a_3-oxygen system ($\Delta G^{\circ\prime} = -24,400$ calories). Thus, if the energy at each of these regions were transferred to ATP formation, this would then mean that the transfer of two electrons through the complete respiratory chain from NADH to oxygen would be sufficient to account for $4ADP + 4P_i \rightarrow 4ATP$ with the formation of one ATP coupled to each of the aforementioned exergonic sites. Similarly, if the chain were primed at the level of $FADH_2$ (via the oxidation of succinate with succinate dehydrogenase, for example), complete oxidation of $FADH_2$ through oxygen should account for $3ADP + 3P_i \rightarrow 3ATP$. One fewer ATPs would be formed in this case, since the entrance of electrons bypasses the NAD-FAD region.

Although the basic principle of this idealized analysis is quite valid, it is not in agreement with experimental studies. Before inspecting data obtained from same, let us briefly examine the experimental system that would be used in the study of oxidative phosphorylation. A typical experimental design is given below. Aside from the usual control of pH, temperature, and ionic strength, the basic requirements are (a) the use of purified mitochondria; (b) the addition of a reduced substrate that will be oxidized by a mitochondrial dehydrogenase; (c) the addition of NAD^+ if the substrate is to be oxidized by an NAD^+-dependent dehydrogenase; (d) the addition of known amounts of ADP and P_i; and (e) the ability to accurately measure the amount of inorganic phosphate consumed or of ATP produced and the amount of oxygen consumed or the amount of reduced substrate consumed. Results are

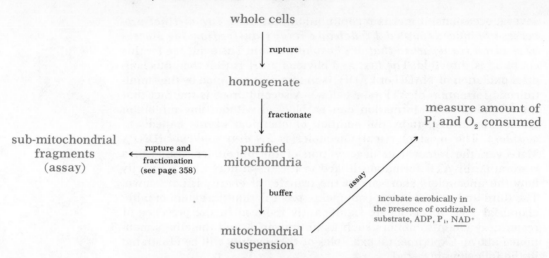

conventionally expressed as a *P/O ratio,* which corresponds to the number of moles of P_i consumed per gram-atom of oxygen consumed. Alternative interpretations would be the number of moles of ATP produced per gram-atom of oxygen consumed or the number of moles of ATP produced per mole of substrate consumed.

Studies of this type typically yield data as summarized in Table 13–2. Although integral values for the P/O ratio are obtained, implying

Table 13–2 Oxidative phosphorylation with intact mitochondria.

Substrate	Dehydrogenase	Inhibitor	P/O ratio
pyruvate	NAD	—	~ 3
isocitrate	NAD	—	~ 3
malate	NAD	—	~ 3
succinate	FAD	—	~ 2
acyl-SCoA	FAD (page 392)	—	~ 2
isocitrate	NAD	antimycin	~ 1
isocitrate	FAD	CN^-	~ 2
succinate	FAD	antimycin	~ 0
succinate	FAD	CN^-	~ 1

that specific sites for ATP formation do exist, note that only three sites are implicated when the chain is primed with NADH—one fewer than was suggested by our idealized analysis. Likewise, two rather than three sites are implicated when the chain is primed with $FADH_2$. Although there have been scattered reports of higher P/O values, the model for oxidative phosphorylation most widely agreed upon is consistent with the data of Table 13–2, namely, a *maximum of three phosphorylation sites.*

In view of our earlier conclusion that four potential phosphorylation sites exist, the next logical question is which three are in fact coupled to ATP formation. Well, actually we have already implicated one site as being contributed by the NAD-FAD region. The basis of this conclusion can be seen from Table 13–2, which indicates that, as predicted, the FAD-dependent oxidation of a reduced substrate is indeed accompanied by a P/O value one unit smaller than that observed for an NAD$^+$-dependent oxidation of a reduced substrate. Accordingly, then, we can assign the NAD-FAD region as phosphorylation site 1. The remaining two sites have been established by measurement of P/O ratios in the presence of respiratory inhibitors with different substrates. For example, the incubation of mitochondria with NAD$^+$-dependent substrates in the presence of antimycin A results in a P/O value of approximately 1. Since the specific site of antimycin A inhibition is the cyt $b \to$ cyt c_1 transfer, a P/O value of 1 suggests that the FAD $\to$ CoQ region is *not* a phosphorylation site. If it were, one would predict a P/O of 2, since the NAD-FAD site alone would account for a P/O of 1. Corroborating this conclusion is the observation that very little P$_i$ is consumed when mitochondria are incubated in the presence of antimycin A and succinate. In addition to ruling out the FAD $\to$ CoQ system, the antimycin effect suggests then that sites 2 and 3 are cyt $b \to$ cyt c_1 and cyt a, $a_3 \to$ oxygen, respectively. The former is, of course, implicated directly by the antimycin effect, since it is the specific site of antimycin inhibition in the transfer of electrons within the respiratory chain. The cyt a, $a_3 \to$ oxygen transfer is similarly confirmed by the addition of respiratory inhibitors of cytochrome oxidase, such as cyanide ion, which yield P/O values of approximately 2 when the respiratory chain is primed with NADH and approximately 1 when the chain is primed with FADH$_2$.

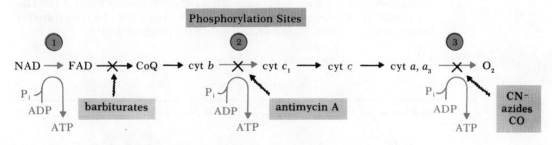

→X→ site of action of respiratory inhibitors

MECHANISM OF COUPLING

The concept of phosphorylation linked to oxidative electron transport was originally proposed about 40 years ago, and quantitative measurements of P/O values began nearly 30 years ago. Although the link is now firmly established and the existence of three localized phosphorylation sites is generally agreed upon, it may surprise you to learn that the exact details of *how the energy is transferred* from electron transfer reactions to ATP formation are still unknown. The main problems in elucidating the mechanism of this coupling are: (a) there is yet no exact knowledge as to the mechanism of action of the individual carriers in the respiratory chain; and (b) the whole process of oxidative phosphorylation occurs in an insoluble multi-enzyme complex localized within the mitochondrial membrane (see a later section). The latter in particular is a major obstacle, since a detailed characterization of molecular function requires a purification of the component from the multi-molecular framework and the presumption that the isolated, solubilized component will exhibit the same or even similar properties in the intact membrane. At the end of this chapter we will review some recent studies that have been successful in this area.

Despite these and other difficulties, many workers have contributed much effort to resolving this problem. Included among this group are A. Lehninger, B. Chance, E. Racker, D. Green, E. Slayter, and D. Griffiths. Among the several theories that have emerged from this effort, the most popular is the proposal that the process is chemical in nature and that the energy is conserved and subsequently transferred via the participation of *intermediate compounds* which have the ability to undergo reversible reactions between low-energy and high-energy states. One specific formulation based on this hypothesis is summarized below, where I represents the *unknown coupling intermediate*. The reduced and oxidized carriers of course refer to those participants at one of the phosphorylation sites along the respiratory chain. In simplified form, the model proposes three steps. First, accompanying the transfer of electrons, the coupling intermediate (I) forms a high-energy complex with either one of the carriers (carrier ∼ I), with the driving force being the energy released in the course of electron transfer. The specification that I binds with (carrier 1)$_{ox}$ is purely arbitrary. In the second step, the carrier ∼ I complex undergoes an exchange reaction with P_i, producing the free form of the carrier and a high-energy phosphorylated form of the coupling intermediate, I ∼ P. Finally, the I ∼ P species undergoes an exchange reaction with ADP to yield free I and ATP. The net effect, of course, is the transfer of energy from the electron transfer between two carriers to the endergonic formation of ATP.

1. (carrier 1)$_{red}$ + (carrier 2)$_{ox}$ + I ⇌ (carrier 1)$_{ox}$ ∼ I + (carrier 2)$_{red}$
2. (carrier 1)$_{ox}$ ∼ I + P_i ⇌ (carrier 1)$_{ox}$ + I ∼ P
3. I ∼ P + ADP ⇌ I + ATP

Net: (carrier 1)$_{red}$ + (carrier 2)$_{ox}$ + ADP + P_i ⇌ (carrier 1)$_{ox}$ + (carrier 2)$_{red}$ + ATP

The chemical identity of the coupling intermediate is obscure. Some workers have proposed that it is a low-molecular-weight substance such as a quinone, and others have suggested that it is a protein. Furthermore, it is not clear whether each step involves an enzyme catalyst. Another uncertainty is whether each of the three phosphorylation sites uses the same type of coupling mechanism and, if they do, whether the coupling intermediate is the same or different in each.

Although there is no evidence decisively favoring this scheme, or any other for that matter, it is a model which *can account for* the action of *uncoupling agents* and other inhibitors of oxidative phosphorylation such as *oligomycin,* a potent antibiotic. For example, the effect of uncouplers like *dinitrophenol* (abolition of ADP phosphorylation with retention of electron transport) has been explained by proposing that DNP could react with the carrier ∼ I complex *prior* to the formation of I ∼ P and ATP. Such a suggestion is supported by experimental evidence indicating that the DNP effect is largely independent of phosphate concentration. Since the electron carrier is regenerated, the operation of the respiratory chain would not be impaired. On the other hand, the inhibition by oligomycin of the combined process of electron transport *and* phosphorylation can be explained by proposing that the oligomycin-sensitive step is either the formation of I ∼ P or the subsequent exchange reaction of I ∼ P with ADP. Either site of action, but particularly the former, would prevent the regeneration of the free electron carrier in levels sufficient for normal electron transport. Of course, both possibilities would short-circuit ATP formation as well.

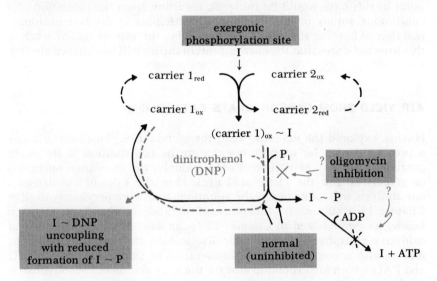

EXTRAMITOCHONDRIAL ATP

Since (a) the complete process of oxidative phosphorylation is *intra*-mitochondrial (specifically associated with the inner mitochondrial membrane); (b) the bulk of ATP-requiring processes are *extra*mitochondrial; and (c) the mitochondrial membrane is impermeable to a direct diffusion of ATP, an obvious question is: How does the ATP get out of the mitochondria? Well, at present we don't really know for sure. One current suggestion is that the membrane contains one or more *transport proteins* which effect a one-for-one translocation of intra-mitochondrial ATP and extramitochondrial ADP. In other words, for each ATP molecule transported out of the mitochondrion to the cytoplasm, one ADP molecule is transported from the cytoplasm into the mitochondrion.

In support of this type of transport system (in fact, part of the basis on which it was originally formulated) are recent studies that show that oxidative phosphorylation of intact mitochondria is strongly inhibited by certain substances, in a fashion wholly unlike that of other inhibitors which *directly* affect the intramitochondrial production of ATP, such as oligomycin. One such inhibitor is an exotic, low-molecular-

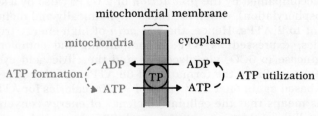

TP = proposed transport protein

weight carbohydrate, called *atractyloside,* found in plants. Presumably, the atractyloside deactivates the ATP-ADP transport protein of the mitochondrial membrane. Thus, the inhibition of oxidative phosphorylation in this case would be *indirect,* resulting from the inhibition of a continuous supply of ADP needed to participate in the last exchange reaction. Whatever the explanation may be, the rate of recent work in this area indicates that the carrier-protein theory will be clarified shortly.

ATP YIELD FROM CARBOHYDRATE CATABOLISM

Having explored the essential features of oxidative phosphorylation as a process per se, let us now re-examine its contribution to the main catabolic pathway of carbohydrates, namely, the combined operation of glycolysis and the citric acid cycle. For the sake of consistency, our analysis will make use of the equations that were previously used in Chapter 12 to summarize this phase of metabolism; these are rewritten below. As emphasized in Chapter 12 (page 319), the metabolic role of oxidative phosphorylation is basically twofold, since the production of ATP is also accompanied by a regeneration of oxidized forms of NAD and FAD which are crucial to sustain the degradation of carbohydrates. At this point, the basis of the latter function should be quite evident.

$$
\begin{array}{ccc}
\underset{\text{glucose}}{C_6H_{12}O_6} & \xrightarrow[\text{citric acid cycle}]{\text{glycolysis, PDC,}} & 6CO_2 \\[2mm]
& \underset{2FAD}{10NAD^+} \qquad \underset{2FADH_2}{10NADH} & \\[2mm]
nATP & \xleftrightarrow[\text{phosphorylation}]{\text{oxidative}} & nADP + nP_i \\[2mm]
& 6H_2O \qquad\qquad 6O_2 &
\end{array}
$$

Given the accepted quantitative relationships of oxidative phosphorylation concerning the uptake of P_i and O_2, it is now possible—in a rather straightforward manner—to *estimate* the efficiency of the combined operations of glycolysis and the citric acid cycle in terms of energy conservation. Since the oxidation of one NADH(H$^+$) unit yields 3 ATPs and one FADH$_2$ unit yields 2 ATPs, the yield of the combined route is 34 ATPs. If you presume that this completes the analysis of the *net total gain* of ATP, you are neglecting three other factors, namely: (a) every molecule of glucose passed through the glycolytic pathway *requires* 2 ATPs; (b) every molecule of glucose passed through the glycolytic pathway *produces* 4 ATPs via substrate-level phosphorylations; and (c) the complete oxidation of 2 units of acetyl-SCoA in the citric acid cycle is accompanied by the *production* of 2 GTPs (also by a substrate-level phosphorylation), which are thermodynamically and metabolically equivalent to 2 ATPs. Hence, the *net gain* of high-energy triphospho-nucleotides, expressed as ATP, accompanying the complete oxidation of glucose to 6CO$_2$ via glycolysis and the citric acid cycle is 38 (34 − 2 + 4 + 2). Since the formation of 38 ATPs would require 277,400 calories (based again on a $\Delta G^{o'}$ value of −7,300 calories for ATP hydrolysis), this means that the cellular efficiency of energy conversion in a metabolically useful form is approximately 40%. Inasmuch as the energy required for *in vivo* ATP formation is probably greater than 7,300 calories per mole (page 246), the figure of 40% is a rather conservative estimate.

$$\begin{array}{lr}
& \Delta G^{\circ\prime} \text{(calories)} \\
38ADP + 38P_i \rightarrow 38ATP & +277,400 \\
\text{glucose} + 6O_2 \rightarrow 6CO_2 + 6H_2O & -686,000 \\
\hline
\text{glucose} + 6O_2 + 38ADP + 38P_i \rightarrow 6CO_2 + 6H_2O + 38ATP & -408,600
\end{array}$$

$\left.\begin{array}{l} \\ \\ \end{array}\right\}$ ~ 40% energy conservation

In performing this efficiency analysis there is one item that merits a brief explanation. Note that in the tally made above, the next production of 38 ATPs includes 6 ATPs that would result from the utilization in electron transport of 2 units of NADH produced during glycolysis. (The other 8 NADHs and 2 FADH$_2$s would be generated in the reactions of the citric acid cycle). Well, in eucaryotic organisms, because glycolysis occurs in the cytoplasm whereas the oxidative phosphorylation occurs in the mitochondrion, you may ask: Why is it legitimate to include the NADH generated by glycolysis in the production of ATP? Moreover, the question is even more pertinent in view of the fact that the mitochondrial membrane is impermeable to a direct transport of NADH. The explanation is that the NADH produced in the cytoplasm can enter the mitochondrion by processes that have been termed *shuttle pathways*. Shuttle pathways provide for an indirect movement of molecules across a membrane. In the case of NADH one of the proposed shuttle pathways is shown below. You will note that it depends on the utilization of NADH in the cytoplasm to reduce oxaloacetate to malate and the malate then enters the mitochondrion. The NAD$^+$-dependent oxidation of malate in the mitochondrion completes the *net* transport of NADH. The enzyme catalyzing each reaction would be the malate dehydrogenase which is contained in each compartment (see page 314). The necessary requirement for oxaloacetate in the formation of malate in the cytoplasm could be satisfied directly by some OAA-generating reaction in the cytoplasm (from the transamination of aspartate, for example) or by another shuttle system which would transfer OAA from the mitochondrion to the cytoplasm. A shuttle system would be required since the mitochondrial membrane is also impermeable to oxaloacetate.

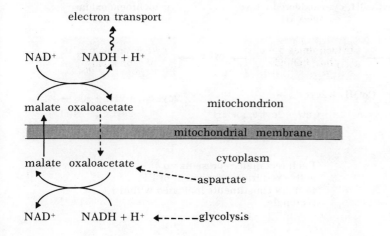

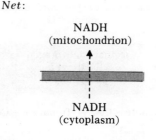

MITOCHONDRIAL COMPARTMENTALIZATION OF OXIDATIVE PHOSPHORYLATION

The fact that oxidative phosphorylation occurs in mitochondria has been known for some years. Since the late 1950's, however, much effort has been expended to determine whether the subcellular compartmentalization is further characterized on an even lower level of submitochondrial compartmentalization. The first evidence in support of this was the finding that oxidative phosphorylation does occur with particulate material obtained from ruptured mitochondria. Moreover, the soluble fraction is inactive. Since virtually all of the particulate material obtained from ruptured mitochondria is fragmented membranous material, the results demonstrated that all of the essential components of oxidative phosphorylation are indeed localized within the mitochondria, specifically in the mitochondrial membrane. Continued studies during the last decade have attempted to pursue the problem one step further by searching for an order of compartmentalization within the membrane itself. The quest has been fruitful and has unraveled one of the most fascinating characteristics in all of nature.

ELECTRON TRANSPORT PARTICLES AND RESPIRATORY COMPLEXES

Following the early success in processing whole mitochondria to yield functional fragments of oxidative phosphorylation, the development of modified rupture and fractionation procedures resulted in the isolation of a particle which had lost the ability of phosphorylation but not that of electron transport. For obvious reasons this isolate was termed the *elementary particle* (EP) of the respiratory chain. Subsequent research resulted in the further dissociation of EP into four *respiratory complexes* (I, II, III, IV), each of which was capable of separately catalyzing a portion of the complete respiratory chain (see below).

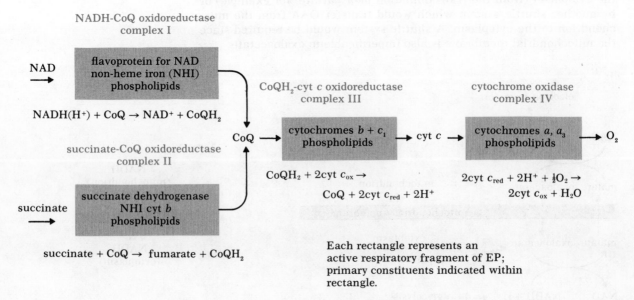

NADH-CoQ oxidoreductase
complex I

NAD →

flavoprotein for NAD
non-heme iron (NHI)
phospholipids

$NADH(H^+) + CoQ \rightarrow NAD^+ + CoQH_2$

succinate-CoQ oxidoreductase
complex II

succinate →

succinate dehydrogenase
NHI cyt b
phospholipids

succinate + CoQ → fumarate + $CoQH_2$

CoQ →

CoQH₂-cyt c oxidoreductase
complex III

cytochromes $b + c_1$
phospholipids

→ cyt c

$CoQH_2 + 2cyt\ c_{ox} \rightarrow$
$CoQ + 2cyt\ c_{red} + 2H^+$

cytochrome oxidase
complex IV

cytochromes a, a_3
phospholipids

→ O₂

$2cyt\ c_{red} + 2H^+ + \frac{1}{2}O_2 \rightarrow$
$2cyt\ c_{ox} + H_2O$

Each rectangle represents an
active respiratory fragment of EP;
primary constituents indicated within
rectangle.

Complex I (NADH-CoQ oxidoreductase) catalyzed the transfer of electrons from NADH to CoQ; complex II (succinate-CoQ oxidoreductase) catalyzed the transfer of electrons from succinate to CoQ; complex III (CoQH$_2$-cytochrome c oxidoreductase) catalyzed the transfer of electrons from CoQH$_2$ to cyt c; and finally, complex IV (cytochrome oxidase) catalyzed the transfer of electrons from cyt c to oxygen. To avoid confusion, it should be noted that measurable activity of each complex presupposes the addition of both reactants. In other words, the complexes themselves do not contain appreciable levels of NAD, CoQ, succinate, and cytochrome c.

The isolation and characterization of these respiratory complexes represented the first decisive proof that the components of the respiratory chain, and probably those materials responsible for the coupling to ATP formation, were highly integrated into some type of *super-ordered molecular assembly* within the mitochondrial membrane. Further support was provided by successful attempts at partial reconstitution by simply mixing together any two appropriate complexes to yield secondary units capable of catalyzing the sum of the reactions typical of each complex, as indicated below.

$$NADH(H^+) + (cyt \cdot c - Fe^{+++})_2 \xrightarrow{I + III} NAD^+ + (cyt \cdot c - Fe^{++})_2 + 2H^+$$

$$succinate + (cyt \cdot c - Fe^{+++})_2 \xrightarrow{II + III} fumarate + (cyt \cdot c - Fe^{++})_2 + 2H^+$$

$$(cyt \cdot c - Fe^{++})_2 + \tfrac{1}{2}O_2 + 2H^+ \xrightarrow{III + IV} (cyt \cdot c - Fe^{+++})_2 + H_2O$$

ULTRASTRUCTURE OF THE MITOCHONDRIAL MEMBRANE

The isolation of a submitochondrial elementary particle and its constituent respiratory complexes has guided much work to determine the *in vivo* arrangement of all the participating components of oxidative phosphorylation *within* the membrane. Aided immeasurably by the use of high-resolution electron microscopy, coupled with refined procedures of fractionation, purification, and analytical techniques, several investigators have contributed greatly toward this objective. The current state of knowledge is diagrammatically summarized in Figure 13–4, which depicts the ultrastructural anatomy of the mitochondrial membrane. An electron micrograph of submitochondrial particles is also shown. The essential points are as follows. First, the process of oxidative phosphorylation is localized within the inner membrane, which is *morphologically* and *functionally distinct* from the outer membrane. Secondly, the active portion of the inner membrane consists of the *cristae*, which contain an ordered array of elementary particles (EP) and phosphorylation factors embedded in a phospholipoprotein environment. Thirdly, the small spheres attached to the cristae in great numbers by small base plates are known to be structural units containing a protein(s) essential for the coupling of phosphorylation to electron transport. Presumably the spheres contain among other things the hypothetical intermediate believed to function in the coupling process. Amazingly, after simply mixing the spheres and the elementary transport particles from the cristae proper—each of which can be isolated separately—one obtains a particle capable of the complete process of oxidative phosphorylation.

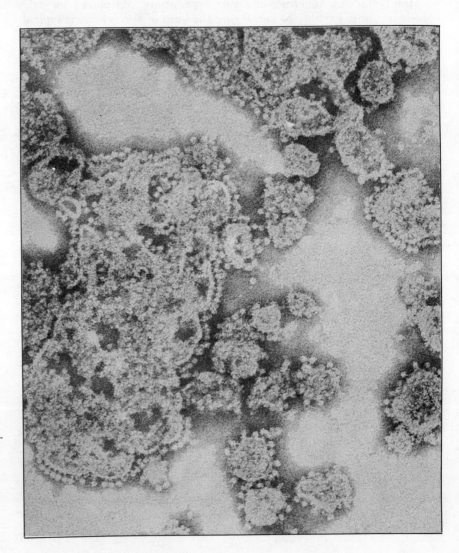

outer membrane (om)

inner membrane (im)

cristae

enlarged

cross-section of
mitochondrion
(see Figure 9–5)

differ in
structure and
function

im   om

☐ = elementary particle
↑ = base stalks and spheres
   attached to cristae
   required for
   phosphorylation

intramembranous
space

Figure 13–4 Top: A diagrammatic
representation of the ultrastructure of a
mitochondrial membrane based on high-
resolution electron microscopy.
Below: An electron micrograph of submitochondrial particles showing the
attachment of numerous spheres and
base stalks at a magnification of
160,000 ×. (Photograph generously
supplied by Dr. E. Racker, Cornell
University.)

It is not our intention here to pursue this diagram and the evidence for it any further. An excellent summary of the key experimental developments can be found in the article by E. Racker cited below. It is hoped that this abbreviated discussion, together with previous examples of the structure–function relationship, will provoke you to wonder and marvel at the profound molecular architecture of nature.

LITERATURE

BALDWIN, E., *Dynamic Aspects of Biochemistry,* Fifth Edition. London-New York: Cambridge University Press, 1967. Chapters 7 and 8 are devoted to enzymes and electron carriers that function in the oxidation of organic compounds and in the transfer of electrons by the respiratory chain. See page 299 for a description of the book.

DICKERSON, R. E., "The Structure and History of an Ancient Protein," *Scientific American,* **226,** 58–72 (1972). A concise discussion of the structure of cytochrome *c* and its evolution as a molecule over 1.2 billion years. The amino acid sequence from 38 different species is examined.

GRIFFITHS, D. E., "Oxidative Phosphorylation," in Volume 1 of *Essays in Biochemistry,* P. N. Campbell and G. D. Greville (eds.), 57–90. New York: Academic Press, 1965. An excellent review article summarizing recent advances in the understanding of the respiratory chain and the coupled process of ATP formation.

LEHNINGER, A. L., *Bioenergetics,* Second Edition. New York: W. A. Benjamin, Inc., 1971. Contains an excellent introductory presentation of oxidative phosphorylation.

LEHNINGER, A. L., *The Mitochondrion.* New York: W. A. Benjamin, Inc., 1965. A comprehensive and more advanced treatment than in the above book.

RACKER, E., "The Two Faces of the Inner Mitochondrial Membrane," in Volume 6 of *Essays in Biochemistry,* P. N. Campbell and F. Dickens (eds.), 1–27. New York: Academic Press, 1970. An excellent review article on the ultrastructure and function of the mitochondrial membrane.

RACKER, E., "The Membrane of the Mitochondrion," *Scientific American,* **218,** 32–39 (1968). Description of the ultrastructure and function of the inner mitochondrial membrane.

WILLIAMS, V. R., and H. B. WILLIAMS, *Basic Physical Chemistry for the Life Sciences.* San Francisco: W. H. Freeman and Company, 1967. Chapter 5 contains an excellent development of principles of oxidation–reduction systems.

EXERCISES

13-1 Calculate the net oxidation-reduction potential and the standard free energy change for each of the following reactions as written from left to right, and indicate whether or not the reaction would tend to occur spontaneously given the proper conditions. (Assume that pH and temperature are as specified in Table 13–1.)

a) $NADH + H^+ + CoQ \rightarrow NAD^+ + CoQH_2$

b) $CoQH_2 + 2[\text{cyt } b \text{ (oxidized)}] \rightarrow CoQ + 2[\text{cyt } b \text{ (reduced)}]$

c) $2(\text{reduced ferredoxin}) + NADP^+ + 2H^+ \rightarrow$
$$2(\text{oxidized ferredoxin}) + NADPH + H^+$$

13-2 The standard reduction potential (pH 7) of the lactate-pyruvate couple is -0.19 volt, which means then that the reaction

$$\text{pyruvate} + 2H^+ + 2e \rightarrow \text{lactate} \qquad \mathscr{E}^{\circ\prime}_{red} = -0.19 \text{ v}$$

is endergonic. Yet, in our analysis of the glycolytic pathway in Chapter 11, we have seen that the reduction of pyruvate to lactate, catalyzed by lactate dehydrogenase, is strongly exergonic. Explain.

$$\text{pyruvate} + \text{NADH} + H^+ \xrightarrow[\text{dehydrogenase}]{\text{lactate}} \text{lactate} + \text{NAD}^+$$

13-3 In physicochemical terms, summarize your understanding of the nature of the respiratory electron transport chain.

13-4 If a respiratory inhibitor functioned at the site of electron transfer between cytochromes c_1 and c, what approximate value for the P/O ratio would be obtained on incubation (aerobically) of intact mitochondria in the presence of malate, ADP, P_i, NAD$^+$, the inhibitor, and a buffer?

13-5 The incubation of mitochondria in the presence of succinate and malonate would result in less oxygen consumption than in the presence of succinate alone, but the P/O ratios would not be significantly different. Explain.

13-6 If respiratory complexes II and IV were incubated together under aerobic conditions in the presence of added succinate, coenzyme Q, and cytochrome c, what overall oxidation–reduction reaction would occur?

13-7 In the system described in the preceding problem, would you expect to detect the formation of any significant amount of reduced cytochrome c_1 during the reaction? Explain.

13-8 What would be the net yield of ATP from the complete aerobic catabolism of *glucose* to 6CO$_2$ according to the hexose-monophosphate shunt, and how does the number compare with the ATP yield from glycolysis linked to the citric acid cycle?

$$6(\text{glucose-6-P}) \xrightarrow{\text{HMS}} 5(\text{glucose-6-P}) + 6CO_2$$
$$\textit{Net:} \quad 1(\text{glucose-6-P}) \rightarrow 6CO_2$$

In this case, although reducing power is generated as NADPH and in the cytoplasm, appropriate mechanisms exist in most cells accounting for the transfer of reducing power from NADPH to NADH in the cytoplasm and then the shuttling of the cytoplasmic NADH into the mitochondrion. (Remember, the calculation is to be made on the basis of the catabolism of free glucose.)

14

Photosynthesis

Photosynthesis is the most important biological process that occurs on the face of the earth. There are two basic reasons for this—both of equal importance. First, the major exogenous source of both carbon and energy—primarily carbohydrate (CH_2O)—on which non-photosynthetic organisms are vitally dependent, is originally made available in nature only through the fixation of atmospheric CO_2 and its subsequent conversion to carbohydrate material by photosynthesizing cells. The second reason is the accompanying production of oxygen which, of course, is indispensable to the existence of all aerobic organisms. Photosynthesis is the only chemical source of oxygen on this planet.

$$6CO_2 + 6H_2O \xrightarrow[\substack{\text{solar} \\ \text{energy}}]{\text{photosynthesis}} (CH_2O)_6 + 6O_2$$

The vital relationship of photosynthesis to aerobic organisms is a reciprocal one, however, since the metabolism of aerobic organisms is mutually important to photosynthetic organisms. Actually the two processes are entirely complementary, inasmuch as the primary products of photosynthesis serve as the primary reactants of aerobic organisms, which in turn yield the primary reactants of photosynthesis. This crucial relationship is generally termed the *carbon cycle*. We emphasize the vital importance of photosynthesis precisely because it begins the carbon cycle and hence, without it, life as we know it would soon cease to exist.

In chemical terms the net effect of photosynthesis is quite simple. Carbon in its most oxidized, low-energy form as carbon dioxide is assimilated by the photosynthetic organism into a more reduced, higher-energy form as carbohydrate material. Thus, the process is *endergonic* (energy requiring) and *reductive* (requires reducing power). Energy is

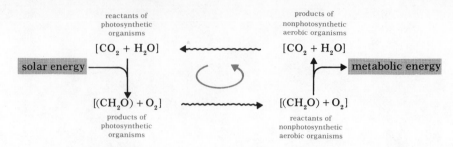

initially supplied from solar radiation as light, and reducing power is initially contributed by water. The major chemical events are believed to occur in two distinct phases termed the *light reaction* and the *dark reaction*. The first evidence for the existence of two separate processes was obtained in 1939 by R. Hill who observed that the rate of oxygen production during photosynthesis was unaffected by the addition or removal of CO_2. The subcellular site of the complete process of photosynthesis is the *chloroplast,* a specialized organelle unique to photosynthetic organisms.

As the name implies, the light reaction is dependent on an input of radiant energy. The complete process, which probably represents the most remarkable chemistry yet known to man, involves many participants, the most important being *chlorophyll,* widely accepted as the initial substance involved in the primary photochemical event. Briefly, the *primary act* is proposed to be the excitation of chlorophyll molecules to a higher energy state by the *absorption of incident light energy*. All reactions immediately subsequent to and dependent on this initial activation are essentially a concerted series of *electron transfer* (oxidation–reduction) steps similar to what happens in the respiratory chain. Specifically, these reactions include the oxidative cleavage of water, the formation of NADPH, and the formation of ATP. The production of ATP is frequently termed *photosynthetic phosphorylation* to distinguish it from the related process of oxidative phosphorylation in aerobic organisms. The dark reaction involves the enzymatic assimilation and conversion of CO_2 into carbohydrate, utilizing the NADPH and ATP formed in the light reaction as the metabolic sources of reducing power and energy, respectively.

Our objective in this chapter will, of course, be to explore the current state of knowledge concerning each of these processes. To establish a proper foundation for such discussions, we will first develop some basic principles dealing with the nature of light and then examine the ultrastructure of the chloroplast. The brief analysis given this subject can be supplemented by additional information from the references cited at the end of the chapter.

results of light reaction:
(directly dependent
on radiant energy)

$$H_2O \rightarrow (2H^+ + 2e) + \tfrac{1}{2}O_2$$
$$NADP^+ + 2H^+ + 2e \rightarrow$$
$$NADPH + H^+$$
$$ADP + P_i \rightarrow ATP$$

results of dark reaction:
(not directly dependent
on radiant energy)

$$CO_2 \xrightarrow{\frac{NADPH}{ATP}} (CH_2O)$$

ELECTROMAGNETIC RADIATION

THE QUANTUM NATURE OF LIGHT

The radiation of solar origin reaching the surface of the earth, commonly referred to as *visible light* (sometimes termed *white light*), comprises a specific region of the complete electromagnetic spectrum (see page 25, Chapter 2), namely, from about 4000Å to 7000Å. According to the principles of modern physics, our concept of any type of electromagnetic radiation is that the radiation is propagated through space as a wave with a certain velocity (c), amplitude (A), and *wavelength* (λ). By definition, the wavelength is the distance required for the wave to propagate one complete cycle (see Figure 14–1). Whereas the velocity of any wave is constant (c = 186,000 miles/sec or 3×10^{10} cm/sec), the ampli-

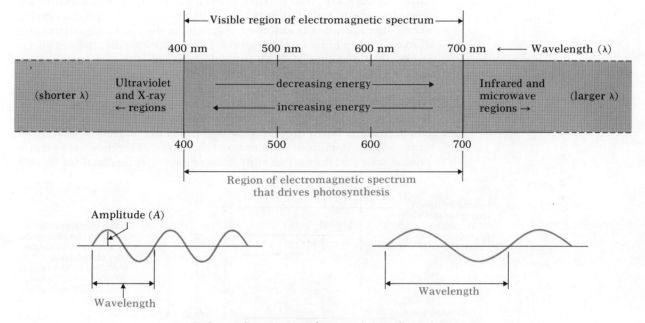

Figure 14–1   An analysis of electromagnetic radiation, particularly in the visible region. See also Figure 2–10.

tude and wavelength are variable. Indeed, it is the wavelength which distinguishes one type of radiation from another. This distinction is also expressed in terms of the *frequency* (ν), the number of cycles of a moving wave that pass a given point per unit of time. The mathematical expression for the frequency is

$$\nu = \frac{c}{\lambda}$$

One of the most revolutionary developments in the early days of modern physics occurred in 1900 when Max Planck suggested that all types of electromagnetic radiation have a dual nature. In addition to its wave character, Planck proposed that radiation is also particulate in the sense that the energy (E) of a wave is emitted in discrete packages called *quanta*. Planck further proposed that the energy value (E) of 1 quantum is directly proportional to the frequency of the radiation. The proportionality constant, h, which for obvious reasons is called Planck's

$$E \propto \nu \qquad E \text{ (1 quantum)} = h\nu \qquad E \text{ (} n \text{ quanta)} = nh\nu$$

constant, is equal to 6.625×10^{-27} ergs/sec. The crux of Planck's hypothesis is quite understandable. It states that, since the energy content of an electromagnetic wave is dependent only on wavelength (λ), the energy content of the entire electromagnetic spectrum is *discontinuous*. In other words, the energy is constantly changing from values of high energy (low wavelength) to values of lower energy (high wavelength). Initially greeted with skepticism, Planck's hypothesis was shortly confirmed by Einstein, who postulated even further that, when matter and electromagnetic radiation interact—a process termed a *photochemical event*—the radiation is absorbed, resulting in the excitation (activation) of molecules to higher energy levels. To be more specific, radiant energy is absorbed, causing an excitation of electrons within the molecule to higher energy levels. For any such transition, Einstein also suggested that the absorption of 1 quantum of radiant energy is required for each electron that is activated to a level of higher energy. It was later proposed that each electronic transition between allowable energy levels can occur only when the molecule is exposed to radiation of exactly the same energy (quantum) content as the energy difference between the ground state and the excited state. This, of course, is the basis for spectro-

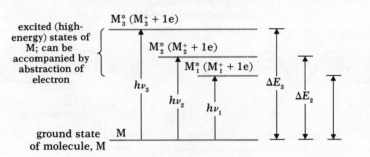

excited (high-energy) states of M; can be accompanied by abstraction of electron

Each transition requires the absorption of a specific quantum ($h\nu$) of radiation matched by the energy difference (ΔE) between permissible activated states.

ground state of molecule, M

scopic investigations that correlate the absorption of radiant energy with the structure of molecules (see page 25, Chapter 2). As we will shortly discover, the same type of phenomenon presumably occurs in photosynthesis. The absorption of radiant energy by the special photosensitive chlorophyll molecules causes a displacement of electrons from these chlorophyll molecules. The electrons are then transferred to special electron carriers.

CHLOROPLASTS—CELLULAR SITE OF PHOTOSYNTHESIS

GENERAL COMMENTS

The complete process of photosynthesis takes place in the *chloroplasts*, highly specialized, subcellular organelles that distinguish photosynthetic cells from non-photosynthetic cells. The initial experimental demonstration that isolated chloroplasts were capable of supporting the *complete* process of photosynthesis was achieved by D. Arnon and co-workers in 1954. However, first credit for the successful use of cell-free extracts in photosynthetic studies is to be given to R. Hill, who demonstrated the photoevolution of oxygen with isolated chloroplasts fifteen years earlier.

In addition to all animal cells and most bacterial cells, certain plant cells are also non-photosynthetic and contain no chloroplasts. These include those cells responsible for plant functions other than the harnessing of solar energy and the fixation of CO_2, such as those found in plant roots, for example. In plants, the process of photosynthesis occurs primarily in the *green leaf cells,* with each cell containing several chloroplasts. On the other hand, since the photosynthetic algae are unicellular organisms, each alga will contain chloroplasts. In contrast to the more advanced algae and green plants, the photosynthetic bacteria (likewise unicellular organisms) do not contain chloroplasts. In these cells the process of photosynthesis occurs in *chromatophores,* which can be thought of as primitive chloroplasts, similar in function but smaller in size and less complex in structure than chloroplasts.

CHLOROPLAST ULTRASTRUCTURE

A cross-sectional view of a fully developed chloroplast as seen in electron microscopy is shown in Figure 14–2. Similar to a mitochondrion, the chloroplast is surrounded by a double (outer and inner) bilayer membrane. (This and other biochemical similarities between chloroplasts

Figure 14–2 The ultrastructure of a fully developed, intact chloroplast as seen in cross-section under the electron microscope. Note the many interconnected grana consisting of stacked lamellae. Samples obtained from mesophyll cells of maize leaf. Magnification: 22,400 ×. (Photograph generously supplied by L. K. Shumway, Department of Botany, Washington State University.)

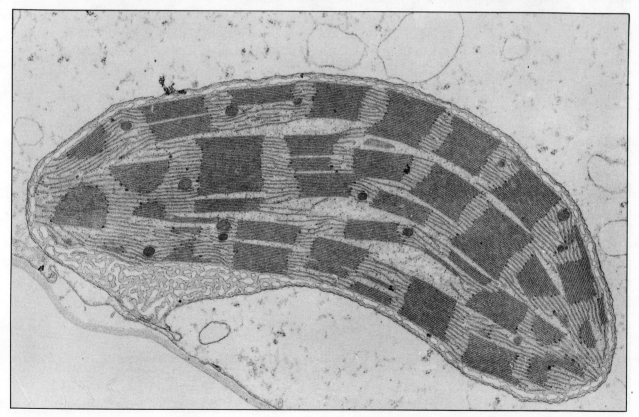

and mitochondria have prompted the suggestion that both organelles evolved from the same origin, probably a primitive symbiotic bacterium. The other similarities referred to include the reported presence of DNA and ribosomes within each organelle and the capacity of each organelle to synthesize protein. Refer to an earlier discussion of mitochondria in Chapter 9, page 225.) The size, shape, and number of chloroplasts vary widely among photosynthesizing cells. In higher plants they are generally cylindrical in shape, ranging anywhere from $5-10\mu$ in length and $0.5-2\mu$ in diameter. A comparison of these dimensions with those of mitochondria reveals that the chloroplasts are much larger. Indeed, among the defined organelles of higher cells, the chloroplast is second in size only to the nucleus.

The most conspicuous feature of the electron micrograph in Figure 14-2 is that the chloroplast, like the mitochondrion, possesses a characteristic and highly organized fine level of ultrastructure, evidenced by the ordered array of several electron-dense bodies throughout its whole interior. These are interpreted as corresponding to flattened *membranous* bodies, called *lamellae* or, more recently, *thylakoid discs*. As with the cristae of mitochondria (see page 224, Chapter 9), the lamellae result from folded protrusions of the inner chloroplast membrane within the core of the chloroplast. In cross-sectional view, they appear as in Figures 14-2 and 14-3, with the latter showing the cross-section

Figure 14-3 Electron micrograph showing grana and lamellae at high magnification. The less electron dense background represents the soluble region of the chloroplast, called the lumen. The chloroplast membrane can be seen at the lower right. Magnification: 124,800 ×. (Photograph generously supplied by L. K. Shumway, Department of Botany, Washington State University, Pullman, Wash.)

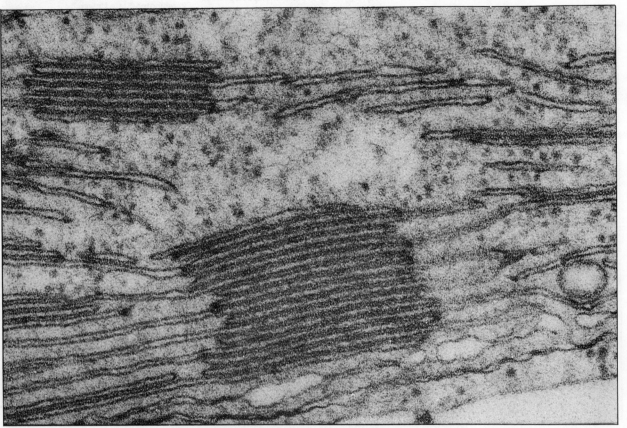

at higher magnification. From a top or bottom view, each lamella (thylakoid) appears as a disc (see drawing in Figure 14–4). The ordered, stacked piles of individual lamellae are called *grana*. As shown in Figure 14–2, the number of stacked lamellae per granum is quite variable.

There are extensive data suggesting that each lamella contains all of the necessary photosensitive pigments, electron carriers, and accessory components for the crucial light reaction of photosynthesis. The bulk of the enzymes and coenzymes responsible for the assimilation of CO_2 into organic material are found in the soluble portion (*lumen*) of the chloroplast. Despite the fact that each lamella—and thus each granum—contains all the materials required for the light reaction, neither an individual lamella nor a granum is suggested as the basic unit of photosynthesis. High-resolution electron microscopic studies of isolated and partially fragmented lamellae suggest that the basic unit (termed a *quantosome*) may be a small, somewhat spherical unit, several of which are embedded in the phospholipoprotein matrix of the lamella membrane (see drawing in Figure 14–4). What the exact composition and arrangement of the quantosomes may be, and whether all quantosomes are identical, are questions yet to be answered. Regardless of these uncertainties, it should be quite obvious to you that the ultrastructure of the chloroplast is another example of the fascinating and, indeed, truly remarkable characteristics of nature. Even more fascinating, however, is what goes on inside the chloroplast.

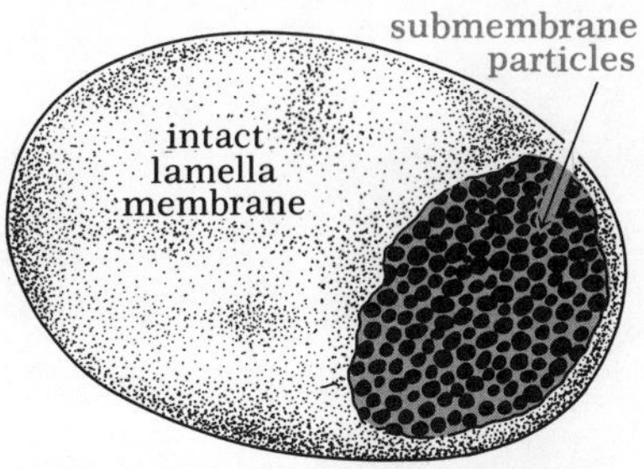

Figure 14–4 Drawing based on electron microscopic studies of chloroplast lamellae. Sketch depicts a top view of individual lamella (disc-shaped) with portion of surface membrane peeled off to reveal ordered array of spherical particles. The latter have been proposed to represent the elementary photochemical structural units, termed *quantosomes*.

THE LIGHT REACTION OF PHOTOSYNTHESIS

The combined effect of the light-dependent phase in all photosynthetic green plants and several algae can be given by the following equation. It is a *net* equation summarizing the four main events of the light reaction:

$$2NADP^+ + mADP + mP_i + 2H_2O \xrightarrow[nh\nu]{chloroplasts} 2NADPH + 2H^+ + mATP + O_2$$

(a) *the **photochemical excitation** of chlorophyll;* (b) *the oxidative cleavage of water–**photo-oxidation**;* (c) *the reduction of $NADP^+$-**photoreduction**;* and (d) *the formation of ATP-**photophosphorylation**.* It will be our objective to describe the sequence of events associated with this overall process. (*Note:* A similar equation could be written for the photosynthetic bacteria. In these organisms, however, the source of reducing power is not H_2O as in the above process, but generally a special inorganic donor such as H_2 or H_2S or certain reduced organic acids. This variation of the photosynthetic bacteria will not be discussed further.)

The equation above is written to show the evolution of 1 unit of molecular oxygen. To avoid unnecessary confusion, this stoichiometry will be used throughout this chapter. Since the production of 1 O_2 involves the transfer of 4 electrons from H_2O to $NADP^+$, the equation also depicts an idealized 2:2 stoichiometry involving H_2O and $NADP^+$. Still uncertain are (a) the number (m) of ATP molecules produced per molecule of oxygen evolved, and (b) the number of light quanta (n) required per molecule of oxygen evolved. For ATP formation, several investigators have suggested a value of 4 for m. Others propose that $m = 2$.

For the amount of light energy, there are likewise two conflicting opinions: $n = 4$ and $n = 8$. According to Einstein's law of photochemical equivalence stating that 1 quantum is required to excite 1 electron, the proposal that $n = 4$ would represent 100% quantum efficiency, whereas $n = 8$ would represent half-efficiency. This controversy has existed since 1922 when O. Warburg first reported, and defended vigorously, that $n = 4$. Fifty years later the controversy still continues.

PRIMARY PHOTOCHEMICAL ACT

The first systematic scheme for the light-dependent phase of photosynthesis was contributed in 1949 by C. B. van Niel, who proposed that the central photochemical event was the photolysis of water to yield a source of reducing power (H) and oxidizing power (OH). The former was then used in the dark for the reductive fixation of CO_2, and the latter was ultimately eliminated as O_2. The basic proposal of van Niel

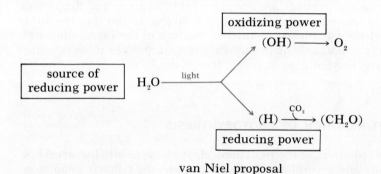

van Niel proposal

proved to be a stimulating and guiding force for future research into the light-dependent reaction. The current view of this process retains the basic principle of van Niel's hypothesis with one key exception. The distinctive feature of the contemporary viewpoint is that the *primary photochemical act is the absorption of radiant energy by chlorophyll molecules, resulting in their activation (excitation) to higher energy states.* This process is currently interpreted as facilitating the extraction and subsequent transfer of electrons from the excited chlorophyll molecules to specialized acceptor molecules, with the latter materials, of course, undergoing reduction (gain in electrons). The electrons are ultimately transferred to $NADP^+$. This initial photochemical event is also accompanied by the oxidative cleavage of H_2O to yield molecular oxygen and a source of protons (H^+), the latter also required for the reduction of $NADP^+$. These generalized statements are summarized in the diagram below. In other words, the cleavage of the hydrogen donor is a *consequence* of the central photochemical act—the excitation of chlorophyll—rather than actually being the central photochemical act as van Niel suggested. Some evidence for the participation of chlorophyll as the "action-molecule" in the primary act of photosynthesis will be discussed shortly. In view of this critical role, it seems appropriate for us to first examine the chemical nature of chlorophyll.

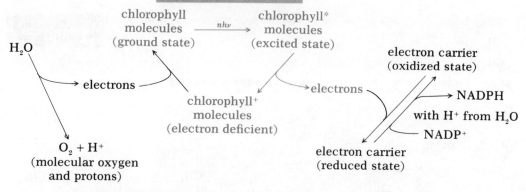

Note: The formation of ATP, coupled to electron transfer reactions, is not indicated in this diagram.

CHLOROPHYLL

It is a unifying biochemical principle of nature that all photosynthesizing cells contain chlorophyll. In fact, with the exception of the photosynthetic bacteria and a few algae, it appears that almost all photosynthetic cells contain identical molecular species of chlorophyll. These species of chlorophyll are two in number with one designated as *chlorophyll a* and the other as *chlorophyll b*. The chloroplasts of algae and higher green plants contain both species. Photosynthetic bacteria presumably contain only one type of chlorophyll—different from both chlorophylls *a* and *b*—called *bacteriochlorophyll*. To conclude, however, that the photosynthetic apparatus is identical from one type of cell to another would be erroneous. In addition to variations in the relative amounts of chlorophylls *a* and *b,* it is quite likely that chloroplasts are also differentiated in terms of the molecular environment of the lamellae that contain the photosensitive chlorophyll pigments.

The basic structure of all chlorophylls is that of a metallo-tetrapyrrole unit already encountered in our discussion of the heme prosthetic group of myoglobin, hemoglobin, and the cytochromes. The chlorophyll molecule, however, is distinctly different from the heme prosthetic group in three respects: (1) in chlorophyll the metal ion coordinated to the tetrapyrrole moiety is Mg^{++} rather than Fe^{++} or Fe^{+++}; (2) chlorophylls are *not* dependent on attachment to a protein grouping for activity; and (3) the chlorophylls contain a characteristic set of pyrrole side-chain groupings. Regarding the side-chain groupings, chlorophylls are most notably distinguished by the presence of (a) a large, non-polar, alcohol grouping (*phytol*) in ester linkage to a propionic acid side-chain residue, and (b) a fused cyclopentanone ring. The non-polar phytol grouping is particularly noteworthy, since it provides the structural basis for a stabilized integration of chlorophyll molecules into the lipoprotein matrix of the lamella membrane. All of these features are depicted in the structures shown below. As indicated, the structural difference between chlorophyll *a* and chlorophyll *b* is merely a variation in only one pyrrole ring substituent.

Y = —CH$_3$ in chl *a*
Y = —CHO in chl *b*

fused cyclopentanone ring

hydrophobic phytol side chain

The distinct physicochemical property of the chlorophyll molecule that is biologically important is, of course, its capacity to absorb light energy from the visible region of the electromagnetic spectrum. Presumably, the electrons excited in this process are those in the conjugated double-bond system of the tetrapyrrole unit. In any event, because of the difference in structure between chlorophylls *a* and *b*, which means a variation in both distribution and excitation of electrons, each type of chlorophyll molecule displays a unique absorption (excitation) spectrum. More important, however, is the effect of the molecular environment on the absorption properties of the chlorophyll molecules within the lamellae. Illustrative of this effect is the fact that *two different forms* of chlorophyll *a* molecules have been detected in the chloroplasts of green plants and algae—one absorbing maximally at 683 nm and the other at 670 nm. These are identical molecules, but they have different light-absorbing properties presumably because they are arranged differently within the lipoprotein matrix of the lamellae membranes. Only *one form* of chlorophyll *b* is known, but it displays absorption maxima at two wavelengths, namely, 650 nm and 480 nm.

The reason for our reference to the light absorption characteristics of chlorophyll is quite relevant, since there is an abundant amount of experimental proof demonstrating that the ability of chloroplasts to produce oxygen with radiation of different wavelengths shows distinct maxima in the visible region at or near 450 nm, 650 nm, and in the range of 670–683 nm. In other words, *the quanta of radiant energy absorbed by chlorophyll are identical to the quanta required for maximum efficiency of oxygen production in the light reaction.* Observations of this type have been reported with many different organisms and have been interpreted to mean that chlorophyl *a* (683) is the *primary* photosensitive pigment (it is more abundant in chloroplasts), while chlorophyll *a* (670) and chlorophyll *b* (both of which are found in lesser quantities) are *accessory* pigments.

EMERSON EFFECT AND THE DUAL-PHOTOSYSTEM HYPOTHESIS

One of the most significant discoveries regarding the role of the different light-absorbing chlorophyll species in photosynthesis was made in the late 1950's by R. Emerson. He found that the efficiency of the photochemical phase, as measured by the amount of oxygen produced per quantum of radiant energy absorbed, was not constant throughout the entire visible spectrum. Rather, a distinct reduction occurred when photosynthesizing cells were exposed to monochromatic (single-wavelength) light sources at the red end of the spectrum beyond 680 nm where the only absorption is due to chlorophyll *a*. (The absorbance of chlorophyll *b* in this region is negligible.) Since the decrease in efficiency occurs at the red end of the spectrum, the effect is generally referred to as the *"red-drop phenomenon."* Emerson subsequently demonstrated that full efficiency could be restored if the cells were *simultaneously* exposed to another light source with a wavelength of 650 nm, a point of maximum absorption in chlorophyll *b*. In other words, when light absorption by chlorophyll *a* was accompanied by light absorption from chlorophyll *b*, the cells displayed an enhancement (*Emerson effect*) in the photoevolution of oxygen as compared to separate light absorption by either chlorophyll *a* or chlorophyll *b*. Emerson suggested then that the light-dependent phase of photosynthesis includes two separate photosystems, both of which must be activated for maximum efficiency of the light-dependent raction. One (photosystem I-PSI) contains largely chlorophyll *a* (683), the other (photosystem II-PSII) mostly chlorophyll *a* (670) and chlorophyll *b*. The Emerson hypothesis of two separate photosystems has since been supported by several different lines of evidence and currently governs much of the modern thinking concerning the photochemical apparatus. The present viewpoint is that both systems are separately localized within each quantosome of the lamella membrane, and that each system participates in a separate phase of the overall light reaction (see p. 374). In addition to the chlorophyll molecules, it is now known that each photosystem, particularly PSII, contains small amounts of other colored substances, such as β-carotene and other carotenoids, which function as *accessory pigments* aiding in the excitation of the active chlorophyll molecules. A more complete description of the composition of each system is beyond the scope of this book.

ELECTRON TRANSPORT IN PHOTOSYNTHESIS

At this point a logical question is: What is the function of each photosystem in the overall light reaction? In order to pursue this subject, it is important that we first recognize the basic type of chemistry that is involved. To analyze this, let us return to the equation given earlier for the net effect of the light reaction. Close examination reveals that the

$$2NADP^+ + mADP + mP_i + 2H_2O \xrightarrow[nh\nu]{\text{chloroplasts}} 2NADPH + 2H^+ + mATP + O_2$$

basic chemistry is an oxidation–reduction reaction involving a transfer of H's (H$^+$'s and electrons) from H_2O (the reduced donor) to NADP$^+$ (the oxidized acceptor). Recalling our discussion in the previous chapter concerning the difference between the NAD⁺–NADH and O₂–H₂O couples, we should also note that the direction of electron transfer involves a transition from a low energy state (H₂O) to a higher energy state (NADPH). It is this unfavorable thermodynamic barrier that is over-

$$
\begin{array}{ll}
\text{NADP}^+ + 2\text{H}^+ + 2e \rightarrow \text{NADPH} + \text{H}^+ & \mathscr{E}^{o\prime}_{red} = -0.34\text{v} \\
\underline{\text{H}_2\text{O} \rightarrow \tfrac{1}{2}\text{O}_2 + 2\text{H}^+ + 2e} & \underline{\mathscr{E}^{o\prime}_{ox} = -0.82\text{v}} \\
\text{NADP}^+ + \text{H}_2\text{O} \rightarrow \text{NADPH} + \text{H}^+ + \tfrac{1}{2}\text{O}_2 & \mathscr{E}^{o\prime}_{net} = -1.16\text{v}
\end{array}
$$

$\mathscr{E}^{o\prime}_{net}$ is negative, therefore, the reaction from
left to right is endergonic

come by the absorption of radiant energy, with the accompanying formation of ATP representing a conservation of part of the absorbed energy. In the pages to follow, our objective will be to elaborate on how these events occur and to explain the suggested participation of photosystems I and II. You will discover shortly that the modes of electron transport and phosphorylation of ADP are identical in design to the events of oxidative phosphorylation in aerobic organisms. In view of our frequent referral to the theme of biochemical unity, you should find this relationship to be a logical one. Our discussion of the whole subject will be somewhat sketchy, in part because of the restricted limits of this book, but also because the complete details of this process have yet to be determined with certitude.

PHOTOREDUCTION (PSI) AND PHOTO-OXIDATION (PSII)

Despite the unknown nature of many phases of the light reaction, there is considerable evidence to suggest that each photosystem fulfills a separate but complementary role. Without reviewing the substance of the experimental proof, these proposed functions are as follows. The activation of photosystem I at wavelengths equal to or greater than 680 nm results in a photoreduction ($2\text{NADP}^+ + 4\text{H}^+ + 4e \rightarrow 2\text{NADPH} + 2\text{H}^+$), whereas the activation of photosystem II at wavelengths less than 680 nm results in a photo-oxidation ($2\text{H}_2\text{O} \rightarrow \text{O}_2 + 4\text{H}^+ + 4e$). In other words, the complementary relationship between the two photosystems involves reducing power and may be summarized in the following manner: *the activation of photosystem II results in a photo-oxidation step which generates reducing power required in the photoreduction step mediated by the activation of photosystem I.*

Although the principle of cooperation contained in this statement is basically correct, the implication that the reducing power required for the reduction of NADP⁺ is supplied directly by the oxidation in photosystem II is partly inaccurate. Actually, a direct linkage between the two systems is proposed to exist only at the level of the protons, with the source of electrons in the photoreduction step of PSI being supplied directly by the photoexcitation of the chlorophyll molecules in photosystem I. What then is the fate of the electrons generated in the photolytic cleavage of H₂O in PSII? According to current interpretations, the electrons generated from the photo-oxidation of H₂O via PSII are returned to the same photosystem, which becomes electron deficient after undergoing excitation (loss of electrons to a higher energy level) by light absorption. The balance between the two photosystems is restored by the transfer of electrons liberated in the excitation of PSII to the electron-deficient photosystem I. It is further proposed that this linkage of electron transport from PSII to PSI is exergonic and is coupled to the phosphorylation of ADP in a fashion quite similar to that of oxidative phosphorylation. The sum and substance of these relationships are represented in the diagram shown below.

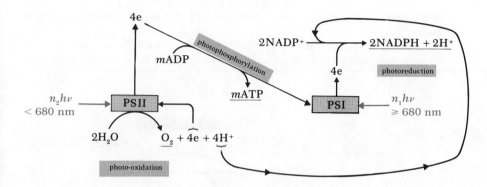

Although the above diagram summarizes the general operation of each photosystem, it leaves many questions unanswered. How are electrons released from each photosystem following light absorption? Are they free electrons or are they transferred to other carriers? How is the light activation of PSII linked to the oxidation of H_2O? How are the electrons released in the oxidation of H_2O returned to PSII? How are the electrons of PSI made available for the reduction of $NADP^+$? How are the electrons transferred from one system to another? What is the mechanism of the ADP phosphorylation? Due to years of effort by many different investigators, partial answers to each question can be given. In general, the basic mechanism of the overall process involves the flow of electrons, abstracted from excited chlorophyll molecules, among specialized carriers.

A more detailed summary of the most widely supported proposal of the events of the light reaction is diagrammed in Figure 14–5. The key to understanding the message of this diagram resides in the A,B and A',B' symbolism in the shaded rectangles. These shaded areas correspond to the two active photosystems, each containing the primary photosensitive chlorophyll molecules and other accessory pigments. To put it simply, the materials symbolized as A, B, A', and B' are proposed to be highly specialized electron carriers unique to each photosystem and obligatorily required for the processes of photo-oxidation, photoreduction, and photophosphorylation. Each photosystem is believed to contain a minimum of two such materials, with one acting as an oxidized *electron acceptor* (A_{ox} in PSII and A'_{ox} in PSI) and the other as a reduced *electron donor* (B_{red} in PSII and B'_{red} in PSI). It is further hypothesized that A_{ox} and A'_{ox} undergo reduction by each receiving an electron from a specialized chlorophyll a molecule excited by the absorption of light energy (Chl^*_a). On the other hand, B_{red} and B'_{red} are hypothesized to act as immediate electron donors to return the electron-deficient chlorophyll molecule (Chl^+_a) to its ground state. The resultant

$$(Chl^*)A_{ox} \xrightarrow[\substack{\text{accepts} \\ \text{electron} \\ \text{from excited} \\ \text{chlorophyll}}]{\text{substance } A} (Chl^+)A^-_{red}$$

(same for A' in PSI)

$$B_{red}(Chl^+) \xrightarrow[\substack{\text{donates} \\ \text{electron} \\ \text{to deficient} \\ \text{chlorophyll}}]{\text{substance } B} B^+_{ox}(Chl)$$

(same for B' in PSI)

formation of the reduced carriers (A_{red}^- and $A_{red}'^-$) represents the raising of electrons to higher energy levels from which they are then transferred to still other specialized acceptors. The electrons from A_{red}^- generated in PSII are ultimately transferred "downhill" (that is, to a lower energy level) to PSI, with the accompanying formation of ATP. The electrons from $A_{red}'^-$ generated in PSI are used in the reduction of NADP+. The resultant formation of B_{ox}^+ and $B_{ox}'^+$ represents the formation of low-energy electron acceptors. B_{ox}^+ can act as a suitable electron acceptor to drive the oxidation of H_2O linked to PSII. In PSI, $B_{ox}'^+$ can act as a suitable terminal acceptor in the transport of electrons from A_{red}^- coming from PSI.

In recent years, many researchers have claimed to have identified these carriers. At one time, A in PSII was thought to be a *plastoquinone*

Figure 14–5 A schematic representation of electron flow in dual-photosystem model of light reaction. See text for discussion of details. (After regeneration of special carriers to original state—*A,B,A',B'*—the process would be repeated.)

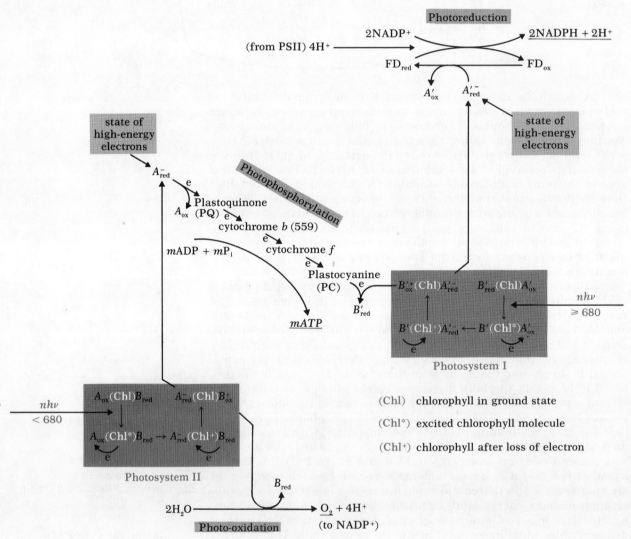

(Chl) chlorophyll in ground state

(Chl*) excited chlorophyll molecule

(Chl+) chlorophyll after loss of electron

(PQ) molecule, but the current feeling is that plastoquinone is the first acceptor of electrons from A_{red}^-, whose identity is still unknown. Others have reported evidence that B is a specialized cytochrome carrier whose immediate electron donor in the electron transport chain is *plastocyanine* (PC), a copper-containing protein, which in turn acts as an acceptor of electrons from *cytochrome f*. Another specialized cytochrome, *cyt b* (559) (the number in parentheses designates a unique absorption maximum of this particular cytochrome) is suggested to likewise operate as a carrier between plastoquinone and cytochrome *f*. The scheme in Figure 14–5 and its specific features constitute, of course, only a working model of the light reaction. This scheme is widely accepted as representative of what is occurring *in vivo*, because it agrees with most experimental studies with illuminated chloroplasts and lamellae preparations.

Regardless of many uncertainties that still exist, such as the nature of A, B, A', B'; the location and number of ATP-generating sites; and the possible existence of other electron carriers, there is universal agreement that electron transfer among specific carriers is an integral part of the light reaction. Moreover, in organisms characterized by the operation of two separate photosystems—presumably this includes virtually all photosynthesizing cells except the photosynthetic bacteria—it should occur to you that, if the scheme in Figure 14–5 is correct, the electron shuttle system between A_{red}^- and $B_{ox}'^+$ is a crucial step of the light reaction, since it constitutes the link between photo-oxidation and photoreduction in addition to serving as the driving force for the formation of ATP, that is, photophosphorylation.

To close our discussion of the dual-photosystem model, let us take note of the participation of the substance symbolized as FD, which is proposed to be the immediate electron acceptor of $A_{red}'^-$ and the immediate electron donor of NADP$^+$ in the photoreduction phase. The FD notation refers to *ferredoxin,* a small, iron-containing protein known to be present in all types of photosynthetic organisms including the photosynthetic bacteria. In fact, recent studies have shown that the ferredoxins isolated from several different sources are remarkably similar in structure. Regardless of the source, ferredoxin has two distinguishing properties in that (1) it can undergo a reversible oxidation–reduction via electron transfer, and (2) the FD_{ox}-FD_{red} couple has a reduction potential even more negative than that of the NADP$^+$-NADPH couple (see margin and Table 13–1, page 339). The latter property is one of the strong arguments for the proposed role of FD_{red} as the immediate donor of electrons to NADP$^+$, since the transfer would be thermodynamically favorable.

Although the scheme depicted in Figure 14–5 is based on an enormous research effort covering the past 15–20 years, it must be emphasized that it is only a working model and an incomplete one at that. No doubt, as work continues, the picture will become more definitive and perhaps even modified. In this regard, D. B. Knaff and D. I. Arnon (the latter being a principal investigator of the light reaction for several years) have recently proposed a new mechanism (see Figure 14-6) suggesting that photosystem II participates in *two* photochemical acts, both activated by light below 680 nm. Their proposal is based on evidence which they interpret as representative of two new cytochrome constituents that function as electron carriers and that had gone pre-

	$\mathscr{E}_{red}^{o'}$ (volts)
$FD_{ox} + 1e \rightarrow FD_{red}$	-0.43 v
oxidized reduced	
ferredoxin ferredoxin	
$NADP^+ + 2H^+ + 2e \rightarrow$	
NADPH + H$^+$	-0.34 v

viously undetected in all other studies. One material (X) participates in a manner such as that proposed earlier for substance A. Electrons from X_{red}^- are than shuttled to the oxidized form of the second substance (Y), likewise located in PSII but in a different region. Presumably, the oxidized form of Y (Y_{ox}^+) is formed via a second light-dependent step occurring within PSII but involving different chlorophyll molecules. By acting as the ultimate acceptor of electrons from X_{red}^-, the role of Y_{ox}^+ is as ascribed earlier to $B_{ox}'^+$ in PSI.

$$H_2O \rightarrow O_2$$
$$\downarrow e$$

$$B(Chl)_{II}X \xrightarrow[<680]{h\nu} B(Chl^*)_{II}X \xrightarrow{e} B(Chl^+)_{II}X_{red}^- \longrightarrow B_{ox}^+(Chl)_{II}X_{red}^-$$

$$\downarrow e$$

$$A'(Chl)_{II}Y \xrightarrow[<680]{h\nu} A'(Chl^*)_{II}Y \xrightarrow{e} A_{red}'^-(Chl^+)_{II}Y \longrightarrow A_{red}'^-(Chl)_{II}Y_{ox}^+$$

$$\downarrow e$$

$$NADP^+ \rightarrow NADPH$$

Note that the two light reactions mediated by PSII in the Knaff-Arnon scheme are proposed to fulfill the combined functions of PSI and PSII in the scheme proposed earlier. As for photosystem I, activated by wavelengths above 680 nm, these workers propose that it constitutes a third light reaction also associated with the photoreduction of ferredoxin, which is then used as a high-energy reduced donor for photophosphorylation. Whether the extent of ATP formation in this step exceeds that in the electron transport between the two active centers in PSII is arguable.

Figure 14–6 Knaff-Arnon model of three light reactions in plant photosynthesis. See text for discussion.

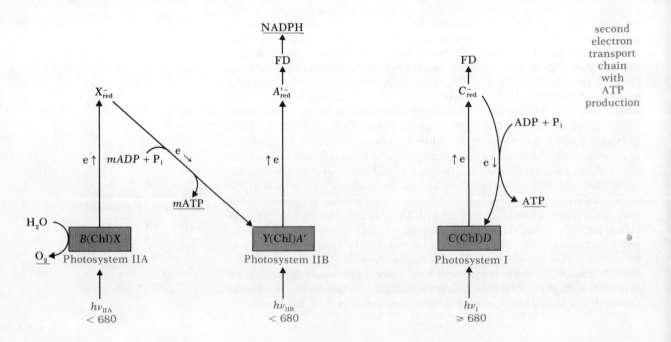

The reason for discussing this scheme involving three photosystems is not because it has displaced the earlier-discussed scheme involving two photosystems as to what is occurring in the light reaction of photosynthesis. Rather, the purpose is only to illustrate that the overall events of the light reaction of photosynthesis—namely, photoexcitation, photo-oxidation, photoreduction, and photophosphorylation—may occur by a process different than that involving two photosystems and two light-dependent reactions. The Knaff-Arnon scheme may be correct and then again it may not. Perhaps, both of the schemes are correct and operate in different species of photosynthetic cells. Furthermore, the possibility that other schemes may exist cannot be ruled out. Regardless of the specific details as to how the events of the light reaction occur, they must account for what occurs. To reiterate, this means that the proposed model must account for (1) the excitation of chlorophyll molecules by the absorption of radiant energy; (2) the formation of oxygen from water; (3) the formation of NADPH; and (4) the formation of ATP.

THE DARK REACTION OF PHOTOSYNTHESIS

INTRODUCTION

A brief and convenient statement of what happens in the dark reaction is given by the following equation.

$$6CO_2 \xrightarrow[\text{(NADPH, ATP)}]{\substack{\text{chloroplast} \\ \text{enzymes}}} C_6H_{12}O_6$$

The process occurs in the chloroplast, involves many enzyme-catalyzed reactions, requires NADPH and ATP, and results in the formation of carbohydrate material ($C_6H_{12}O_6$) from inorganic CO_2. Although the equation is quite useful in summarizing the overall effect, it can be misleading since it implies (a) that the carbon atoms of each of six separate molecules of CO_2 become part of the same hexose molecule, and (b) that the dark reaction is limited to this one type of metabolic activity. Actually, neither of these implications is correct. Regarding the former, we will shortly discover that the relationship of $6CO_2 \rightarrow C_6H_{12}O_6$ represents only a *net* conversion rather than a *de novo* synthesis of a single hexose molecule from 6 molecules of CO_2. As for the latter, it should occur to you that the complete enzymatic metabolism of a plant cell must consist of more than the fixation and conversion of CO_2 to carbohydrates. While a significant portion of the assimilated carbon will be stored as sucrose and utilized for the biosynthesis of cellulose, the remainder—by being channeled into central metabolic pathways such as the citric acid cycle—will serve as a chemical source of energy and a carbon source for the anabolism of other carbohydrates, amino acids, proteins, fatty acids, lipids, purine and pyrimidine nucleotides, nucleic acids, and even the tetrapyrrole moiety of chlorophyll itself. In other words, the original carbon of CO_2 is ultimately incorporated into the entire metabolism of the whole organism.

EXPERIMENTAL HISTORY

Investigations into the mechanism of photosynthetic CO_2 fixation began in earnest only about 25 years ago. The chief pioneering researchers were M. Calvin, A. A. Benson, and J. A. Bassham. Although it had been known since the last century that CO_2 was converted into carbohydrate, there was lively debate as to whether the process was directly dependent on the absorption of light energy. In this sense, there was considerable significance to Hill's discovery that the light-dependent phase of photosynthesis did not require the presence of CO_2, but instead was characterized by the photo-oxidation of water accompanied by the reduction of various electron acceptors such as $NADP^+$. Since the nicotinamide adenine dinucleotides were then known to be obligatory coenzymes for dehydrogenase enzymes, this suggested that the reducing power produced in the light reaction was made available for an enzymatic conversion of CO_2 to carbohydrate which could occur in the dark.

The most fundamental questions you can ask regarding the flow of carbon in photosynthesis—indeed, the very questions to which the Calvin group addressed itself—are as follows: (a) What is the identity of the substance that acts as the initial acceptor of CO_2? (b) What is the immediate product that appears after CO_2 fixation? (c) How is the immediate product then converted to simple sugars?

In attacking these problems, Calvin, Benson, and Bassham studied the flow of carbon in single-celled algae of the genera *Chlorella* and *Scendesmus*. *Chlorella* is particularly useful for photosynthetic studies since it can be easily and reproducibly cultured. The key and indispensable feature of their experiments was the utilization of radioactive CO_2 ($C^{14}O_2$) as the carbon source. Their studies are classic representations of the use of radioactive tracer substances in the elucidation of cellular metabolism (see page 26, Chapter 2). The overall experimental design was simple but ingenious. $C^{14}O_2$ was injected into illuminated glass tubes through which an algae suspension was flowing. After exposure to $C^{14}O_2$, the suspension was run into hot alcohol. On contact with the alcohol, all enzymatic reactions within the cells were brought to a halt. By adjusting the time between the injection of $C^{14}O_2$ and the final mixing with alcohol, it was possible to limit exposure of the cells to the carbon source to any desired interval from a few minutes to a fraction of a second. Afterwards, samples of the alcohol solution, which contained dissolved compounds extracted from the cell, were analyzed chromatographically for the appearance of C^{14}-labeled compounds.

As you might expect, with prolonged exposure times (10 minutes), the extract contained a tremendous assortment of C^{14}-labeled compounds including many simple carbohydrates (mostly phosphorylated sugars), several amino acids, all of the major nucleotides, and others. Shorter exposure intervals (30 seconds) considerably reduced the number of labeled materials, with virtually all of the C^{14} being found in a restricted number of phosphorylated carbohydrates. Those identified were: trioses (dihydroxyacetone phosphate, glyceraldehyde-3-phosphate, 3-phosphoglycerate); a tetrose (erythrose-4-phosphate); pentoses (ribose-5-phosphate, ribulose-5-phosphate, ribulose-1,5-diphosphate, xylulose-5-phosphate); hexoses (fructose-1,6-diphosphate, fructose-6-phosphate, glucose-6-phosphate); and heptoses (sedoheptulose-7-phosphate, sedoheptulose-1,7-diphosphate). When the exposure period was reduced even further to only a fraction of a second, the extract was found to contain only a single compound with any appreciable C^{14} content, namely, *3-phosphoglycerate*. Although the initial studies were done with algae, there is now considerable evidence that the initial formation of 3-phosphoglycerate and its subsequent metabolism constitute the primary metabolic pathway utilized by most green plants as well. Recent studies have uncovered the existence of at least one major alternate pathway in plants which we will examine briefly at the end of the chapter (see page 384). Photosynthetic bacteria use alternate routes as well.

Although the appearance of 3-phosphoglycerate as the primary product of CO_2 assimilation suggested that the initial acceptor was probably a C_2 compound, Calvin and coworkers subsequently demonstrated that the acceptor molecule was by *ribulose-1,5-diphosphate,* a C_5 compound. In other words, the initial flow of carbon was: $1C_5 + CO_2 \rightarrow 2C_3$. Moreover, the flow of carbon during periods of light and dark indicated that the acceptor → product relationship was *cyclic* in nature, with cellular levels of labeled diphosphate decreasing in the dark, and levels

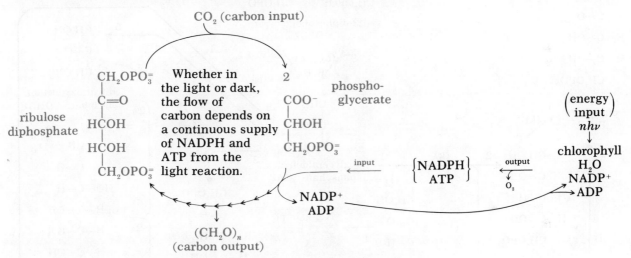

of phosphoglycerate increasing. The label pattern during dark periods thus suggested that the subsequent metabolism of 3-phosphoglycerate, particularly the regeneration of ribulose-1,5-diphosphate, was limited by factor[s] supplied only during periods of illumination. These factors are now known to be NADPH and ATP. After several years of study, the Calvin group eventually proposed a scheme identifying all the steps between 3-phosphoglycerate and ribulose-1,5-diphosphate. The task was extremely difficult, because the constituent reactions do not occur in a linear sequence but rather in a complicated, highly branched fashion. For traditional reasons, the sequence is frequently called the *Calvin-Benson-Bassham cycle.*

PRIMARY PATH OF CARBON IN PHOTOSYNTHESIS

The assimilation of CO_2 into carbohydrate material by photosynthetic cells according to the Calvin-Benson-Bassham scheme is shown in

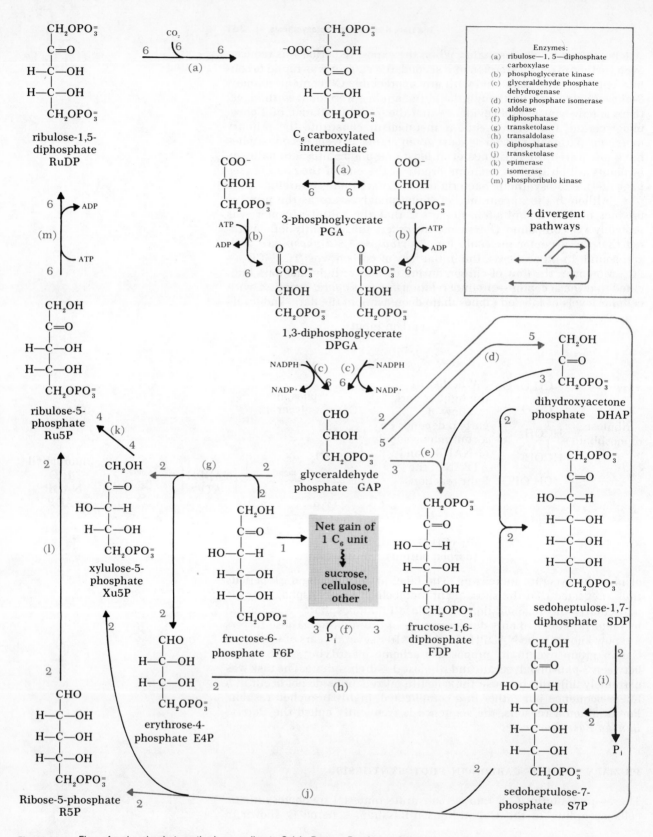

Figure 14-7 Flow of carbon in photosynthesis according to Calvin-Benson-Bassham scheme.

Figure 14–7. At first glance, the composite diagram may strike you as being an incomprehensible maze of structures and arrows. Despite its complexity, don't let it bewilder you, because a distinct metabolic pattern does exist. The first reaction, catalyzed by *ribulose-1,5-carboxylase* (sometimes called *carboxydismutase*), is the carboxylation of ribulose-1,5-diphosphate to yield an unstable six-carbon intermediate which is then cleaved hydrolytically to give 2 units of 3-phosphoglycerate (reaction (a)). This immediate formation of 3-phosphoglycerate from the CO_2 fixation step is, of course, consistent with the results of the radioactive feeding experiments described earlier. The crucial nature of this reaction is evidenced by the fact that the carboxylase enzyme is known to occur in fantastically large amounts within the chloroplasts, accounting for roughly one-sixth of all the soluble protein in the lumen.

Although 3-phosphoglycerate could leave the chloroplast and be metabolized further by soluble enzymes of the glycolytic pathway to yield pyruvate, which could then enter the citric acid cycle in the mitochondria, the primary and immediate metabolic fate of 3-phosphoglycerate occurs *within* the chloroplast. This step is believed to be a two-stage conversion to glyceraldehyde-3-phosphate involving two enzymes already encountered in glycolysis (phosphoglycerate kinase and triosephosphate dehydrogenase) which function here in reverse. The former requires ATP and the latter NADPH, both of which are supplied from the light reaction.

As you can see, the subsequent metabolism of glyceraldehyde-3-phosphate diverges through four distinct *branches* (reactions (d), (e), (g), (j)). Note that the overall chemistry of these and all subsequent reactions, involves only the modification and interconversion of various simple phosphorylated sugars. These reactions include isomerizations, an epimerization, transfers between aldoses and ketoses, dephosphorylations, and a phosphorylation. Note also that each type of interconversion was encountered in our earlier discussion of glycolysis and the hexose monophosphate shunt. As with the shunt pathway, the characteristic of this non-oxidative phase is the participation of the *transaldolase* and *transketolase* enzymes. Although each of the four branches of glyceraldehyde-3-phosphate metabolism is important, the isomerization to (reaction (d)) and condensation with (reaction (e)) dihydroxyacetone phosphate are especially crucial, since they account for the incorporation of the C of the original CO_2 into hexose units which are then metabolized further via glycolysis and the citric acid cycle, stored in the form of sucrose, or utilized in the biosynthesis of cellulose. Ultimately, all of these conversions (reactions (c) through (k)) converge on the production of ribulose-5-phosphate. The ribulose-5-phosphate is then phosphorylated in an ATP-dependent kinase-catalyzed reaction to yield the original diphosphate, thus closing the cycle. As in the formation of glyceraldehyde-3-phosphate, the ATP required in this step is supplied from the light reaction.

Since the Calvin-Benson-Bassham cycle is not composed of individual reactions acting in sequence, the metabolic significance of the flow of carbon through the many divergent and convergent steps can best be considered by developing an idealized analysis utilizing a non-unit stoichiometry. A convenient approach is to begin with the assimilation of 6 CO_2 units by 6 units of ribulose diphosphate. Then, by distributing the further metabolism of 12 units of glyceraldehyde-3-phosphate as indicated in Figure 14–7, all of the component enzymatic steps of the pathway can be written separately as shown below. When the net result is tabulated, the overall chemical effect becomes obvious. The *equivalent* of 1 hexose molecule is produced from 6 molecules of CO_2, with 2 molecules of NADPH and 3 molecules of ATP being required for every CO_2 molecule that is assimilated.

$$6RuDP + 6CO_2 \xrightarrow{(a)} 6[\text{INTERMEDIATE}] \xrightarrow{(a)} 12PGA$$
$$12PGA + 12ATP \xrightarrow{(b)} 12DPGA + 12ADP$$
$$12DPGA + 12NADPH(H^+) \xrightarrow{(c)} 12GAP + 12NADP^+ + 12P_i$$
$$5GAP \xrightarrow{(d)} 5DHAP$$
$$3DHAP + 3GAP \xrightarrow{(e)} 3FDP$$
$$3FDP \xrightarrow{(f)} 3F6P + 3P_i$$
$$2F6P + 2GAP \xrightarrow{(g)} 2Xu5P + 2E4P$$
$$2E4P + 2DHAP \xrightarrow{(h)} 2SDP$$
$$2SDP \xrightarrow{(i)} 2S7P + 2P_i$$
$$2S7P + 2GAP \xrightarrow{(j)} 2Xu5P + 2R5P$$
$$4Xu5P \xrightarrow{(k)} 4Ru5P$$
$$2R5P \xrightarrow{(l)} 2Ru5P$$
$$6Ru5P + 6ATP \xrightarrow{(m)} 6RuDP + 6ADP$$

Net: $\quad 6CO_2 + 12NADPH(H^+) + 18ATP \xrightarrow[\text{steps}]{13} \text{fructose-6-phosphate(F6P)}$
$$+ 12NADP^+ + 18ADP + 17P_i$$

Subsequently:

fructose-6-P $\longrightarrow$ glucose-6-P $\rightarrow\rightarrow\rightarrow\rightarrow\rightarrow$ sucrose, cellulose, and
general metabolism via glycolysis and citric acid cycle

ALTERNATE PATHWAY OF CO_2 ASSIMILATION

Although the Calvin-Benson-Bassham sequence is supported by an over-whelming amount of experimental evidence as being the *major* pathway of photosynthetic CO_2 fixation, it apparently is *not the only* pathway. Recent studies of the fate of $C^{14}O_2$ fed to certain tropical plants showed that, after short-term exposure, the primary C^{14}-labeled products were *malate* and *aspartate* rather than 3-phosphoglycerate and phosphoryl-ated sugars. Eventually the latter materials were produced, but only after prolonged incubation times. The key feature of the pathway that has been proposed to explain these observations is that the primary acceptor of CO_2 is *phosphoenolpyruvate* (PEP) rather than ribulose-1, 5-diphosphate, and that the immediate product is *oxaloacetate* (OAA) rather than 3-phosphoglycerate. Strong evidence in support of this alter-

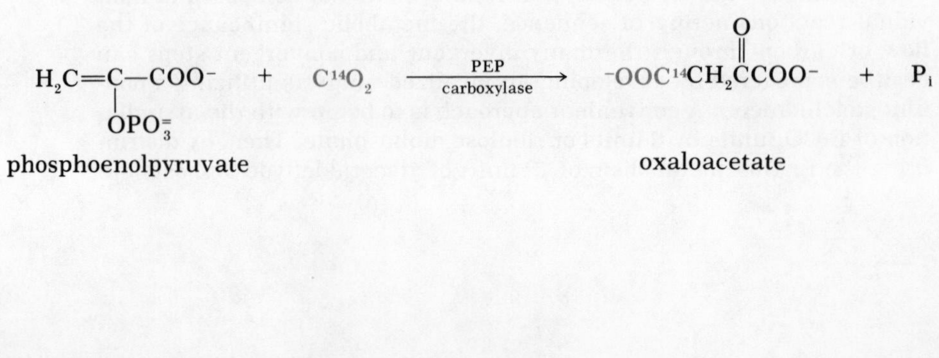

$$H_2C{=}C{-}COO^- \;+\; C^{14}O_2 \xrightarrow[\text{carboxylase}]{\text{PEP}} {}^-OOC^{14}CH_2\overset{\overset{\textstyle O}{\|}}{C}COO^- \;+\; P_i$$
$$\underset{\displaystyle OPO_3^=}{|}$$

phosphoenolpyruvate $\qquad\qquad\qquad\qquad\qquad\qquad$ oxaloacetate

nate carboxylation step was obtained with the isolation of *phosphoenol-pyruvate carboxylase,* the enzyme that presumably catalyzes the re-action.

This reaction would, of course, account for the early appearance of both malate and aspartate, both of which could be produced directly from oxaloacetate—malate by reduction of oxaloacetate and aspartate by a transamination (see page 321, Chapter 12). The later formation of 3-phosphoglycerate and the sugar phosphates has been accounted for by the suggestion that the C^{14} label in oxaloacetate could eventually be shunted into the regular Calvin-Benson-Bassham cycle by a *trans-carboxylation* between oxaloacetate and ribulose-1,5-diphosphate, accompanied by hydrolytic cleavage. Supporting this suggestion—as well as the entire PEP carboxylase pathway—is the recent demonstra-tion that the green leaf cells of these plants contain another enzyme (*pyruvate phosphate dikinase*) capable of catalyzing the conversion of pyruvate to phosphoenolpyruvate and thus closing the cycle.

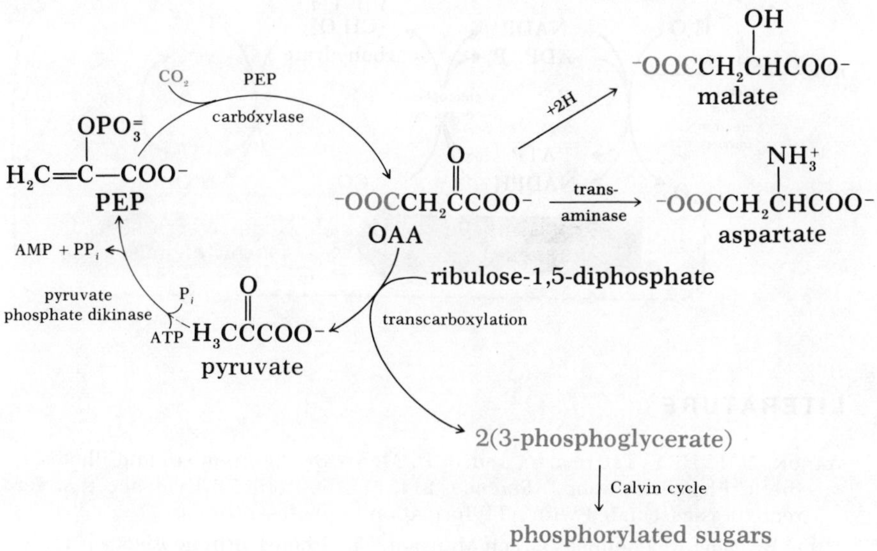

Whether or not the PEP → OAA pathway has a universal or limited occurrence in photosynthetic cells is uncertain. Also uncertain is what metabolic advantage—if any—is conferred on these plants in which it is known to operate as the primary pathway. Much work still remains to be done.

PHOTOSYNTHESIS—A SUMMARY

Because of the complex biochemistry of photosynthesis, let us close our discussion of this subject by briefly reviewing the major events (see diagram below). Photosynthesis consists of two separate but related processes, the so-called light reaction and dark reaction, with the latter being absolutely dependent on the former. In the light reaction, solar light energy is harnessed by chlorophyll-containing photosystems compartmentalized within the lamellae membranes, resulting in the formation of metabolically useful reducing power as NADPH and metabolically useful energy as ATP. The ultimate source of the reducing power is H_2O. In the dark reaction, occurring in the lumen of the chloroplasts, the ATP and NADPH are utilized in the enzymatic assimilation of CO_2 into organic material, with the major acceptor molecule being ribulose-1,5-diphosphate. The subsequent oxidation of the photosynthetically produced carbohydrates by aerobic, non-photosynthetic organisms completes the major biochemical relationship in our biosphere.

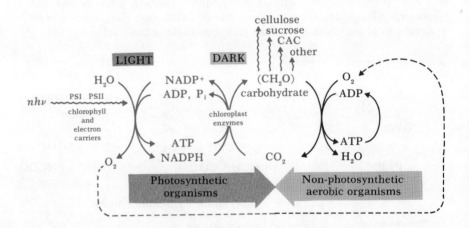

LITERATURE

ARNON, D. I., H. Y. TSUJIMOTO, and B. D. McSWAIN, "Ferredoxin and Photosynthetic Phosphorylation," *Science,* **214,** 562–566 (1967). Evidence that ferredoxin is associated with ATP formation in photosynthesis.

HILL, R., "The Biochemist's Green Mansion: The Photosynthetic Electron Transport Chain in Plants," in Volume 1 of *Essays in Biochemistry,* P. N. Campbell and G. D. Greville (eds.), 121–152. New York: Academic Press, 1965. A review article with historical perspective of the light reaction by one of the pioneering researchers in the field.

KAMEN, M. D., *Primary Processes in Photosynthesis.* New York: Academic Press, 1963. A short paperback offering a thorough introductory treatment of the light reaction of photosynthesis.

LEVINE, R. P., "The Mechanism of Photosynthesis," *Scientific American,* **221,** 58–70 (1969). A good summary of the important features of the light reaction of photosynthesis, some of which are not treated in this chapter.

MACHLIS, L. (ed.), *Annual Review of Plant Physiology.* Palo Alto: Annual Reviews, Inc. An annual publication containing review articles of current developments on various aspects of plant physiology and biochemistry.

RABINOWITCH, E. I., and GOVINDJEE, "The Role of Chlorophyll in Photosynthesis," *Scientific American,* **213,** 74–83 (1965). A description of experiments that resulted in the suggestion of two separate photosystems.

EXERCISES

14-1 Summarize your understanding of each of the following:
    a) the primary photochemical event of photosynthesis
    b) quantosome particles
    c) dual photosystems
    d) photosynthetic phosphorylation
    e) the role of ribulose-1,5-diphosphate in photosynthesis
    f) the relationship of the light and dark reactions of photosynthesis

14-2 Which of the reactions in the Calvin cycle also occur in
    a) the hexose monophosphate shunt pathway
    b) the glycolytic pathway

14-3 Summarize your understanding of the relationship between photosynthetic and respiratory organisms.

15

Lipid Metabolism

In the preceding four chapters, our concern has been largely confined to the areas of carbohydrate metabolism and bioenergetics in both non-photosynthetic and photosynthetic organisms. While it is true that our analysis of the metabolic role of the citric acid cycle led us into other areas of metabolism, our treatment of these was, by and large, rather sketchy. In this and subsequent chapters we will now examine these other areas in greater detail. We begin here with the metabolism of lipids.

Lipid metabolism is an extensive subject. There are a large number of structurally distinct lipids, and each could be described in terms of its unique anabolic and catabolic pathways. A consideration of all these is not our objective. Rather, we will explore only certain facets, with particular emphasis given to major pathways of *fatty acid metabolism*. The basis for this emphasis is threefold. First, the fatty acids are the chief components of simple and compound lipids. This common structural feature thus necessitates a common phase of metabolism. Secondly, the metabolic turnover of the fatty acid residues in simple and compound lipids is generally greater than that of the alcohol moiety. Thirdly, when we speak of an organism utilizing and storing lipid material as a source of carbon and energy, the metabolic description of this is, by and large, translated into the catabolism and anabolism of fatty acids, respectively. In other words, a large segment of lipid metabolism is synonymous with the metabolism of fatty acids.

Although our emphasis will be on fatty acids, we will investigate other aspects of lipid metabolism such as (a) the *biosynthesis of phospholipids,* (b) the *biosynthesis* of some of the important *derived lipids*—cholesterol in particular, and (c) the ability of many organisms to convert *lipids to carbohydrates.* In addition to some practical implications regarding body weight control, the last subject will provide an opportunity for a brief but informative reinvestigation of the principle of metabolic integration, in this instance with a modified form of the citric acid cycle, namely, the glyoxylate cycle.

Despite the obvious fact that the reactions of lipid metabolism are unique to lipids, there is much more to be learned from this study than merely a new set of pathways. Our analysis of fatty acid metabolism will, for example, provide a clear example of the general principles which differentiate catabolic and anabolic pathways (see page 260). In addition, we will encounter another example of the role of multi-enzyme complexes and also some principles of enzyme action not treated in previous chapters.

CATABOLISM OF FATTY ACIDS

EXPERIMENTAL HISTORY

The first serious attempt to study the catabolism of fatty acids was made at the turn of the century by F. Knoop, a German biochemist, who proposed that *fatty acids were oxidatively degraded by sequential removal of two-carbon units proceeding from the carboxyl end of the molecule.* His experimental design was ingenious. Not having access to radio-isotopes, he utilized a chemical label by synthesizing a series of straight-chain carboxylic acids of even and odd chain length, each containing a *phenyl* grouping at the non-carboxyl end of the molecule. These acids were then fed to experimental animals, after which the urine was collected and assayed for the fate of the phenyl group label. The use of the phenyl grouping was important, because short-chain phenyl-substituted acids are not metabolized by animals but excreted as waste products. The results were as follows. With even-numbered acids *phenylacetate* accumulated, whereas odd-numbered acids resulted in

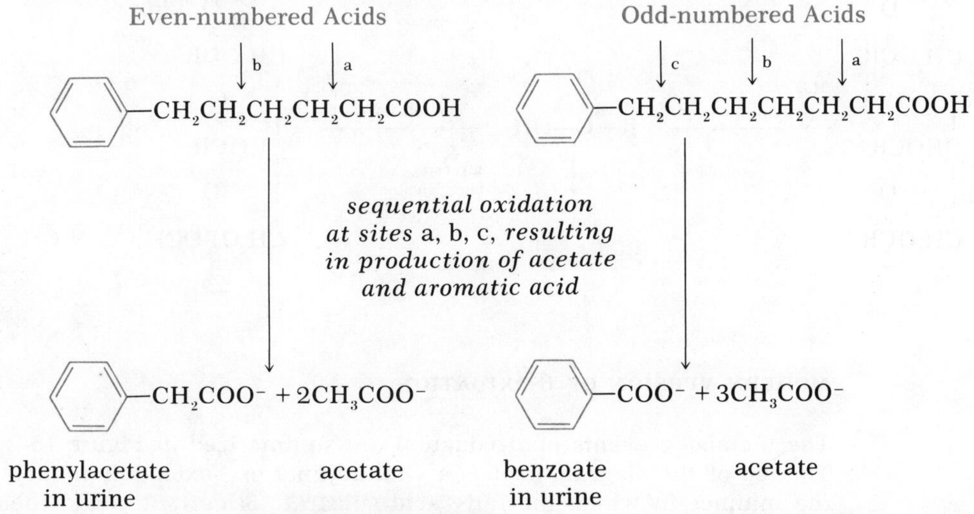

Even-numbered Acids   Odd-numbered Acids

$$\text{C}_6\text{H}_5\text{—CH}_2\text{CH}_2\text{CH}_2\text{CH}_2\text{CH}_2\text{COOH} \qquad \text{C}_6\text{H}_5\text{—CH}_2\text{CH}_2\text{CH}_2\text{CH}_2\text{CH}_2\text{CH}_2\text{COOH}$$

*sequential oxidation
at sites a, b, c, resulting
in production of acetate
and aromatic acid*

$$\text{C}_6\text{H}_5\text{—CH}_2\text{COO}^- + 2\text{CH}_3\text{COO}^- \qquad \text{C}_6\text{H}_5\text{—COO}^- + 3\text{CH}_3\text{COO}^-$$

phenylacetate   acetate   benzoate   acetate
in urine   in urine

the accumulation of *benzoate.* Both observations fit the proposed pattern outlined above. Knoop termed the process *β-oxidation,* signifying that the oxidative cleavage occurred at the C^β—C^α bond in the original acid and in each subsequent shorter acid. *Acetate* would be produced in each chain-shortening step.

At present, the process of β-oxidation is recognized as the primary catabolic pathway of fatty acids in all organisms. While the modern version of β-oxidation incorporates the essential principles of Knoop's original proposal, it was not fully developed until nearly fifty years after his pioneering studies. The key discoveries were that the process is *enzymatic,* occurs within the *mitochondria,* and is *ATP-dependent* (1941), and that the fatty acids as well as all intermediates are processed as *thioesters of CoASH* rather than as free acids (1951). Since then all of the intermediates and their metabolic sequence have been identified, and all of the enzymes involved have been isolated and studied in purified form.

CELLULAR SOURCE OF FATTY ACIDS

Obviously, the catabolism of fatty acids presupposes their presence within the cell. However, as pointed out in Chapter 8, free fatty acids do not occur in nature in any significant amounts, but rather are present in ester linkage primarily as acylglycerols and phosphoacylglycerides (see page 195). The former class represents the primary endogenous storage form of fatty acids, whereas the latter are essential components of biological membranes. The process whereby all cells degrade both lipid classes is quite direct, involving the action of two specialized groups of enzymes called *lipases* and *phospholipases.* The only point we wish to make regarding these enzymes is summarized below. Their action is essentially hydrolytic, resulting in the formation of the free fatty acids which can be reutilized in anabolic pathways or degraded via β-oxidation. Our concern here is with the latter process.

MODERN VERSION OF β-OXIDATION

The metabolic events of β-oxidation are summarized in Figure 15–1. The top of the diagram depicts a vital adjunct to β-oxidation, namely, the manner in which the fatty acid substrate is *activated* and then *gains entry* to the inside of the mitochondria. Since the hydrolytic lipases are extramitochondrial, the entry phase is a prerequisite to the subsequent intramitochondrial oxidation.

Activation and Entry Fatty acids must be converted to thioesters of CoASH prior to their participation in any type of cellular reaction. As pointed out in Chapter 10, the acyl-SCoA metabolites are *high-energy compounds* more susceptible to reaction than the free acid or the oxo-ester. Particular increases in reactivity are observed in (a) reactions involving a condensation at the carbonyl carbon and (b) elimination or addition reactions involving the α and β carbons of the acyl group (see page 251).

The most widely distributed activation process involves an ATP-dependent *fatty acid thiokinase* (top of Figure 15–1). The overall reaction is a classical example of a coupled reaction involving an actual transfer of energy (see page 255). At least three different thiokinases, varying in substrate specificity, are known to exist in nature. One is highly specific for acetate, a second for acids of medium chain length $(C_4\text{-}C_{12})$, and the third for long-chain acids $(C_{14}\text{-}C_{22})$. The latter two act on both saturated and unsaturated acids. Regardless of type, the activating thiokinases are known to be particulate enzymes localized in cellular membranes. In higher organisms specifically, it is proposed that they are found in the outer mitochondrial membrane.

For several years it was believed that the activated acyl group crossed the mitochondrial membrane via simple diffusion. This viewpoint is no longer held. The key factor in the development of the current proposal was the discovery that fatty acid oxidation was greatly stimulated by a substance called *carnitine*. Subsequent studies have correlated this effect to the process of β-oxidation by suggesting that carnitine esters of fatty acids serve as *carriers of the acyl group* across the mitochondrial membrane. A fact consistent with this role is the isolation of *carnitine acyltransferases* which catalyze the formation of carnitine-fatty acid esters. The localization of these enzymes in the membrane of mitochondria, the reversibility of the reaction, and the ability of carnitine to freely cross the membrane further support this role. It is not clear whether the same acyltransferase (E_A) operates on both sides of the membrane, or whether a different enzyme (E_B) catalyzes the intramitochondrial thiolytic hydrolysis of the carnitine ester. The intramitochondrial carnitine can return to the cytoplasm by simple diffusion or

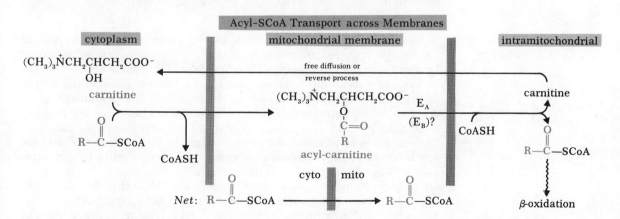

by acting in reverse and mediating the removal of acyl-SCoA compounds from the mitochondria.

OXIDATIVE SEQUENCE

Once inside the mitochondrion, acyl-SCoA compounds are degraded through the action of four enzymes (Figure 15–1). The chemistry of this set of reactions is rather straightforward: (A) *elimination of hydrogen* to yield an α,β unsaturated acyl-SCoA; (B) *hydration* to yield a β-hydroxy-acyl-SCoA; (C) *oxidation* to yield a β-ketoacyl-SCoA; and (D) *thiolytic cleavage* to yield acetyl-SCoA and a second acyl-SCoA now shortened by a two-carbon unit. Note that, although both oxidative steps (A and C) are catalyzed by dehydrogenases, the first is FAD-dependent and the second is NAD$^+$-dependent. Both steps represent sites of conservation of energy that is ultimately utilized in ATP formation (see below). The shortened acyl-SCoA could then go through the same reaction sequence, generating a second acetyl-SCoA unit and another shortened acyl-SCoA which would be recycled for still another pass. This cyclic pattern of β-oxidation would continue through the formation of the C_4 β-keto metabolite, acetoacetyl-SCoA (CH_3—$\overset{\overset{\displaystyle O}{\|}}{C}$—$CH_2$—$\overset{\overset{\displaystyle O}{\|}}{C}$—S—CoA). Thiolytic cleavage of this material would yield 2 units of $\overset{\overset{\displaystyle O}{\|}}{C}H_3$—$\overset{\overset{\displaystyle O}{\|}}{C}$—SCoA and thus complete the process. As indicated in Figure 15–1, with stearyl-SCoA as a starting material, the overall effect would be the complete conversion to 9 units of acetyl-SCoA. All of the enzymes have been isolated in pure form. The interested student is referred to other sources such as *Methods in Enzymology* for details concerning structural and catalytic properties.

The use of stearyl-SCoA with a fully saturated acyl group as an example raises the obvious question as to the degradation of unsaturated acids such as palmitoleic, oleic, and linoleic acids. Suffice it to say that these are processed by a combination of a special group of enzymes plus the four shown in Figure 15–1. The details of this aspect of fatty acid metabolism can be found in several of the literature sources listed at the end of the chapter. For our purpose, it is sufficient only to note that the overall effect would be the same as for stearyl-SCoA, that is, the unsaturated acids would be oxidized completely to acetyl-SCoA.

Energetics An ideal analysis of the bioenergetics of fatty acid catabolism requires an assumption that the fate of acetyl-SCoA would be entry into the citric acid cycle where it would be oxidized completely to CO_2. The assumption is not unrealistic. Indeed, such would be the case when the physiological state of the organism and/or dietary factors dictate that lipids rather than carbohydrates be utilized as the primary energy source. Moreover, remember that the enzymes of the citric acid cycle are also localized in the mitochondria. In this context our analysis is straightforward. For reasons of consistency with Figure 15–1, stearic acid will be retained as the initial substrate.

The pertinent equations are as follows. (Note that no distinction is made between the metabolic sources of FADH$_2$ and NADH in the equation for their coupled reoxidation to ATP formation. Regardless of

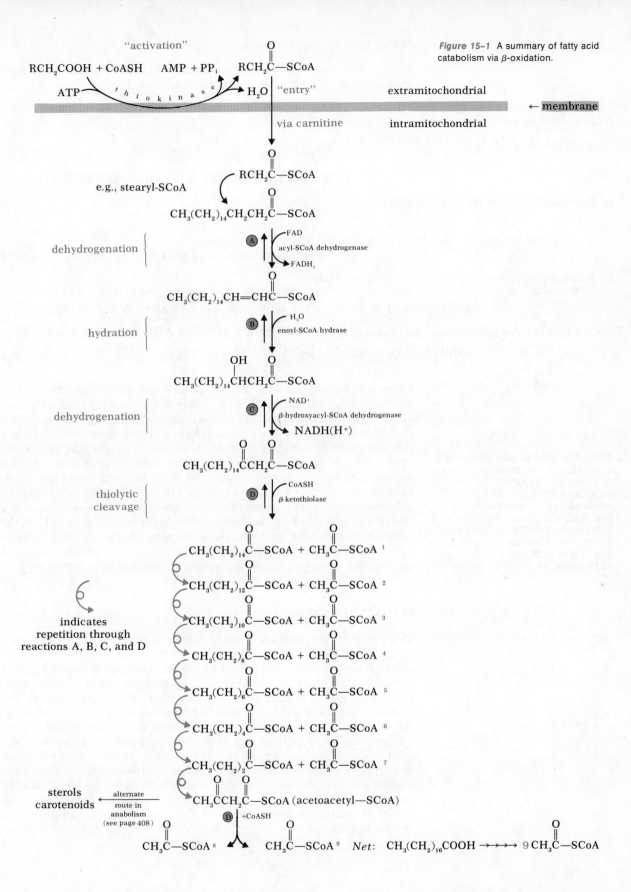

Figure 15-1 A summary of fatty acid catabolism via β-oxidation.

source, they are metabolically equivalent. That is to say, the P/O ratios are identical—2 for $FADH_2$ and 3 for $NADH + H^+$.)

A. Balanced equation for activation and β-oxidation:

$$CH_3(CH_2)_{16}COOH + ATP + 8FAD + 8NAD^+ + 8H_2O + 9CoASH \rightarrow$$

$$9CH_3\overset{\overset{\displaystyle O}{\|}}{C}SCoA + AMP + PP_i + 8FADH_2 + 8NADH + 8H^+ + H_2O$$

B. Balanced equation for citric acid cycle:

$$9CH_3\overset{\overset{\displaystyle O}{\|}}{C}SCoA + 9FAD + 27NAD^+ + 9GDP + 9P_i + 27H_2O \rightarrow$$

$$18CO_2 + 9CoASH + 9FADH_2 + 27NADH + 27H^+ + 9GTP$$

C. Balanced equations for oxidative phosphorylation:

$$17FADH_2 + 8.5O_2 + 34ADP + 34P_i \rightarrow 17FAD + 17H_2O + 34ATP$$

$$35NADH + 35H^+ + 17.5O_2 + 105ADP + 105P_i \rightarrow 35NAD^+ + 35H_2O + 105ATP$$

A + B + C: Net balanced equation (assuming GDP = ADP and GTP = ATP) and $AMP + PP = ADP + P_i$:

$$CH_3(CH_2)_{16}COOH + 26O_2 + 147ADP + 147P_i \rightarrow 18CO_2 + 147ATP + 18H_2O$$

Note: The specification in reaction B for $3H_2O$ being required per mole of acetyl-SCoA oxidized by the citric acid cycle includes one H_2O required in the condensation of acetyl-SCoA with oxaloacetate, one H_2O required in the hydrolysis of succinyl-SCoA to succinate, and one H_2O required in the hydration of fumarate to malate.

Using a value of −7.3 kcal for $\Delta G^{\circ\prime}$ of ATP hydrolysis as a basis, the net production of 147 units of ATP represents a conservation of energy equivalent to 1,073 kcal (147×7.3). Since the complete, uncoupled oxidation of stearic acid to CO_2 and H_2O can potentially yield 2,660 kcal, the biological efficiency of energy conservation in fatty acid oxidation is approximately 40%. Once again, however, this figure is a conservative estimate, since the energy required for ATP formation *in vivo* may be considerably greater than 7.3 kcal/mole. In any case, the fact is that the actual amount of ATP production accompanying the oxidative degradation of 1 long-chain fatty acid molecule is significantly greater than that from the catabolism of 3 hexose molecules (see page 357). In other words, under aerobic conditions and when the need arises, fatty acids are capable of serving as effective energy-yielding substrates.

GLYOXYLATE CYCLE

The entry of acetyl-SCoA from β-oxidation into the citric acid cycle would seem to provide a basis for the *in vivo* conversion of lipids into other classes of compounds such as amino acids and hexoses. To determine whether this is so requires that you recognize that this possibility will occur only if a cycle intermediate, suitable as a biosynthetic precursor, is removed *after* the point of entry of acetyl-SCoA and *before* the cycle is closed with oxaloacetate (OAA) formation. In the case of priming the cycle at the level of acetyl-SCoA, such a situation would exist with α-ketoglutarate. As it was formed, it would be bled off for use as a precursor of glutamate and related amino acids. As long as an anaplerotic reaction was operable to maintain catalytic levels of OAA, the net production of amino acids from the carbon atoms of fatty acids would be quite possible. In fact, such a conversion is common to all aerobic organisms.

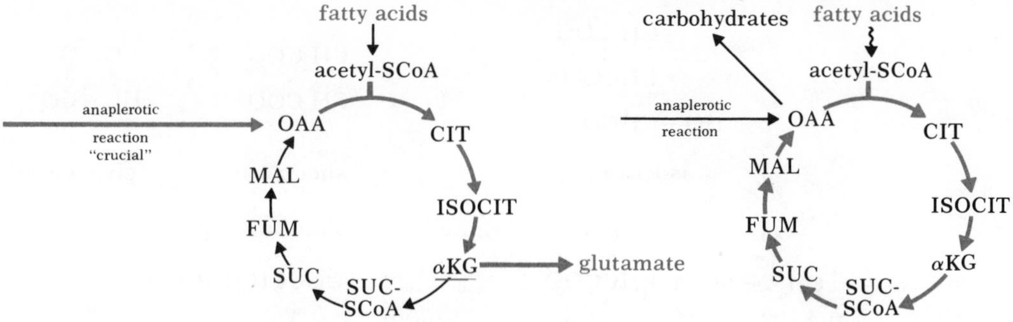

significant removal of carbons of
acetyl-SCoA before cycle
is closed

minimal removal of carbons of
acetyl-SCoA since cycle is
closed

On the other hand, a link of the carbon atoms of acetyl-SCoA to hexoses requires a complete turn of the cycle to OAA formation. In this case, we have in one complete turn a replenishment of an intermediate used in the initial condensation with acetyl-SCoA. The point is that there would be *no net production of additional* OAA that could be bled off for the biosynthesis of carbohydrates. The OAA that was formed would be required to react with additional acetyl-SCoA. One might argue that this should not make any difference since the OAA could be bled off, with the anaplerotic reaction providing the necessary OAA for condensation with acetyl-SCoA. The latter argument presupposes, however, that the cell will select a specific OAA molecule for carbohydrate biosynthesis and another for reaction with acetyl-SCoA. Suffice it to say that living organisms are not that clever. Another factor that would tend to minimize a lipid → carbohydrate conversion is that, when fatty acids are being utilized as a carbon source, the bulk of the acetyl carbon will be removed at the level of α-ketoglutarate for glutamate production, with only a small percentage ever being incorporated into oxaloacetate. In summary then, a significant net production of carbohydrate from lipid seems to be ruled out. What do we find in nature? Well, animal organisms are just so characterized. Lipid is not converted to carbohydrate to any appreciable degree. (Unfortunately, for most of us, the reverse process does occur and rather efficiently.) Unlike in animals, however, an efficient conversion of lipid to carbohydrate does occur in many plants and bacteria. Having just determined that this should not occur, we must now explain why it does.

The basis of this phenomenon is the fact that plants and bacteria contain two auxiliary enzymes for which there are no known counterparts in animals. The enzymes are *isocitritase* and *malate synthetase*, which catalyze the reactions shown above. By themselves the reactions have little meaning. To understand their role, it is necessary to examine their participation in connection with other enzymes of the citric acid cycle as shown in Figure 15–2. The key to this pathway (commonly called the *glyoxylate cycle*) is twofold: (a) the shunting of isocitrate from its usual fate in the citric acid cycle by isocitritase to yield glyoxylate and succinate; and (b) the subsequent condensation of the glyoxylate with a second unit of acetyl-SCoA to yield malate, which can then be converted to OAA, thus closing the cycle. The important point

$$\underset{\text{isocitrate}}{\overset{2}{C}H_2COO^- \atop \overset{3}{\underset{4}{C}}HCOO^- \atop HO-\overset{5}{C}HCOO^-} \xrightarrow{\text{isocitritase}} \underset{\text{succinate}}{\overset{2}{C}H_2COO^- \atop \overset{3}{\underset{6}{C}}H_2COO^-} + \underset{\text{glyoxylate}}{\overset{O}{\overset{\|}{H\overset{4}{C}}}-\overset{O}{\overset{\|}{\overset{5}{C}O^-}}}$$

$$\underset{\text{acetyl-SCoA}}{CH_3\overset{O}{\overset{\|}{C}}-SCoA} + \underset{\text{glyoxylate}}{H\overset{O}{\overset{\|}{C}}COO^-} \xrightarrow[\text{synthetase}]{\text{malate}} \underset{\text{L-malate}}{^-OOCCH_2\overset{OH}{\overset{|}{C}}HCOO^-}$$

to realize is that this pathway will be accompanied by a net increase in the production of succinate, which can then be converted to OAA by the usual CAC enzymes. This constitutes a *net gain* of OAA originating from the carbon atoms of acetyl-SCoA. The OAA can then be used in the biosynthesis of carbohydrates and amino acids as well. Of course, the glyoxylate cycle by itself is also capable of generating reducing power for ATP conversion, due to the NAD^+-dependent conversion of malate $\rightarrow$ OAA.

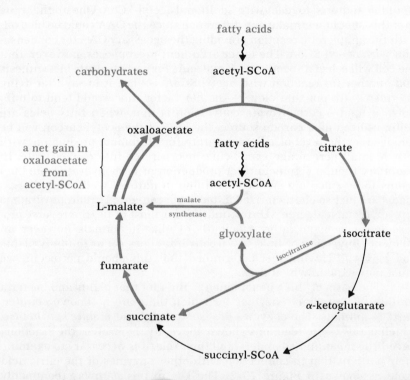

Figure 15–2 The glyoxylate cycle. The activity of malate synthetase and isocitritase results in the formation of OAA in excess of what is required to sustain the formation of citrate. Consequently the excess OAA can be used for carbohydrate biosynthesis.

A special feature of bacterial isocitritase and malate synthetase is that both are *inducible enzymes*. Inducible enzymes are enzymes that are produced in considerable amounts only when their substrates are present in considerable amounts. When the substrates are not present or when they are present in very low levels, the synthesis of these enzymes is repressed. Recall that the induction and repression of protein biosynthesis is another mode of metabolic regulation. We will explore this phenomenon in greater depth in Chapter 18.

ANABOLISM OF FATTY ACIDS

RELATIONSHIP TO β-OXIDATION

It is a well-documented fact that feeding acetate (C^{14}) to any type of organism will result in the production of fatty acids containing the C^{14} label. In fact, every carbon atom of the newly synthesized acid will be labeled. Given these data, if you had to predict the type of pathway responsible for the biosynthesis of fatty acids from acetyl units, an obvious suggestion would be that the hydrocarbon chain is assembled by a reversal of β-oxidation. Aside from the fit with the above data, further support for this proposal is that all of the β-oxidation enzymes can catalyze the reverse reactions.

Despite the obvious, there is, however, one predicament. The biosynthesis of fatty acids from acetyl-SCoA does not occur with purified preparations of mitochondria that contain the β-oxidation enzymes, but rather with soluble (cytoplasmic) extracts. Since it is unlikely that the same set of enzymes are localized in two different cellular compartments, it would appear that the biosynthesis of fatty acids is accomplished by a different set of enzymes, that is, by an anabolic pathway other than the simple reversal of β-oxidation. In recent years this pathway has been elucidated. We will investigate it shortly. Finally, however, it should be noted that the reversal of β-oxidation within the mitochondria does play a part in fatty acid biosynthesis. In particular, it is believed that the mitochondrial system is the main pathway responsible for the extension of long-chain fatty acids (C_{16} and up) via a direct condensation with acetyl-SCoA and subsequent reduction.

INTRACELLULAR SOURCE OF ACETYL-SCoA

As stated above, an extracellular supply of acetate will be converted into fatty acid. You should realize, however, that the same event can occur with an intracellular supply of acetate, that is, acetyl-SCoA. In fact, under normal environmental conditions, the major and in many cases the only source of acetate as acetyl-SCoA is intracellular, coming from the reaction: pyruvate $\xrightarrow{-CO_2}$ acetyl-SCoA. But, since (a) the decarboxylation of pyruvate occurs in the mitochondria, (b) the enzymes for fatty acid biosynthesis are in the cytoplasm, and (c) the mitochondrial membrane is impermeable to the free diffusion of acetyl-SCoA, we have a problem. How does acetyl-SCoA get across the membrane to participate in anabolism? Well, based on previous material given in this chapter and in Chapter 12, we can propose two possible explanations. One involves the diffusion of citrate from the mitochondria followed by the action of the *citrate-cleaving enzyme* (see page 325). The second involves the *acyl-carnitine transport* system just described on page 391. Both processes are shown at the top of the next page.

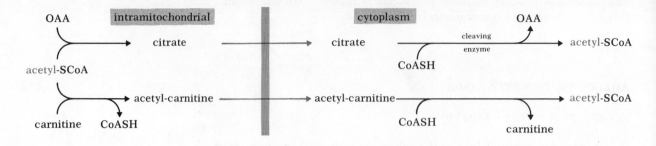

SOLUBLE ANABOLIC PATHWAY—MALONYL-SCoA FORMATION

Most of the knowledge in this area of biochemistry has been recently acquired; that is, most of the productive research has been done within the past five to ten years. The first significant development was the observation by Wakil and coworkers in 1958 that the incorporation of acetyl-SCoA into long-chain acyl groups by soluble extracts was dependent on ATP, NADPH, and Mn^{++}, as well as being greatly stimulated by CO_2. Subsequently, Wakil's group provided the explanation for much of their data by isolating the enzyme, *acetyl-SCoA carboxylase,* which catalyzed the ATP-dependent, irreversible carboxylation of acetyl-SCoA to yield *malonyl-SCoA.* It is now well documented that this is the *initial* reaction of fatty acid biosynthesis. Although Mn^{++} is required for optimal activity, a unique feature of acetyl-SCoA carboxylase is that it is absolutely dependent on a substance called *biotin.* The role of biotin had been implicated by earlier work which showed that acetyl-SCoA utilization was strongly inhibited by *avidin,* a protein that selectively binds with biotin.

$$CH_3\overset{\overset{\textstyle O}{\|}}{C}{-}SCoA + ATP + CO_2 \xrightarrow[Mn^{++},\ biotin]{acetyl\text{-}SCoA\ carboxylase} {}^-OOCCH_2\overset{\overset{\textstyle O}{\|}}{C}{-}SCoA + ADP + P_i$$
$$\text{malonyl-SCoA}$$

In this reaction, biotin, a water-soluble vitamin with an intriguing structure (see below), participates as an obligatory coenzyme firmly attached to the enzyme via the ϵ-amino group of a lysine residue. Although other biotin-dependent enzymes are known, the total number is small (approximately 10). The mode of action of biotin in the acetyl-SCoA carboxylase reaction is summarized below. The proposed reaction mechanism is twofold. The first step (A) involves the energy-dependent carboxylation of the biotin-enzyme complex. Note that the site of carboxylation is the biotin moiety. The resultant product is a high-energy form of the one-carbon unit and is termed *"activated CO_2."* In the second step (B), the CO_2 unit is condensed with acetyl-SCoA. With a little reflection, it should be apparent that the coenzyme function of biotin is to act as a carrier (transfer agent) of the one-carbon unit. The site of CO_2 attachment to biotin has been shown to be the N atom most distant from the aliphatic side chain.

Recent studies on purified preparations of acetyl-SCoA carboxylase have revealed that the enzyme is probably a key regulatory site in lipid metabolism. Metabolites acting as activators are citrate and isocitrate. Malonyl-SCoA and long-chain acyl-SCoA materials are feedback inhib-

A $\quad$ $CO_2 + \text{Biotin}\sim\text{Enzyme} + ATP \xrightarrow{Mn^{++}} CO_2\sim\text{Biotin}\sim\text{Enzyme} + ADP + P_i$

B $\quad$ $CH_3\overset{\overset{\displaystyle O}{\|}}{C}-SCoA + CO_2\sim\text{Biotin}\sim\text{Enzyme} \longrightarrow {}^-O_2CCH_2\overset{\overset{\displaystyle O}{\|}}{C}-SCoA + \text{Biotin}\sim\text{Enzyme}$

Net: $\quad$ $CO_2 + CH_3\overset{\overset{\displaystyle O}{\|}}{C}-SCoA + ATP \xrightarrow[\text{enzyme}]{\text{biotin}} {}^-OOCCH_2\overset{\overset{\displaystyle O}{\|}}{C}-SCoA + ADP + P_i$

malonyl-SCoA

carboxyl group
linked to protein
via $\epsilon-NH_3^+$ of
lysine residue

Biotin $\qquad\qquad\qquad\qquad$ CO_2 Biotin

itors. Since the enzyme is oligomeric, all effects are probably allosteric. Having previously explored allosterism in the regulation of carbohydrate metabolism (page 329), we will not indulge in a similar exercise at this time. Suffice it to say that the effects mentioned above are metabolic signals consistent with an efficient control of fatty acid biosynthesis as an integrated pathway with the whole of metabolism. For example, consider the following reasoning regarding the activation by citrate and isocitrate. When the energy (ATP) demands of the organism are great, acetyl-SCoA would best be funneled into the citric acid cycle, since it is the citric acid cycle that provides the bulk of reducing power necessary for ATP formation. As long as the ATP demand remained great, the intracellular levels of citrate, isocitrate, and the other cycle intermediates would not increase despite the continued input of acetyl-SCoA. The concentrations of these materials would remain low and relatively constant because they would be rapidly utilized and reformed in the cycle reactions. When the energy demands of the organism diminish, the need for a rapid oxidation of acetyl-SCoA by the citric acid cycle would also be diminished. This diminished need for energy is signaled by increased ratios of ATP/ADP and NADH/NAD$^+$. Recall that these signals would result in a negative control (inhibition) of isocitrate dehydrogenase (see page 330). This of course would result in increases in the cellular levels of isocitrate and its immediate precursor, citrate. These increases would in turn act as signals resulting in a positive control (activation) of acetyl-SCoA carboxylase. (In eucaryotic cells these changes would be localized in the mitochondrion and would require the diffusion of citrate and isocitrate out of the mitochondrion into the cytoplasm, where the carboxylase is localized.) Thus, the excess acetyl-SCoA, no longer required to satisfy a large need for metabolic energy, would be diverted into fatty acid biosynthesis for storage.

$\quad$ This type of reasoning is but one of several that may explain the physiological significance of the regulatory properties of acetyl-SCoA carboxylase as determined from kinetic studies on highly purified

preparations of the enzyme. These and additional regulatory properti
of some of the other enzymes that participate in fatty acid biosynthes.
may also account for the alterations of fatty acid metabolism in starve
animals, in diabetic animals, and in animals on a high-fat, low-carbo
hydrate diet.

Acyl Carrier Protein The initial formation of malonyl-SCoA is
only one of the many features which distinguish the soluble biosynthetic
pathway from a reversal of β-oxidation. A second is that none of the acyl-
SCoA intermediates are metabolized as CoASH thioesters, but rather as
special thioesters involving a carrier substance called the *acyl carrier
protein* (ACP-SH). This is a low-molecular-weight protein containing an
active sulfhydryl group which reacts with free acyl-SCoA to yield acyl-
S-ACP derivatives. The distinguishing feature of the ACP-SH is that it
contains a functional sulfhydryl (-SH) grouping contributed not by a
cysteine residue but by a grouping called *4'-phosphopantetheine* which
is covalently attached to the polypeptide chain via a serine residue. The
interesting aspect of this is that 4'-phosphopantetheine, you will recall,
is the same grouping found in the structure of CoASH (page 250). The
best way to describe this reaction is as a transacylation—an acyl group
is transferred from a CoASH thioester to another active -SH group to
form a second thioester. The transacylations involving acetyl-SCoA and
malonyl-SCoA are known to be catalyzed by separate enzymes—*acetyl
transacylase* and *malonyl transacylase,* respectively.

Reaction Sequence Since all of the subsequent reactions involve
acyl-S-ACP derivatives, it is now appropriate to direct our attention to the
metabolic sequence of the anabolic pathway. In so doing, other distinguishing characteristics will emerge. The complete pathway is illustrated
in Figure 15–3.

The immediate fate of malonyl-S-ACP is a condensation with
acetyl-S-ACP, catalyzed by *β-ketoacyl-S-ACP synthetase,* resulting in
the production of acetoacetyl-S-ACP. You will note that the chemistry
of this reaction, as shown by the use of C^{14}-labeled substrates in the
presence of the purified enzyme, is such that the carbonyl and α carbons
of the malonyl group are in the same position in the β-ketoacyl compound. Of prime significance in this reaction is the formation of CO_2 and
ACP-SH. Since both materials are required in two previous steps, the

$$\text{ACP—S—}\overset{\overset{\displaystyle O}{\|}}{C}\text{—CH}_3 \; + \; ^{-}\text{OOC}^{14}\text{—C}^{14}\text{H}_2\text{—}\overset{\overset{\displaystyle O}{\|}}{C^{14}}\text{—S—ACP} \qquad C^{14}O_2$$

$$\xrightarrow[\text{ACP—SH}]{\substack{\beta\text{-ketoacyl-S-ACP} \\ \text{synthetase}}} \text{CH}_3\text{—}\overset{\overset{\displaystyle O}{\|}}{C}\text{—C}^{14}\text{H}_2\text{—}\overset{\overset{\displaystyle O}{\|}}{C^{14}}\text{—S—ACP} + C^{14}O_2$$

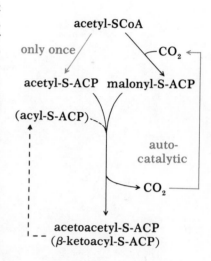

pathway is rendered *autocatalytic*. The regeneration of CO_2 is most important, since it is essential for the formation of malonyl-SCoA, which in turn is critical to the initiation of the whole process. Further evidence for the autocatalytic role of CO_2 has been established by radio-isotope studies which have shown that the CO_2 coming off in the synthetase reaction is the same unit of CO_2 used initially in the acetyl-SCoA carboxylase reaction. In other words, the carbon atom of CO_2 does not become part of the carbon skeleton of fatty acids. It merely keeps the pump primed, so to speak.

    In vitro studies with highly purified preparations of β-ketoacyl-S-ACP synthetase have shown that the enzyme is strongly inhibited by iodoacetamide (see page 118), thus indicating that the cysteine sulfhydryl grouping is required for activity. This inhibition is not observed if the enzyme is first incubated in the presence of acetyl-S-ACP. It has been proposed therefore that the condensation of the acetyl and malonyl moieties is preceded by a transacylation involving acetyl-S-ACP and a cysteine residue of the synthetase enzyme (see below). This results in the formation of an acetylated enzyme as an intermediate and it is the

**synthetase enzyme
with free cysteine
sulfhydryl group**

acetyl-S-ACP   HS—CH₂—ENZ   acetoacetyl-S-ACP + CO₂

step 1: *transacylation*   step 2: *condensation*

ACP-SH   acetyl—S—CH₂—ENZ   malonyl-S-ACP

**acetylated synthetase
enzyme**

Net:

    acetyl-S-ACP + malonyl-S-ACP $\xrightarrow{\text{synthetase}}$ acetoacetyl-S-ACP + CO₂ + ACP-SH

acetylated enzyme which then participates in the condensation with malonyl-S-ACP. In other words, the reaction involving acetyl-S-ACP and malonyl-S-ACP is not a direct condensation. The detail given this point is not intended to confuse nor to complicate the issue. Rather, the intent is to illustrate the various and specific roles of enzymes as catalytic agents. It particularly illustrates the role of amino acid residues at the active site of the enzyme in reactions characterized by the formation of a covalently bonded enzyme-substrate intermediate.

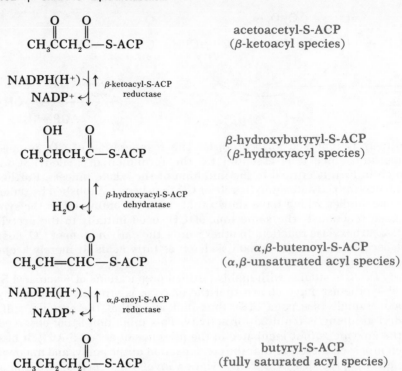

acetoacetyl-S-ACP
(β-ketoacyl species)

β-hydroxybutyryl-S-ACP
(β-hydroxyacyl species)

α,β-butenoyl-S-ACP
(α,β-unsaturated acyl species)

butyryl-S-ACP
(fully saturated acyl species)

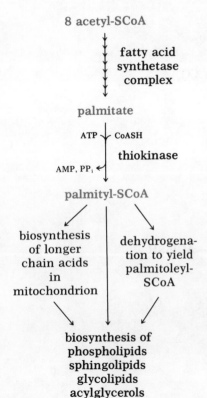

The fate of acetoacetyl-S-ACP is ultimate conversion to the fully saturated butyryl-S-ACP via three enzymes acting in sequence—first, a *β-ketoacyl-S-ACP dehydrogenase;* then a *β-hydroxyacyl-S-ACP dehydratase;* and finally an *α,β-enoyl-S-ACP dehydrogenase.* Although we are now dealing with different thioesters, you should recognize that the reaction sequence of the acyl moieties is exactly the reverse of β-oxidation. The differences are the enzymes and coenzymes involved and their cellular localization. The two dehydrogenases are particularly noteworthy because they are NADPH-dependent. (Recall the requirement of NADPH in Wakil's early work with soluble extracts.) Their counterpart in the reversal of the β-oxidation pathway, on the other hand, would be NADH and FADH$_2$-dependent. Presumably, the source of the required NADPH is the hexose monophosphate shunt, the enzymes of which are also found in the cytoplasm. The complete pathway is diagrammed in Figure 15–3.

With one pass through this cycle completed, the butyryl-S-ACP would then be recycled by condensing with a second unit of malonyl-S-ACP. As shown in Figure 15–3, this pattern would presumably continue until palmityl-S-ACP was formed (7 cycles). Although it is not included in the diagram, the condensation of the elongated acyl-S-ACP with malonyl-S-ACP would in each turn involve the formation of an acylated intermediate via the active cysteine sulfhydryl group of β-ketoacyl-S-ACP synthetase, as previously explained for the condensation between acetyl-S-ACP and malonyl-S-ACP.

Due to the nature of the β-ketoacyl synthetase reaction, it should be clear that the acyl chain is elongated by the successive addition of a two-carbon unit from the terminal methyl carbon towards the carbonyl end. Recall that the reverse pattern is typical of β-oxidation.

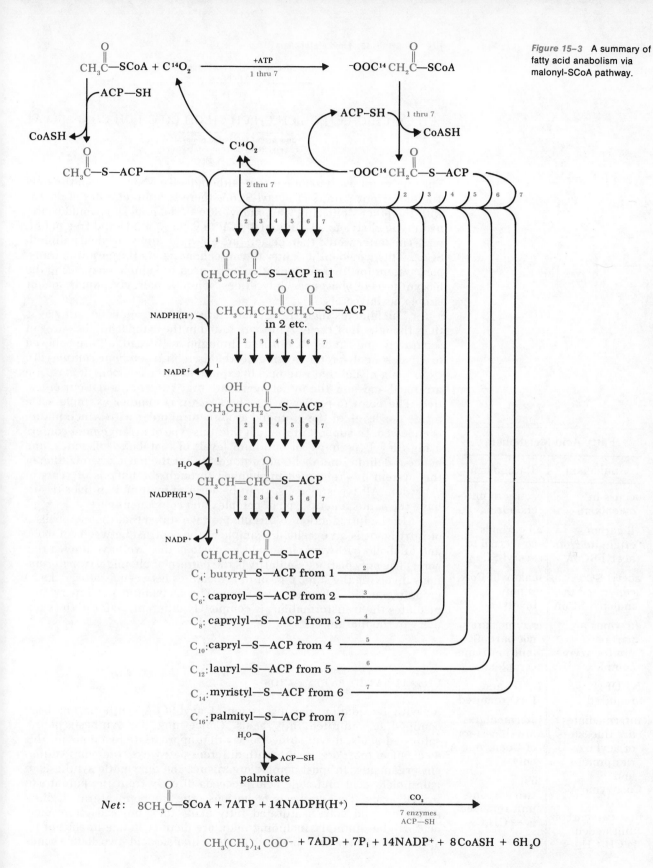

Figure 15–3 A summary of fatty acid anabolism via malonyl-SCoA pathway.

direction of sequential addition
of acetyl-SCoA units in anabolism →

$$CH_3CH_2CH_2CH_2CH_2CH_2CH_2CH_2CH_2CH_2CH_2CH_2CH_2CH_2CH_2\overset{O}{\underset{\|}{C}}—SCoA$$

← direction of sequential removal
of acetyl-SCoA units in catabolism

The important point to note is that, although all carbon atoms ultimately originate from 8 units of acetyl-SCoA, there is a direct entry of only 1, with the other 7 entering via malonyl-SCoA. The final step would be the hydrolytic cleavage of palmityl-S-ACP to yield ACP-SH and free palmitate. The latter would then be activated by a thiokinase to yield palmityl-SCoA. This would either enter the mitochondria via the carnitine transport system for further elongation or be used by soluble enzymes in the biosynthesis of phosphoacylglycerides, sphingolipids, glycolipids, and/or simple acylglycerols.

The final distinguishing characteristic of the anabolic pathway is that, though all of the enzymes are found in the cytoplasm, they are not separately and randomly diffused throughout. Instead, *all* are believed to exist as a poly-protein aggregate, that is, a *multi-enzyme complex*. To examine a model that attempts to explain how the component parts are arranged and how the intact aggregate may function is not our objective. The point to realize is that here again is another example, on a molecular level, of the profound architectural order with which nature is endowed. In support of the fact that this type of arrangement confers a high level (perhaps an optimum level) of metabolic efficiency, and hence a definite metabolic advantage, is that the basic organization of this system has remained unchanged through the billions of years of evolution. All types of cells, from bacteria to mammalian liver tissue, have the same general type of complex and component parts.

In the introduction to this chapter, we stated that the metabolism of fatty acids is an excellent example of the contrast between catabolic and anabolic pathways. It should be obvious that we have proved this point. The only distinct similarity is the pattern of chemical transformations involving the same type of intermediates between a saturated acyl grouping and a β-ketoacyl grouping. The enzymatic machinery that mediates the transformations is completely different. Refer to the summary in the margin.

UNSATURATED FATTY ACIDS

As with β-oxidation, our discussion of acyl-SCoA synthesis has been confined to saturated fatty acids. Concerning the synthesis of unsaturated acids, it will suffice to say that appropriate reactions for this do occur in most organisms, with different pathways common to different organisms. In most aerobic organisms, the enzymatic synthesis of palmitoleic acid and oleic acid proceeds directly from the parent saturated acids. The synthesis of various other monounsaturated, diunsaturated, and polyunsaturated fatty acids then proceeds from oleic acid. Higher animals, including man, are distinct in one important respect, namely, they are unable to produce linoleic acid (two double bonds

Fatty Acid Metabolism	
Anabolism	**Catabolism**
occurs in cytoplasm	occurs in mitochondrion
all carbons originate from acetyl-SCoA	all carbons converted to acetyl-SCoA
acetyl-SCoA converted to malonyl-SCoA	malonyl-SCoA is not involved
enzymes are part of multi-enzyme complex	enzymes are not part of multi-enzyme complex
NADPH required	NAD+ and FAD required
intermediates are thioesters of acyl carrier protein and Coenzyme A	intermediates are thioesters of Coenzyme A only
first two-carbon unit added is CH_3CH_2~	first two-carbon unit removed is ~ $CH_2\overset{\|}{\underset{O}{C}}$—

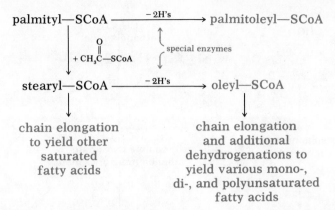

at positions $C_{9,10}$ and $C_{12,13}$) from oleic acid. Since linoleic acid is a substance that is essential for normal growth and development, mammals depend on a dietary supply of it. The requirement is satisfied primarily by the ingestion of plant material. The conversion of oleic acid to linoleic acid does occur in plants. It is probable that small amounts of other polyunsaturated acids are also required as part of a normal dietary intake.

BIOSYNTHESIS OF OTHER LIPIDS

PHOSPHOACYLGLYCERIDES

Despite the fact that phosphoacylglycerides occur throughout nature as vital structural and functional components of biological membranes, very little was known about their biosynthesis until recently. Current knowledge in this area, while still far from complete, is now rather extensive. Some of the important relationships are shown in Figure 15–4. Although they are not specified, each reaction is catalyzed by an enzyme. Other sources should be referred to for additional details.

The key reactions (*) are the formation of *cytidine diphosphate diglyceride* and *cytidine diphosphate choline* (ethanolamine). It is quite clear then that CTP is an obligatory coenzyme. Moreover, it is quite a specific coenzyme in these reactions since most other nucleotides will not substitute for CTP. The experimental history behind the discovery of this role of CTP is rather interesting. In 1955 E. Kennedy and S. Weiss were using cell-free systems in their investigations of the biosynthesis of phosphatidyl choline. One of the components which they added to their incubation mixture was ATP. (Previous studies had indicated that the incorporation of choline phosphate into phosphatidyl choline was ATP-dependent.) In the course of their work, it was observed that identically prepared systems gave variable results when incubated under the same conditions which included adding the same amount of ATP. Eventually the basis for the discrepancy was traced to the purity of the ATP that was added. Specifically, it was discovered that certain of the commercial sources of ATP that were used in the studies were contaminated with CTP. Noting that the incorporation of choline phosphate into lipids was greater with the CTP-contaminated sources,

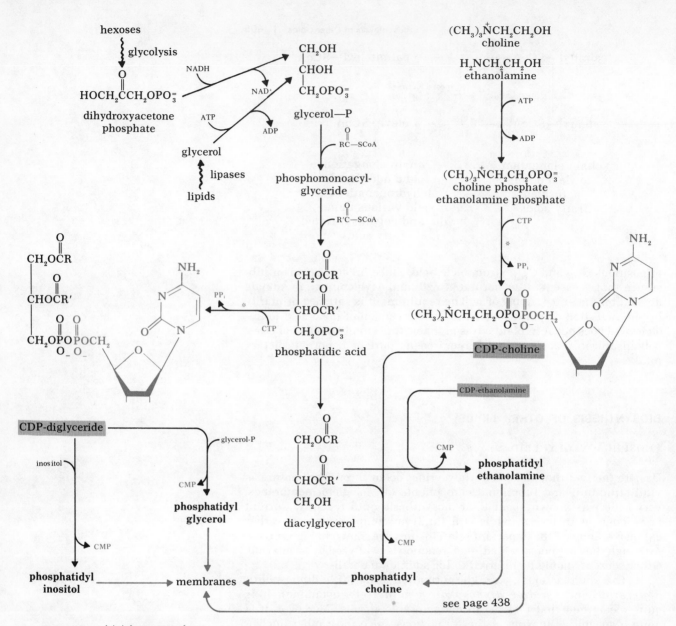

Figure 15-4 A brief summary of some anabolic pathways of phosphoacylglycerides. Crucial CTP-dependent reactions are indicated with ∗.

pure CTP and pure ATP were then utilized. The addition of pure CTP resulted in a considerable stimulation of choline phosphate incorporaation whereas the addition of pure ATP was without effect. Further studies by Kennedy, Weiss, and other workers (a) confirmed the specificity of the stimulatory effect of CTP on the utilization of choline phosphate in phosphatidyl choline formation; (b) determined that CTP had a similar effect on the incorporation of ethanolamine phosphate into phosphatidyl ethanolamine; (c) defined the details as to how CTP participated in these processes as an essential coenzyme; and (d) determined that the incorporation of phosphatidic acid into other lipids such as phosphatidyl inositol and phosphatidyl glycerol was also stimulated by and thus dependent on CTP.

If you are interested in more detail concerning phospholipid biosynthesis and the biosynthesis of other compound lipids such as the sphingolipids and glycolipids, you are referred to more advanced text-books and the essay by Lawson (see references at the end of the chapter).

CHOLESTEROL, STEROIDS, AND CAROTENOIDS

Despite the fact that the net chemistry is rather straightforward, the processes of nucleic acid biosynthesis and protein biosynthesis often leave the greatest impression on students of biochemistry. In each process monomeric units are linked together by the formation of identical types of bonding—the phosphodiester bond for nucleic acids and the peptide bond for proteins. Of course, the remarkable feature is that each process is highly programmed for the ordered production of a polymer comprised of a specific sequence of monomeric units. From the stand-point of the chemistry involved, however, perhaps the most fascinating anabolic pathway in all of nature is that responsible for the biosynthesis of cholesterol and other lipids.

Before considering the specific sequence of reactions involved, let us briefly summarize what they account for. The biosynthesis of choles-terol will be our frame of reference. In this context, the net effect of this pathway can be stated rather simply: All of the carbon atoms of choles-terol (a total of 27) are derived from the two carbon atoms of the acetyl unit of acetyl-SCoA (see below). The initial observation of this precursor-

$$CH_3 \!-\! \overset{\overset{\displaystyle O}{\|}}{C} \!-\! SCoA \longrightarrow$$

carbonyl carbon (c)

methyl carbon (m)

cholesterol

product relationship was made in 1950 by studying the utilization of uniformly labeled (C^{14}) acetate by liver cells for the production of cholesterol. Two experimental approaches were employed. One approach involved the feeding of the C^{14}-acetate to rats whose livers were later removed. The second involved the incubation of fresh liver slices in the presence of the labeled acetate. In both instances the cholesterol iso-lated from the liver cells was completely labeled with C^{14}, proving con-clusively that the entire carbon skeleton of cholesterol originates from the two carbons of acetate. Subsequent studies determined that the pattern of incorporation was very specific, with each carbon atom in cholesterol originating from either the carbonyl carbon (c) or the methyl carbon (m) of the acetyl unit.

The elucidation of the anabolic pathway responsible for this pat-tern required nearly ten years. It turned out to be a milestone in the de-velopment of biochemistry, because it is a major pathway found in all types of organisms, accounting for the biosynthesis of a host of bio-molecules besides cholesterol. The key development occurred in the late 1950's with the discovery that *mevalonic acid* (3-methyl-3,5-dihydroxy-valerate) was an intermediate of the pathway. The complete sequence

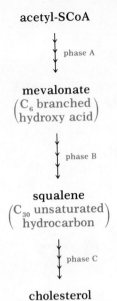

acetyl-SCoA

phase A

mevalonate
$\left(\begin{array}{c} C_6 \text{ branched} \\ \text{hydroxy acid} \end{array}\right)$

phase B

squalene
$\left(\begin{array}{c} C_{30} \text{ unsaturated} \\ \text{hydrocarbon} \end{array}\right)$

phase C

cholesterol

Figure 15–5 A brief summary of cholesterol biosynthesis.

of this pathway is summarized in Figure 15–5. We will investigate this by dividing the whole process into three phases: A—the *formation of mevalonate;* B—the *formation of squalene;* and C—the *formation of cholesterol.*

In phase A, three units of acetyl-SCoA condense to give mevalonate. The process is not direct, but involves (see Figure 15–6) the intermediate formation of acetoacetyl-SCoA and then *β-hydroxy-β-methylglutaryl-SCoA,* a substituted dicarboxylic acid. The latter is then converted to mevalonate via a step dependent on two units of NADPH. One NADPH functions in the reduction of the carbonyl grouping to a hydroxyl group, and the second unit participates in the reductive cleavage of the carbon-sulfur bond yielding CoASH and mevalonate in the free form. (In 1963 a second route of mevalonate formation was discovered involving the same chemical intermediates except that they were processed as acyl groups attached to a protein containing an active sulfhydryl group.)

In phase B (Figure 15–7), mevalonate is first activated by a trio of ATP-dependent kinases to yield *3-phospho-5-pyrophosphomevalonate.* The latter is extremely unstable and undergoes a decarboxylation and a dephosphorylation to yield *isopentenyl pyrophosphate,* which isomerizes further to give *dimethylallyl pyrophosphate.* The latter two compounds are crucial intermediates. In effect, four units of isopentenyl pyrophosphate and two units of dimethylallyl pyrophosphate condense with each other to yield *squalene,* a C_{30} unsaturated hydrocarbon. The condensation is not direct, but rather involves the intermediate formation of two units of *geranyl pyrophosphate* and five units of *farnesyl pyrophosphate* (C_{15}). One of the farnesyl units is then isomerized to yield *nerolidol pyrophosphate,* which in turn condenses with the second farnesyl unit to finally give squalene. Knowledge of this latter process is rather sketchy, with only a requirement of NADPH being well documented. In most plants and in many microbes, a special branch of this pathway occurs at the point of farnesyl pyrophosphate due to its

Figure 15–6 Phase A of cholesterol biosynthesis. Formation of mevalonic acid.

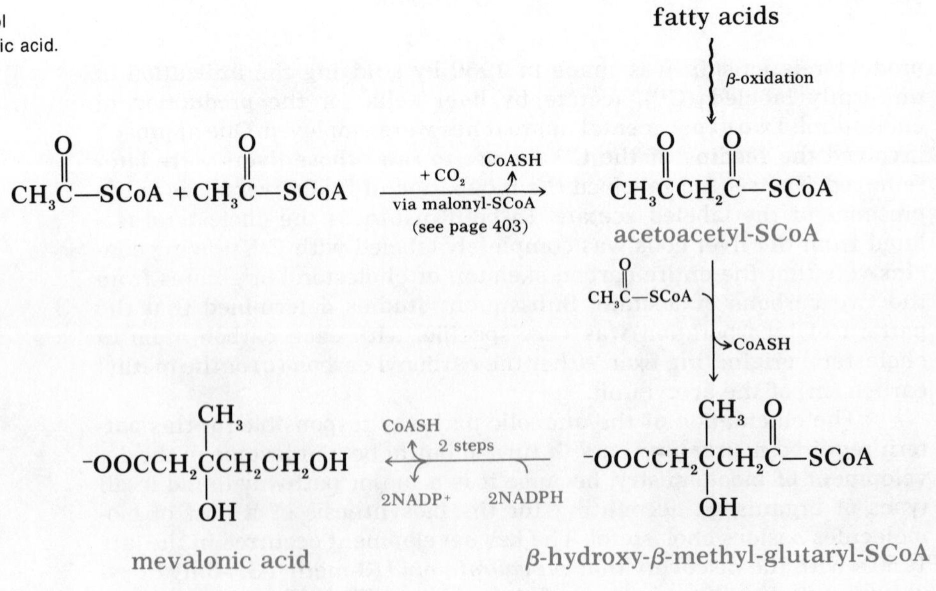

fatty acids

β-oxidation

$$\underset{\text{O}}{\overset{\text{O}}{\text{CH}_3\text{C}}}\text{—SCoA} + \underset{\text{O}}{\overset{\text{O}}{\text{CH}_3\text{C}}}\text{—SCoA} \xrightarrow[\substack{\text{via malonyl-SCoA} \\ \text{(see page 403)}}]{\substack{+ \text{CO}_2 \quad \text{CoASH}}} \underset{\text{acetoacetyl-SCoA}}{\overset{\text{O} \quad\quad \text{O}}{\text{CH}_3\text{CCH}_2\text{C}}\text{—SCoA}}$$

$$\overset{\text{O}}{\text{CH}_3\text{C}}\text{—SCoA}$$

CoASH

$$\underset{\text{OH}}{\overset{\text{CH}_3}{\text{-OOCCH}_2\text{C}\text{CH}_2\text{CH}_2\text{OH}}} \underset{\substack{2\text{NADP}^+ \quad 2\text{NADPH}}}{\overset{\text{CoASH} \quad 2\text{ steps}}{\longleftarrow}} \underset{\text{OH}}{\overset{\text{CH}_3 \quad \text{O}}{\text{-OOCCH}_2\text{C}\text{CH}_2\text{C}}\text{—SCoA}}$$

mevalonic acid   β-hydroxy-β-methyl-glutaryl-SCoA

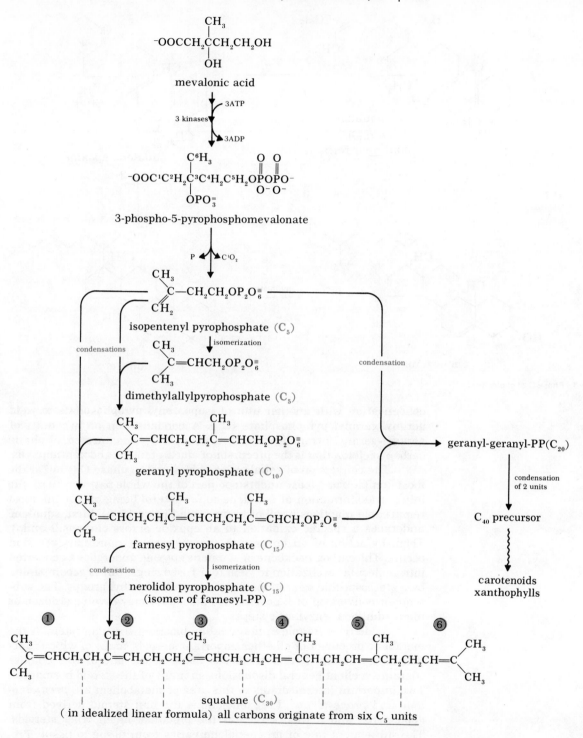

Figure 15–7 Phase B of cholesterol biosynthesis. Formation of squalene.

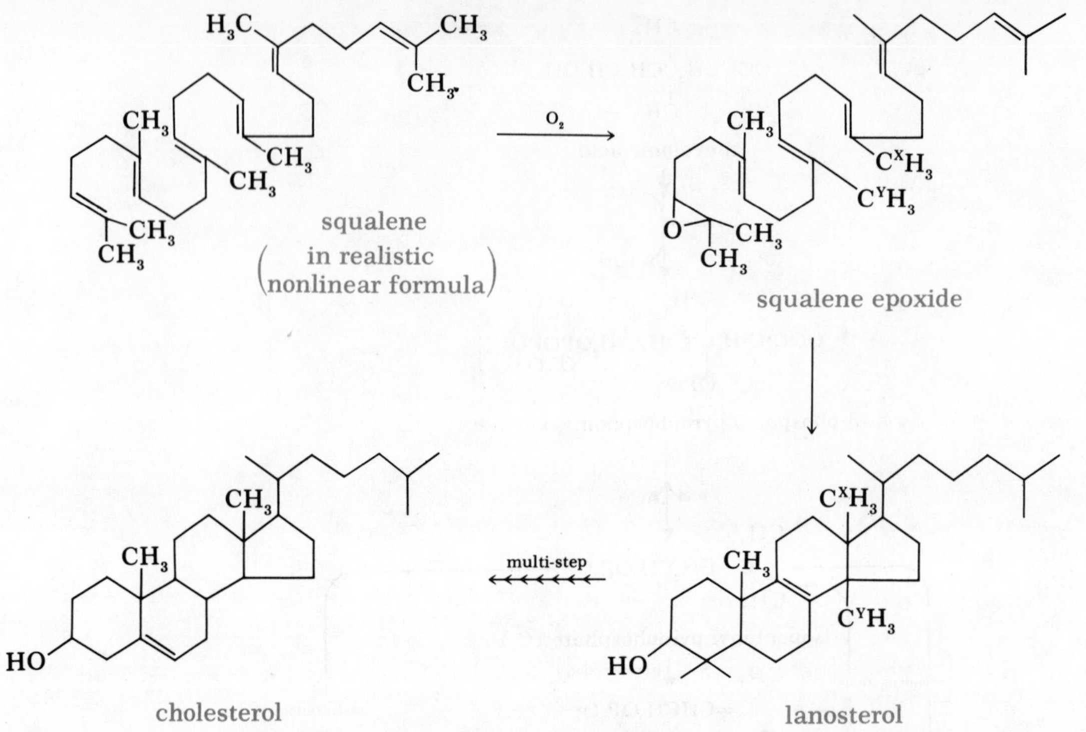

Figure 15–8 Phase C of cholesterol biosynthesis.

condensation with another unit of isopentenyl pyrophosphate to yield geranyl-geranyl pyrophosphate (C_{20}). A condensation of two units of geranyl-geranyl pyrophosphate then yields a C_{40} unsaturated, aliphatic carbon skeleton that is the precursor of all carotenoids and xanthophylls.

The conversion of squalene to cholesterol in phase C is by far the most complex and least understood part of the whole pathway, with the initial transformation of squalene to *lanosterol* being one of the most remarkable reactions in all of nature (see Figure 15–8). First, squalene undergoes a specific oxidation to an epoxide across carbons 2 and 3. Then, by action of an enzyme or enzymes, an extraordinary reaction occurs. The carbon backbone of squalene epoxide undergoes a concerted intramolecular cyclization to yield four fused rings; this is accompanied by a stereospecific migration of two particular methyl groups. The subsequent conversion of lanosterol to cholesterol may involve a dozen or more additional enzymatic steps.

Aside from its role in mammalian biochemistry, cholesterol is the metabolic precursor of all other important steroids, many of which function as hormones. (Other textbooks listed at the end of this chapter contain excellent general discussions on many of the steroid hormones.) Two important intermediates in this area of metabolism are *pregnenolone* and *progesterone*. Pregnenolone is the first steroid derived from cholesterol, and it then serves as the precursor of all other steroids. The subsequent fate of pregnenolone varies from tissue to tissue. Produced by the adrenal gland, for example, are *aldosterone* and *cortisone* (cortisol). The former influences electrolyte and water metabolism, whereas the latter regulates the metabolism of carbohydrates, fatty acids, and proteins. The ovaries and testes, respectively, elaborate the estrogens (*estrone*) and androgens (*testosterone* and *androsterone*), both classes being responsible for the development of sex characteristics (see page 208). In addition, the corpus luteum of the ovaries is the chief site of progesterone production in the female. One cannot resist the comment that, because of these relationships, it should be obvious that each of us has a special identity with the metabolic pathway of acetyl-SCoA→ mevalonate→ squalene→ cholesterol pathway.

POSTSCRIPT

By reflecting on both the content of this chapter and our previous analysis of the metabolic relationships of the citric acid cycle in Chapter 12, one can appreciate that there is something rather special about the metabolic role of acetyl-SCoA as an individual metabolite. We can summarize this quite readily. Acetyl-SCoA is *the* compound which is at the very nucleus of metabolism, acting both as a metabolic receiving and

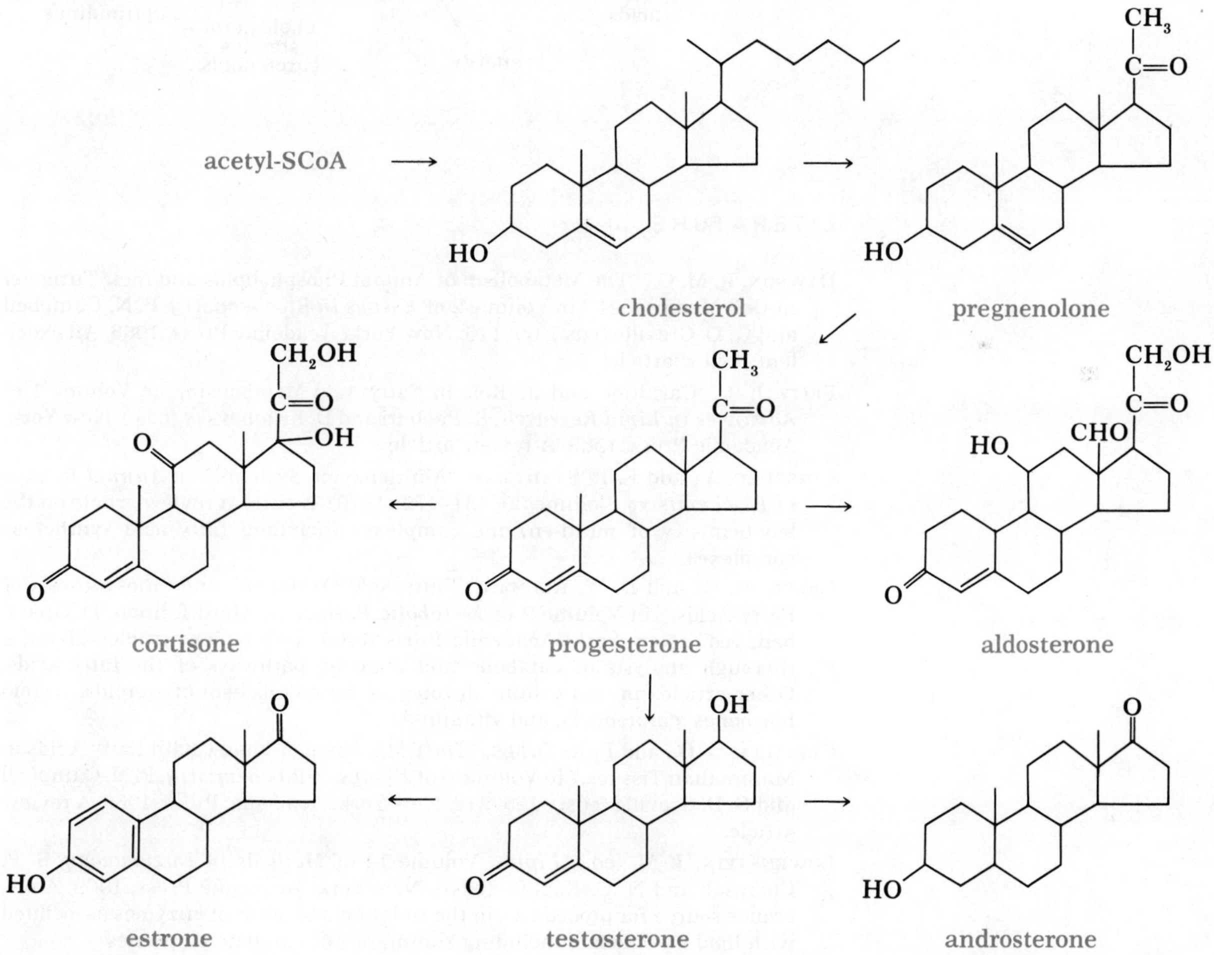

acetyl-SCoA $\longrightarrow$

cholesterol

pregnenolone

cortisone

progesterone

aldosterone

estrone

testosterone

androsterone

shipping department, so to speak, for the carbon of all classes of bio-molecules and as a major source of useful metabolic energy. The general theme of these relationships is diagrammatically summarized below. On inspecting the diagram, remember that, though all processes can and do occur simultaneously, there is (probably in all organisms) a complex set of regulatory checks and balances, as previously described for the major pathways of carbohydrate metabolism, that modulates the extent to which each process occurs in the presence of the others.

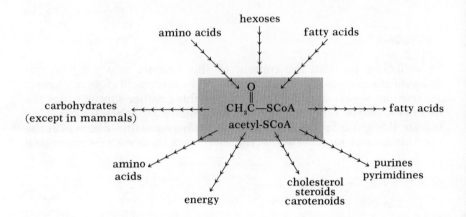

LITERATURE

DAWSON, R. M. C., "The Metabolism of Animal Phospholipids and their Turnover in Cell Membranes," in Volume 2 of *Essays in Biochemistry*, P. N. Campbell and G. D. Greville (eds.), 69–116. New York: Academic Press, 1966. An excellent review article.

FRITZ, I. B., "Carnitine and its Role in Fatty Acid Metabolism," in Volume 1 of *Advances in Lipid Research*, R. Paoletti and D. Kritchevsky (eds.). New York: Academic Press, 1963. A review article.

GINSBURG, A., and E. R. STADTMAN, "Multienzyme Systems," in *Annual Review of Biochemistry*, Volume 39, 431–472 (1970). A current review article on the biochemistry of multi-enzyme complexes including fatty acid synthetase complexes.

GREEN, D. E., and D. W. ALLMAN, "Fatty Acid Oxidation" and "Biosynthesis of Fatty Acids," in Volume 2 of *Metabolic Pathways*, Third Edition, D. Greenberg (ed.). New York: Academic Press, 1968. Two review articles giving a thorough analysis of catabolic and anabolic pathways of the fatty acids. Other articles in this volume devoted to the metabolism of steroids, steroid hormones, carotenoids, and vitamin A.

GREVILLE, G. D., and P. K. TUBBS, "The Catabolism of Long-Chain Fatty Acids in Mammalian Tissues," in Volume 4 of *Essays in Biochemistry*, P. N. Campbell and G. D. Greville (eds.), 155–212. New York: Academic Press, 1968. A review article.

LOWENSTEIN, J. M. (ed.), *Lipids*. Volume 14 of *Methods in Enzymology*, S. P. Colowick and N. O. Kaplan, (eds.). New York: Academic Press, 1969. A reference source for procedures in the isolation and assay of enzymes associated with lipid metabolism including summaries of catalytic properties.

MAJERUS, P. W., and P. R. VAGELOS, "Fatty Acid Biosynthesis and the Acyl Carrier Protein," in Volume 5 of *Advances in Lipid Research,* R. Paoletti and D. Krtichevsky (eds.). New York: Academic Press, 1967. A review article.

WAKIL, S. J. (ed.), *Lipid Metabolism.* New York: Academic Press, 1970. A comprehensive treatise containing articles that investigate in detail the biochemistry and enzymology of the metabolism of various lipids in animals, plants, and microorganisms. A chapter on the prostaglandins is included.

EXERCISES

15–1 If only the first of eight molecules of acetyl-SCoA used in the biosynthesis of palmitic acid were labeled with C^{14}, which of the following would represent the location of the label in palmitic acid?

$$^-OOC^{14}C^{14}H_2CH_2CH_2CH_2CH_2CH_2CH_2CH_2CH_2CH_2CH_2CH_2CH_2CH_2CH_3$$

or

$$^-OOCCH_2CH_2CH_2CH_2CH_2CH_2CH_2CH_2CH_2CH_2CH_2CH_2CH_2C^{14}H_2C^{14}H_3$$

15–2 Determine the *net yield* of ATP molecules from the complete aerobic oxidation of one molecule of myristyl-SCoA to CO_2. Also determine the number of ATP's *required* in this process.

15–3 If the palmitic acid produced in Exercise 15–1 were degraded to acetyl-SCoA via β-oxidation, would the labeled acetyl-SCoA unit be produced from the thiolytic cleavage of β-ketomyristyl-SCoA or the thiolytic cleavage of acetoacetyl-SCoA?

15–4 The metabolism of aspartate is linked to the citric acid cycle by the following reversible transamination reaction.

$$\text{aspartate} + \alpha\text{-keto acid} \xrightleftharpoons[\text{aminase}]{\text{trans-}} \text{oxaloacetate} + \text{amino acid}$$

Given this information and referring back to Figure 12–4, suggest a reaction sequence that will account for the fact that some of the carbons of aspartate are eventually converted to a metabolite which can then be used in the biosynthesis of *either* fatty acids or carbohydrates.

15–5 In the situation posed in the preceding exercise, what is the only possible explanation for the conversion of carbons in aspartate to carbons in fatty acids according to the following reaction sequence?

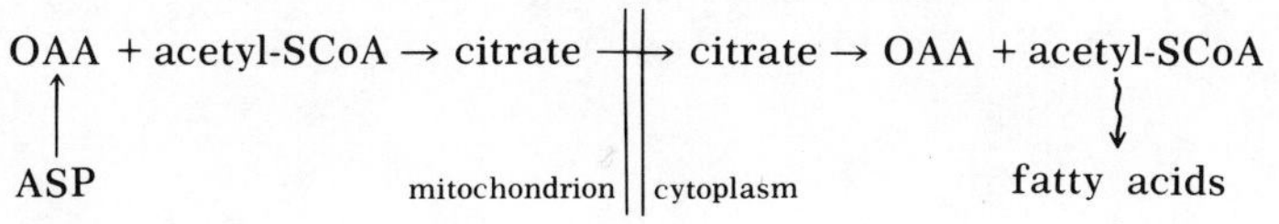

15–6 How do the following reactions differ?

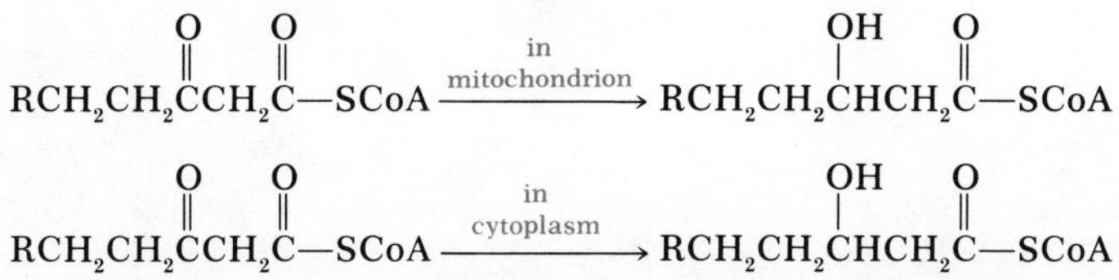

15–7 If a molecule of uniformly labeled acetyl-SCoA (C^{14}) condensed with acetoacetyl-SCoA to form β-hydroxy-β-methyl-glutaryl-SCoA which was then converted to mevalonate, what would be the pattern of the C^{14} label in mevalonate?

15–8 Considering the description of the properties of β-ketoacyl-S-ACP synthetase, what result would you predict for each of the following experiments? Express the results with or without the inhibition of acetoacetyl-S-ACP formation. Also indicate which system(s) would probably be characterized by the greatest and least amount of inhibition. Assume that in each instance the preincubation period was 10 minutes and that the amount of acetoacetyl-S-ACP formation formed was measured 2 minutes after the additions were made.

    a) iodoacetamide and acetyl-S-ACP are added to a previously incubated mixture of the synthetase and malonyl-S-ACP;

    b) the synthetase is added to a solution—not previously incubated—containing iodoacetamide, acetyl-S-ACP, and malonyl-S-ACP;

    c) acetyl-S-ACP is added to a previously incubated mixture of the synthetase, malonyl-S-ACP, and iodoacetamide;

    d) malonyl-S-ACP is added to a previously incubated mixture of the synthetase, acetyl-S-ACP, and iodoacetamide;

    e) iodoacetamide is added to a previously incubated mixture of the synthetase, malonyl-S-ACP, and acetyl-S-ACP.

15–9 The biosynthesis of cholesterol and other steroids is known to be subject to regulation in the cell. One aspect of this regulation is a feedback inhibition by cholesterol on one of the enzymes functioning in phase A. Now, whereas the mevalonic acid is a metabolite unique to this overall anabolic pathway and is formed only from β-hydroxy-β-methyl glutaryl-SCoA, the latter can be utilized in other ways as well as being formed via other routes, such as by the catabolism of leucine. Given this information, discuss which of the reactions in phase A would be the most logical site for regulation. In addition, discuss why it would be more efficient to regulate the pathway in phase A rather than in phase B.

15–10 According to the outline of the anabolic pathway given in this chapter, estimate the amount of energy required to produce one molecule of cholesterol from acetyl-SCoA. Make the estimate in terms of the number of high-energy compounds that are required, expressing each in terms of its ATP equivalent. Assume that an acyl-SCoA compound is thermodynamically equivalent to one ATP, and that one molecule of NADH or NADPH is potentially equivalent to three ATP's. Of course, ATP is ATP.

16

Amino Acid Metabolism

In Chapter 4 it was stated that the most important reaction of amino acids in a living cell is their covalent condensation with each other to form the polypeptide backbone of proteins. In view of your understanding of the many vital biological functions of proteins, particularly as enzymes, the basis for that statement should be obvious at this point. However, the formation of proteins is not the only important aspect of amino acid metabolism. Also important are those reactions involved in the degradation and synthesis of amino acids. In addition, many amino acids undergo reactions responsible for specialized metabolic and physiological functions in the cell. The significance of all these reactions to the normal metabolism of the whole organism cannot be overemphasized.

For example, the catabolism of amino acids serves as the major intracellular source of nitrogen needed for the biosynthesis of critical nitrogen-containing compounds such as purines, pyrimidines, and tetrapyrroles. Furthermore, since their degradation yields intermediates of the citric acid cycle, the amino acids can also serve as effective intracellular sources of both carbon and energy. The biosynthesis of amino acids is especially significant since their formation is an obvious prerequisite to their utilization in protein biosynthesis. Most plants and bacteria can synthesize all of the amino acids required for proteins. This is a rather crucial aspect of the biochemical design of our biosphere, since animal organisms are capable of synthesizing only certain of the amino acids, and hence are dependent for their existence on a supply of the others in the form of ingested proteins from plants and other animals. Whether it be a total or a limited capability, the biosynthesis of amino acids is also linked to the central process of the citric acid cycle. In this case, the cycle provides carbon intermediates originating from carbohydrate or lipid to serve as anabolic precursors for all or part of the amino acid carbon skeleton. In other words, both the catabolic and anabolic reactions of amino acids are integrated into the mainstream of the whole of metabolism.

The subject of amino acid metabolism is extremely complex, because, unlike the hexoses and the fatty acids, which share common pathways, each amino acid basically has a separate pathway for degradation and biosynthesis. Moreover, the special metabolic functions of amino acids are due to still other reaction pathways. Since the scope and thrust of this book preclude a thorough coverage of this area, our objective in this chapter will be to consider selected segments that are representative of the principles stated above. The material also includes an analysis of certain other coenzymes not yet encountered in earlier discussions, a major pathway for the excretion of nitrogen, and some principles of nutrition.

UNIFYING PRINCIPLES OF AMINO ACID METABOLISM

Although amino acid metabolism is one of the most massive areas for discussion in general biochemistry courses (for example, inspect Figure 16–2, which summarizes only part of the metabolism of just two amino acids, phenylalanine and tyrosine), it is possible to unify the subject to some extent. The most distinctive common denominator is, of course, their role as biosynthetic precursors of the proteins. What about the broader area of amino acid metabolism? Here also unifying elements exist, two of which will be considered here. First, as previously considered in Chapter 12 (see Figure 12–4) and summarized in the diagram shown below, the metabolism of amino acids is integrated into the mainstream of metabolism by (a) an *input* to the citric acid cycle of a portion of, or the entire carbon skeleton of, nearly all the common amino acids during their catabolism, and (b) an *output* of carbon from the citric

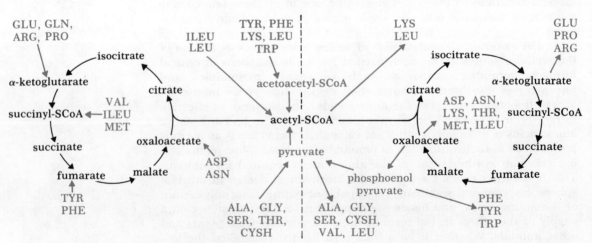

Entrance of carbon into the mainstream
of metabolism from amino acid degradation

Removal of carbon from the mainstream
of metabolism for amino acid formation

acid cycle in the form of cycle intermediates that serve as precursors of the carbon skeletons of many amino acids during their anabolism. Because of the individuality of the pathways involved, a multitude of reactions would be necessary to define each type of link for all the amino acids. While it is not our intent to do that, a few words are in order concerning the general metabolic significance of these relationships. As for the several catabolic links to the citric acid cycle, these account for the fact stated earlier that amino acids can be effective intracellular sources of both metabolic energy (ATP) and carbon for the formation of carbohydrates and lipids. Both factors, accompanied by a depression of the hunger sensation, account for the success of weight control diets that are high in protein and low in carbohydrate and lipid. The anabolic link, of course, accounts for just the reverse, namely, that the carbons of amino acids can originate from carbohydrates and lipids.

During catabolism, if the amino acid carbons are shunted largely into carbohydrates, the parent amino acids are termed *glycogenic* (carbohydrate formation). If the carbons are more efficiently incorporated into lipid material, the amino acids are termed *ketogenic* (lipid formation). The only requirement for classification as glycogenic is that the amino acid be converted directly or indirectly to *pyruvate*. This requirement is met by nearly two-thirds of the common amino acids. Those which yield pyruvate directly are glycine, alanine, cysteine, serine, and threonine. The indirect route is based on the formation of oxaloacetate or any citric acid cycle intermediate that would eventually be converted to oxaloacetate. Glycogenic amino acids in this category are aspartate, asparagine, glutamate, glutamine, arginine, methionine, valine, isoleucine, tyrosine, and phenylalanine. The potential ketogenic amino acids are those that yield *acetyl-SCoA* or *acetoacetyl-SCoA*. Included here are tyrosine, phenylalanine, leucine, isoleucine, lysine, and tryptophan. Note that although several amino acids are only glycogenic, some are both glycogenic and ketogenic. Leucine is the only amino acid that is ketogenic but not glycogenic.

The second element of unity is that, although there are a great number of reactions associated with the metabolism of amino acids as a group, there is considerably less diversity in the *type of reactions* involved. Actually, if we limit our attention to those reactions that involve amino acids directly, the number of reaction types is small indeed. They include *transamination, decarboxylation,* and *deamination.* Of these three, transamination reactions play a major role and hence will be discussed first and in greater depth.

TRANSAMINATION

Frequently the first and last chemical event occurring during the degradation and synthesis of amino acids, respectively, is a *transamination.* As the word implies, a transamination reaction is characterized by the transfer of an amino grouping. To be more specific: an *amino grouping is transferred from a donor amino acid to an acceptor α-keto acid to yield the α-keto acid of the donor amino acid and the amino acid of the original α-keto acid acceptor.* The reaction is catalyzed by an enzyme called *transaminase* that requires a metal ion and *pyridoxal phosphate* (see below) for activity. As you might expect, the reaction is readily reversible.

$$\underset{\text{amino acid}}{R-\overset{\overset{\displaystyle NH_3^+}{|}}{C}H-COO^-} + \underset{\alpha\text{-keto acid}}{R'-\overset{\overset{\displaystyle O}{\|}}{C}-COO^-} \underset{\substack{\text{pyridoxal}\\\text{phosphate}\\(M^{++})}}{\overset{\text{transaminase}}{\rightleftharpoons}} \underset{\alpha\text{-keto acid}}{R-\overset{\overset{\displaystyle O}{\|}}{C}-COO^-} + \underset{\text{amino acid}}{R'-\overset{\overset{\displaystyle NH_3^+}{|}}{C}H-COO^-}$$

Although several different transaminases occur in nature, they do not display an absolute level of substrate specificity. On the contrary, most transaminases have a broad range of specificity. However, many enzymes show a preference for utilizing α-ketoglutarate as the acceptor keto acid, yielding glutamate, or vice versa. Although the reaction from

$$\underset{}{R-\overset{\overset{\displaystyle NH_3^+}{|}}{C}H-COO^-} + \underset{\alpha\text{-ketoglutarate}}{^-OOCCH_2CH_2-\overset{\overset{\displaystyle O}{\|}}{C}-COO^-} \overset{\text{transaminase}}{\rightleftharpoons} R-\overset{\overset{\displaystyle O}{\|}}{C}-COO^- + \underset{\text{glutamate}}{^-OOCCH_2CH_2-\overset{\overset{\displaystyle NH_3^+}{|}}{C}H-COO^-}$$

left to right (→) accounts for the direct biosynthesis of glutamate from a citric acid cycle intermediate, and the reverse reaction (←) explains how the complete carbon skeleton of glutamate gets into the citric acid cycle for further metabolism (a similar transformation and explanations exist for the oxaloacetate ⇌ aspartate set), the metabolic role of the α-ketoglutarate ⇌ glutamate transamination system is much broader in scope. In amino acid catabolism, for example, it is believed that α-ketoglutarate is the major amino group acceptor for most of the amino acid transaminations. In other words, α-ketoglutarate acts as a "collection compound" for amino acid nitrogen. The subsequent metabolic fate of the amino group of glutamate is quite varied (see diagram below). One course is a reutilization of the nitrogen in the biosynthesis of amino acids, also via a transamination reaction. Another route, catalyzed by an ATP-dependent *glutamine synthetase,* is amidation to form glutamine. The glutamine then serves as a nitrogen donor in the biosynthesis of several biomolecules, most notably the purines and pyrimidines (see Chapter 17). A third path results from the action of *glutamate dehydrogenase* (see page 422), which converts glutamate to α-ketoglutarate and free ammonia. The ammonia can then be used in certain anabolic reactions as an important nitrogen source (glutamine biosynthesis; pyrimidine biosynthesis) or excreted from the organism as ammonia or urea (see page 423). A fourth main pathway is a specific

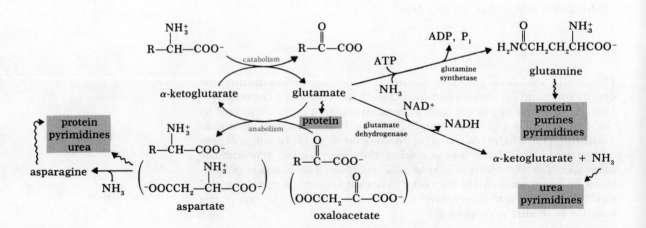

transamination with oxaloacetate to yield aspartate. The aspartate can also be amidated to give asparagine, an amino acid found in most proteins. Alternatively, the aspartate can lose its nitrogen, also in the form of urea. The nitrogen and carbon skeleton of aspartate are also utilized in the biosynthesis of pyrimidines.

Because it does have a central role in amino acid metabolism, and because the reaction mechanism is understood in some detail, let us consider the process of transamination in greater depth. The main feature is the participation of *pyridoxal phosphate* as a coenzyme. Although our immediate concern is its role in transamination reactions, pyridoxal phosphate also functions as a required coenzyme in other types of amino acid transformations such as decarboxylation and racemization (L-amino acid $\rightleftarrows$ D-amino acid). Consistent with our discussions of other coenzymes throughout previous chapters, note that pyridoxal phosphate represents the metabolically active form of a vitamin. In this instance, the parent substance is *vitamin B$_6$*. As shown below, vitamin B$_6$, sometimes called *pyridoxine* or *pyridoxol,* is a substituted pyridine. Oxidation of one hydroxymethyl group ($-CH_2OH$) to an aldehyde linkage and phosphorylation of the second yields pyridoxal phosphate. The active site of pyridoxal phosphate resides in the aldehyde grouping, which is susceptible to undergoing covalent interaction with free amino groupings (such as that contributed by amino acids, for example) to form what is called a *Schiff base* species with a character-

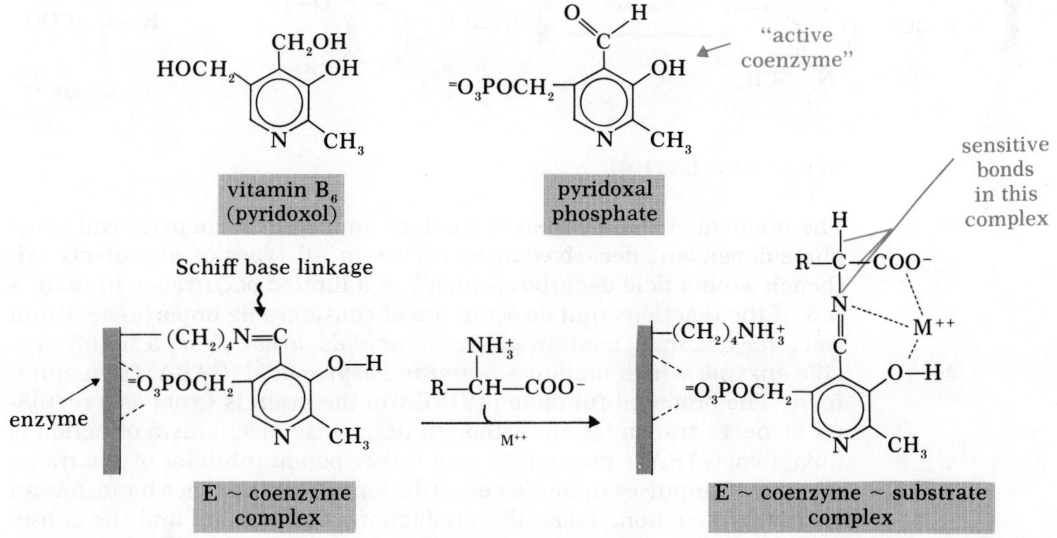

istic imino linkage ($-\overset{\overset{\displaystyle H}{|}}{C}=N-$). In fact, it is believed that, prior to reaction with a substrate amino acid, the pyridoxal phosphate is covalently bound to the enzyme by just such a linkage, with the amino grouping being contributed by the ϵ-amino group of a lysine side chain in the polypeptide chain. The first stage of a reaction involves attack by the substrate amino acid at the imino bond between the coenzyme and enzyme, resulting in the formation of a new Schiff base species between the coenzyme and the substrate amino acid. The new covalent Schiff base complex is stabilized by a metal ion and presumably remains attached to the enzyme by non-covalent interactions between the coenzyme and the polypeptide chain. Aside from explaining the initial mechanism of all pyridoxal phosphate-dependent transformations of amino acids, this system offers a clear illustration of what is meant by the basic concept of an enzyme-coenzyme-substrate intermediate complex in biocatalysis.

The subsequent fate of the complex during the rest of the reaction is controlled by the specificity of the enzyme-active site, which is ultimately based on the amino acid sequence. The events that describe the mode of action of the transaminase enzyme are diagrammed below. At first glance the proposed mechanism may appear complex. Actually, it is quite simple and can be described as occurring in two stages. First, the amino acid (substrate 1) is converted to its α-keto acid by the rearrangement of the imino linkage and then hydrolysis. Note that the amino grouping remains with the enzyme-coenzyme system as *pyridoxamine phosphate*. The second stage is just the reverse of the first, beginning with a Schiff base formation involving the acceptor α-keto acid (substrate 2). The net result of this cyclic process is the transfer of an amino group from the donor amino acid to an acceptor keto acid.

DECARBOXYLATION

The removal of the α-carboxyl group of amino acids via pyridoxal phosphate-dependent decarboxylases occurs in all types of organisms. Although amino acid decarboxylation has a limited occurrence in man, a few of the reactions that do occur are of considerable importance. Brain cells, for example, contain *glutamic acid decarboxylase,* a highly specific enzyme which produces γ-amino butyric acid (GABA) from glutamate. The proposed function of GABA in the brain is to act as a regulator of nerve transmission. Although its precise mechanism of action is unknown, GABA is recognized as a rather potent inhibitor of the transmission of impulses in nerve cells. Glutamate, on the other hand, has an excitatory function. Thus, the production of glutamate and the subsequent glutamate → GABA conversion may serve as major control signals in the neurophysiology of the brain.

$$\text{-OOCCH}_2\text{CH}_2\overset{\overset{\displaystyle \text{NH}_3^+}{|}}{\text{CH}}\text{COO}^- \xrightarrow[\text{(pyridoxal-P)}]{\begin{array}{c}\text{glutamate}\\\text{decarboxylase}\end{array}} \text{-OOCCH}_2\text{CH}_2\text{CH}_2\text{NH}_3^+ + \text{CO}_2$$

L-glutamate   γ-aminobutyrate
                                 (GABA)

The decarboxylation of aromatic amino acids such as histidine, tryptophan, 5-hydroxytryptophan, and 3,4-dihydroxyphenylalanine are also of importance. (The latter two amino acids are normal metabolic intermediates produced during the metabolism of tryptophan and phenylalanine or tyrosine, respectively.) The product of histidine decarboxylation is *histamine*. Excessive production of histamine occurs during hypersensitive allergic reactions, and its symptoms are unfortunately familiar to many individuals. The decarboxylation product of 5-hydroxytryptophan is *5-hydroxytryptamine,* commonly called *serotonin*. The bulk of serotonin production is confined to the brain, intestine, and platelet cells of blood. Although its mode of action is not completely clear, serotonin has long been implicated as an agent that plays an important role in the regulation of the nervous system. Tryptophan itself is also decarboxylated in brain cells to yield *tryptamine,*

histidine → histamine

5-hydroxytryptophan → 5-hydroxytryptamine (serotonin)

tryptophan → tryptamine → (plants) → indole acetic acid

3,4-dihydroxyphenylalanine (DOPA) → 3,4-dihydroxyphenylethylamine (dopamine)

another neurologically active amine. In plants, tryptamine is a biosynthetic precursor of *indole acetic acid* (the major site of production is the tip of roots), a very potent plant hormone that promotes plant growth. *3,4-dihydroxyphenylethylamine* (also called *dopamine*), another amine with neurological activity, is produced from the decarboxylation of 3,4-dihydroxyphenylalanine (DOPA). In a later section we will consider some proposals regarding the physiological significance of serotonin, tryptamine, and dopamine production.

OXIDATIVE DEAMINATION

A secondary route for the conversion of L-amino acids to the corresponding α-keto acids (remember that the primary route is transamination) is *oxidative deamination,* a process catalyzed by either an NAD+-dependent dehydrogenase or a flavin-dependent oxidase. The most important and widespread dehydrogenase is *glutamate dehydrogenase* (see below). Although the reaction is readily reversible, its primary role seems to be deamination. Although the liberated ammonia could be reused in other reactions, such as the amidation of glutamate and aspartate to glutamine and asparagine, most is excreted as ammonia or urea (see urea cycle). An interesting characteristic of this enzyme is that, although glutamate is the favored substrate, the enzyme can utilize

$$\text{L-glutamate} + \underset{\substack{\text{or}\\(\text{NADP}^+)}}{\text{NAD}^+} \xrightarrow[\text{dehydrogenase}]{\text{glutamate}} \alpha\text{-ketoglutarate} + \text{NH}_3 + \underset{\substack{\text{or}\\(\text{NADPH})}}{\text{NADH(H}^+)}$$

either NAD+ or NADP+ as the coenzyme. Hence, in addition to its role in nitrogen metabolism, the enzyme can also serve as an intracellular source of NADPH needed for anabolism. Two different types of flavin-dependent oxidases exist. One utilizes FAD as the electron acceptor and the other uses FMN. The FAD oxidase acts on D-amino acids whereas the FMN-dependent oxidase acts on L-amino acids. The biological significance of these reactions is not clear, since the production of reducing power does not appear to have any metabolic value. Rather, the reduced flavoprotein reacts directly and irreversibly with oxygen, producing hydrogen peroxide, a substance with a potent toxicity. A safety valve does exist, however, in the form of a special enzyme, called *catalase,* which catalyzes the decomposition of hydrogen peroxide to water and oxygen.

FMN (flavin mononucleotide) is a second coenzyme form of riboflavin with a similar but simpler structure than FAD. FMN is composed of riboflavin, ribitol, and one phosphate grouping. FAD has an additional AMP grouping (see page 312, Chapter 12).

$$\text{L-amino acid} + \text{E—FMN} \xrightarrow{\text{oxidase}} \alpha\text{-Keto acid} + \text{NH}_3 + \text{E—FMNH}_2$$

$$\text{D-amino acid} + \text{E—FAD} \xrightarrow{\text{oxidase}} \alpha\text{-Keto acid} + \text{NH}_3 + \text{E—FADH}_2$$

$$\underset{(\text{E—FADH}_2)}{\text{E—FMNH}_2} + \text{O}_2 \longrightarrow \underset{(\text{E—FAD})}{\text{E—FMN}} + \text{H}_2\text{O}_2$$

$$\text{H}_2\text{O}_2 \xrightarrow{\text{catalase}} \text{H}_2\text{O} + \tfrac{1}{2}\text{O}_2$$

An enzyme widespread in the animal kingdom and important to normal brain metabolism is *monoamine oxidase* (MAO). This enzyme is related in action, but not in structure, to the amino acid oxidases. MAO catalyzes the oxidative deamination of primary amines to the corresponding aldehydes (see below). The significance of this reaction is discussed further on pages 432 and 433.

$$RCH_2NH_2 + O_2 \xrightarrow[\text{oxidase}]{\text{monoamine}} RCHO + NH_3 + H_2O_2$$

UREA CYCLE

Excess or unused nitrogen resulting from amino acid degradation is excreted from an organism in the form of ammonia, urea, and uric acid. As was pointed out above, the primary source of ammonia is deamination of glutamate by glutamate dehydrogenase. Urea is formed by a special group of enzymes whose combined operation constitutes the *urea cycle,* which will be examined here. Uric acid is not a direct end product of amino acid metabolism, but rather originates from the degradation of purines (see page 460). The inclusion of uric acid as an excretory form of amino acid nitrogen is based on the fact that the nitrogen in purines originates from amino acids. Although the major end product varies from one type of organism to another, certain generalizations are possible. For example, most bacteria, plants, and fish are ammonia excreting, whereas birds and most invertebrates secrete uric acid. In most mammals including man, the primary product is urea, due to the operation of the enzymes of the urea cycle. In mammals these enzymes are localized in the liver. From the liver, the urea is passed into the circulating blood, which is eventually dialyzed in the kidneys, resulting in loss of the low-molecular-weight urea to the urine. The urea is excreted in the urine where it represents 80–90% of the total urine nitrogen. For man the average daily urea excretion is approximately 30 grams. This is roughly 20 times the combined amounts of ammonia and uric acid, and 150 times the amount of free amino acids excreted in the same period. An obvious question is: What happens to all this urea? Well, eventually it is used as a nitrogen source by plants and bacteria, which possess the enzyme *urease* that converts urea to ammonia and carbon dioxide. Why isn't the urea reused by mammals? Simply because mammals do not produce urease.

The urea cycle itself is composed of only five reactions, each catalyzed by a different enzyme. As indicated in the net reaction given below: (a) the immediate source of urea nitrogen is twofold, namely, ammonia and the amino group of aspartate; (b) the urea carbon originates from CO_2, which thus can be thought of as the nitrogen acceptor; and (c) the process is significantly endergonic, requiring 3 ATP's per molecule of urea produced.

$$CO_2 + NH_3 + H_2O + \underset{(N)}{\text{aspartate}} \xrightarrow[\underset{\text{3ATP}}{\overset{\text{AMP, PP}_i}{}}]{\overset{\text{5 enzymes}}{\underset{\text{2ADP, 2P}_i}{}}} H_2N\overset{\overset{\displaystyle O}{\|}}{—C}—NH_2 + \text{fumarate}$$
$$\text{urea}$$

As we have found on other occasions, however, a net reaction relates nothing at all about the sequence of events that intervene between reactants and products. These are diagrammed in Figure 16–1. An analysis of how this metabolic sequence results in urea formation best begins by considering the formation of *carbamyl phosphate* from

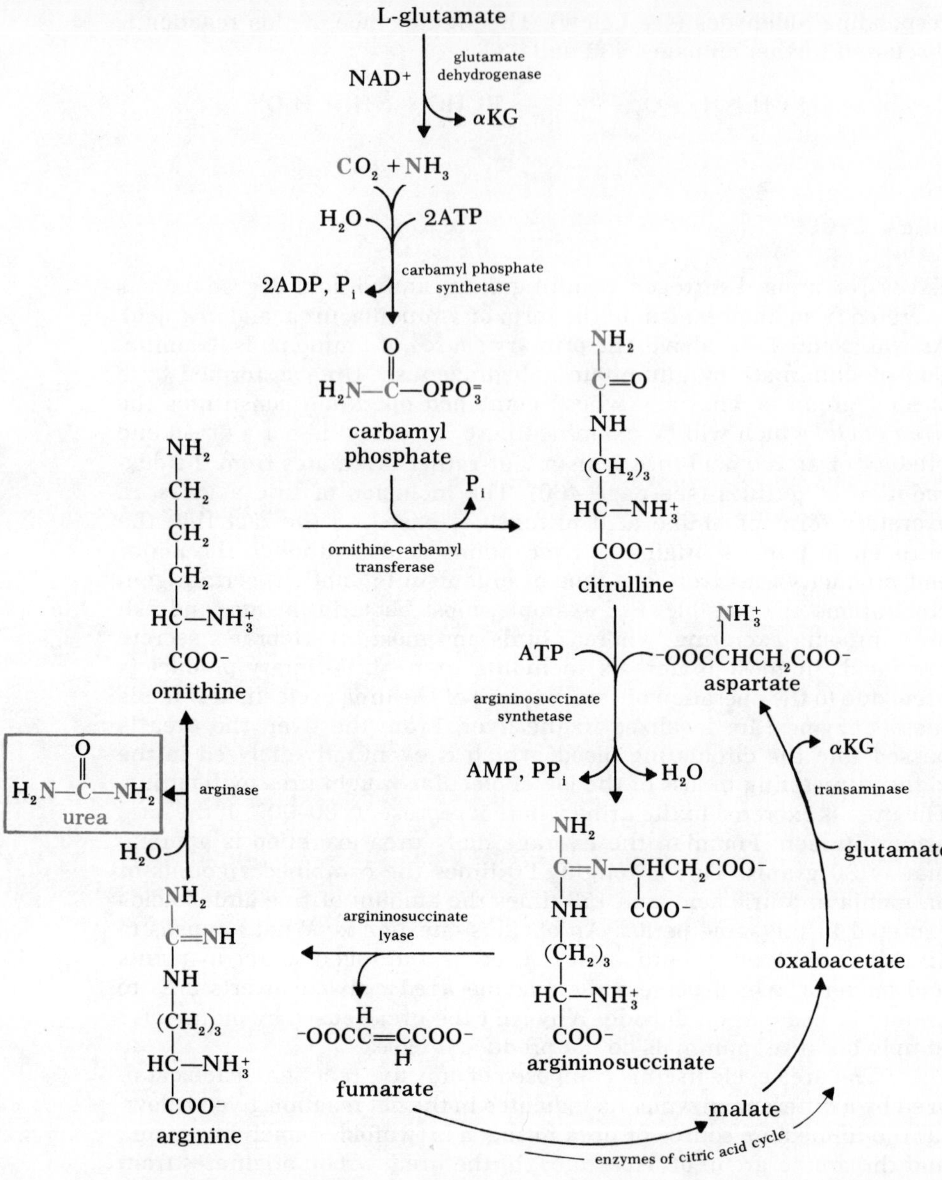

Figure 16-1 The urea cycle. Reactions of urea cycle proper shown by heavy arrows. Ancillary reactions shown by lighter arrows. Flow of carbon and nitrogen to urea shown by C and N.

CO_2, NH_3, and ATP as the first reaction. The enzyme involved is *carbamyl phosphate synthetase* and, as you can see, it requires two molecules of ATP. Once formed, carbamyl phosphate condenses with *ornithine* to form *citrulline*. Both of these substances are basic alpha amino acids found in most organisms but not known to occur in any of the cellular proteins. In the second ATP-dependent reaction, citrulline condenses with aspartate (the second N source) to yield *argininosuccinate,* which in turn is converted to arginine and fumarate. The key and unique step in the urea cycle is the hydrolysis of arginine by the enzyme *arginase.* Not only is it the step wherein urea is formed, but the production of ornithine serves to close the cycle. Non-urea–producing organisms are so because they lack this enzyme. The other enzymes are widely distributed in nature and participate in pathways other than the urea production. Carbamyl phosphate synthetase, for example, catalyzes the first step in the biosynthesis of the pyrimidine nucleotides (see page 451).

Although ammonia and aspartate are the immediate nitrogen sources, note that both can be traced back to glutamate. Glutamate dehydrogenase accounts for the formation of ammonia. Aspartate can acquire its amino nitrogen from glutamate by a simple transamination involving oxaloacetate as the acceptor keto acid. Since oxaloacetate can be formed from fumarate by enzymes of the citric acid cycle, none of the intermediates of the urea cycle is wasted.

METABOLISM OF SPECIFIC AMINO ACIDS

Having examined the major types of metabolic transformations common to most amino acids, we will now consider some of the specific reactions describing the metabolism of individual amino acids. Although our coverage will be limited to only a small number of amino acids, the subject matter is rather illustrative in a specific fashion of the general principles of amino acid metabolism.

PHENYLALANINE, TYROSINE, AND TRYPTOPHAN

One aspect of amino acid metabolism that students of biochemistry find rather interesting is the myriad reactions associated with the metabolism of the three aromatic acids, phenylalanine, tyrosine, and tryptophan. A quick glance at Figures 16–2 and 16–3, which summarize the major metabolic relationships (a few minor ones exist) of these amino acids, indicates why. Though the composite diagram of the two figures may initially appear as an incomprehensible maze of reactions, it is not that at all. Briefly, Figure 16–2 summarizes the anabolism of the three amino acids and the major catabolic pathway of tyrosine and phenylalanine, and Figure 16–3 summarizes the principal catabolic pathways of tryptophan and additional catabolic pathways of tyrosine and phenylalanine, each of which has some special biological significance.

Study of the diagram best begins by recognizing that the nucleus of these reactions is a direct relationship between phenylalanine and tyrosine, namely, tyrosine is produced from phenylalanine. It is an irreversible process and hence phenylalanine is not formed from tyrosine. Thus, the phenylalanine → tyrosine conversion is rather significant. The only link between the metabolism of phenylalanine and tyrosine and the metabolism of tryptophan is that both phenylalanine and tryptophan share part of the same anabolic biosynthetic pathway.

The phenylalanine → tyrosine conversion is catalyzed by *phenylalanine hydroxylase*. As you might expect, the enzyme is specific in its action, resulting in a hydroxylation of only the para position of the phenyl ring to yield para-hydroxyphenylalanine, that is, tyrosine. If it were not specific, hydroxylation would also occur at any of the other four positions in the phenyl ring yielding both ortho-hydroxyphenylalanine and meta-hydroxyphenylalanine. This strict specificity for one of several possible hydroxylation sites in the substrate is characteristic of hydroxylases in general. Recall, that hydroxylases are also typified by a requirement for a co-oxidizable substrate which acts as a hydrogen donor (see Chapter 13, page 341). In the case of phenylalanine hydroxylase this role is fulfilled by a substance called *tetrahydrobiopterin*. During the course of the reaction it is oxidized to dihydrobiopterin. (The structures of both biopterin species are shown below. Chemically, the biopterin structure would be described as a *substituted pteridine*, the parent heterobicyclic compound [see margin]. *Tetrahydrofolic acid*, another pteridine-derived coenzyme of immense importance in the metabolism of amino acids, purines, and pyrimidines, is discussed in the next section.) Although the immediate co-oxidizable substrate for phenylalanine hydroxylase is tetrahydrobiopterin, the reducing power originates from NADPH. As shown in the diagram, this is accomplished by the reducing power in NADPH being utilized to form tetrahydrobiopterin from dihydrobiopterin. Note that the NADPH:dihydrobiopterin reaction is catalyzed by a specific dehydrogenase and not phenylalanine hydroxylase.

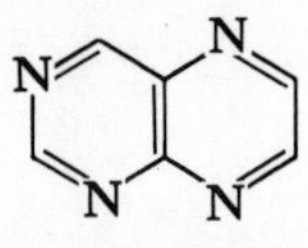

pteridine

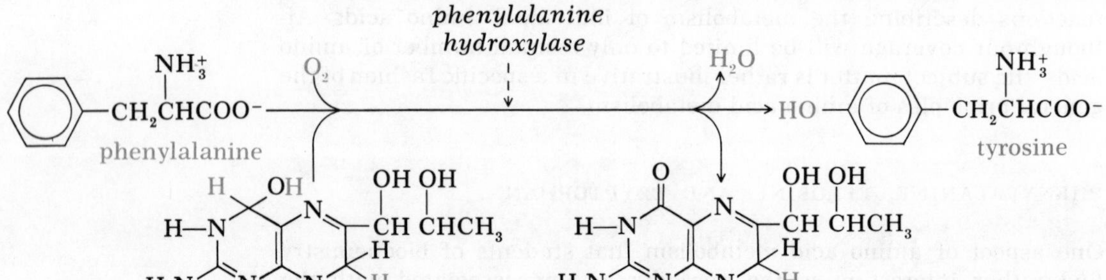

Phenylalanine hydroxylase occurs in all types of organisms including man. Accordingly, tyrosine is not classified as an *essential amino acid* that must be supplied in the daily diet of man. Phenylalanine, on the other hand, is required, since the enzymes for the biosynthesis of phenylalanine (Figure 16–2) are not present in man. In fact, the dietary requirement of phenylalanine applies to most mammals, with the necessary anabolic enzymes being found primarily in plants and bacteria. The complete amino acid dietary requirements of man are summarized at the end of this chapter (see page 444).

Unfortunately, because of a hereditary genetic defect, not all individuals possess the hydroxylase enzyme, or they produce it in levels too low to support normal metabolism. Consequently, a metabolic blockage is created resulting in elevated levels of phenylalanine in the body tissues and fluids. This situation in turn results in an increase in the levels of phenylpyruvate, phenyllactate, and phenylacetate (route H in

Figure 16-3). Under normal conditions the production of these acids is very small. The complication results from the fact that these substances are toxic, with the damaging effects being primarily directed against developing brain cells. Severe cases of this condition, called *phenyl-ketonuria* (PKU), are characterized by an extensive degree of mental retardation and an early death. Since the brain damage is particularly rapid and irreversible in infants, an early diagnosis is mandatory in order for treatment to be effective. Fortunately both are possible. The diagnosis, which is now a generally routine procedure done shortly after birth, is based on a simple diaper test to detect the presence of high levels of phenylalanine in the baby's urine. The treatment of PKU infants is to limit the intake of phenylalanine by the use of specially formulated diets with a low phenylalanine content. In adult life there is less need for dietary control since the toxic products apparently are excreted with greater efficiency.

Phenylketonuria is but one of several hereditary diseases associated with disorders of amino acid metabolism. In fact, there are four different diseases associated with the metabolism of phenylalanine and tyrosine alone (see below). Furthermore a number of metabolic diseases exist that are associated with the metabolism of compounds other than amino acids. For example, recall our earlier discussions in Chapter 8 of hereditary metabolic diseases associated with the abnormal degradation of cerebroside and ganglioside lipids. A listing of these and several other conditions is given in Appendix III.

Rather than proceed with a blow-by-blow account of the other pathways shown in Figures 16-2 and 16-3, only a brief synopsis of each is given below. Although the mention of a few specifics cannot be avoided, a thorough analysis of all details is avoided. Despite the appearance of this diagram, it is not intended to impress you with details. The primary objective, using phenylalanine, tyrosine, and tryptophan as specific examples, is to illustrate the varied and specialized nature of amino acid metabolism and its relationship to the metabolism of the whole organism. A complete family of similar diagrams could be constructed for many of the amino acids. Some would be more extensive, others less so.

1. Route A (Figure 16-2) depicts the main catabolic pathway of tyrosine and phenylalanine. The very first reaction in this sequence is a transamination to yield *para-hydroxyphenylpyruvate,* the α-keto acid of tyrosine. In two rather complex reactions, each catalyzed by a different oxidase enzyme, hydroxyphenylpyruvate is first converted to *homogentisic acid* and then to *maleylacetoacetate.* A rare metabolic disease, called *alkaptonuria,* resulting from an inability to produce homogentisic acid oxidase, causes an accumulation of homogentisic acid which is then excreted in the urine. On exposure to alkali and oxygen, the urine turns black due to the oxidation of homogentisic acid. This condition is not known to be associated with any adverse physiological effects. An isomerization of maleylacetoacetate to *fumarylacetoacetate,* followed by hydrolysis to yield *fumarate* and *acetoacetate,* completes the catabolic sequence. The fumarate can then enter the citric acid cycle for further degradation to CO_2 or incorporation into carbohydrate. Thus, phenylalanine and tyrosine are glycogenic. The acetoacetate fragment, after conversion to acetoacetyl-SCoA, can be used in the biosynthesis of fatty acids or sterols. Hence, phenylalanine and tyrosine are ketogenic.

Recent studies provide evidence that the biochemical basis of brain damage associated with phenylketonuria may be an inhibition, specifically in brain cells, by phenylpyruvate of pyruvate dehydrogenase, the multi-enzyme complex that catalyzes the conversion of pyruvate to acetyl-SCoA (see Chapter 12, page 316). Since this is the primary source of acetyl-SCoA formation in brain cells, this means that significantly reduced amounts of acetyl-SCoA would be available for entering the citric acid cycle for energy production. Less acetyl-SCoA would also be available for the biosynthesis of fatty acids and cholesterol, both of which are important constituents of nerve tissue in the brain. In short, the inhibition of the pyruvate → acetyl-SCoA conversion would severely affect the normal metabolism, development, and function of the brain.

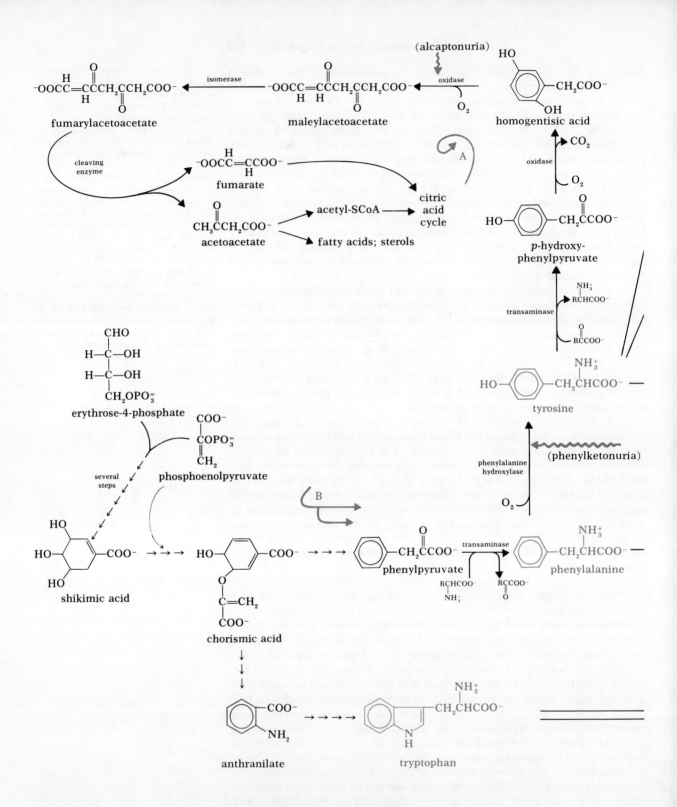

Figure 16–2 A summary of the main catabolic pathway of tyrosine and phenylalanine (A) and the anabolic (B) pathways of all three aromatic amino acids. Wavy arrows (〜) mark the locations of hereditary metabolic defects.

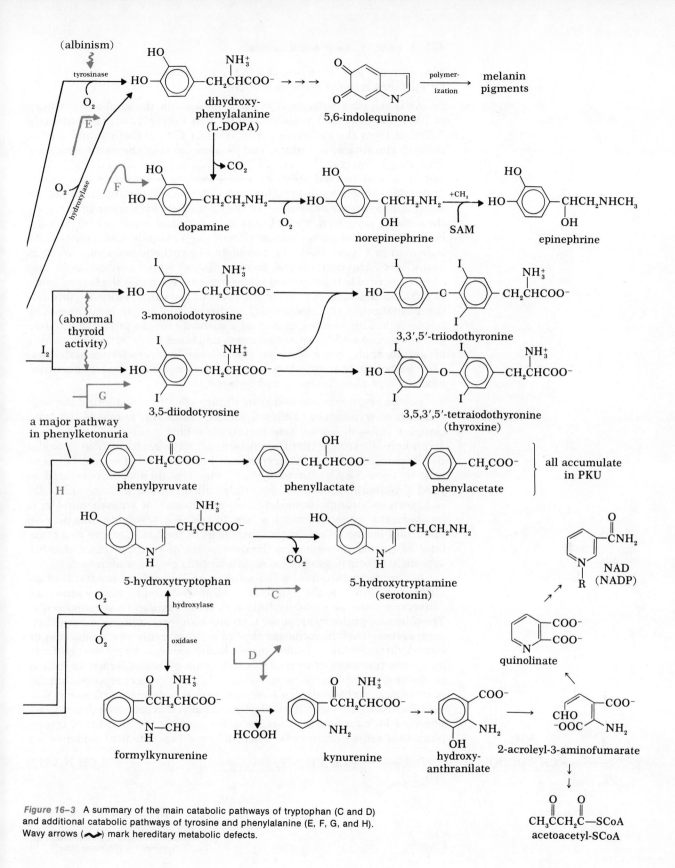

Figure 16–3 A summary of the main catabolic pathways of tryptophan (C and D) and additional catabolic pathways of tyrosine and phenylalanine (E, F, G, and H). Wavy arrows (〰) mark hereditary metabolic defects.

Alternatively, the acetoacetyl-SCoA can be converted to acetyl-SCoA for entrance into the citric acid cycle.

2. As is the case with most of the amino acids, the anabolic pathway of phenylalanine and tyrosine (route B in Figure 16–2) is completely different from the catabolic pathway. Only the catabolism and anabolism of glutamate, aspartate, and alanine involve the same reactions operating in reverse. In each of these instances, the amino acid is converted to and formed from its corresponding α-keto acid in a transamination reaction: α-ketoglutarate ⇄ glutamate; oxaloacetate ⇄ aspartate; pyruvate ⇄ alanine. In the case of phenylalanine production, the carbons arise from *phosphoenolpyruvate* and *erythrose phosphate*, both of which in turn originate from the catabolism of hexoses. As indicated in Figure 16–2, the complete biosynthetic sequence involves many steps through several intermediates, with *shikimic acid* and *chorismic acid* being the most characteristic. Note that the last reaction is a transamination step. Note that part of the same pathway (through the formation of chorismic acid) is also utilized in the biosynthesis of tryptophan. This sharing of part of a pathway for the production of two or three amino acids is not uncommon, and takes place with other groups of amino acids. Such sharing also occurs in degradative pathways. The catabolism of tryptophan, however, does not share the homogentisic acid route of phenylalanine and tyrosine.

3. Let us begin our discussion of Figure 16–3 by considering the degradation of tryptophan (routes C and D). Since this is one of the most complex areas of amino acid metabolism, only a skeleton summary is given here. First note that the initial reaction in each pathway is oxidative in nature. In route C, tryptophan is hydroxylated on the benzene ring to yield *5-hydroxytryptophan,* which is then decarboxylated to yield *5-hydroxytryptamine,* generally called *serotonin.* Since serotonin is known to strongly stimulate the constriction of smooth muscle, it has been the subject of much study. In addition, serotonin may play an important hormonal role in the physiology of the brain, acting as a regulator of neural transmission. Despite years of study, neither of these actions nor their physiological significance is clearly understood.

Very recent studies by C. Frohman and coworkers suggest that an alternate pathway to the tryptophan → 5-hydroxytryptophan → serotonin conversion may be causally linked in some fashion to schizophrenia. The alternate pathway proposed is tryptophan → tryptamine → *dimethyltryptamine.* They hypothesize that in schizophrenia the production of dimethyltryptamine, a known potent hallucinogenic agent, results from an excess transport of tryptophan into brain cells and hence an excess production of tryptamine in the brain cells. It is further proposed that the biochemical malfunction in schizophrenia is a defective transport process for tryptophan into the cells. Specifically, it is proposed that schizophrenics lack an enzyme that normally controls the amount of tryptophan that enters brain cells. There is some experimental evidence for

tryptophan →($-CO_2$)→ tryptamine →(methylation)→ dimethyltryptamine

(Is this the molecular agent responsible for the symptoms of schizophrenia?)

these suggestions, but additional investigation is necessary for confirmation as well as clarification. It should be noted that there are other theories about the cause of schizophrenia. One of these proposals is that the causal agent is produced from the abnormal metabolism of tyrosine (see item 5 below).

In the other catabolic pathway (route D), the indole ring is oxidatively cleaved to yield *formylkynurenine,* which in turn is converted to *kynurenine.* The loss of carbon as formic acid (HCOOH) in this step links the catabolism of tryptophan to an important area of metabolism termed *one-carbon metabolism.* We will return to this subject in a later section (page 436). The further catabolism of kynurenine proceeds through a complex series of reactions, with the first principal intermediate being *3-hydroxyanthranilate.* After a ring cleavage to yield *2-acroleyl-3-amino fumarate,* a branching in the pathway occurs. The less important route eventually results in the production of *acetoacetyl-SCoA,* which can then enter the citric acid cycle. Of greater importance, however, is the cyclization of 2-acroleyl-3-amino fumarate to yield *quinolinate,* which then serves as the biosynthetic precursor of the *nicotinamide* moiety of NAD and NADP. The tryptophan → NAD(NADP) pathway operates under normal conditions and is a supplement to the dietary requirement of nicotinic acid which is used directly in the formation of NAD and NADP. It does not, however, replace the dietary requirement.

4.   Route E depicts one of the specific roles of tyrosine metabolism that occurs in a specialized group of cells which are variously called *melanocytes, melanoblasts,* or simply *pigment cells.* These cells are responsible for producing the so-called *melanin* pigments, which are the substances imparting the coloration of skin, eyes, and hair. Melanin pigments appear to be polymeric forms of *indole-5,6-quinone,* but the exact structure and extent of polymerization are unknown. As shown, the formation of melanin initially depends on the hydroxylation of tyrosine to yield *3,4-dihydroxy-L-phenylalanine* (L-DOPA). This process is catalyzed by the enzyme *tyrosinase,* which as you might expect is quite abundant in melanocytes. An inability of the melanocytes to produce tyrosinase, because of a defective and hereditary gene, is responsible for the condition known as *albinism.*

5.   Route F summarizes a second special feature of tyrosine metabolism, namely, the formation of physiologically active hormones, termed the *catecholamines,* which include *L-dopamine, norepinephrine* (noradrenalin), and *epinephrine* (adrenalin). Recall that we have already discussed the major metabolic effect of epinephrine, namely, the ability to accelerate the catabolism of carbohydrates by stimulating the production of cyclic-AMP, which in turn stimulates the action of glycogen phosphorylases (see page 275). The production of catecholamines is particularly prominent in the cells of brain tissue, nerve tissue, and the adrenal gland. As in melanin production, the key reaction is the initial formation of L-DOPA, which then undergoes a decarboxylation to yield *L-dopamine.* The hydroxylation of L-dopamine and a subsequent methylation reaction (see a later section, page 437) yield norepinephrine and epinephrine, respectively. Although the melanin and catecholamine pathways both begin with the conversion of tyrosine to L-DOPA, note that two different enzymes are involved. The hydroxylase catalyzing the transformation in the catecholamine pathway appears to be quite

similar to the hydroxylase involved in the conversion of phenylalanine to tyrosine. The fact that the administration of L-DOPA offers relief to individuals suffering from Parkinson's disease (see page 72) suggests that this affliction is related to an inability of certain cells to produce adequate levels of L-DOPA. It further suggests that in these cells tyrosine hydroxylase may be (a) produced in low levels or not at all, or (b) produced in a defective form.

The subsequent fate of dopamine, norepinephrine, and epinephrine is primarily excretion in the urine. However, only small levels of the free amines are found in the urine. Rather, they are excreted as the corresponding acids and, in the case of norepinephrine and epinephrine, also as the methylated derivatives of the corresponding acids. The acids are formed by the action of *monoamine oxidase*, to which we referred earlier in the chapter (page 422). In the case of dopamine, the action of monoamine oxidase forms the corresponding aldehyde, which is then oxidized to the acid, dihydroxyphenylacetate, by an NAD^+-dependent dehydrogenase. Earlier, we discussed the possibility that the cause of schizophrenia may be related to abnormal metabolism of tryptophan, and stated that another theory has been proposed. Well, it is in this area of tyrosine metabolism for which there is some evidence that the causal agent of a schizophrenia may be produced. Included among the suspected catecholamine compounds are 3,4-dimethoxyphenylethylamine and 6-hydroxydopamine (that is, 3,4,6-trihydroxyphenylethylamine).

H_3CO—⬡(OCH_3)—$CH_2CH_2NH_2$

3,4-dimethoxyphenylethylamine

HO—⬡(OH)(HO)—$CH_2CH_2NH_2$

3,4,6-trihydroxyphenylethylamine

dopamine $\xrightarrow[O_2]{\text{monoamine oxidase}}$ (aldehyde) $\xrightarrow[NAD^+ \rightarrow NADH^+]{\text{dehydrogenase}}$ CH_2COO^-

norepinephrine $\xrightarrow[O_2]{\text{monoamine oxidase}}$ (CHCHO) $\xrightarrow[+CH_3, O_2]{\text{methylation and monoamine oxidase}}$ $CHCOO^-$

main excretion products

$\xrightarrow[]{\text{"+CH}_3\text{" methylation}}$ H_3CO—...—$CHCH_2NH_2$ $\xrightarrow[O_2]{\text{monoamine oxidase}}$

epinephrine $\xrightarrow[]{\text{"+CH}_3\text{" methylation}}$ H_3CO—...—$CHCH_2NHCH_3$ $\xrightarrow[O_2]{\text{monoamine oxidase}}$ H_3CO—...—$CHCHO$ $\xrightarrow[NAD^+ \rightarrow NADH]{\text{dehydrogenase}}$

6. The thyroid gland is another site of a specialized and extremely important facet of tyrosine metabolism, namely, the formation of a group of low-molecular-weight iodinated compounds called the *thyroid hormones* (route G). Although the exact sequence of events is more complex than that shown in Figure 16–3, the process can be broken down into two stages: (a) *iodination* to yield 3-monoiodotyrosine and 3,5-diiodotyrosine, and (b) *conjugation* of these species to yield 3,5,3'-triiodothyronine and 3,5,3',5'-tetraiodothyronine (*thyroxine*). The latter

two materials are the active thyroid hormones. In the thyroid gland, triiodothyronine and thyroxine are present almost exclusively in peptide linkage in a protein called *thyroglobulin*. When the thyroid is stimulated, the thyroglobulin molecule is hydrolyzed by proteolytic enzymes in the gland, and the hormones are secreted into the circulating blood and carried to other tissues. By processes yet unknown, the thyroid gland profoundly influences a broad spectrum of metabolic and physiological processes. Actually, there are few phases of the general growth and development of man that are not regulated to some extent by these hormones.

PHENYLALANINE-TYROSINE METABOLISM AND ALCOHOLISM

Alcoholism is one of the most common diseases of man. Although the factors that turn an individual to alcohol are many and varied, recent studies have shown that the onset and persistence of a state of alcohol dependence (alcoholism) may have a biochemical explanation. Using the many similarities between the withdrawal symptoms of individuals dependent on either alcohol or the addictive alkaloid drugs such as morphine, it was hypothesized that alcohol dependence may be caused by the formation of a substance similar in effect to the addictive alkaloids. To test the hypothesis, laboratory rats were maintained on a steady diet of ethyl alcohol to induce a state of dependency. Thereafter, the animals were sacrificed and cell-free homogenates of brain tissue were prepared. The hypothesis proved to be correct with the isolation from the homogenate of *tetrahydropapaveroline* (THP), an alkaloid (see next page). Brain homogenates from non-alcohol-fed control animals contained none of this substance.

A biochemical explanation for this is related to the metabolism of dopamine, which we have just discussed as being a normal intermediate of phenylalanine-tyrosine metabolism (see Figure 16-3). We have seen that the further catabolism of dopamine normally yields dihydroxyphenylacetate by the consecutive action of two enzymes, namely, monoamine oxidase and an NAD^+-dependent dehydrogenase. The acid is then excreted in the urine. Under abnormal conditions—in this case in the presence of elevated levels of ethyl alcohol—it is proposed that the oxidation of dihydroxyphenylacetaldehyde to the corresponding aromatic acid is inhibited by a competition between the aromatic aldehyde dehydrogenase which catalyzes this reaction and another NAD^+-dependent dehydrogenase which catalyzes the oxidation of ethyl alcohol to acetaldehyde. In other words, the limited intracellular supply of NAD^+ is depleted by the presence of ethyl alcohol. In still other words, ethyl alcohol acts as a scavenger of NAD^+. The immediate result is a decrease in the activity of the aromatic aldehyde dehydrogenase. That is to say, the dihydroxyphenylacetaldehyde → dihydroxyphenylacetate conversion is blocked. The resulting increased level of the aromatic aldehyde in the presence of its precursor, dopamine, is then proposed to yield tetrahydropapaveroline by a direct condensation of the two materials. This event is probably enzyme independent, since reactions between primary amines and aldehydes occur quite easily even under the mild conditions of the physiological state.

Although it is yet undetermined whether THP is a compound with addictive properties, it is known that THP is a biosynthetic precursor

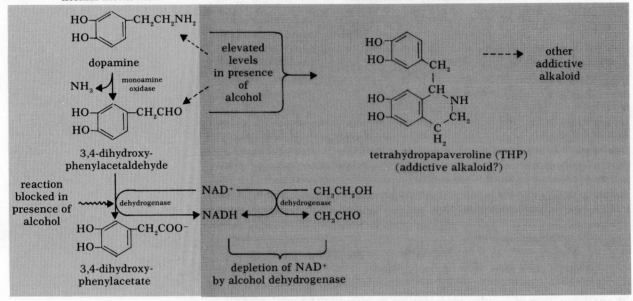

normal metabolism

abnormal metabolism

dopamine

3,4-dihydroxy-
phenylacetaldehyde

reaction
blocked in
presence of
alcohol

3,4-dihydroxy-
phenylacetate

elevated
levels
in presence
of
alcohol

depletion of NAD⁺
by alcohol dehydrogenase

tetrahydropapaveroline (THP)
(addictive alkaloid?)

other
addictive
alkaloid

of morphine in the opium poppy plant. Thus, if THP is not itself addictive, the possibility does exist that in the brain it may be converted to another alkaloid that is addictive. Indeed, there is debate as to whether this type of pathway has any causal relationship to alcoholism. An alternate school of thought is that the preference for alcohol is associated with an increased production of serotonin in addicted animals. Whatever the case, there is considerable evidence that alcoholism does have a biochemical explanation—be it the production of addictive alkaloids, the elevated production of serotonin, or the elevated production of some other agent. Additional research offers the possibility of a solution and with it the possibility of developing a more satisfactory treatment of withdrawal from a state of alcohol dependency. Knowing the biochemical basis for a physiological disorder, the search for an effective treatment can be more organized.

At this point you ought to appreciate the validity of earlier statements that the amino acids are not merely monomeric units of proteins. True, this is their critical and primary role, but it is not—as clearly illustrated by the metabolism of phenylalanine, tyrosine, and tryptophan —their only role. As further evidence of this point, let us now examine other examples in the event that the false impression is made that these specialized roles are confined only to the metabolism of the *aromatic* amino acids.

GLYCINE AND TETRAPYRROLE BIOSYNTHESIS

The functional importance of the porphyrin (tetrapyrrole) grouping in all types of living cells cannot be questioned. So far we have seen that it is the active structural moiety of hemoglobin, myoglobin, chlorophyll, and all the cytochromes. It is also the structural backbone of vitamin B_{12} (see page 441). Accordingly, it is only appropriate that we consider its biosynthetic origin. The subject is well suited to this chapter, since the sole anabolic precursors are *glycine* and *succinyl-SCoA*. A few of the main steps are shown in Figure 16–4. The process begins with a condensation of succinyl-SCoA and glycine to form *α-amino-β-ketoadipic acid*. This in turn is decarboxylated (the CO_2 lost comes from the glycine carboxyl group) to yield δ-*aminolevulinic acid*. The next step involves an ordered intermolecular condensation of two molecules of aminolevulinic acid to yield *porphobilinogen*, a substituted pyrrole. Four molecules of porphobilinogen are then condensed

Figure 16–4 Biosynthesis of heme groupings. A partial pathway.

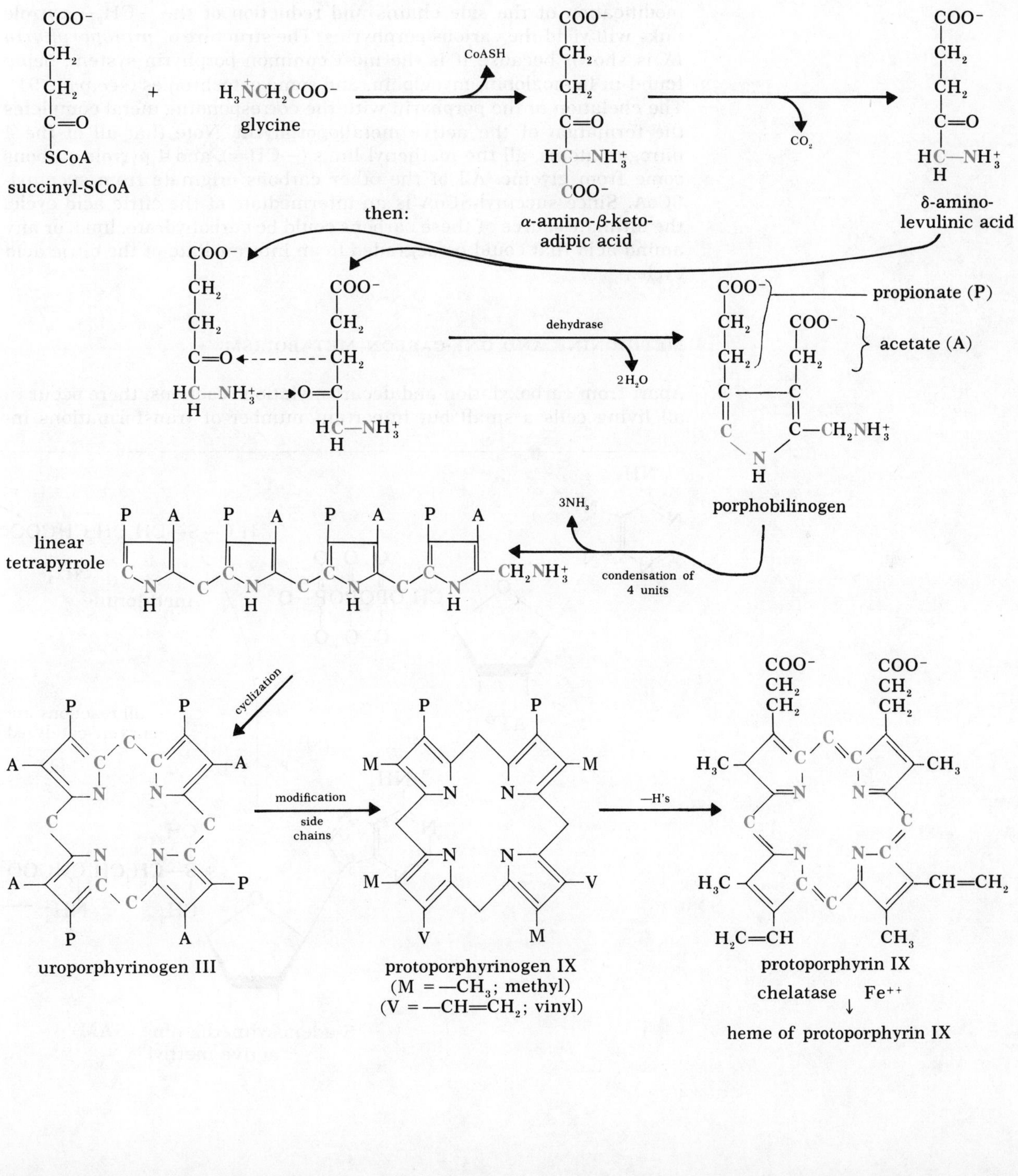

COO⁻ CH₂ CH₂ C=O SCoA succinyl-SCoA + H₃NCH₂COO⁻ glycine —CoASH→ COO⁻ CH₂ CH₂ C=O HC—NH₃⁺ COO⁻ α-amino-β-keto-adipic acid —CO₂→ COO⁻ CH₂ CH₂ C=O HC—NH₃⁺ H δ-amino-levulinic acid

then: linear tetrapyrrole P A P A P A P A C N C C N C C N C C N CH₂NH₃⁺ H H H H ←condensation of 4 units— 3NH₃ porphobilinogen propionate (P) acetate (A) —dehydrase 2H₂O→

uroporphyrinogen III —modification side chains→ protoporphyrinogen IX (M = —CH₃; methyl) (V = —CH=CH₂; vinyl) —H's→ protoporphyrin IX chelatase ↓ Fe⁺⁺ heme of protoporphyrin IX to form a *linear tetrapyrrole,* which then undergoes a ring closure to produce a *cyclic tetrapyrrole* species. Depending on the specificity of the enzymes that catalyze this latter step, the ring closing either can occur by a direct joining of the two ends of the linear tetrapyrrole or, as shown in Figure 16–3, be accompanied by a flipping of the pyrrole unit at the non-amino end into a different position before ring closure. The latter thus causes the pyrrole side chains to be arranged in a non-alternating fashion, that is: A-P; A-P; A-P; P-A rather than A-P; A-P; A-P; A-P. In other words, a specific isomer is produced, called *uroporphyrinogen III.* From this point, a specific combination of reactions involving modification of the side chains and reduction of the —CH$_2$— pyrrole links will yield the various porphyrins. The structure of *protoporphyrin IX* is shown because it is the most common porphyrin system, being found in hemoglobin, myoglobin, and some cytochromes (see page 91). The chelation of the porphyrin with the corresponding metal completes the formation of the active metalloporphyrin. Note that all of the 4 nitrogen atoms, all the methenyl links (—CH=), and 4 pyrrole carbons come from glycine. All of the other carbons originate from succinyl-SCoA. Since succinyl-SCoA is an intermediate of the citric acid cycle, the ultimate source of these carbons could be carbohydrate, lipid, or any amino acid that could be degraded to an intermediate of the citric acid cycle.

METHIONINE AND ONE-CARBON METABOLISM

Apart from carboxylation and decarboxylation reactions, there occur in all living cells a small but important number of transformations in-

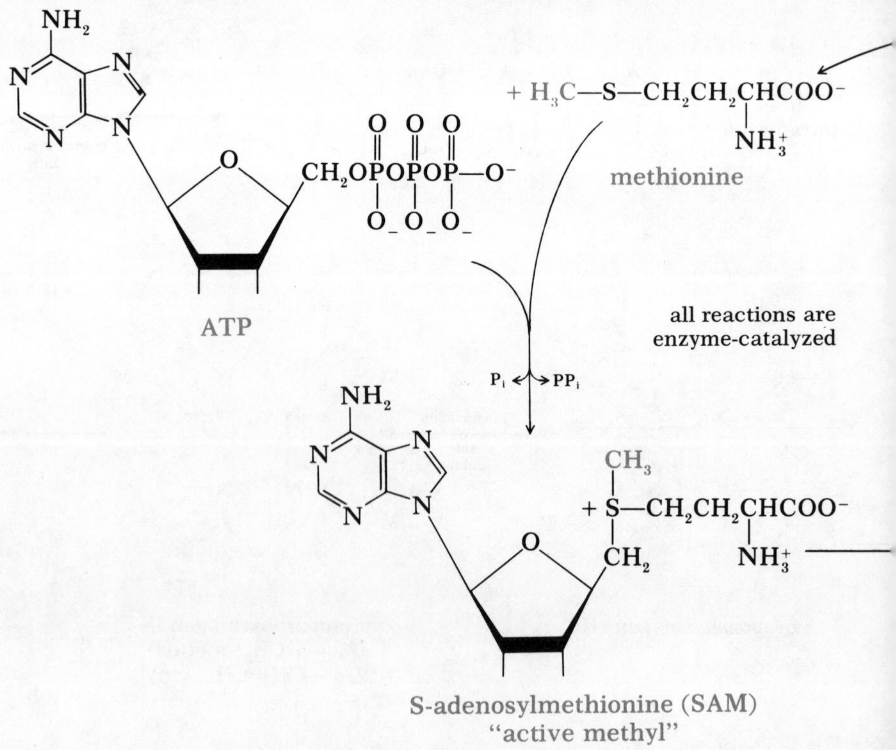

ATP

+ H$_3$C—S—CH$_2$CH$_2$CHCOO$^-$
 NH$_3^+$
methionine

all reactions are enzyme-catalyzed

P$_i$ ⇌ PP$_i$

S-adenosylmethionine (SAM) "active methyl"

volving the transfer of a one-carbon unit between two substrates. Included in this group are reactions wherein there are transfers of *methyl* (—CH$_3$), *hydroxymethyl* (—CH$_2$OH), *formyl* (—CHO), and *formimino* (—CH=NH) groups. Of these, methyl group transfer reactions, termed *transmethylations,* are most abundant.

A general representation of a transmethylation reaction can be given as follows. Under the influence of a *transmethylase* (sometimes called a methyltransferase), the complete methyl group is transferred from a donor to an acceptor molecule.

$$\text{A} \quad + \quad \text{D} \sim \text{CH}_3 \quad \xrightarrow[\text{transferase}]{\text{methyl}} \quad \text{A} \sim \text{CH}_3 \quad + \quad \text{D}$$

$$\begin{matrix} \text{acceptor} & \text{methyl} & & \text{methylated} & \text{demethylated} \\ \text{substrate} & \text{donor} & & \text{acceptor} & \text{donor} \end{matrix}$$

The reason for considering transmethylation reactions in this chapter is that the primary methyl donor is *S-adenosylmethionine,* often symbolized simply as SAM. This substance is present in all types of cells, where it is formed directly from methionine and ATP. Chemically, SAM would be classified as an unstable *sulfonium* compound in which the —S—CH$_3$ linkage is quite labile. Accordingly, S-adenosylmethionine is frequently termed an *active methyl species*. Note that S-adenosylmethionine is converted to *S-adenosylhomocysteine* (SAH) during the transmethylation reaction. S-adenosylhomocysteine is then enzymatically hydrolyzed to homocysteine and adenosine. The homocysteine is then converted to methionine by another type of transmethylation reaction. However, the methyl donor in this reaction is not S-adenosylmethionine. We will discuss this reaction shortly.

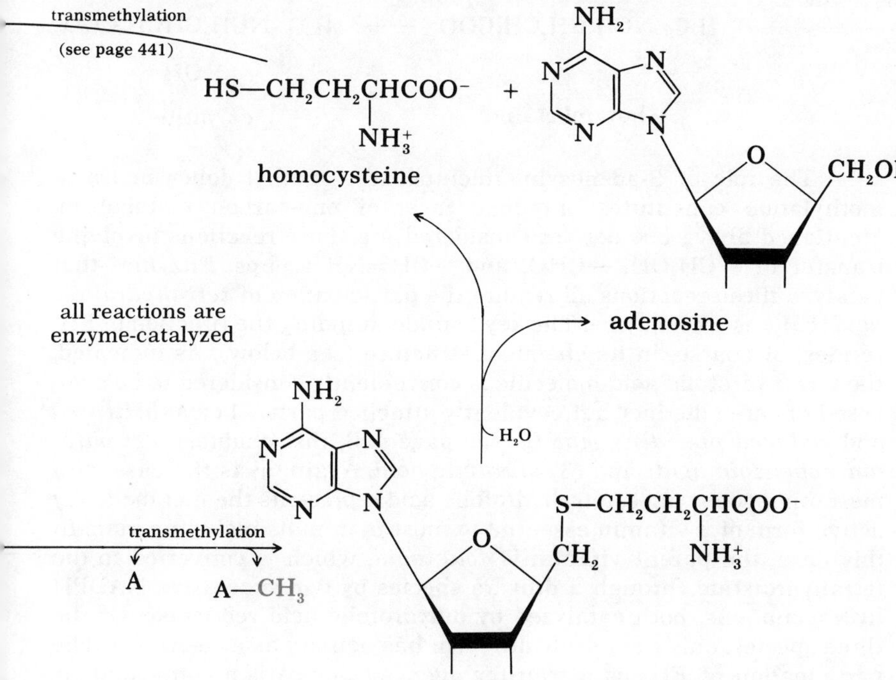

transmethylation
(see page 441)

HS—CH$_2$CH$_2$CHCOO$^-$ +
|
NH$_3^+$
homocysteine

CH$_2$OH

adenosine

all reactions are enzyme-catalyzed

H$_2$O

transmethylation

A   A—CH$_3$

S—CH$_2$CH$_2$CHCOO$^-$
| |
CH$_2$ NH$_3^+$

S-adenosylhomocysteine (SAH)

Some of the reactions illustrative of transmethylation in metabolism are given below. These include methylation of phosphatidyl ethanolamine to yield phosphatidyl choline—a major phospholipid of cellular membranes and the source of choline in the biosynthesis of sphingolipids; the methylation of guanidoacetic acid to yield creatine—a substance important in the flow of energy in muscle tissue (see page 290); and the methylation of γ-amino butyric acid to yield γ-butyrobetaine, which in turn is oxidized to yield L-carnitine—the substance involved in the transport of acyl groupings across biological membranes (see page 391). Another is the formation of epinephrine from norepinephrine, which we discussed previously (section 5 on page 432).

$$
\begin{array}{ccc}
\mathrm{CH_2OCOR} & & \mathrm{CH_2OCOR} \\
| & & | \\
\mathrm{CHOCOR'} & & \mathrm{CHOCOR} \\
| & & | \\
\mathrm{O} & \xrightarrow[\substack{\text{3 successive} \\ \text{methylations}}]{} & \mathrm{O} \\
\| & & \| \\
\mathrm{CH_2OPOCH_2CH_2NH_3^+} & & \mathrm{CH_2OPOCH_2CH_2\overset{+}{N}(CH_3)_3} \\
| & & | \\
\mathrm{O^-} & & \mathrm{O^-}
\end{array}
$$

phosphatidyl ethanolamine $\qquad\qquad$ phosphatidyl choline

$$
\text{arginine + glycine} \longrightarrow \underset{\substack{\\ \text{guanidoacetate}}}{\mathrm{H_2N-\overset{\overset{\displaystyle\overset{+}{N}H_2}{\|}}{C}-\underset{\underset{H}{|}}{N}-CH_2COO^-}} \xrightarrow[\mathrm{SAM}]{\mathrm{SAH}} \underset{\substack{\\ \text{creatine}}}{\mathrm{H_2N-\overset{\overset{\displaystyle\overset{+}{N}H_2}{\|}}{C}-\underset{\underset{CH_3}{|}}{N}-CH_2COO^-}}
$$

$$
\underset{\substack{\\ \gamma\text{-aminobutyric acid}}}{\mathrm{H_3\overset{+}{N}CH_2CH_2CH_2COO^-}} \xrightarrow[\mathrm{SAM}]{\mathrm{SAH}}\!\!\xrightarrow[\mathrm{SAM}]{\mathrm{SAH}}\!\!\xrightarrow[\mathrm{SAM}]{\mathrm{SAH}} \underset{\substack{\\ \gamma\text{-butyrobetaine}}}{\mathrm{(H_3C)_3\overset{+}{N}CH_2CH_2CH_2COO^-}} \xrightarrow{\mathrm{O_2}} \underset{\substack{\\ \text{carnitine}}}{\mathrm{(H_3C)_3\overset{+}{N}CH_2\underset{\underset{OH}{|}}{C}HCH_2COO^-}}
$$

The role of S-adenosylmethionine as a methyl donor in transmethylation constitutes only one facet of one-carbon metabolism. Mentioned above but not yet considered are those reactions involving transfer of $-CH_2OH$, $-CHO$, and $-CH{=}NH$ groups. Enzymes that catalyze these reactions all require the participation of *tetrahydrofolic acid* (FH_4) as a coenzyme. The key to understanding the function of FH_4 resides, of course, in its chemical structure (see below). As indicated, the tetrahydrofolic acid molecule is conveniently considered to be composed of three distinct but covalently attached parts: (1) a *substituted* and *reduced pteridine moiety* (see page 426, this chapter); (2) *para-aminobenzoic acid;* and (3) *glutamic acid.* Again, as is the case with most other coenzymes, tetrahydrofolic acid represents the metabolically active form of a vitamin essential to most mammals including man. In this case, the parent vitamin is *folic acid,* which is converted to the tetrahydro state through a dihydro species by two successive NADPH hydrogenations, both catalyzed by dihydrofolic acid reductase. Of the three species, only the tetrahydro form has activity as a coenzyme. The participation of FH_4 as a transfer agent of one-carbon compounds is due to its capability to form single-bonded covalent adducts at the nitrogen atoms at positions 5 and 10 or a bridged adduct between positions 5 and 10.

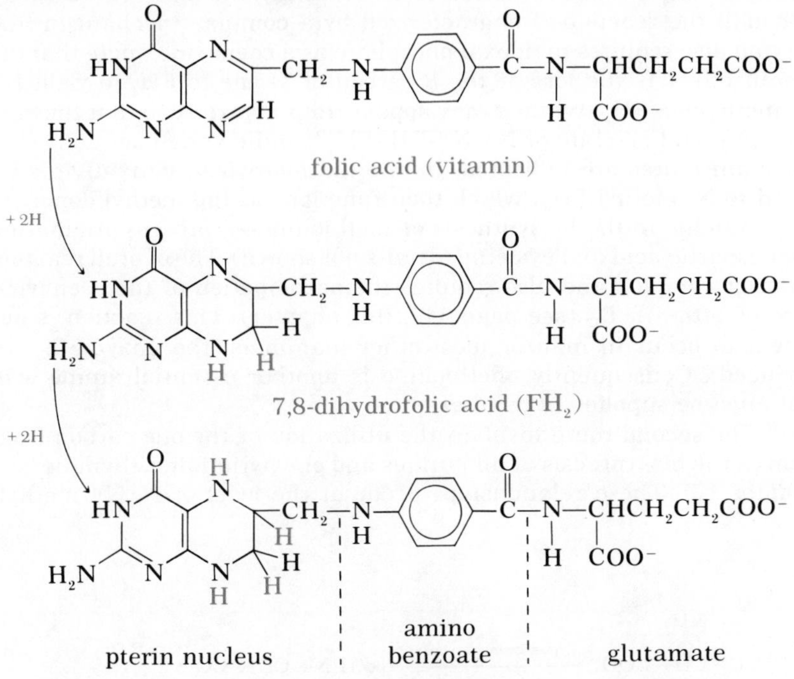

folic acid (vitamin)

+ 2H

7,8-dihydrofolic acid (FH$_2$)

+ 2H

pterin nucleus   amino benzoate   glutamate

5,6,7,8-tetrahydrofolic acid (FH$_4$)
(active coenzyme)

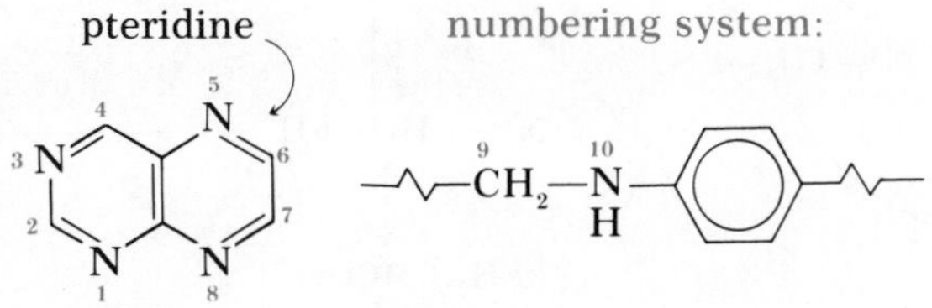

pteridine   numbering system:

one-carbon–FH$_4$ adducts:

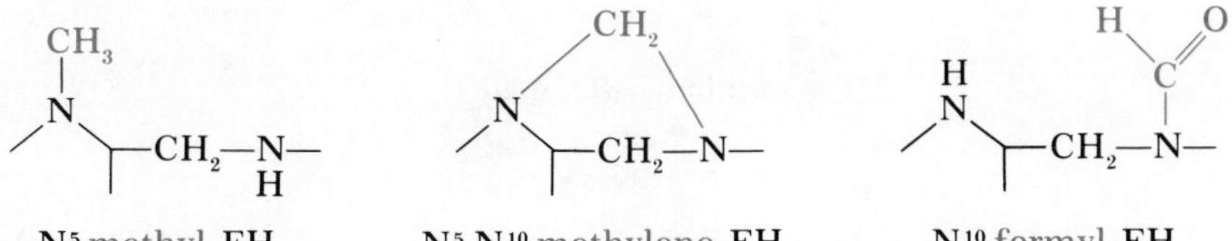

N^5-methyl-FH$_4$ N^5,N^{10}-methylene-FH$_4$ N^{10}-formyl-FH$_4$

A brief analysis of the role of tetrahydrofolic acid in metabolism is difficult, since it is involved in several reactions and in many different ways. The approach employed here begins by considering the participation of FH_4 in the conversion of serine to glycine (see Figure 16–5). Although the reaction is characterized by a complex mechanism (the enzyme also requires pyridoxal phosphate as a coenzyme), note that the overall effect is the loss of the β carbon of serine to FH_4 to yield N^5, N^{10}-methylene-FH_4. While it may appear from Figure 16–5 that the subsequent metabolic fate of N^5, N^{10}-CH_2-FH_4 is quite varied, actually only two main routes are indicated. In one the methylene derivative is reduced to N^5-methyl-FH_4, which then functions as the methyl donor for homocysteine in the biosynthesis of methionine—a process originating from aspartic acid and cysteine (details not shown). The overall reaction is rather complex and also requires the participation of the coenzyme form of *vitamin B_{12}* (see page 442, this chapter). This reaction is not known to occur in man or most other mammals (the enzyme is not produced). Consequently, methionine is another essential amino acid that must be supplied in the diet.

The second route involves the utilization of the one-carbon fragment in the biosynthesis of all purines and one pyrimidine, thymine (see Chapter 17). These relationships occur at the level of N^5,N^{10}-methyl-

Figure 16–5 A partial summary of the role of tetrahydrofolic acid in one-carbon metabolism. All transformations are enzyme catalyzed.

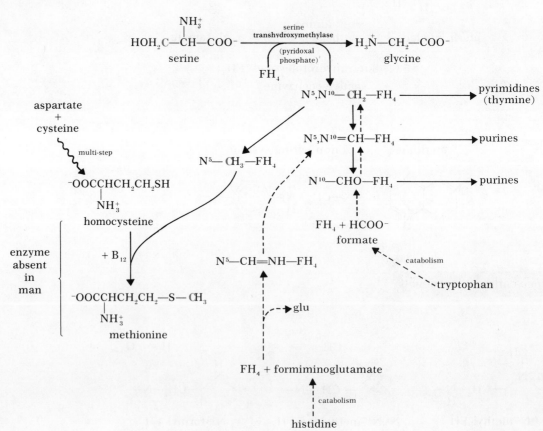

ene-FH$_4$, N^5,N^{10}-methenyl(—CH≡)-FH$_4$, and N^{10} formyl-FH$_4$. As indicated in Figure 16–4, the latter two species are enzymatically and sequentially formed from the methylene derivative. The supply of one-carbon fragments for thymine and purine biosynthesis is the most vital aspect of the biological function of FH$_4$. Illustrative of *how* vital is the effect of many sulfa drugs, which act as potent inhibitors in the microbial biosynthesis of folic acid. Presumably, the basis of the inhibition is competitive, preventing the incorporation of the para-aminobenzoic acid moiety into the compound (see page 117, Chapter 5). The blockage is fatal to the organism. Man cannot synthesize folic acid and hence it must be supplied from another source. Recommended daily dietary levels are rather low, however, since the bulk of man's requirement is satisfied by synthesis carried out by the bacteria of the intestinal tract.

Although we have considered the serine → glycine conversion as the major starting point, note that the FH$_4$ intermediates can also be produced from other sources. The basis for this is the reversibility of the reactions involving the interconversions of the FH$_4$ derivatives. One source occurs from formic acid, a product of tryptophan catabolism. Another is formiminoglutamate, a product of histidine catabolism.

VITAMIN B$_{12}$

In the preceding section, mention was made of a requirement for vitamin B$_{12}$ as a coenzyme in the last reaction in the biosynthesis of methionine.

$$\text{homocysteine} + \text{N}^5\text{-methyl-FH}_4 \xrightarrow[\text{B}_{12}]{\text{enzyme}} \text{methionine} + \text{FH}_4$$

Vitamin B$_{12}$ is a complex tetrapyrrole compound (see below). The three most characteristic features of its structure are: (a) rather than the usual four interpyrrole methenyl (—CH≡) bridges, the cyclic tetrapyrrole moiety contains only three, with two pyrrole units linked directly; to distinguish it from the porphyrin ring, this system is called a *corrin* ring system; (b) the corrin tetrapyrrole system is coordinated to *cobalt;* and (c) the presence of a nucleotide-like structure as *5,6-dimethyl-benzimidazole,* which is covalently attached to one of the pyrrole side chains and also coordinated to the fifth position of the central cobalt atom. The active coenzyme form of vitamin B$_{12}$ found in most organisms contains a 5'-deoxyadenosyl grouping coordinated to the sixth position of cobalt. During isolation this adenosyl grouping is usually displaced by a cyanide grouping. Vitamin B$_{12}$ is synonymously called *cobalamine,* and hence the cyanide form would be *cyano-cobalamine* and the coenzyme form would be *5'-deoxyadenosylcobalamine.*

In the homocysteine → methionine conversion, the methyl group is first transferred from N^5-methyl-FH$_4$ to the coenzyme form of B$_{12}$ by displacement of the deoxyadenosyl grouping. The resultant methylated species of B$_{12}$ then serves as the immediate methyl donor of homocysteine. The number of other B$_{12}$-dependent reactions in all of metabolism is quite sparse. Since these are more appropriately the subject of advanced textbooks and courses, they are not covered here. Although

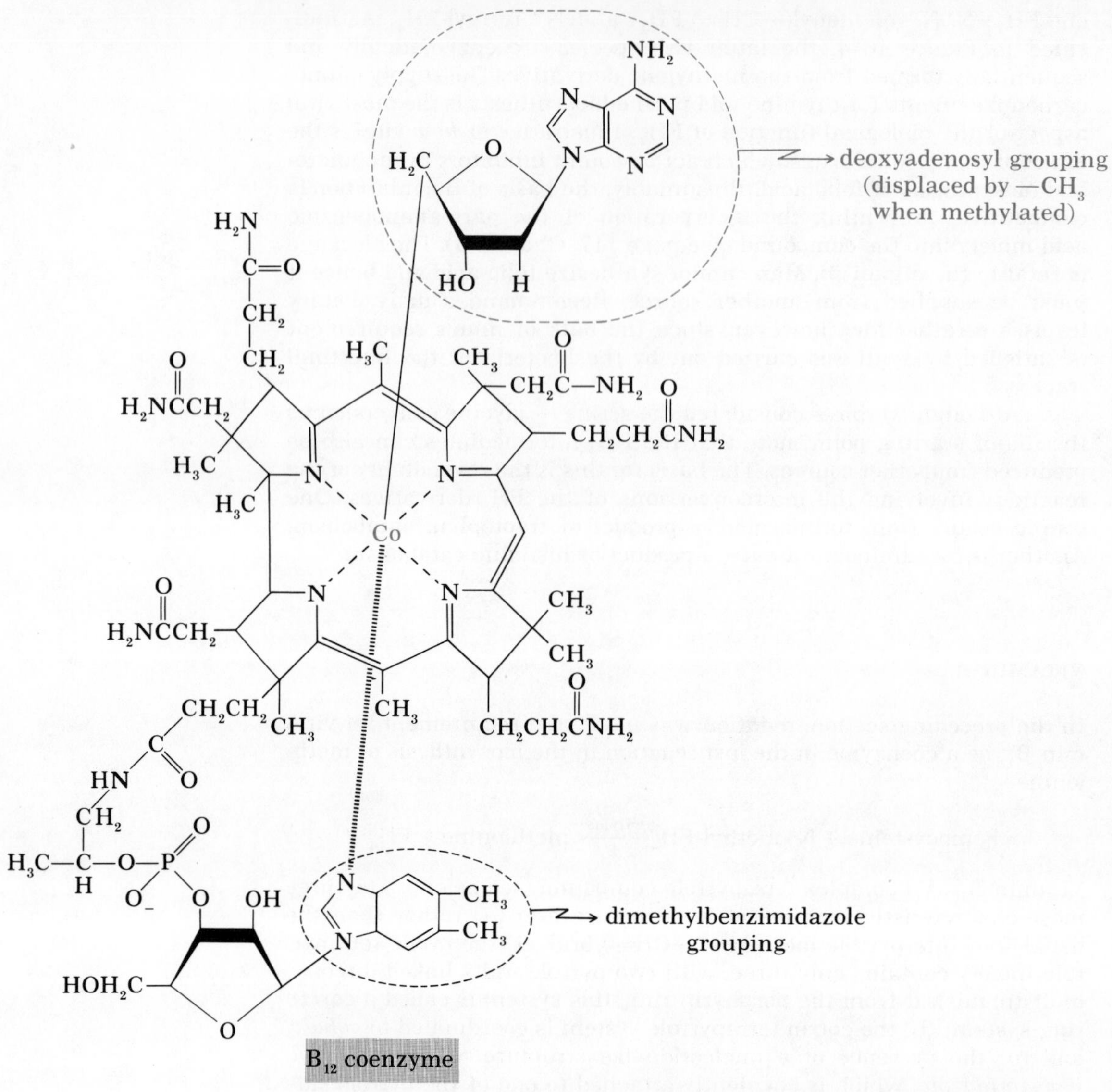

→ deoxyadenosyl grouping
(displaced by —CH₃
when methylated)

→ dimethylbenzimidazole
grouping

B₁₂ coenzyme

the daily intake requirement of B_{12} for man is not known, the state of pernicious anemia brought on by a deficiency of the vitamin can be prevented by an intake of approximately 0.1 μg (0.0000001 gram) per day.

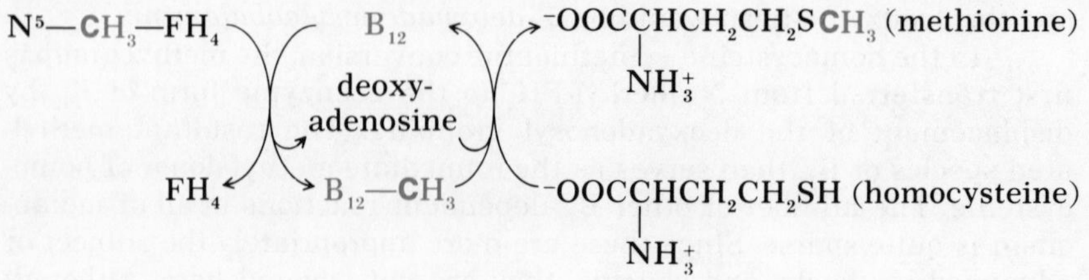

N^5—CH_3—FH_4 B_{12} $^-OOCCHCH_2CH_2SCH_3$ (methionine)

deoxy-
adenosine NH_3^+

FH_4 B_{12}—CH_3 $^-OOCCHCH_2CH_2SH$ (homocysteine)

   NH_3^+

NUTRITIONAL CONSIDERATIONS

Obviously every organism requires a supply of the amino acids for normal growth and development. In many cases, this requirement is satisfied by the organism itself due to an enzymatic ability to synthesize each of the amino acids from other sources. Most microbes and the photosynthetic plants are prime examples. In fact, given supplies of carbon, energy, inorganic nitrogen, and varied inorganic nutrients, these organisms can produce not only all of the amino acids but also every other substance necessary for normal growth and development. On the other hand, animal organisms—and man in particular—are not quite so versatile. Many substances—the exact ones varying from one organism to another—must be supplied in the diet since the organisms lack the necessary enzymes for their biosynthesis.

Two especially critical aspects of man's nutrition are concerned with an intake of the vitamins and several amino acids. As we have encountered on several occasions throughout the last few chapters, the vitamins are required for many life processes in the area of general metabolism where they function as coenzymes. At this point it is suggested that you return to our first treatment of coenzymes where the relationship to vitamins was initially discussed (pages 106–109 in Chapter 5). In view of your understanding of how coenzymes participate in metabolism, the review can now be made with a greater perspective. Moreover, certain vitamins are involved in specialized physiological processes, such as vitamin A in vision, vitamin D in bone development, vitamin E in the function of the kidneys and male genital organs, and vitamin K in blood clotting. The need for amino acids is, of course, obvious. Thousands of different proteins must be synthesized, and as evidenced by the last section, many amino acids have specialized metabolic functions. The major exogenous supply of amino acids is protein. The amino acids are made available during digestion due to the action of the proteolytic enzymes of the gastrointestinal secretions such as trypsin, chymotrypsin, pepsin, carboxypeptidase, and aminopeptidase. The free amino acids are then transported across the intestinal wall and conveyed throughout the whole body in the blood stream.

An obvious question at this point is: Which of the 20 common amino acids are required by man? The answer is provided in Table 16–1 and, as you can see, the list is not small. Also note that the amounts required for an adult are appreciably less than those for an infant. In addition, the number of amino acids required is one fewer for the adult.

The effects of malnutrition are varied, and many are not even understood. A deficiency of each vitamin is usually manifested by a complex set of symptoms. A prolonged deficiency of nutritive protein—that is, protein rich in the essential amino acids—results in a particularly tragic disease called *kwashiorkor*. If untreated in early life, this is most frequently an irreversible and terminal state. Since most of the common food sources contain some of the essential amino acids, the general cause of this condition is not a total lack of *all* the essential amino acids in the diet. Although such a situation would certainly cause this condition, kwashiorkor can also result from the absence or sub-minimal presence of only *some* of the essential acids. To satisfy the need, the body

L-Amino Acid	Infants (mg/kg body wt.)	Male Adult (grams)	Female Adult[4] (grams)
Histidine	30	0	0
Tryptophan	20	0.25	0.16
Phenylalanine[3]	90	1.1	0.22
Lysine	100	0.80	0.50
Threonine	90	0.50	0.31
Methionine	45	1.1	0.35
Leucine	150	1.1	0.62
Isoleucine	130	0.70	0.45
Valine	110	0.80	0.65

[1] Recommended levels are generally twice the minimal values.
[2] Small quantities of arginine are required under certain conditions.
[3] Since much of the physiological function of phenylalanine requires its conversion to tyrosine, roughly 75% of the phenylalanine requirement can be covered by tyrosine.
[4] Greater intake of all acids is recommended during pregnancy and lactation.

tissues begin to degrade their own protein. The results are impaired development and function of all vital organs. An early death is quite common, particularly in infants feeding from a mother who herself is subsisting on a deficient diet. The hideous problem of malnutrition is widespread, but is especially severe in underdeveloped countries. Efforts to increase the production of high-quality nutritive food from the oceans, or in the form of algae or other microbes grown on plentiful resources such as crude petroleum deposits and waste products, have the potential to rid our world society of these intolerable conditions.

LITERATURE

DAVIS, V. E., and M. J. WALSH, "Alcohol, Amines, and Alkaloids: A Possible Biochemical Basis for Alcohol Addiction," *Science,* **167,** 1005–1007 (1970). The original article describing the detection of tetrahydropapaveroline in rat brain extracts incubated with alcohol or acetaldehyde.

GREENBERG, D. M., and W. W. RODWELL, "Carbon Catabolism of Amino Acids" and "Biosynthesis of Amino Acids and Related Compounds," in Volume 3 of *Metabolic Pathways,* Third Edition, D. Greenberg (ed.). New York: Academic Press, 1969. Two review articles giving a thorough analysis of catabolic and anabolic pathways of all the amino acids. Other articles in this volume devoted to nitrogen metabolism of amino acids, sulfur metabolism, and metabolism of porphyrin compounds.

LEHNINGER, A. L., *Biochemistry.* New York: Worth Publishers, 1970. Chapters 20 and 24 contain an excellent summary of the main catabolic and anabolic pathways of the amino acids.

MEISTER, A., *Biochemistry of the Amino Acids,* Second Edition. New York: Academic Press, 1965. A treatise in two volumes containing a comprehensive treatment of amino acid metabolism.

SOBER, H. A. (ed.), *Handbook of Biochemistry,* Second Edition. Cleveland: The Chemical Rubber Company, 1970. A listing is given on pages K-50 through K-52 of the recommended daily dietary allowances of protein and vitamins for humans as revised in 1968 by the Food and Nutrition Board of the National Academy of Sciences and the National Research Council.

STANBURY, J. O., J. B. WYNGAARDEN, and D. S. FREDRICKSON (eds.). *The Metabolic Basis of Inherited Disease,* Second Edition. New York: McGraw-Hill Book Company, 1966. All types of metabolic diseases due to genetic defects are discussed.

WHITE, A., P. HANDLER, and E. L. SMITH, *Principles of Biochemistry,* Fourth Edition. New York: McGraw-Hill Book Company, 1968. Chapters 23 through 26 of this textbook contain an excellent summary of all aspects of amino acid metabolism.

UMBARGER, H. E., "Regulation of Amino Acid Metabolism," in *Annual Review of Biochemistry,* Volume 38, 323–370 (1969). A review article describing metabolite-mediated regulation of enzyme activity in multifunctional pathways in general, and pathways of amino acid metabolism in particular.

EXERCISES

16-1 Complete each of the following.

a) arginine + α-ketoglutarate $\xrightarrow{\text{transaminase}}$

b) valine + α-ketoglutarate $\xrightarrow{\text{transaminase}}$

c) L-lysine + FMN $\xrightarrow[\text{oxidase}]{\text{amino acid}}$

d) cysteine + α-ketoglutarate $\xrightarrow{\text{transaminase}}$

e) leucine $\xrightarrow[\text{decarboxylase}]{\text{leucine}}$

g) pyruvate + NADH + H$^+$ + NH$_3$ $\xrightarrow{\text{dehydrogenase}}$

16-2 What relationship exists between the reactions given below, known to occur in liver, and the lack of a dietary requirement for arginine in adults?

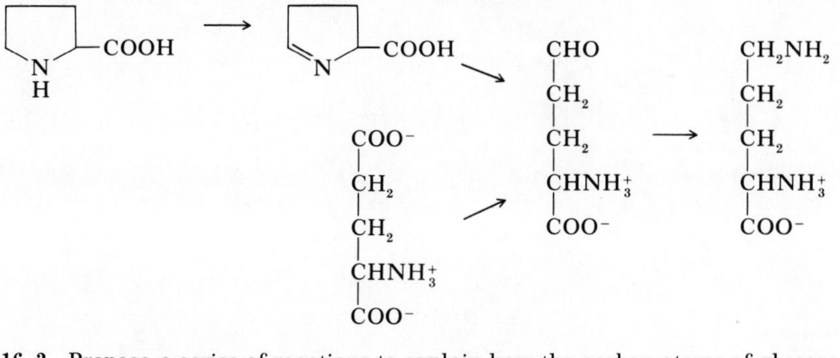

16-3 Propose a series of reactions to explain how the carbon atoms of glucose could be converted to γ-aminobutyrate.

16-4 Propose a series of reactions to explain how a carbon atom of tryptophan could eventually be utilized in the biosynthesis of epinephrine. What specific carbon atom of tryptophan is involved?

16-5 In many organisms, the immediate biosynthetic precursor of L-lysine is α,ϵ-diaminopimelic acid (structure below). What type of enzyme would catalyze this reaction, what coenzyme would be required, and what type of enzyme-substrate complex would be formed?

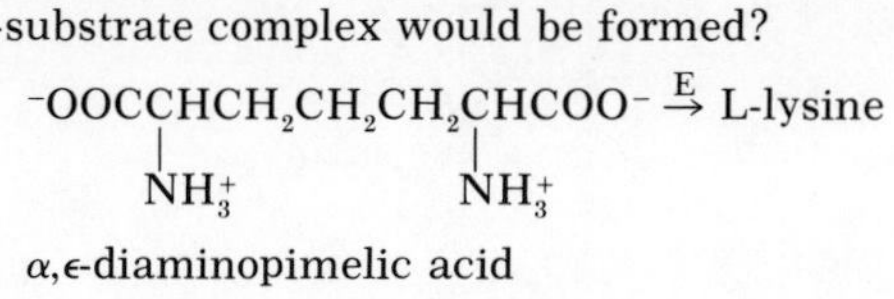

$$^-\text{OOCCHCH}_2\text{CH}_2\text{CH}_2\text{CHCOO}^- \xrightarrow{\text{E}} \text{L-lysine}$$
$$\text{NH}_3^+ \qquad\qquad \text{NH}_3^+$$

α,ϵ-diaminopimelic acid

16-6 Tryptophan is known to be converted into indole acetic acid, a potent growth hormone in plants, by the action of tryptophan decarboxylase, monoamine oxidase, and an NAD-dependent dehydrogenase in that order. Reproduce the complete pathway showing the structures of all intermediate metabolites.

indole acetate

16-7 What relationship exists between the metabolism of phenylalanine and tyrosine and the production of morphine in the opium poppy?

16-8 Propose a reaction sequence to account for the utilization of carbon from fatty acids in the biosynthesis of porphyrin compounds.

16-9 If patients suffering from alcaptonuria are fed homogentisic acid, what do you predict would happen to this compound after it entered the blood stream?

16-10 Mastocytosis is a physiological disorder resulting from the infiltration of mast cells into skin and organs such as the liver, spleen, and kidney. Clinically, a patient with this condition may possess an enlarged liver and spleen containing unusually high amounts of histamine. It has been suggested that the latter is caused by an excessive production of histamine as a result of the invading mast cells, rather than by a block in the degradation of histamine, which would likewise result in its accumulation. If this is so, what enzyme would you expect to find in large amounts in mast cells?

17

Nucleotide and Nucleic Acid Biosynthesis

The formation of a professional relationship between James Watson and Francis Crick was based on their sharing the attitude that the center of biology was the gene and its control of cellular metabolism. In this context the main challenges in understanding the biology of the living cell were to understand (a) the process of gene replication, and (b) the functional role of the genes in controlling—as it was hypothesized at the time —the biosynthesis of proteins. To study these problems in any meaningful way first required that the chemical structure of a gene be unraveled; this meant solving the structure of DNA. Their elucidation of the correct double-helix conformation for DNA in 1953 reinforced their position and has guided research into the molecular nature of the living cell for the past two decades. No other single discovery has had such an impact on modern biology.

Although many questions concerning various details of the replication of genes and their role in the biosynthesis of proteins still remain unanswered, much has been learned about each process, with most of the significant advances having been made only in the past ten to fifteen years. The current state of knowledge is often summarized as the so-called *central dogma of molecular biology,* which can be diagrammatically represented as follows:

$$\text{DNA} \xleftarrow[\substack{triphospho\text{-}\\deoxyribonucleotides}]{replication} \boxed{\text{DNA}} \xrightarrow[\substack{triphospho\text{-}\\ribonucleotides}]{transcription} \boxed{\text{RNA}} \xrightarrow[\substack{amino\\acids}]{translation} \text{protein}$$

In effect, these relationships summarize the molecular foundation of all living cells starting with the now undisputed fact that the genetic individuality of every living cell is contained in the structure of DNA, specifically in the sequence of nitrogen bases contributed by the monomeric nucleotides. On a molecular level then, the reproduction of the gene-containing chromosomes is reduced to the reproduction of DNA molecules. In other words, *gene replication is synonymous with the biosynthesis of deoxyribonucleic acid molecules from the monomeric deoxyribonucleotides with all the nucleotide units arranged in the proper sequence.* The functional role of the genes is likewise reduced to a molecular level involving two distinct phases. First, the genetic information contained in the nitrogen base sequence of DNA is rewritten as the base sequence in the other type of nucleic acid, RNA. That is to say, the genetic specificity originally in a DNA molecule is copied in the form of a RNA molecule. This process is called *transcription* and is synonymous with the DNA-directed biosynthesis of ribonucleic acid from the monomeric ribonucleotides. Then the genetic information now contained in RNA is utilized to direct the formation of proteins. In other words, in this process, called *translation,* the original language of genetic specificity and function, that is, the sequence of nucleotides in a nucleic acid, is converted into the language of protein specificity and function, namely, the sequence of amino acids in a polypeptide chain. Thus, to repeat a basic tenet of molecular biology: the genetic individuality of any organism is ultimately expressed by the proteins it is capable of producing.

Our purpose in this chapter will be to examine certain aspects of the processes involving nucleic acid biosynthesis, namely, replication and transcription. First, however, we will explore some features concerning the anabolism of purine and pyrimidine nucleotides. Since these are the substrates of DNA and RNA biosynthesis, this represents a logical beginning. The subject of nucleotide biosynthesis will also provide us with another opportunity to discuss (a) the important participation of coenzymes in metabolism; (b) the integration of metabolic pathways; and (c) the regulation of metabolism by allosteric enzymes. The details of the translation process—that is, protein biosynthesis—will be treated in the next chapter. A brief summary of all these events was given previously in Chapter 6 (see page 162). This plus the sections on DNA and RNA structure would be a good review at this time.

NUCLEOTIDE BIOSYNTHESIS

GENERAL FEATURES

The biosynthetic pathways of both pyrimidine and purine nucleotides have been completely elucidated. Much of the early work, started over 20 years ago, was done with mammalian systems and later extended to other types of organisms. Now there is extensive evidence that the same basic steps occur in nearly all organisms. Actually two separate pathways are involved—one accounting for the biosynthesis of pyrimidine nucleotides and the other for the biosynthesis of purine nucleotides. The chief end-product of the pyrimidine pathway is *uridine-5'-monophosphate* (UMP), which then serves as the precursor of all other pyrimidine ribonucleotides and deoxyribonucleotides. The principal end-product of the purine pathway is *inosine-5'-monophosphate* (IMP), which is then converted to all other purine ribonucleotides and deoxyribonucleotides.

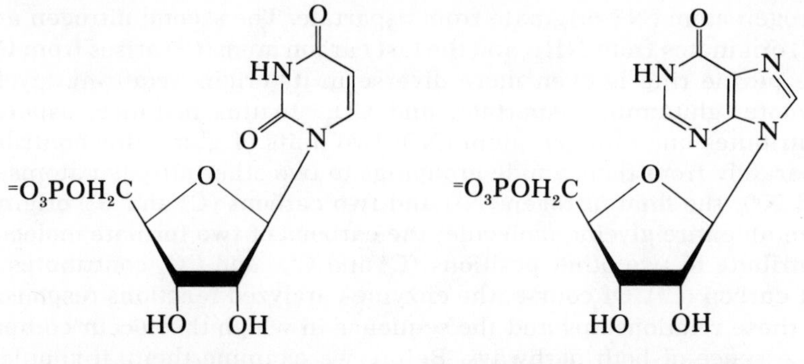

uridine-5'-monophosphate
(UMP)

*precursor of all
pyrimidine
nucleotides*

inosine-5'-monophosphate
(IMP)

*precursor of all
purine
nucleotides*

Although the end-product of each pathway is a monophosphate nucleotide, the part of the nucleotide that is actually being assembled is the heterocyclic nitrogen base moiety. The base assembled in UMP is *uracil,* of course. In IMP the base assembled is *hypoxanthine* (6-oxopurine). In both processes, the phosphopentose component is contributed by *5-phosphoribosyl-1-pyrophosphate* (PRPP), which in turn originates from ribose-5-phosphate in an ATP-dependent pyrophosphorylation reaction. The ribose phosphate in turn originates from glucose by such

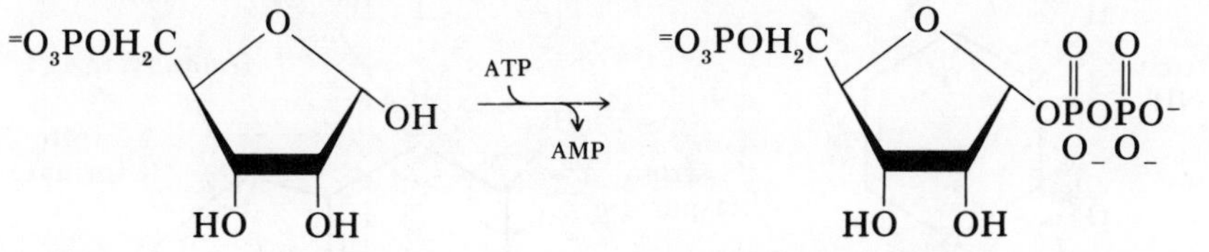

β-ribose-5-phosphate

5-phosphoribosyl-1-pyrophosphate
(PRPP)

pathways as the hexose-monophosphate shunt (see Chapter 11). Consequently, it is more logical to examine each pathway in the context of how the pyrimidine and purine ring systems are put together.

ANABOLIC ORIGINS OF PYRIMIDINES AND PURINES

As we have seen on several occasions now, the atoms of the ultimate end products of anabolic pathways are derived from smaller precursors: pyruvate → glucose (glycogen); acetyl-SCoA → fatty acids; acetyl-SCoA → cholesterol. Moreover, often different precursors are involved as in the biosynthesis of the tetrapyrrole grouping from glycine and succinate and the formation of the aromatic amino acids from phosphoenolpyruvate and erythrose-4-phosphate. Two of the clearest examples of both these principles are represented in the production of the uracil and hypoxanthine ring systems. The former is built up from aspartate, CO_2, and NH_3. As shown below, three carbons (C^4, C^5, C^6) and one nitrogen atom (N^1) originate from aspartate. The second nitrogen atom (N^3) originates from NH_3, and the last carbon atom (C^2) arises from CO_2. The purine ring is even more diverse in its origin, requiring glycine, formate, glutamine, aspartate, and CO_2. In this instance, aspartate contributes one nitrogen atom (N^1); two units of glutamine contribute separately from their amide groupings to two other nitrogen atoms (N^3 and N^9); the final nitrogen (N^7) and two carbons (C^4 and C^5) originate from an entire glycine molecule; the carbons of two formate molecules contribute to two other positions (C^2 and C^8); and CO_2 contributes the last carbon (C^6). Of course, the enzyme-catalyzed reactions responsible for these relationships and the sequence in which they occur comprise the essence of both pathways. Before we examine them, it should be noted that both processes are endergonic and thus will require an expenditure of energy supplied by a coupling of ATP hydrolysis in specific steps.

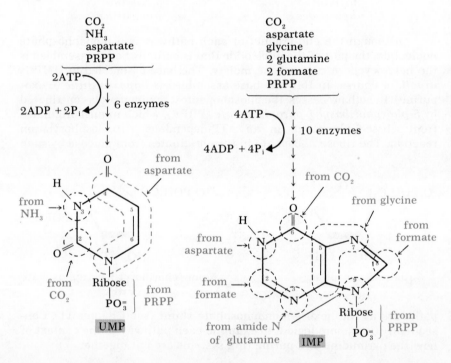

COMPARISON OF UMP AND IMP BIOSYNTHESIS

In order that you can examine the biochemistry of UMP and IMP biosynthesis, the complete pathways are diagrammed in Figures 17–1 (UMP) and 17–2 (IMP). Aside from the similarity that in both cases it is the heterocyclic nitrogen base moiety that is being assembled, the two pathways are completely different. The greater complexity of the IMP pathway is quite obvious. The first specific difference between the two is the point of insertion of the phosphoribose moiety. In the IMP

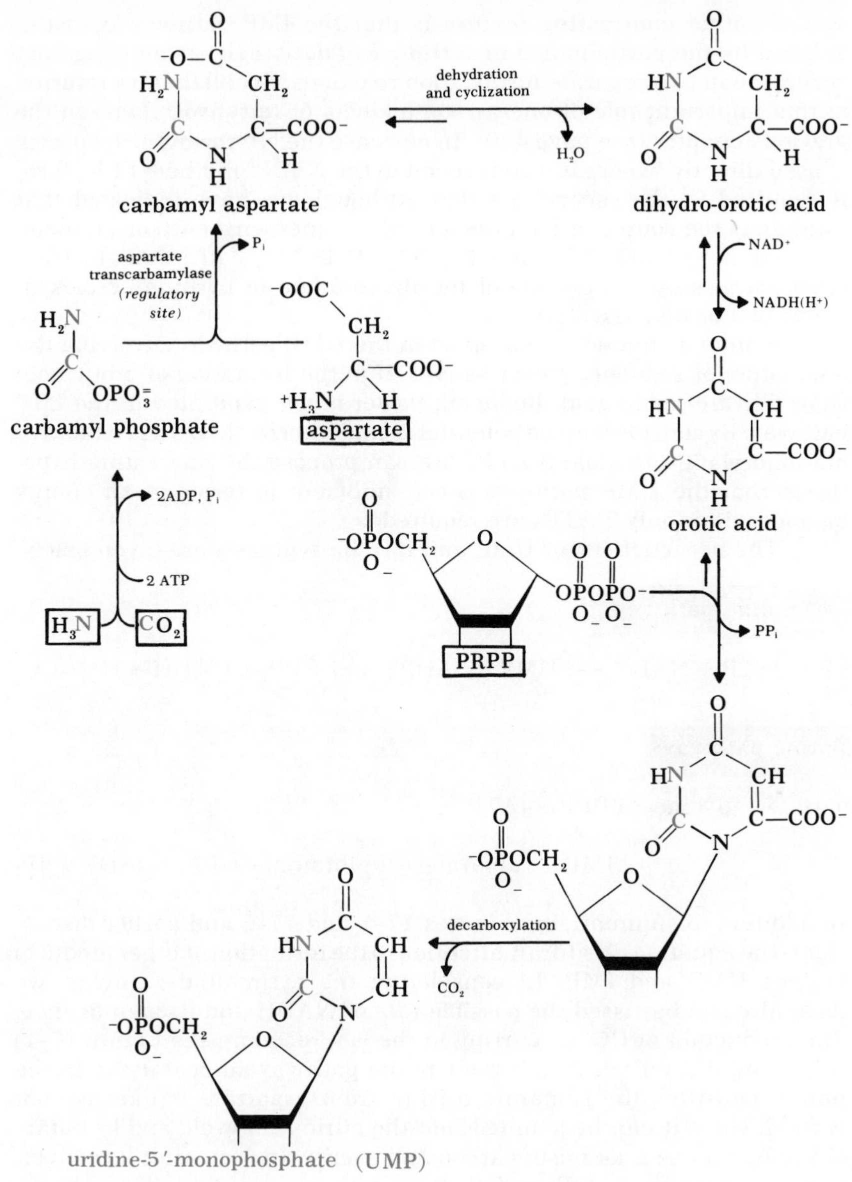

carbamyl aspartate

dehydration and cyclization

H_2O

dihydro-orotic acid

aspartate transcarbamylase (regulatory site)

P_i

carbamyl phosphate

aspartate

NAD^+

$NADH(H^+)$

orotic acid

2ADP, P_i

2 ATP

H_3N CO_2

PRPP

PP_i

decarboxylation

CO_2

uridine-5′-monophosphate (UMP)

Figure 17–1   Anabolic pathway of UMP, precursor to all pyrimidine nucleotides. Considering the formation of carbamyl phosphate, the overall process requires 6 distinct enzyme-catalyzed steps. The heterocyclic ring is assembled before the utilization of PRPP.

pathway, the PRPP is involved in the very first reaction resulting in the formation of *β-5-phosphoribosyl-1-amine,* an anomeric amino derivative of ribose-5-phosphate. In other words, the phosphopentose component is inserted prior to the formation of the purine ring. All subsequent reactions involve the progressive buildup of the purine ring from this position. Included among these reactions are two ring closures. Eventually the carbon-nitrogen linkage in 5-phosphoribosyl-1-amine becomes the characteristic $C^{1'}(\beta)$—N^9 glycosidic bond of the purine nucleotide. In the UMP route, on the other hand, the PRPP is utilized in the next to last reaction after the pyrimidine ring (as orotic acid) is formed. Note here the formation of the $C^{1'}(\beta)$—N^1 glycosidic linkage common to pyrimidine nucleotides.

Another contrasting feature is that the IMP pathway is distinguished by the participation of *tetrahydrofolate* (FH_4) as an obligatory coenzyme in two separate formylation reactions. Recall that we referred to this important role of one-carbon adducts of tetrahydrofolate in the previous chapter (see page 440). In one case the N^{10}-formyl-FH_4 species is used directly, whereas a conversion to the N^5, N^{10}-methenyl-FH_4 form is required in the second reaction. Although we have indicated that formate is the source of both the formyl and methenyl carbons, remember that N^{10}—CHO—FH_4 and N^5, N^{10}=CH—FH_4 can originate from other sources. A special role of tetrahydrofolate in pyrimidine biosynthesis will be discussed later.

A final distinction is observed in the UMP pathway involving the production of reducing power as NADH in the formation of orotic acid from dihydro-orotic acid. Reducing power is not generated in the IMP pathway. By considering the potential reoxidation of NADH via oxidative phosphorylation to yield 3 ATPs, we can propose the interesting hypothesis that the UMP pathway is self-sufficient in terms of an energy balance, since only 2 ATPs are required.

The net reactions of UMP and IMP biosynthesis are given below.

pyrimidine pathway:

$$CO_2 + NH_3 + \text{aspartate} + PRPP + 2ATP + NAD^+ \longrightarrow UMP + 2ADP + 2P_i + PP_i + NADH + H^+ + CO_2$$

purine pathway:

$$CO_2 + 2\,\text{glutamine} + 2HCOO^- + \text{aspartate} + \text{glycine} + PRPP + 4ATP \xrightarrow{FH_4}$$

$$IMP + \text{fumarate} + 2\,\text{glutamate} + PP_i + 4ADP + 4P_i$$

In addition to summarizing Figures 17–1 and 17–2 and earlier discussions, the equations also draw attention to the formation of other products besides UMP and IMP. In considering the pyrimidine pathway, we have already discussed the possible fate of NADH and its significance. The production of CO_2 (occurring in the last reaction; see Figure 17–1) is also significant because it renders the pathway autocatalytic. In the purine pathway, the fumarate arising from aspartate is likewise not wasted, since it can be shunted into the citric acid cycle and be catabolized further as a source of carbon and energy. In fact, after its conversion to oxaloacetate followed then by a transamination, it can be reconverted to aspartate. Many things can happen to the glutamic acid arising from glutamine. However, by the action of glutamine synthetase, it would be reconverted to glutamine for further use in IMP production. In both cases the ADP produced would be returned to the mitochondria for phosphorylation back to ATP.

BIOSYNTHESIS OF UTP, CTP, GTP, AND ATP

The pathways for UMP and IMP biosynthesis together represent only the first of three equally important phases of nucleotide biosynthesis. A second phase consists of the conversion of UMP to UTP and CTP, and of

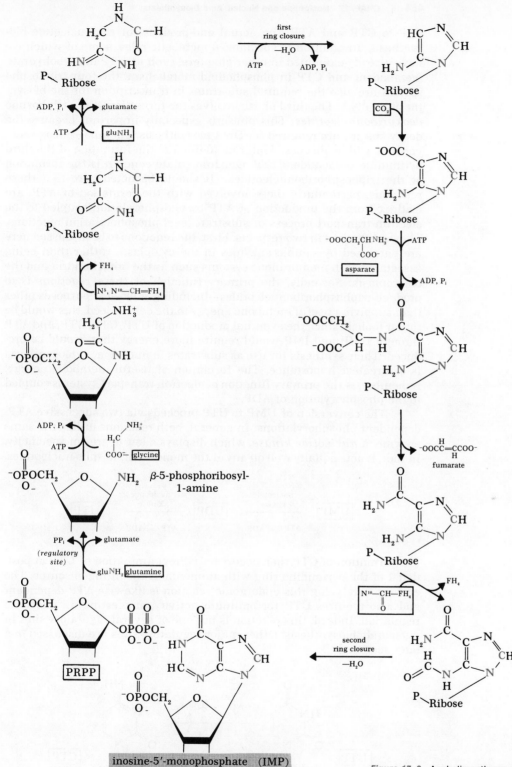

inosine-5′-monophosphate (IMP)

Figure 17–2 Anabolic pathway of IMP, precursor to all purine nucleotides. The overall process requires 10 distinct enzyme-catalyzed steps. The assembly of the purine ring system follows the utilization of PRPP in the first step.

IMP to GTP and ATP, the actual end-products of ribonucleotide bio-synthesis. In addition to specialized metabolic roles, some of which we have already examined in other chapters, such as UTP in carbohydrate metabolism and CTP in phospholipid metabolism, the four triphospho species are also the required substrates in transcription for the biosynthesis of RNA. The third phase involves the formation of the triphospho *deoxyribonucleotides*. This phase is especially important because the deoxy species are required for DNA biosynthesis. The ribo → deoxy conversions will be discussed later in addition to the formation of the third pyrimidine nucleotide, dTTP. Our immediate concern is the formation of the triphosphoribonucleotides. (It should be noted here that these reactions, particularly those involved with the formation of ATP, are distinct from the production of ATP by phosphorylation coupled to the electron transport process or substrate level phosphorylation reactions. They are distinct in two respects. First, the reactions to be discussed here are catalyzed by soluble enzymes in the cytoplasm rather than being associated with membranous systems such as the mitochondria and the chloroplasts. Secondly, the primary function of these reactions is to produce triphosphoribonucleotides—including ATP—for purposes other than supplying useful metabolic energy to the cell. Indeed, this would be rather foolish, since the eventual production of UTP, CTP, GTP, and ATP through UMP and IMP would require more energy than would be produced. Their synthesis for use as substrates in nucleic acid biosynthesis is of greatest importance. The formation of useful metabolic energy, remember, is the primary function of electron transport systems coupled to the phosphorylation of ADP.)

The conversion of UMP to UTP proceeds via two successive ATP-dependent phosphorylations. In general, both reactions utilize the same enzyme, a *nucleotide kinase,* which displays a low degree of specificity. In fact, it acts equally well on any of the mono- or diphospho nucleotides.

The formation of CTP then occurs by a direct amination of UTP at position 4 of the pyrimidine ring with ammonia as the nitrogen source. The enzyme catalyzing this endergonic reaction is likewise ATP-dependent and also requires GTP for optimum activity, suggesting an allosteric regulation. Indeed, this reaction is but one of several regulatory sites in nucleotide biosynthesis. Other major regulatory sites are discussed in a later section.

The biosynthesis of the triphospho purine nucleotides, GTP and ATP, involves two different pathways from the same IMP precursor. Both are diagrammed below. In each case, the hypoxanthine ring of IMP is first modified to yield the appropriate monophosphonucleotides, AMP and GMP. The latter are then phosphorylated, as described above for UMP, to ultimately yield ATP and GTP. Note that AMP and GMP are likewise formed by amination reactions, but each in a fashion unlike that of the UTP→CTP transformation. The amination to yield AMP

utilizes aspartate as a nitrogen source and requires two separate steps. After a necessary oxidation of the hypoxanthine ring forming a carbonyl grouping at position 2 (yielding *xanthosine-5'-monophosphate*—XMP), the amination step to GMP—as it occurs in higher organisms—utilizes glutamine as the nitrogen donor. Lower organisms, on the other hand, employ ammonia directly. In any case, the effect is the same, namely, XMP → GMP.

BIOSYNTHESIS OF dCTP, dGTP, dATP, AND dTTP

DNA biosynthesis depends on a supply of the four triphosphodeoxyribonucleotides—dCTP, dGTP, dATP, and dTTP—as substrates. Although it was proposed at one time that the reaction pathways responsible for biosynthesis of the deoxynucleotide precursors were similar to but independent of the UMP and IMP pathways, it is now quite clear that the major process (if not the only process) for the formation of the deoxynucleotides occurs *directly* from the preformed ribonucleotides. In other words, the reductive conversion of β-D-ribose to β-2-D-deoxyribose occurs at the nucleotide level rather than at the level of the free sugars.

The formation of dCTP, dGTP, and dATP proceeds by a two-stage process originating from the corresponding diphosphoribonucleotides, which in turn, as we have just seen, originate from UMP and IMP. The route to dTTP follows a slightly more complex course.

The key breakthrough in deciphering the basis of deoxyribonucleotide biosynthesis was made by P. Reichard and coworkers in 1964 with the demonstration that a soluble protein component obtained from *E. coli,* called *thioredoxin,* could serve as a hydrogen donor in the enzymatic reduction of ribonucleotides to deoxyribonucleotides. Thioredoxin is a small protein (MW = 11,700) composed of a single polypeptide chain containing one disulfide bond. However, the protein does not function in this, the oxidized state, symbolized below as TR-S$_2$. First, the disulfide bond is reduced to give reduced thioredoxin containing two thiol groupings. This process requires NADPH and a flavoprotein enzyme called *thioredoxin reductase.* Reduced thioredoxin, symbolized below as TR-(SH)$_2$, then participates in the reduction of the ribosyl moiety of a diphosphoribonucleotide to the deoxy state. The reductase enzyme catalyzing this reaction, acting *specifically* on the 2' position of diphosphonucleotides but showing no preference for the nitrogen base moiety, was originally discovered in bacteria but is now known to be widely distributed. Note that the reduced thioredoxin would be oxidized to the disulfide state, which would then be reduced once again to keep the reaction circuit closed.

(1)

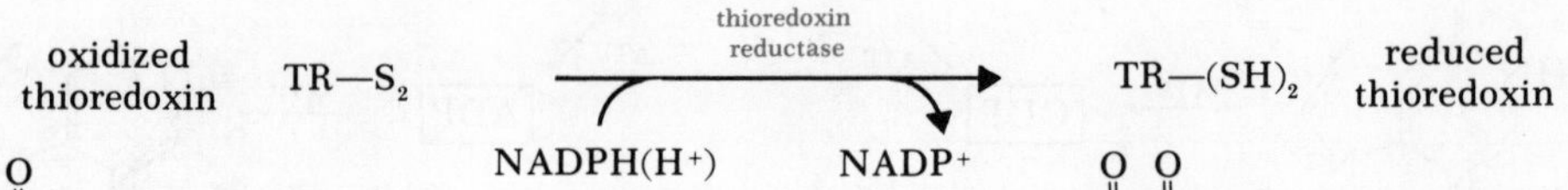

(2)

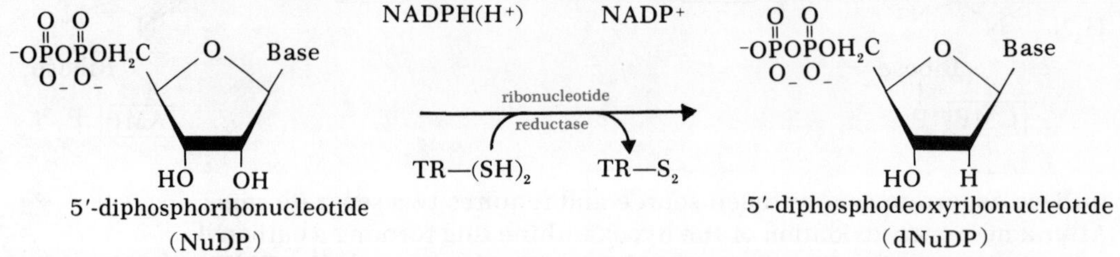

(overall)

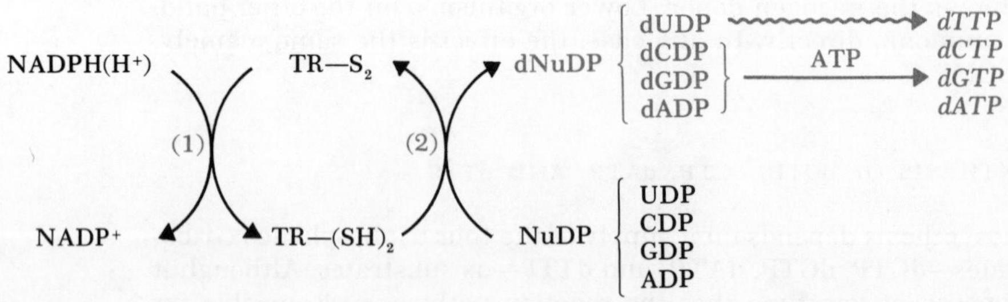

The final step in the biosynthesis of dCTP, dGTP, dATP, and dTTP is a kinase-catalyzed phosphorylation of the corresponding diphospho species, three of which (dCDP, dGTP, dADP) are produced directly in the thioredoxin reaction. What about dTTP? Indeed, we have not yet indicated how thymine itself is produced, despite the fact that we have already examined the formation of the pyrimidine nucleotides. The reason for delaying discussion of thymine formation until now was that it occurs at the level of a deoxyribonucleotide rather than of a ribonucleotide. First, dUDP is hydrolyzed to dUMP. Then the uracil moiety is methylated to yield dTMP via a process involving N^5N^{10}-methylene-FH_4 as the methyl donor. (Recall our mention of this in the last chapter; see page 440.) The stepwise phosphorylation of dTMP to yield dTTP completes the transformation.

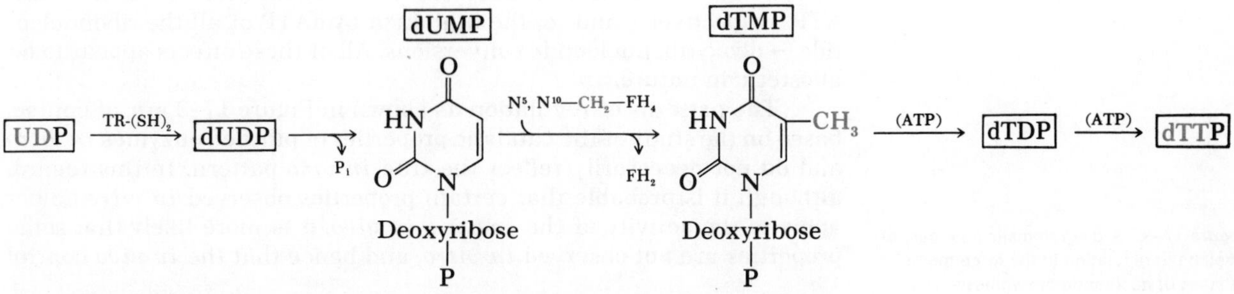

$$\boxed{\text{UDP}} \xrightarrow{\text{TR-(SH)}_2} \boxed{\text{dUDP}} \xrightarrow{\quad P_i \quad} \boxed{\text{dUMP}} \xrightarrow{N^5, N^{10}-CH_2-FH_4 \quad FH_2} \boxed{\text{dTMP}} \xrightarrow{\text{(ATP)}} \boxed{\text{dTDP}} \xrightarrow{\text{(ATP)}} \boxed{\text{dTTP}}$$

dUMP (Deoxyribose-P) and dTMP (with CH_3, Deoxyribose-P) pyrimidine ring structures shown.

Our frequent mention of the importance of coenzymes in metabolism—indeed, their importance to the very life of a cell—is neatly summed up by considering the role of tetrahydrofolate in nucleotide biosynthesis. Without the participation of the tetrahydrofolate adducts as donors of one-carbon units, the production of ATP, GTP, dATP, and dTTP would be blocked. In turn, this would impede DNA and RNA biosynthesis directly and protein biosynthesis indirectly. Recall our earlier discussions as to the mechanism of action of the sulfa drugs as effective chemotherapeutic agents in combating infectious organisms by inhibiting the biosynthesis of tetrahydrofolic acid (see page 117, Chapter 5).

REGULATION OF NUCLEOTIDE BIOSYNTHESIS

The biosynthesis of pyrimidine and purine nucleotides is under strict intracellular control. The basic strategy used is that of *feedback inhibition,* with certain of the nucleotide end-products having the ability to reduce the catalytic activity of certain key enzymes, thus reducing the overall rate of their own formation. For example, CTP is a potent inhibitor of aspartate transcarbamylase, ATCase (carbamyl phosphate + aspartate → carbamyl aspartate), which would then lead to a decrease in the production of UMP; this in turn would result in a decreased production of UTP, CTP, dCTP, and dTTP. The CTP-ATCase control point is not new to us. Recall that we used it as a model system in developing the theory of allosterism, which explains the regulatory properties of enzymes in terms of secondary binding sites in active and inactive conformational states of proteins (Chapter 5, pages 124–38).

Since our introduction of this phenomenon, we have encountered several examples of how this tactic is employed in nature to guarantee the efficient production and utilization of energy and other resources within the living cell. The regulation of nucleotide biosynthesis is another example of this principle, but a rather remarkable example at that. In addition to the CTP effect on the control of UMP production, other regulatory signals and sites are known to exist. The major ones are summarized in Figure 17–3 and include (a) the stimulation by ATP of ATCase, and thus of pyrimidine biosynthesis; (b) the feedback inhibition by adenine and guanine nucleotides—AMP, ADP, ATP, GMP, GDP, GTP— of the enzymes catalyzing the first reaction in the biosynthesis of IMP; (c) the feedback inhibition by AMP and GMP of the enzymes responsible for converting IMP to each of these purine nucleotides; (d) the stimulation of AMP and GMP formation from IMP by the presence of GTP and ATP, respectively; and (e) the inhibition by dATP of all the ribonucleotide → deoxyribonucleotide conversions. All of these effects appear to be allosteric in nature.

The patterns of regulation as shown in Figure 17–3 are, of course, based on the study of the catalytic properties of purified enzymes *in vitro* and do not necessarily reflect the true *in vivo* pattern. In this regard, although it is probable that certain properties observed *in vitro* do not apply to the activity of the enzyme *in vivo*, it is more likely that some properties are not observed *in vitro*, and hence that the *in vivo* control

Figure 17–3 A diagrammatic summary of metabolic regulation in the three major phases of nucleotide biosynthesis.

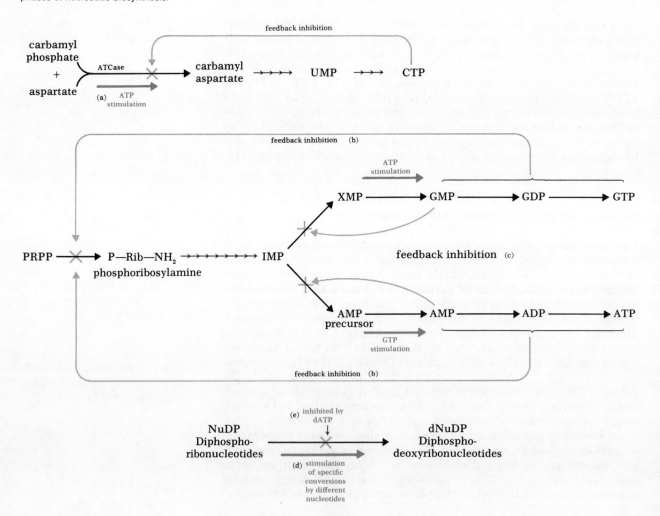

pattern is even more complex than that summarized in Figure 17–3. Whatever the real situation, it is apparent that the many reactions responsible for the biosynthesis of nucleotides are highly tuned to the changing needs of the cell, and that there is no waste of metabolic resources. In periods of active nucleic acid biosynthesis, the enzymes of the anabolic pathways are actively churning out the required triphosphonucleotides. In this situation, the nucleotides do not operate as allosteric feedback inhibitors, but instead are preferentially utilized as substrates in the assembly of polynucleotides. When, for one reason or another, the requirement for nucleic acid synthesis is reduced, the substrate nucleotides built up then serve a group of signals which, figuratively speaking, turn off their own biosynthesis. When the level of DNA and/or RNA biosynthesis picks up again, the inhibitory signals are removed by the utilization of the nucleotides and the anabolic pathways are turned on.

The importance of this type of system of checks and balances to a living cell cannot be overemphasized. In addition to accounting for a general state of metabolic economy, the principle also explains the mode of action of many hormones and pharmacological agents that control various physiological processes in man and other higher organisms. It is also possible that the principle accounts in part for the uncontrolled metabolism and cell division in certain types of cancer cells. Much more research is needed in all these areas in order to achieve a greater understanding.

NUCLEOTIDE CATABOLISM

Having completed coverage of nucleotide biosynthesis, the first of two major objectives of this chapter, we will shortly consider the second, namely, how these nucleotides are utilized in the biosynthesis of DNA and RNA. Before that, however, we shall examine some aspects of the degradation of these substances. Our attention shall focus on the degradation of nucleotides with particular emphasis given to the catabolic fate of the purine and pyrimidine bases. The area of nucleic acid catabolism will receive no attention except the brief note that all cells contain enzymes with the combined action of catalyzing the hydrolysis of polynucleotide chains to yield the constituent monophosphonucleotides. Each of these enzymes is classified as either an *endonuclease,* if it acts at phosphodiester bonds within a polynucleotide chain, or an *exonuclease,* if it acts at a phosphodiester bond at the end of a chain. This classification was discussed earlier in Chapter 6 as was the property of phosphodiester bond specificity (see Table 6–1, page 155). Brief mention was also made then of the various biological roles of nucleases. Now, however, the only point to be emphasized is that the monophosphonucleotides are the final hydrolysis products of polynucleotides. Although the monophosphonucleotides can be reused for RNA and DNA

$$\text{nucleic acids} \xrightarrow[\text{and endonucleases}]{\substack{\text{combined action} \\ \text{of exonucleases}}} \text{monophosphonucleotides}$$

biosynthesis, our objective here is to consider their further degradation to other products. Owing to several types of reactions associated with the degradation of deoxyribonucleotides, we will narrow our treatment even further by specifically examining the catabolism of ribonucleotides. Reactions that would apply to the catabolism of purine and pyrimidine bases originating from deoxyribonucleotides will be mentioned, however.

PURINE CATABOLISM

The further degradation of purine-containing ribonucleotides, GMP and AMP, occurs in all organisms as part of their normal metabolism. In fact, in most organisms the primary degradative pathways for GMP and AMP involve the same set of separate reactions which converge on the production of *xanthine* (see below). The conversion of guanine from GMP to xanthine is rather direct, whereas the formation of xanthine from adenine of AMP is indirect. After a dephosphorylation of AMP, the adenine moiety of adenosine is then converted to hypoxanthine to yield *inosine*. Inosine is then hydrolyzed to yield *hypoxanthine* as the free base, which is finally converted to xanthine. Although the details are not considered here, xanthine could also originate from the guanine and adenine of the corresponding deoxyribonucleotides, dGMP and dAMP, respectively.

Depending on the organism, the subsequent fate of xanthine is varied (see below). In most primates—including man, birds, certain reptiles, and the majority of insects—xanthine is converted to *uric acid*, which is excreted as the final end product of purine catabolism. In all other land animals *allantoin* is the final end product being formed by the further oxidation of uric acid. In amphibians and fish allantoin is further degraded to *allantoic acid*. In many microorganisms allantoic acid is converted to *glyoxylate* and *urea*. All these reactions are catalyzed by specific enzymes and clearly illustrate the themes of biochemical unity and diversity.

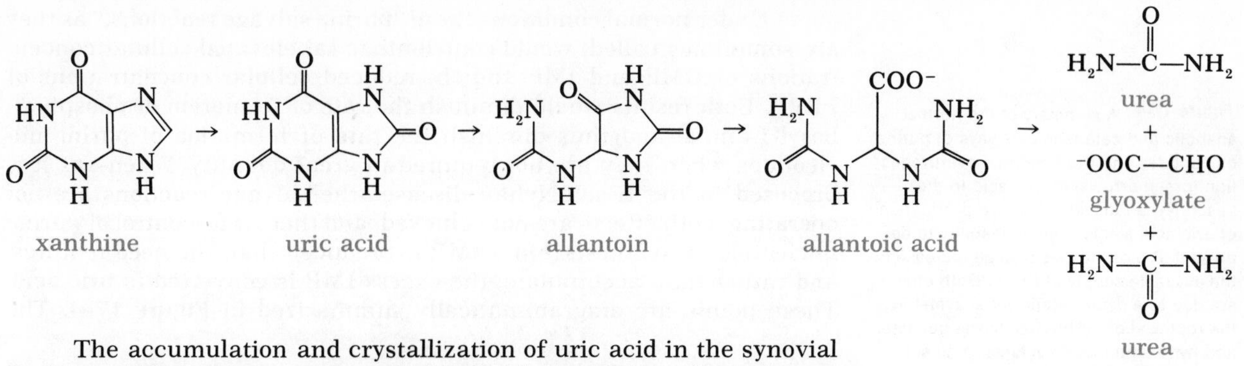

The structures shown, left to right: xanthine → uric acid → allantoin → allantoic acid → urea + ⁻OOC—CHO (glyoxylate) + urea.

The accumulation and crystallization of uric acid in the synovial fluid around bone joints are responsible for the painful condition known as *gout*. A hereditary disease, gout results from an overproduction of uric acid plus a failure of the kidneys to eliminate uric acid in large amounts. The biochemical basis for the overproduction of uric acid is not yet known. There is some evidence, however, that in some individuals this metabolic abnormality may be due to an inability to depress the biosynthesis of purine nucleotides by the normal feedback inhibition. Recall that the activity of the enzyme catalyzing the initial reaction of the anabolic pathway of purine nucleotides—namely, the formation of β-5-phosphoribosyl-1-amine from 5-phosphoribosyl-1-pyrophosphate (PRPP) and glutamine—is normally under strong negative control (it is inhibited) by GMP, AMP, and IMP (see page 458). The malfunction in this normal control point may be a defective enzyme that catalyzes this reaction. The enzyme may be defective in the sense that it is not capable of binding to and hence not capable of being regulated by the feedback inhibitors.

Another explanation would be that the AMP and IMP cellular levels required for inhibition to occur are not attained despite the fact that purine biosynthesis is occurring at an increased rate. Indeed, this type of malfunction has recently been documented as being the basis of the *Lesch-Nyhan syndrome,* a rare genetic disease related to gout. Among other things, the disease is characterized by excessive anxiety, aggressiveness, mental retardation, and a compulsion toward self-mutilation of the lips, tongue, and fingers. The biochemical defect in Lesch-Nyhan patients is the lack of *hypoxanthine-guanine phosphoribosyltransferase (HPRT),* an enzyme which normally catalyzes the reuse of the free purine bases, guanine and hypoxanthine, in the biosynthesis of GMP and IMP, respectively. The reactions, both of which utilize PRPP as the phosphoribosyl donor, are as follows:

$$\text{guanine} + \text{PRPP} \xrightarrow[\text{phosphoribosyltransferase}]{\text{hypoxanthine-guanine}} \text{GMP} + \text{PP}_i$$

$$\text{hypoxanthine} + \text{PRPP} \xrightarrow{\text{same enzyme}} \text{IMP} + \text{PP}_i$$

A separate enzyme that specifically catalyzes a similar reaction for adenine to yield AMP is present in both normal individuals and victims of the Lesch-Nyhan syndrome.

$$\text{adenine} + \text{PRPP} \xrightarrow[\text{phosphoribosyltransferase}]{\text{adenine}} \text{AMP} + \text{PP}_i$$

Under normal conditions these "purine salvage reactions," as they are sometimes called, would contribute to (a) elevated cellular concentrations of GMP and IMP and (b) reduced cellular concentrations of PRPP. Both results would diminish the rate of formation of phosphoribosyl-1-amine and thus diminish the rate of formation of purine nucleotides when they are not required in great quantity. When—as it is proposed in the Lesch-Nyhan disease—the salvage reactions are not operating, both effects are not achieved, and there is no control of purine nucleotide biosynthesis. More IMP is produced than the need requires, and rather than accumulate, the excess IMP is converted to uric acid. These points are diagrammatically summarized in Figure 17–4. The

Figure 17–4 A summary of the normal anabolic and catabolic pathways of purine nucleotides and the abnormal overproduction (green arrows) of uric acid in the Lesch-Nyhan disease. The overproduction of uric acid stems from an inability to depress IMP biosynthesis plus an increase in the available supply of PRPP. Both effects are due to a defect (deficient enzyme) in the reutilization of the free bases guanine and hypoxanthine. Structures of all substances can be found elsewhere in this chapter.

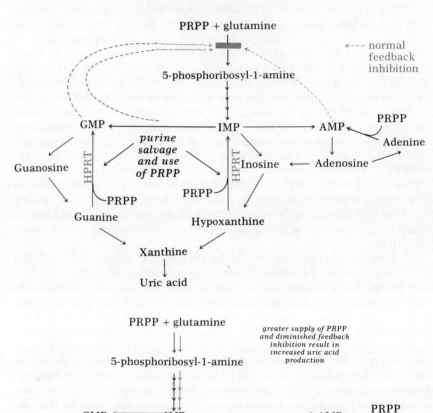

above information and the summary in Figure 17–4 provide an obvious example of the complexity of metabolism and its control. In addition, here is an interesting example of how one specific biochemical defect can have a severe disruptive effect on a whole area of metabolism and normal body growth and development. The details associated with the HPRT deficiency and the neurological abnormalities in the Lesch-Nyhan disease are not yet known.

PYRIMIDINE CATABOLISM

The catabolism of pyrimidine bases originating from pyrimidine-containing nucleotides apparently proceeds through one of several different pathways, depending on the organism. One of the major pathways, occurring, for example, in man and other animals, involves the reduction of uracil or thymine to yield a fully hydrogenated heterocyclic ring. The degradation of cytosine follows the same route after an initial deamination to yield uracil. Ring cleavage of the product resulting from uracil (cytosine) yields *carbamyl-β-alanine,* which is further hydrolyzed to CO_2, NH_3, and β-alanine. All of the products would be either excreted as waste products or reused in other areas of metabolism. For example, β-alanine could be reused in the biosynthesis of Coenzyme A.

uracil   β-alanine

thymine would yield:

$$CO_2, NH_3, \text{ and } {}^-OOCCHCH_2NH_2$$
$$| $$
$$CH_3$$

cytosine is first converted to uracil

DNA BIOSYNTHESIS—GENE REPLICATION

GENERAL PRINCIPLES: SEMI-CONSERVATIVE REPLICATION

Once it had been proven that DNA was the carrier of genetic information, the problem of chromosomal inheritance was immediately reduced to determining how DNA was reproduced. In other words, how does the biosynthesis of a DNA molecule occur such that the newly formed DNA is a duplicate copy of the original DNA and has the same genetic information? The first meaningful hypothesis as to how this might occur was made by Watson and Crick in 1953 a few weeks after they announced their model for the structure of DNA. They proposed that, if their model of DNA as a double helix of complementary polynucleotide strands was correct, this immediately suggested that the molecule should be capable of *self-replication*. The key to this suggestion was the complementary nature of the two chains. Their proposed scheme was quite simple. Prior to replication, the interchain hydrogen bonds are broken and then the chains unwind and separate. Each chain would then act independently as a template for the ordered positioning of nucleotides into a new complementary chain. The result would be the production of two DNA molecules identical to the original one.

The Watson-Crick hypothesis has been supported by extensive research during the past two decades. The most conclusive proof of their proposal was obtained in the late 1950s by M. Meselson and F. W. Stahl, who, in a brilliantly conceived set of experiments, demonstrated that in dividing *E. coli* cells the bacterial chromosome was duplicated according to what was then termed a *semi-conservative* scheme of replication. In this process (see Figure 17–5), which was the one suggested by Watson and Crick, each strand of the original DNA molecule separately directs the formation of its complement and then combines with it. Each of the two new double-helix molecules would thus consist of a newly synthesized polynucleotide chain intertwined with its complementary chain

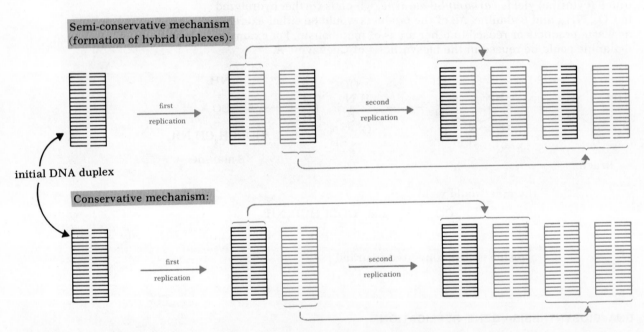

Figure 17–5 A comparison of two possible mechanisms for DNA replication.

of the original molecule. In other words, each new DNA produced would be a *hybrid* of old and new. This is distinct from a *conservative* scheme of replication wherein both of the newly formed strands were thought to be present in the same double helix. In other words, no hybrids of new and old chains would be produced. Each chain of the original DNA molecule would direct the formation of a new complementary chain, but then the two new chains would combine with each other.

The Meselson-Stahl experiment was based on attempting to prove or disprove the formation of hybrid duplexes and to thus prove one of the two possible schemes. To do this, they first grew *E. coli* cells in a medium containing $N^{15}H_4Cl$ as the sole nitrogen source. N^{15} is a stable heavy isotope of the most abundant natural form of nitrogen, N^{14}. Consequently, after growth in such a medium, all nitrogen-containing compounds will eventually be "labeled" with N^{15}. The DNA of the cells will be extensively labeled, because each molecule will contain several thousand N^{15} atoms in the many purine and pyrimidine nitrogen bases. Because of this, N^{15}-DNA will have a greater density (it will be heavier) than N^{14}-DNA or any hybrid of DNA containing a portion of N^{14} and a portion of N^{15}, and should then be separable by density gradient ultracentrifugation.

A diagrammatic outline of the Meselson-Stahl experiment is given in Figure 17–6. After the cells were labeled in N^{15} medium, they were washed and transferred to a similar medium containing only $N^{14}H_4Cl$, and growth was continued for several generations. Every time the population doubled—that is, with the production of every new generation of

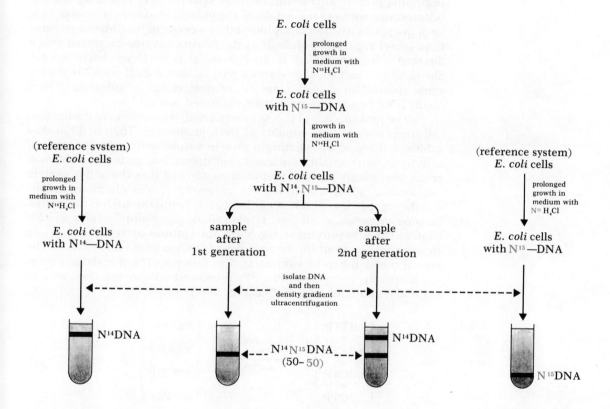

cells—a sample was removed and the DNA assayed for its content of N^{14} and N^{15}. Ultracentrifugal analysis of the DNA obtained after one generation revealed only one zone in the tube, which was 50% lighter than the completely N^{15}-DNA and 50% heavier than the completely N^{14}-DNA. No other bands were present in significant amounts. This suggests then that after one doubling all of the DNA molecules were 50–50 hybrids of N^{14} and N^{15}. Furthermore, the DNA obtained after the second generation displayed two bands. One was equivalent to the band obtained after the first generation and the second was equivalent to

Figure 17–6 Diagrammatic summary of Meselson-Stahl experiment proving the semiconservative mechanism of DNA replication.

N^{14}-DNA. Moreover, both were present in equal amounts. All of these data proved the formation of hybrid DNA's that could have arisen only by a semi-conservative scheme of replication. The complete loss of the original DNA containing only N^{15} also eliminates the conservative mechanism. The original experiments of Meselson and Stahl have since been successfully repeated on *E. coli* and other microbes, as well as with higher organisms. Thus, it appears probable that the process has a universal occurrence.

ENZYMOLOGY OF DNA BIOSYNTHESIS

At the time Meselson and Stahl were studying the nature of DNA biosynthesis using living whole cells, Arthur Kornberg and coworkers were beginning investigations with cell-free systems of *E. coli* in an attempt to determine some of the details of the process. Answers were sought to such questions as: Can DNA biosynthesis occur in a cell-free system or is an intact organism required? Is the process enzyme-catalyzed or is it directed solely by DNA? If an enzyme(s) is involved, what are the chemical and biological properties, that is, how does it work? Is the enzyme specific for a certain species of nucleotides as substrates? How might DNA be used in an enzyme-catalyzed process?

The first success of the Kornberg group was in demonstrating that cell-free systems were capable of DNA production. Then in 1958 they achieved the goal of isolating a protein extract with a high degree of activity in polymerizing nucleotide substrates into an intact DNA molecule. Moderately purified preparations showed that the active protein component, called simply a *DNA polymerase,* was characterized by specific properties which included (a) a requirement for the simultaneous presence of all four *triphosphodeoxyribonucleotides* as substrates; (b) a requirement for Mg^{++} for optimal activity; and (c) an absolute requirement for the presence of DNA to prime the reaction. The overall reaction can be summarized as follows. (The metabolic fate of the inorganic pyrophosphate, PP_i, produced in the reaction will be examined in a later section. See page 486.)

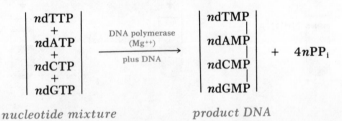

$$nucleotide\ mixture \qquad product\ DNA$$

By thinking about the nature of a polynucleotide chain, you should recognize that the condensation of the constituent nucleotides could possibly occur so that the chain is extended in a $5' \rightarrow 3'$ direction, in a $3' \rightarrow 5'$ direction, or in both directions. Well, it was found that the action of DNA polymerase results in elongation of the chain proceeding only in the $5' \rightarrow 3'$ direction. In other words, every time a new phosphodiester bond is formed, the phosphorus atom is contributed by the *incoming* 5'-triphosphodeoxyribonucleotide (see facing page).

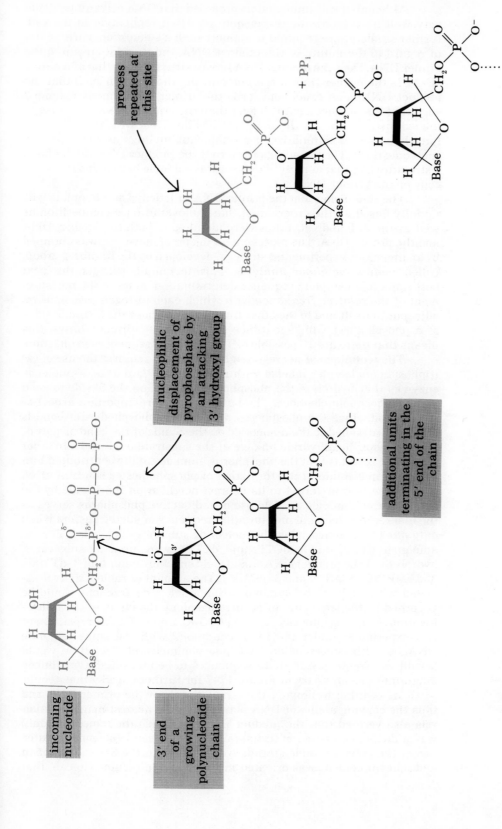

Although it was immediately proposed that DNA polymerase could very well be the enzyme responsible for DNA replication in the cell, further studies were required to support such a suggestion, particularly in regard to the nature of the product DNA and its relationship to the primer DNA. Does the product DNA have a structure like that of a native DNA? Is the primer DNA a *template* during the reaction such that the product DNA is an exact copy, or is the primer DNA merely extended such that the product DNA is bigger than the original DNA? Because of the extensive nature of the many studies involved, we are of necessity forced to merely summarize the significant findings as they apply to such questions. These findings were that the product DNA (a) did have a structure like that of native DNA—it was a double helix—and (b) was a copy of the primer DNA.

The conclusion that the primer DNA functioned as a template was initially based on the observation that the overall base composition as well as the A/T and G/C ratios were identical in both the product DNA and the primer DNA. The most convincing proof, however, was obtained by an ingenious experimental strategy, developed by the Kornberg group, called *nearest-neighbor analysis*. This technique permits the next best thing to a complete sequence determination, namely, the measurement of the *relative frequency* with which each nitrogen base appears adjacent to itself and to the other three bases on both the 3' and 5' sides of a phosphodiester linkage. Since there are four nitrogen bases, this means that there are 16 possible (4^2) dinucleotide sequences in question.

The technique of nearest-neighbor analysis requires the use of (a) triphosphonucleotides labeled with radioactive P^{32}, and (b) 5'-nuclease enzymes that hydrolyze the phosphodiester bond on the 5' side to yield 3'-monophosphonucleotides. The latter is the more important aspect of the method, since the phosphorus atom of the phosphodiester bond is originally attached to the nucleotide on the 5' side of the bond as part of the 5'-triphosphoanhydride linkage of the substrate nucleotide. In other words, the result is that the phosphorus atom originally contributed by a substrate nucleotide in the formation of phosphodiester bonds by DNA polymerase is transferred to its nearest neighbor on the 5' side by the action of the 5'-nucleases. The use of radioactive phosphorus serves as the marker to detect and measure the frequency of such transfers when *only one* of the four triphosphonucleotide substrates is labeled. For example, if dTTP, dATP, dGTP, and $dCTP^{32}$ were used as substrates, hydrolysis of the product DNA would yield specific amounts of 3'-$dTMP^{32}$, 3'-$dAMP^{32}$, 3'-$dGMP^{32}$, and 3'-$dCMP^{32}$. The amount of radioactivity associated with each of the 3'-monophosphonucleotide fractions would be governed by the frequency of occurrence along the chain of the following dinucleotide sequences: TpC, ApC, GpC, and CpC. The repetition of this experiment under the same conditions with the same template DNA, but with a different labeled triphosphonucleotide each time, would permit the frequency of all 16 sequences to be measured. Consult the diagrammatic summary in Figure 17–7 for further clarification.

In addition to proving the template role of the primer DNA and thus the copying ability of DNA polymerase, the nearest-neighbor analysis also verified that the product DNA (and thus the template DNA) was a duplex composed of antiparallel polynucleotide strands. That is, one of the polynucleotide strands was oriented in the 5' → 3' direction and its complement was oriented in the 3' → 5' direction. (Recall, that

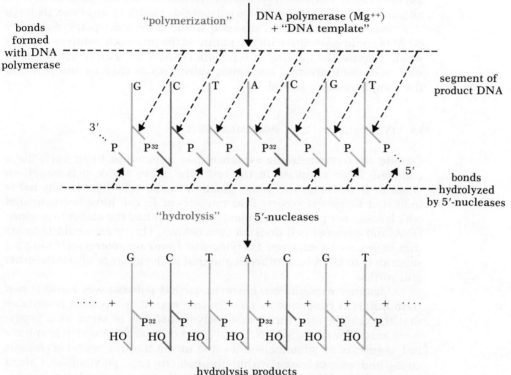

dGTP, dATP
dTTP, dCTP³²

mixture of
nucleotide substrates
(one contains 5′-P³²P³²P³²)

"polymerization" | DNA polymerase (Mg⁺⁺)
+ "DNA template"

Figure 17–7 A summary of the experimental approach of nearest-neighbor analysis.

bonds
formed
with DNA
polymerase

segment of
product DNA

bonds
hydrolyzed
by 5′-nucleases

"hydrolysis" | 5′-nucleases

hydrolysis products
(mixture of 3′-monophosphonucleotides)

"analysis" | a) separation by ion exchange chromatography
b) determine amount of P³² in dGMP, dAMP, dTMP, and dCMP

1st trial with dCTP³²: calculate frequency of GpC, ApC, TpC, CpC
2nd trial with dTTP³²: calculate frequency of GpT, ApT, TpT, CpT
3rd trial with dATP³²: calculate frequency of GpA, ApA, TpA, CpA
4th trial with dGTP³²: calculate frequency of GpG, ApG, TpG, CpG

this characteristic of DNA structure is termed, *opposite polarity*). This conclusion was based on the fact that the frequency of occurrence of each of the sixteen dinucleotide sequences in the 5′ → 3′ direction was identical to the frequency of occurrence of its complementary dinucleotide sequence in the 3′ → 5′ direction, rather than the 5′ → 3′ direction. For example (see margin), the frequency of occurrence of TpG was equal to that of CpA and not ApC; the occurrence of GpA was equal to that of TpC and not CpT; and so on.

In recent years DNA polymerase preparations have been obtained from various sources, and all have properties similar to those of the enzyme isolated from *E. coli* by Kornberg. However, the *E. coli* enzyme has been studied the most and hence, is best understood. Since it was the

$(5')\overrightarrow{TpG}(3')$
$(5')\underrightarrow{ApC}(3')$

ApC would be the
dinucleotide complement
of TpG if the two
strands were oriented
in the same direction

$(5')\overrightarrow{TpG}(3')$
$(3')\underleftarrow{ApC}(5')$

CpA would be the
dinucleotide complement
of TpG if the two
strands were oriented
in opposite directions

first to be isolated, and also because at least two separate polymerases are now known to occur in *E. coli* (see below), the original Kornberg enzyme is now generally referred to as *polymerase I*. As a protein, polymerase I is a rather large molecule having a molecular weight of approximately 100,000. It is not clear, however, whether the protein is an oligomer or simply one massive polypeptide chain. In any case, its large size (assuming a spherical shape, it would have a diameter of roughly 60 Å) is commensurate with the nature of the process it catalyzes, which would require the binding of template DNA, itself a large molecule, as well as of the individual nucleotide substrates as they are inserted into the complementary strand.

IN VIVO ROLE OF DNA POLYMERASE I

Despite the overwhelming evidence that polymerase I can duplicate a complete DNA template in the test tube, so to speak, it is uncertain whether it performs the same function in the cell. That it may not is indicated by recent reports that mutants of *E. coli* have been isolated which could not produce polymerase I but still had the ability to produce DNA and undergo cell division (see below). This then would indicate that at least two enzymes (*polymerase I* and *polymerase II*) may act separately in DNA biosynthesis, and that in the absence of one the other still works.

Another explanation, however, is that polymerases I and II perform different functions *in vivo*. In this regard, it has been postulated that the real *in vivo* function of polymerase I is to serve as a *repair* mechanism for damaged DNA, that is, for cellular DNA which may have lost segments of oligonucleotides due to the natural action of various endo- and exonucleases within the cell. In fact, polymerase I itself possesses the ability to function catalytically as an exonuclease. In combination with its known polymerization properties, this would then mean that polymerase I could bind to an adulterated DNA (it might contain localized regions of mismatched base pairs arising from a mutation, or perhaps so-called thymine dimers resulting from exposure to UV radiation—see later section), first excise the damaged segment, and then replace it with the correct sequence or a dimer-free sequence. The repair role is further supported by the fact that the most efficient samples of primer DNA *in vitro* are those that have been slightly denatured prior to use by the introduction of nicks in one of the strands with an accompanying partial unfolding, or by the removal of a short segment from the end of one of the strands. Indeed, an intact DNA double helix is known to be relatively inactive *in vitro*. A single linear or circular strand of a DNA duplex works quite well, however.

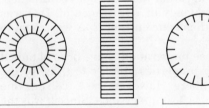 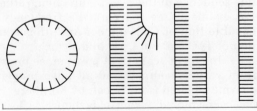

inactive templates   active templates

Although the exact biological role of polymerase I is questionable, a remarkable experiment performed by M. Goulian, Kornberg, and R. L. Sinsheimer in 1967 strongly suggests that an enzyme very similar to polymerase I (if not I itself) is involved in DNA replication. The objective of the experiment was to duplicate *in vitro* an intact DNA molecule obtained from a known biological source, and then to test whether the synthetic copy was biologically active. The DNA chosen as a template was the single chromosome of a tiny bacterial virus, designated ϕX174. With approximately 5,500 nucleotides arranged in specific sequence, the ϕX174 viral DNA would appear to be a massive template. In comparison to other chromosomal DNAs, however, the size of ϕX174 DNA is quite small. Most other viral chromosomes are larger. On the cellular level, the fact that the single chromosome of an *E. coli* cell contains approximately 10,000,000 nucleotides further indicates the smallness of the ϕX174 DNA. The DNA from higher organisms would, of course, be even larger.

Nature aided considerably in the design of the experiment, because it so happens that the ϕX174 chromosome exists in both a *non-replicative* state and a *replicative* state. The former is a circular molecule consisting of only one polynucleotide strand (+). That is, it is single stranded. The replicative state, however, consists of two intertwined complementary strands (+ and −). That is, it is double stranded. Thus, the objective was to first use the (+) strand as a template to make a synthetic (−) strand and to then use the (−) strand to make a synthetic (+) strand. If the DNA polymerase were truly competent, then the synthetic (+) strand should be identical to the original template (+) strand. In other words, the synthetic (+) strand should carry all of the genetic information of ϕX174 and hence be biologically active ϕX174 viral-DNA.

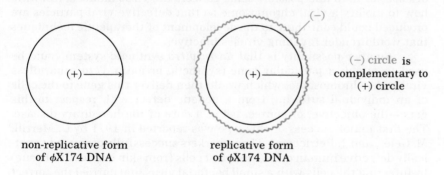

non-replicative form
of ϕX174 DNA

replicative form
of ϕX174 DNA

(−) circle **is**
complementary to
(+) circle

To test this, a brilliant technique was devised which in part required the closure of the newly synthesized DNA molecule to give an intact circular (−) strand and then an intact circular (+) strand. This was done enzymatically by use of a *joining enzyme,* called *DNA ligase,* which was also isolated from *E. coli.* The closure to yield an intact circular duplex was then followed by controlled treatment of the duplex product with DNAase. This was done to produce a nick in the strand that was being copied in each phase. Since the action of DNAase is not selective for either of the strands, and since some duplex molecules would escape the DNAase action, a mixture of products was obtained. Mild exposure to heat was then used to unravel the nicked strands from the duplexes. Under the conditions used, the intact duplex remained unchanged. The intact circular synthetic strand was then isolated by

deoxybromouridine
triphosphate (dBUTP)

O
‖
HN—⟍
     ⟍—Br
O=⟍ ⟋
     N

deoxyribose-P-P-P

deoxythymidine
triphosphate (dTTP)

O
‖
HN—⟍
     ⟍—CH₃
O=⟍ ⟋
     N

deoxyribose-P-P-P

density gradient ultracentrifugation. The separation of strands was made possible by the use of *deoxybromouridine triphosphate* (BUTP) in place of deoxythymidine triphosphate in the first polymerization step. Bromouracil is a structural analog of thymine that will enter into complementary base pairing with an adenine residue. Thus, during assembly wherever a thymine would have been inserted, bromouracil was inserted instead. The product DNA then becomes labeled because bromouracil is much heavier than thymine (the Br atom is heavier than the —CH₃ grouping). Consequently, the presence of several bromouracil residues should produce a DNA strand of different density that could be separated from those strands not containing bromouracil. The pattern of the experiment is diagrammed in Figure 17–8. The final result of the experiment was that the synthetic (+) strand infected E. coli cells and resulted in the production of additional (+) strands that were identical to the native (+) strand used as a template in the first place. In other words, the product was biologically active.

Expectedly, the announcement of this achievement caused quite a stir in the scientific community. Although a considerable effort was made to acquaint the non-scientific public with the significance of the work, the reaction fell far short of the expected effect. Unfortunately, the implications of the achievement are not as readily appreciated, nor are they as dramatic, as those of a successful heart transplant, which the public had been exposed to only a few months earlier. Nevertheless, the experiment does create immediate potentials for exciting research. For example, it should be feasible to manipulate the process so as to produce modified forms of a chromosome and to determine how its biological properties are affected. Investigations of this sort with viral chromosomes could yield valuable information, since many infectious diseases of man and possibly some cancers are virus induced. Knowing how to modify a viral chromosome so that defective viral particles are produced could contribute to the development of therapeutic techniques that would render invading viruses inactive.

Another possibility is that an *in vitro* synthetic system could be used to attach a particular gene (synthetic or natural) to a harmless viral-DNA chromosome, which would then deliver this gene to the cells of an individual suffering from a genetic defect with respect to this gene—the objective, of course, being a cure of the hereditary disease. The first major success of this type was reported in 1971 by C. Merrill, M. Geier, and J. Petricciani. These workers successfully corrected genetically defective human cells (fibroplast cells from skin connective tissue) by infecting the cells with a small bacterial virus that carried the correct gene, acquired by a previous infection of bacteria. The fibroplast cells were obtained from a patient afflicted with galactosemia, a genetic disease characterized by the inability to produce galactose-1-phosphate uridyl transferase (see page 282). Without concern about how the virus or viral chromosome entered the cells or about whether the genetic information carried by the viral chromosome was incorporated into the DNA of the fibroplasts, they did demonstrate that after treatment with the virus the defective human cells had acquired the ability to produce the enzyme and convert galactose-1-phosphate to UDP-galactose. In repeated experiments the amount of enzyme produced in these cells was anywhere from 10 to 75 times as great as that produced in uninfected cells or in cells infected with a virus not carrying the correct gene.

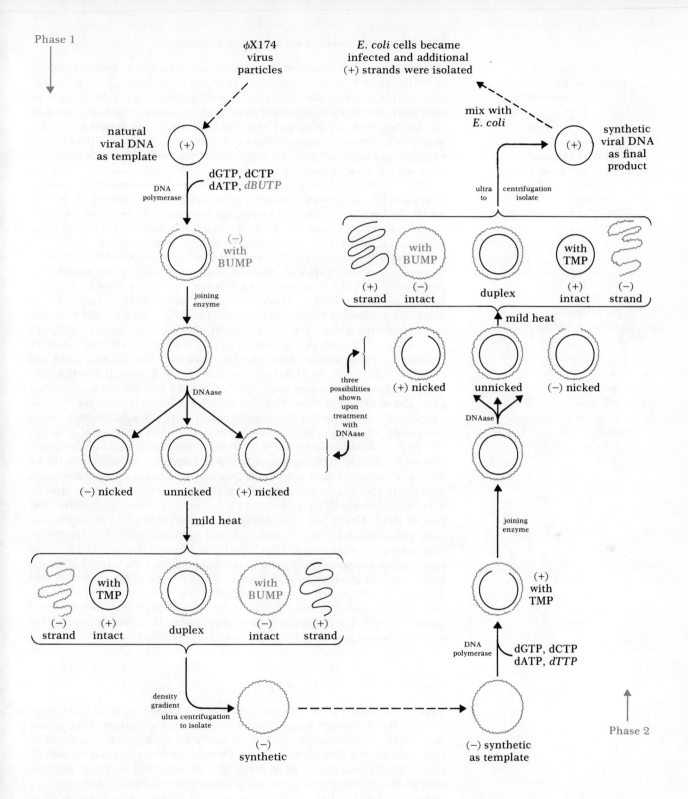

Phase 1

φX174
virus
particles

E. coli cells became
infected and additional
(+) strands were isolated

mix with
E. coli

natural
viral DNA
as template

(+)

(+)

synthetic
viral DNA
as final
product

DNA
polymerase

dGTP, dCTP
dATP, *dBUTP*

ultra
to

centrifugation
isolate

(−)
with
BUMP

with
BUMP

(−)
intact

duplex

with
TMP

(+)
intact

joining
enzyme

(+)
strand

(−)
strand

mild heat

three
possibilities
shown
upon
treatment
with
DNAase

(+) nicked

unnicked

(−) nicked

DNAase

DNAase

(−) nicked

unnicked

(+) nicked

joining
enzyme

mild heat

(+)
with
TMP

(−)
strand

(+)
intact

with
TMP

duplex

(−)
intact

with
BUMP

(+)
strand

DNA
polymerase

dGTP, dCTP
dATP, *dTTP*

density
gradient
ultra centrifugation
to isolate

Phase 2

(−)
synthetic

(−) synthetic
as template

Figure 17–8 A diagrammatic summary of
the *in vitro* synthesis of a biologically
active DNA.

bacterial cells
capable of producing
GIP-uridyl transferase

virus
infection

isolate viruses
carrying the gene from
bacteria for the
production of
GIP-uridyl transferase

defective human
fibroplast cells
unable to
produce the
enzyme

human fibroplast cells
capable of producing
the enzyme

cells divided with
retention of ability
to produce the enzyme

Moreover, the acquisition of this ability persisted during nearly 6 weeks of culturing, which included twice splitting the culture. To summarize (see margin): A nondefective gene was transferred by a virus to human cells that contained a defective gene. The bacterial gene functioned in the human cells by directing the biosynthesis of the missing protein, and also underwent replication as the human cells divided. Because of experiments such as this, the capacity to manipulate genetic material by design is now becoming a real possibility and not merely scientific fantasy. As our knowledge in this area of genetic engineering advances to higher levels, several ominous questions will be created on social, moral, and ethical levels as to how this knowledge is to be used for the betterment of mankind. It would be wise to consider such questions now so that, hopefully, the knowledge will be used properly.

Despite the uncertainty as to the actual biological role of polymerase I, studies with this enzyme have unraveled many significant clues regarding the mechanism of DNA biosynthesis. However, many aspects of the process of DNA replication still remain a mystery. For example, it is not yet known for sure how the DNA unwinds, and whether the unwinding occurs prior to the start of replication or is concurrent with replication. Another feature of the *in vivo* process for which there is clear experimental evidence is that *both strands* of the duplex are *copied simultaneously.* How this occurs is also unknown. It would seem, however, that the enzyme responsible for DNA replication should then have the ability to synthesize polynucleotide chains in both the $5' \rightarrow 3'$ and $3' \rightarrow 5'$ directions. In this regard, one of the main arguments against the role of polymerase I in replication is that it can't do this—at least not *in vitro.* It works only in the $5' \rightarrow 3'$ direction. Although Kornberg has offered a possible explanation of how polymerase I, working only in the $5' \rightarrow 3'$ direction, could copy both strands of a duplex simultaneously, support is shifting to the proposition that polymerase II is the true *in vivo* replicase for DNA and that polymerase I operates primarily in repair of DNA. Recall the evidence cited earlier concerning mutants that lack polymerase I activity but can still synthesize DNA. The recent demonstration that one of these mutants has a defective DNA repair mechanism supports this repair function of polymerase I. In what seems to be a staged production of the saga of DNA replication, M. Gefter and Thomas Kornberg, the son of Arthur, have even more recently announced the isolation from *E. coli* of a polymerase preparation different from Arthur's. They propose it to be polymerase II. It will be interesting to await the report of their studies on its catalytic properties.

CHEMICAL SYNTHESIS OF DNA

Ever since genes were established as being segments of a DNA molecule, it has long been a goal of molecular biology to synthesize an intact gene from its nucleotide precursors solely by a chemical route and to then test for its biological activity. (Note that the synthesis of ϕX174 DNA, which contains 5 or 6 genes linked together, was not really a chemical laboratory synthesis but a biological synthesis using enzymes and a template DNA in a cell-free system.) In 1970 the first objective was achieved by G. Khorana and coworkers after five years of work with the assembly of the gene that presumably codes for an alanine transfer-

RNA molecule in yeast. No biological template was used. The template in this case was merely a sequence of 77 nitrogen base pairs that could be written on a piece of paper with the sequence of bases in one strand being complementary to the sequence of bases in alanine transfer-RNA. The base sequence of ala-tRNA had been previously elucidated in 1965 (see page 498, Chapter 18). In a living cell, the tRNA gene would be transcribed to yield the intact alanine transfer-RNA molecule (see next section).

In contrast to the Merrifield solid-phase method for the chemical synthesis of polypeptide chains based on the successive addition of amino acid residues one at a time from the C-terminus, the technique developed by Khorana involved the separate assembly of fifteen small oligonucleotides of desired sequence, which in turn were then pieced together in the proper order. In addition to developing suitable chemical methods for the formation of 3'—5' phosphodiester bonds between adjacent nucleotides, each of the nitrogen bases had to be protected from undergoing reactions throughout the many steps. Isolation, purification, and characterization were also required after each segment was assembled. Moreover, two separate strands had to be synthesized.

The details as to how these many operations were performed are not our concern. The important thing is that they have been accomplished. Thus, the basic techniques are available for possible use in producing genetic material in the laboratory. The only requirement would be the sequence of bases in the gene or in the segment of the gene that is desired. This, however, depends on whether or not the synthetic material has any biological activity, and that has yet to be determined. Based on the successful chemical synthesis of biologically active peptides (such as vasopressin and oxytocin) and proteins (such as ribonuclease and the human growth hormone), what would you expect?

MUTATIONS

GENERAL PRINCIPLES

A mutation can occur as a natural spontaneous process or it can be induced by *mutagenic agents*. Whereas natural mutations occur at a very low frequency, those arising from exposure to mutagenic agents occur at a rather high frequency. In either case, however, the overall biological effect is basically the same: the mutation results in an alteration (a change) in one or more inheritable characteristics caused by an alteration in one or more genes of the chromosome. On a biochemical or molecular level, the alteration in the gene is an alteration of the nitrogen base sequence. The result of this is that the ultimate product of a gene, that is, a particular protein, is altered with respect to its amino acid sequence and possibly its biological activity. In addition, the altered gene may be one that is not programmed for messenger-RNA and then protein, but rather for either ribosomal-RNA or transfer-RNA. Our discussion here will center on the relationship to proteins.

The degree of change in the biological activity of the protein will depend on whether the modification in amino acid sequence is minimal or extensive, and whether it involves essential or non-essential residues.

Mutations that result in the change of only one amino acid residue do not generally yield defective proteins. That is to say, the modified protein still has nearly the same degree of biological activity as the original. Such a mutation is referred to as being *silent*. However, if the particular amino acid has a critical role in the protein as an essential structural, binding, or catalytic residue, the change will most likely yield a defective protein. This type of mutation is said to be *lethal*. For example, recall our earlier discussion of the single amino acid substitution in position 6 of valine for glutamic acid in the β chain of hemoglobin, resulting in the defective hemoglobin molecule of individuals with sickle cell anemia (see page 87, Chapter 4). With mutations that produce multiple changes in the amino acid sequence, the likelihood is greatly increased that the protein will be defective.

THE NATURE OF A MUTATION

The most fundamental questions relative to this subject refer to the when and how of the mutation process. Does it occur at the level of an intact chromosome or while the chromosome is being replicated? Does it require the simultaneous change of several nitrogen base pairs or can it occur as the result of a change in only a single pair? Do the changes involve only replacements of nitrogen base pairs, that is, a substitution of one complementary pair for another, or can there be additions and deletions? Exactly how do the changes occur?

The first question is answered in part by the fact that mutations occur only in growing organisms. That is to say, the cells must be metabolically active. More detailed studies have shown that in particular the cell must be synthesizing DNA. Thus, the formation of mutated genes occurs during the assembly of DNA. However, as we will discover below, the process may begin by an initial modification of nitrogen bases in the intact chromosome. Even so, this must be followed by an active phase of DNA synthesis so that the change can be completed.

The second question was resolved by a brilliant series of experiments by Seymour Benzer and his colleagues during the late 1950s. Without analyzing the strategy involved (refer to Benzer's article listed at the end of this chapter), suffice it to say that, in studies with a particular genetic segment of the chromosome of a bacterial virus, Benzer was able to prove that the smallest mutatable unit in a gene was in all probability a single nitrogen base pair. Thus, during the replication of DNA, a mutated gene can result from a single mistake involving a change of a single complementary pair of nucleotides.

The third question has been settled by investigations designed to determine the mode of action of different mutagenic agents. From such studies it is known that all three types of alterations can occur—*base pair substitutions, base pair additions,* and *base pair deletions*. Of the three types, substitution mutations are the least likely to result in a mutated gene with a program for a defective protein. Single additions or deletions, however, will both generally result in a lethal mutation.

In order to respond to the last question, it is best that we consider the mode of action of specific mutagenic agents. One of the most powerful mutagenic agents is nitrous acid (HNO_2). It acts at the level of the intact chromosome by causing a chemical transformation of certain nitrogen bases, namely, adenine, cytosine, and guanine. Each of these three bases contains a $\diagdown$C—NH$_2$ grouping which, on treatment with HNO$_2$, is oxidatively deaminated to a $\diagdown$C=O grouping. See Figure 17–9.

In other words, modified nitrogen bases are produced in intact DNA— *hypoxanthine from adenine; uracil from cytosine;* and *xanthine from guanine.* The action of HNO$_2$ is essentially random and any of the adenine, guanine, and cytosine residues on either of the two strands will be so modified. During subsequent DNA biosynthesis, this causes alterations in the nitrogen base sequence because each of the modified residues has a complementary partner different from that of the original nitrogen base. For example, cytosine normally pairs with guanine. Treatment with HNO$_2$ converts cytosine to uracil, which prefers to pair with adenine. In the first replication of DNA, the uracil would direct the insertion of adenine in its complementary strand. In the second replication, the adenine in turn would direct the insertion of its complementary base, thymine. Thus, the net effect would be the change of a G–C pair to an A–T pair. This represents a mutation. Because the alteration involves the replacement of one purine-pyrimidine pair by another, this type of change is termed a *transitional mutation* and is the most common type of substitution. Other mutagenic agents that result in transitional substitutions are bromouracil, 2-aminopurine, and hydroxylamine. In addition to characterizing the effect of most mutagenic agents, transitional mutations also represent most natural mutations.

Two of the most deleterious mutagenic agents are the *acridines* and *nitrogen mustards,* causing base pair additions and deletions, respectively. Termed *frame-shift mutations,* these changes are gener-

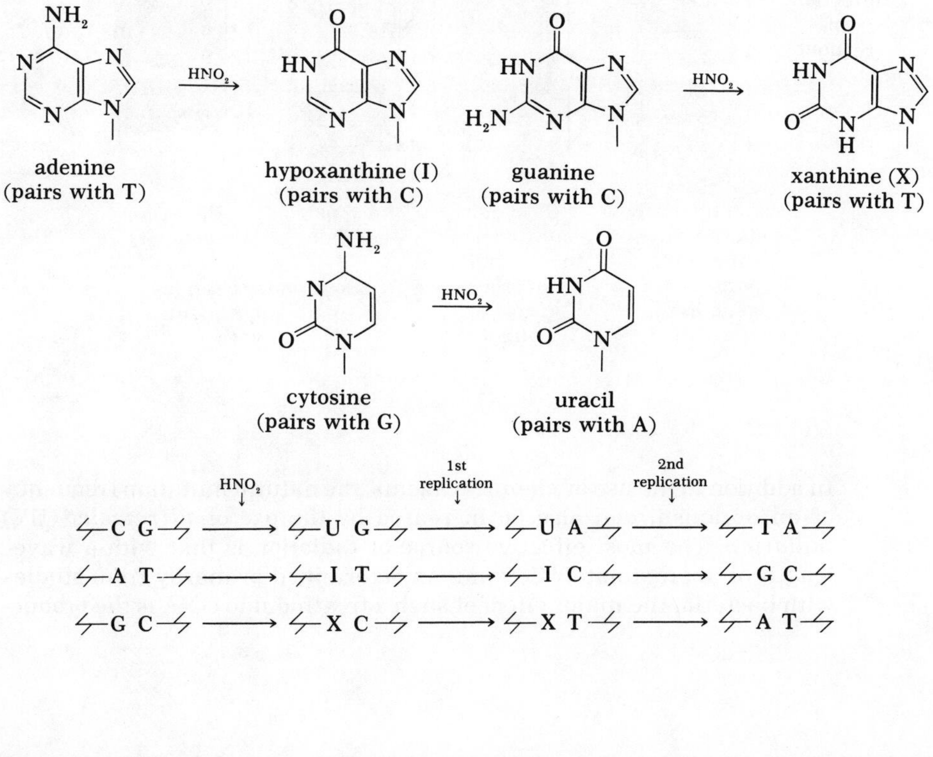

Figure 17–9 A summary of the mutagenic effect of HNO$_2$.

adenine
(pairs with T)

hypoxanthine (I)
(pairs with C)

guanine
(pairs with C)

xanthine (X)
(pairs with T)

cytosine
(pairs with G)

uracil
(pairs with A)

ally lethal, because when either occurs, the entire genetic program is changed beyond the point of the addition or deletion. To appreciate the truth of this, we must introduce something about how the genetic program is read. That is, how does the genetic program specify the amino acid sequence of a protein? In the next chapter we will consider this question in greater detail. For now, we will merely state what is known, namely, that the sequence of amino acids in a protein is coded in the gene by a continuous sequence of groups of three nucleotides, called *triplets*. Each triplet, consisting of a specific sequence of the three nucleotides, determines the positioning of a specific amino acid. Thus, a single transitional mutation resulting in a localized change of only one base pair will change the sequence of only one triplet, and only one amino acid residue will be affected (see diagram below). On the other hand, a single frame-shift mutation will change the sequence of all triplets beyond the point of mutation (the reading frame of triplets is shifted), and thus several residues of the amino acid sequence will be affected. Indeed, if the frame-shift mutation occurs at the beginning of the gene where transcription begins, then nearly the entire amino acid sequence of the resultant protein will be modified.

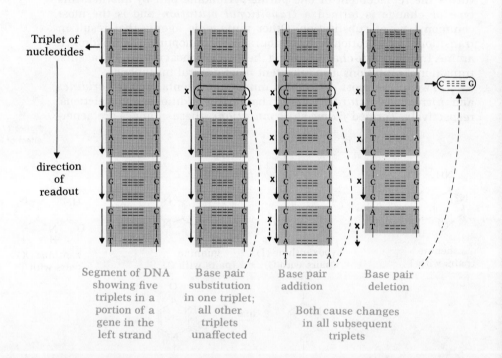

Triplet of nucleotides

direction of readout

Segment of DNA showing five triplets in a portion of a gene in the left strand

Base pair substitution in one triplet; all other triplets unaffected

Base pair addition

Base pair deletion

Both cause changes in all subsequent triplets

THYMINE DIMERS

In addition to the use of chemical agents, the natural mutation frequency of an organism can also be increased by the use of *ultraviolet* (UV) *radiation*. The most effective source of radiation is that with a wavelength of approximately 260 nm. As determined primarily from studies with bacteria, the major effect of such a treatment to DNA is the production of a particular type of lesion, called *thymine dimers*. This means that two thymine bases occupying adjacent positions in the same polynucleotide strand covalently interact with each other to form a structure as shown below. If the dose of radiation is large enough, and hence associated with an extensive formation of thymine dimers, the overall

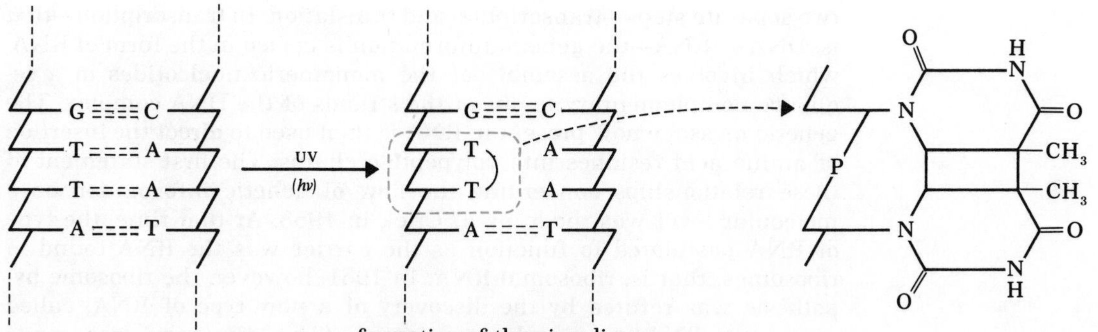

formation of thymine dimer
(structure at right)

effect is lethal—the organism dies. With smaller, sublethal doses the organism can repair (DNA polymerase I?) the damage by first removing the thymine dimer lesion as a short oligonucleotide segment and then building a new piece. If a mistake occurs here, a mutation results. Alternatively, both the dimer lesion and its complementary segment in the unaltered strand may be removed without any resynthesis, thus resulting in a frame-shift, deletion mutation. Actually, precise explanations for the mutagenicity and lethality of UV radiation are unknown, and it is possible that both may involve events other than the formation of thymine dimers.

THE USE OF MUTANT ORGANISMS

Mutant bacteria and viruses with a particular defect have played an extremely valuable role in the growth of our understanding concerning biochemical processes. The underlying philosophy in their use is that one way to understand what normally goes on in a normal organism is to study abnormal processes in abnormal (mutated) organisms. Many metabolic pathways and catalytic functions have been elucidated by this approach. Consider the previously cited work with the polymerase I mutants, for example. The discoveries of gene control mechanisms—indeed, our complete understanding of the nature of the gene—have also resulted from the use of mutants. Mutant organisms have proved beneficial at the industrial and agricultural levels as well. At the industrial level, mutant microorganisms have been used to produce higher yields of desired fermentation products. At the agricultural level, mutant plants have resulted in producing larger and more nutritious crops. Unfortunately, although all of these areas are interesting for further discussion, they are too complex for suitable treatment in an introductory text.

RNA BIOSYNTHESIS—GENE TRANSCRIPTION

GENERAL PRINCIPLES

As we stated earlier in the chapter, the utilization of the genetic information in DNA in controlling the biosynthesis of protein proceeds through two separate steps—transcription and translation. In transcription—that is, DNA → RNA—the genetic information is copied in the form of RNA, which involves the assembly of the monomeric nucleotides in a sequence complementary to one of the strands of the DNA complex. The genetic message now present in RNA is then used to direct the insertion of amino acid residues into polypeptide chains. The first statement of these relationships concerning the flow of genetic information on a molecular level was made by F. Crick in 1958. At that time, the type of RNA postulated to function as the carrier was the RNA found in ribosomes, that is, ribosomal-RNA. In 1961, however, the ribosome hypothesis was refuted by the discovery of a new type of RNA, called *messenger-RNA,* previously undetected. (The discovery was made simultaneously but independently by two groups: S. Brenner, F. Jacob, and M. Meselson; and F. Gros, J. Watson, and coworkers.) Thus, the ideas of genetic expression were changed from the ribosomal hypothesis to the *messenger hypothesis,* first enunciated by F. Jacob and J. Monod in 1961. In essence, the messenger hypothesis stated that the *primary gene product was a messenger-RNA molecule.* At present, this is a well-documented law of molecular biology. It should be pointed out, however, that the general process of transcription also accounts for the formation of ribosomal-RNA and transfer-RNA, as well as messenger-RNA. That is to say, all three types of RNA are transcription products of DNA and are presumably formed via the same general mechanism. Thus, all three are complementary copies of genes in DNA, but apparently only messenger-RNA carries the code specifying the amino acid sequence.

ENZYMOLOGY OF RNA BIOSYNTHESIS

The basic process of DNA transcription is very much like that of DNA replication. A mixture of the four nucleotides as substrates (specifically the triphosphoribonucleotides), a DNA primer, and a Mg^{++}-dependent polymerase enzyme are all required. For reasons that should be clear at this point, the enzyme is termed a *DNA-dependent–RNA polymerase.* (Frequently the term *transcriptase* is used.) Originally discovered in rat liver by S. Weiss and coworkers in 1959, preparations of this enzyme

$$
\left|\begin{array}{c} n\text{UTP} \\ + \\ n\text{ATP} \\ + \\ n\text{CTP} \\ + \\ n\text{GTP} \end{array}\right| \xrightarrow[\text{plus DNA}]{\substack{\text{RNA polymerase} \\ (Mg^{++})}} \left|\begin{array}{c} n\text{UMP} \\ | \\ n\text{AMP} \\ | \\ n\text{CMP} \\ | \\ n\text{GMP} \end{array}\right| \;+\; 4n\text{PP}_i
$$

nucleotide mixture   *product RNA*

have been detected in virtually all types of natural sources. Although the above similarities exist, the processes of DNA replication and DNA transcription are considerably different. Some of the distinguishing details of the transcription process will be described shortly.

The belief that transcriptase is directly responsible for the *in vivo* transcription of DNA is based upon much evidence obtained from *in vitro* studies demonstrating that the RNA product is complementary in base sequence to the primer DNA. That is to say, the primer DNA functions as a template which is copied during synthesis. Although this relationship was suggested by a comparison of the base compositions of product RNA and primer DNA and by nearest-neighbor analysis, the strongest evidence has been provided by *hybridization* experiments. In the hybridization technique, a mixture containing both RNA and DNA is heated quickly and then cooled slowly. On heating, the DNA duplex unwinds to yield disordered polynucleotide strands. RNA molecules will likewise lose whatever conformational structure they possess, be it helical or otherwise. On slow cooling, the disordered chains can align with each other via complementary hydrogen bonding of base pairs to form stable duplexes. Thus, if this were done with a pure DNA solution, the DNA duplex would be destroyed and then reformed. If, on the other hand, one were to start with a mixture of DNA and RNA to yield a mixture of denatured DNA and RNA strands, and if the RNA had a base sequence complementary to that of one of the DNA strands, then slow cooling should result in the formation of a few DNA-RNA hybrid duplexes. If the RNA were originally labeled with radioactive atoms, the detection and isolation of such a duplex could be easily achieved by ultracentrifugation in a density gradient. This is precisely what was observed in hybridization studies between the product RNA and primer DNA of the RNA polymerase reaction, confirming that the former was a complementary copy of the latter.

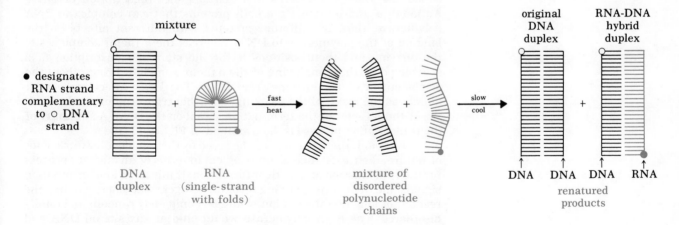

The original *in vitro* studies with RNA polymerase showed by the hybridization technique that both strands of the template DNA were copied. That is, two DNA-RNA hybrids could be detected. There is clear evidence, however, that such is not the situation *in vivo*. Rather, only one of the strands of the native DNA duplex is copied. Which of the two strands is transcribed is argumentative. The important point to realize, however, is that each strand would yield a transcription product with a unique nitrogen base sequence.

The details of DNA transcription are more clearly understood than those of DNA replication. One reason for this is that more is understood about the properties of RNA polymerase than about those of DNA polymerase, despite the fact that, structurally speaking, the former is a larger (MW = approximately 500,000) and more complex molecule. In *E. coli,* the active form of RNA polymerase is currently viewed as being an oligomer composed of five different polypeptide chains, one of which is present twice. Thus, the molecule is hexameric. One of the keys to understanding the transcription process was recently discovered in 1969 by E. Bautz and collaborators. They observed that one of the polypeptide subunits, called the *sigma (σ) factor,* can be easily dissociated from the native hexameric polymerase to yield a pentameric species which still has complete catalytic activity. In other words, the sigma factor has no catalytic function in the formation of RNA. Yet, it is required for normal transcription to occur.

What then is the function of the σ factor, if it is not involved in the catalytic process? Remarkable as it may seem, it is proposed that its function is to recognize specific nitrogen base sequences along DNA that represent *transcription initiation signals.* That is, the σ factor is a protein with a specific conformation that can reversibly bind with specific segments of a polynucleotide chain. When the σ factor is complexed to the catalytically active oligomeric core of RNA polymerase, the result is that the polymerase is positioned for binding to the DNA at the start of the gene or group of genes that will be transcribed.

The demonstration of the recognition of a transcription starting signal by the σ factor stimulated the search for an analogous substance that would recognize a *transcription termination signal.* Success was achieved recently with the detection in bacteria of a soluble protein, called the *rho (ρ) factor,* which disrupts the transcription of DNA. Although σ and ρ factors are both proteins that can complex to RNA polymerase, they are different proteins with different effects on the binding of the polymerase to DNA. Whereas the σ factor complexes to the enzyme and then positions it for the start of transcription at a specific point, the complexing of the ρ factor somehow brings about the displacement of the enzyme from DNA. The latter effect may occur merely as the result of the blocking of further transcription by the binding of the ρ factor to the termination signal on the DNA. A summary of the transcription process is diagrammed in Figure 17–10.

Although there is reason to be awed by these molecular intricacies of nature, their existence is quite logical in terms of an efficient process for the transmission of genetic information. If initiation and termination signals and their corresponding recognition agents did not exist, then the readout of genetic information would be completely random and totally disordered. The RNA polymerase would bind at any site on DNA and begin transcribing to any other site. Thus, transcription could start within one gene and stop within the next gene, resulting in a hybrid and meaningless message. With signals specifying "start" and "stop," the transcription of intact genes is guaranteed. Although this type of reasoning appeared years ago, it has been verified only recently with the isolation of the σ and ρ factors. Continued research is still needed to deter-

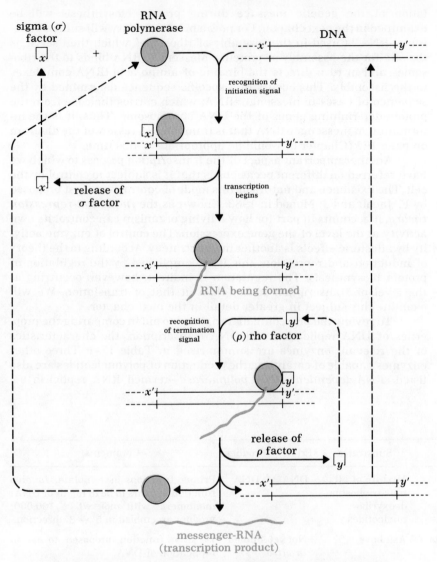

x = binding site in σ factor recognizing initiation signal (x') in DNA
y = binding site in ρ factor recognizing termination signal (y') in DNA

(-- $\rightarrow$ indicates recycling of participants)

Figure 17–10 A diagrammatic summary of DNA transcription by RNA polymerase.

mine whether additional factors operate in the same or different processes, and whether there is only one or several species of σ and ρ factors per cell.

As we pointed out earlier, the transcription of DNA results in at least three different types of RNA products—ribosomal-RNA, transfer-RNA, and messenger-RNA. The role of each of these RNA's in the translation of the genetic message during protein biosynthesis will be examined in the next chapter. For now a brief summary will suffice. Ribosomal-RNA is used in the assembly of ribosomes which then serve as the site for the assembly of proteins. Messenger-RNA binds to the ribosomes and in turn directs the binding of amino acid-tRNA complexes to the assembly. This occurs in a specific sequence determined by the sequence of bases in messenger-RNA, which carries the code from the protein-determining genes of the DNA chromosome. Thus, it is the information in messenger-RNA that is translated. A review of the diagram on page 162 (Chapter 6) would be appropriate at this time.

Another important aspect of the transcription process to which we have referred on different occasions is that it is subject to control by the cell. The existence and nature of this mode of control were first proposed by F. Jacob and J. Monod in 1963. Known as the *induction-repression theory,* it accounts in part for how a living organism can control its own activity at the level of the gene expression. The control of enzyme activity by allosteric effects is another major strategy. According to the theory of induction and repression, this is accomplished by the regulation of protein biosynthesis. The regulation is indirect, however, occurring at the level of transcription rather than at that of translation. We will examine this subject in greater detail in the next chapter.

To review the preceding material and to aid in comparing the properties of DNA replication and DNA transcription, the characteristics of the relevant enzymes are summarized in Table 17–1. Three other enzymes capable of catalyzing the production of polynucleotides are also listed. *RNA-dependent–RNA polymerase*—termed RNA replicase be-

Table 17–1 A comparison of polynucleotide polymerases.

Enzyme	Occurrence	Substrates	Primer	Product	Comments
DNA polymerase I (repair enzyme)	All types of organisms	Mixture of all four triphospho-deoxyribo-nucleotides	DNA	DNA	Primer functions as template; *in vivo* function appears to be in repair of DNA; monomeric with mol. wt. $\approx$ 100,000; product assembled in $5' \rightarrow 3'$ direction.
DNA polymerase II (DNA replicase)	Only bacteria to present	As above	Not yet studied *in vitro*		*In vivo* function proposed to be in replication of DNA.
DNA-dependent–RNA polymerase (transcriptase)	All types of organisms	Mixture of all four triphospho-ribonucleotides	DNA	RNA	Primer functions as template; requires non-catalytic protein factors for normal operation; oligomeric with mol. wt. $\approx$ 500,000; assembly in $5' \rightarrow 3'$ direction.
RNA-dependent–RNA polymerase (RNA replicase)	Virus-infected bacteria	As above	RNA	RNA	Primer functions as template; responsible for replication of RNA bacterial virus in host cell.
RNA-dependent–DNA polymerase (reverse transcriptase)	RNA tumor viruses	Mixture of all four triphospho-deoxyribo-nucleotides	RNA	DNA	Proposed to be related to transformation of normal cells to tumor cells.
Polynucleotide Phosphorylase	Microorganisms	Diphospho-nucleotides	RNA	RNA	Biological role is unknown; role of primer is variable; used in the study of the genetic code.

cause it produces RNA from an RNA template as distinguished from a DNA replicase producing DNA from a DNA template—has been isolated only from microorganisms infected with an RNA virus. Recall that the storage of genetic information in RNA instead of in DNA is a known property unique to certain viruses (see page 165). In some manner not yet clear, the infection of the host cell by the viral-RNA causes the production of the RNA-dependent–RNA polymerase, which then replicates the viral-RNA within the host cell.

Although its precise biological role is as yet unknown, *polynucleotide phosphorylase* merits our consideration for two reasons. Initially, it was the first enzyme discovered that was capable of assembling nucleotide units into a polynucleotide chain (in 1955 from bacteria by M. Grunberg-Manago and S. Ochoa). A primer polyribonucleotide is required and the product is RNA. However, unlike the RNA polymerases, the RNA produced is not a copy of the primer. In fact, the insertion of the nucleotides is largely random. Thus, the primer does not serve as a template. The exact role of the primer is somewhat complex and will not be covered here. The second reason for our mention of this enzyme will be elaborated on in the next chapter. For now, suffice it to say that it has proved to be an extremely valuable experimental tool in the elucidation of the nature of the *genetic code* (see page 515). (In 1959 the Nobel Prize in Physiology and Medicine was jointly awarded to S. Ochoa and A. Kornberg for their independent pioneering investigations into the *in vitro* production of nucleic acids.)

The discovery in 1970 of an *RNA-dependent–DNA polymerase* represents one of the most significant findings of recent years. In effect, the enzyme is a *reverse transcriptase* in that it is capable of forming DNA from an RNA template. In other words, the central dogma of the flow of information as originally enunciated by Crick in 1958 has proved to be an oversimplification. The process apparently is reversible, at least between DNA and RNA, that is, $DNA \rightleftarrows RNA$. On an applied level, a more significant aspect of this enzyme, however, is due to the fact that it was originally detected in an RNA tumor virus and since then has been detected in about half a dozen more. This has prompted the suggestion that the ability of these viruses to transform normal cells into stable cancer cells may result from the transcription of viral-RNA first into a DNA molecule by its own reverse transcriptase, which becomes active on infection of a host cell. The viral-DNA may then be incorporated into the chromosome of the normal host cell, which transforms it into a tumor cell.

Such a relationship received further support from the recent discovery that viral particles, isolated from and proposed to be responsible for human breast cancers, contain reverse transcriptase activity. These findings offer the hope that certain types of cancer—in this case, those induced by RNA viruses—will be better understood and possibly susceptible to chemotherapeutic treatment. If the above hypothesis proves to be true, then it should be possible to find substances that would inhibit the activity of the viral reverse transcriptase and to thus prevent the transformation of other cells. The first objective in working toward such a goal will be to isolate the enzyme and study its catalytic properties. Studies are also in progress in an attempt to determine whether similar enzymes occur in normal cells. So far the known occurrence of the reverse transcriptase is restricted to the RNA tumor viruses.

METABOLIC FATE OF PYROPHOSPHATE IN REPLICATION
AND TRANSCRIPTION

In the preceding sections, we have seen that the enzymes that function
in replication and transcription require triphosphonucleotides as substrates. This results in the cleavage of the triphosphoanhydride linkage
such that inorganic pyrophosphate (PP$_i$) is produced for each added
nucleotide. What is the metabolic fate of this pyrophosphate and is there
any significance associated with it? The presence of *pyrophosphatase*
in virtually all types of cells answers the first part of the question. This
enzyme catalyzes the hydrolysis of inorganic pyrophosphate to two units

$$
\underset{\text{PP}_i}{\text{HO}-\overset{\overset{\displaystyle O}{\|}}{\underset{\underset{\displaystyle O^-}{|}}{P}}-O-\overset{\overset{\displaystyle O^-}{\|}}{\underset{\underset{\displaystyle O}{\|}}{P}}-\text{OH}} \xrightarrow[\text{H}_2\text{O}]{\text{pyrophosphatase}} \underset{\text{P}_i}{\text{HO}-\overset{\overset{\displaystyle O}{\|}}{\underset{\underset{\displaystyle O^-}{|}}{P}}-O^-} + \underset{\text{P}_i}{{}^-O-\overset{\overset{\displaystyle O^-}{\|}}{\underset{\underset{\displaystyle O}{\|}}{P}}-\text{OH}} + 2\text{H}^+
$$

of inorganic orthophosphate (P$_i$). The latter, of course, can then be
utilized in various phosphorylation reactions.

Probably of greater significance is that the $\Delta G^{\circ\prime}$ of the reaction is
approximately −8,000 calories per mole. That is, the reaction is highly
exergonic. Considering that the biosynthesis of a nucleic acid—indeed,
the biosynthesis of any biopolymer—will be an extremely endergonic
process, the enzymatic hydrolysis of pyrophosphate can thus serve in a
coupled fashion as an important force in driving the overall reaction to
completion. It would, however, be only one of two such forces, with the
other being the initial hydrolysis of the triphosphonucleotide substrates.
In case you wonder why triphosphonucleotides are the preferred substrates of DNA and RNA polymerases, this analysis provides a possible
explanation in thermodynamic terms. The utilization of the triphospho
species in the biosynthesis of polynucleotides can provide two exergonic
driving forces coupled to the endergonic anabolic process, whereas the
use of diphosphonucleotides would provide only one.

	$\Delta G^{\circ\prime}$
NuTP → NuMP + PP$_i$	−7,700 cal/mole
PP$_i$ → 2P$_i$	−8,000
versus:	
NuDP → NuMP + P$_i$	−7,000

LITERATURE

BALTIMORE, D., "RNA-Dependent–DNA Polymerase in Virions of RNA Tumor
    Viruses"; Temin, H., and S. Mizutani, "RNA Dependent–DNA Polymerase
    in Virions of Rous Sarcoma Virus," *Nature,* **226,** 1209–1211; 1211–1213
    (1970). Two research papers announcing the independent isolation of a
    reverse transcription enzyme from animal tumor viruses.

BENZER, S., "Fine Structure of a Gene," *Scientific American,* **206,** 70–84 (1962). A synopsis of classical experiments with bacterial viruses that revolutionized our understanding of genes.

BLAKELY, R. L., and E. VITOLS, "The Control of Nucleotide Biosynthesis," in *Annual Review of Biochemistry,* Volume 38, 210–224 (1968). A review article summarizing the many regulatory enzymes associated with the pathways of nucleotide biosynthesis.

BURGESS, R. R., "RNA Polymerase," in *Annual Review of Biochemistry,* Volume 40, 711–740 (1971). A review article of the current status of knowledge concerning the biochemistry of DNA-dependent RNA–polymerase and the necessary protein factors that participate in the transcription process.

CAIRNS, J., "The Bacterial Chromosome," *Scientific American,* **214,** 36–44 (1966). A description of the *in vivo* experiments showing that the two polynucleotide strands of the *E. coli* DNA chromosome are replicated simultaneously, and a proposed mechanism of how this occurs.

CRICK, F., "Central Dogma of Molecular Biology," *Nature,* **227,** 561–563 (1970). A restatement and defense of Crick's original theory accounting for the flow of genetic information among DNA, RNA, and protein in view of new discoveries since 1958.

DUPRAW, E. J., *Cell and Molecular Biology.* New York: Academic Press, 1968. A highly regarded textbook offering an advanced treatment of the activities of living organisms at the level of the cell and the participating molecules. Chapter 13 deals with the replication and transcription of DNA. Chapter 18 considers the organization and expression of genetic material in eucaryotic chromosomes.

GOULIAN, M., "Biosynthesis of DNA," in *Annual Review of Biochemistry,* Volume 40, 855–898 (1971). A review article of the role of various protein factors that participate in the biosynthesis of DNA, and current views on the mechanism of DNA biosynthesis.

HANAWALT, P. C., and R. H. HAYNES, "The Repair of DNA," *Scientific American,* **216,** 36–43 (1967). A description of experiments proving that living cells have the ability to repair damaged DNA.

KORNBERG, A., "Active Center of DNA Polymerase," *Science,* **163,** 1410–1418 (1969). A review of the structural and catalytic properties of DNA polymerase by its discoverer and primary investigator. Emphasis given to polymerase I from *E. coli* with a proposal as to how it might function in the replication of DNA *in vivo.*

KORNBERG, A., "The Synthesis of DNA," *Scientific American,* **219,** 64–78 (1968). A non-technical account of thus epoch achievement by the principal investigator. The article also contains a brief historical survey of the events that led to the discovery of DNA polymerase.

MESELSON, M., and F. W. STAHL, "The Replication of DNA in *Escherichia coli, Proc. Natl. Acad. Sci. U.S.,* **44,** 671–682 (1958). The original paper describing the experimental approach used to establish the semi-conservative scheme of DNA replication.

SINSHEIMER, R. L., "The Prospect for Designed Genetic Change," *American Scientist,* **57,** 134–142 (1969). An interesting paper describing the possibilities for genetic engineering using viruses as carriers of synthetic or natural DNA. The author discusses the subject in relation to the disease of diabetes.

STENT, G. S., *Molecular Genetics—An Introductory Narrative.* San Francisco: W. H. Freeman and Company, 1971. A new textbook designed for undergraduate courses in molecular biology and genetics. The author, an authority, uses an historical approach tracing the growth of knowledge from important pioneering studies to the present day.

Transcription of Genetic Information, Volume 35 of *Cold Spring Harbor Symposia on Quantitative Biology.* New York: Cold Spring Harbor Laboratory, 1970. A collection of approximately 100 papers delivered by primary researchers on investigations of various aspects of transcription in different types of organisms. Highly recommended to the student interested in pursuing the subject at the technical level. Volume 33 of this series (1968) is devoted to DNA replication in microorganisms.

WATSON, J. D., *Molecular Biology of the Gene,* Second Edition. New York: W. A. Benjamin, Inc., 1970. The best available introductory treatment of the molecular aspects of gene function that should be in the library of every biological scientist. Chapters 9 and 11 are devoted to replication and transcription.

WATSON, J. D., and F. H. C. CRICK, "Genetical Implications of the Structure of Deoxyribonucleic Acid," *Nature,* **171,** 964–967 (1953). The original paper by the discoverers of DNA structure proposing how a DNA duplex molecule could be replicated.

EXERCISES

17-1 How do you account for the fact that certain of the carbon atoms of glucose-6-phosphate ultimately appear as the carbon atoms in the pyrimidine ring that are known to be contributed by aspartate?

17-2 What possible role does the hexose monophosphate shunt play in the conversion of ribonucleotides to deoxyribonucleotides?

17-3 What is your prediction of the relative ability of system A and system B (see below) to form dADP? Explain.

System A	System B
5′-ADP	5′-ADP
thioredoxin (-SH)$_2$	thioredoxin (-SH)$_2$
ribonucleotide reductase	ribonucleotide reductase
buffer	*p*-chloromercurobenzoate
	buffer

17-4 Assuming that the chromosome of *E. coli* replicates according to the *conservative* scheme, which of the drawings below, numbered 1 through 6, will represent the density gradient ultracentrifugation pattern of the cellular DNA obtained in the Meselson-Stahl experiment from (a) the first generation of cells, that is, after one replication, and (b) the second generation of cells, that is, after two replications? Explain.

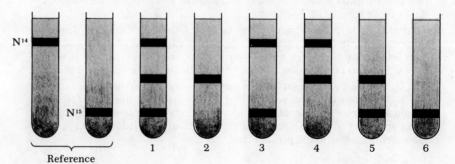

17-5 In the Meselson-Stahl experiment proving the *semi-conservative* scheme for the replication of DNA, which of the above patterns would correspond to the density gradient pattern obtained from the third generation of cells, that is, after three replications? In addition, describe the relative proportions of each type of DNA that would be present in the extract.

17-6 Under certain conditions, *E. coli* cells can multiply quite rapidly. For example, in a nutritionally luxuriant broth the generation time at 37℃ is approximately 30 minutes. Assuming that the same time is required for replication of DNA, calculate and then reflect upon the number of nucleotides that are added in phosphodiester linkage per minute. There are approximately 4.4 million nitrogen base pairs in the single *E. coli* chromosome.

17-7 If DNA polymerase were incubated with a mixture of dGTP, dCTP, dTTP, and dATP^{32} in the presence of a single-stranded primer DNA that possessed in part the sequence of bases given below, how many units of 3'-dGMP^{32}, 3'-dCMP^{32}, 3'-dTMP^{32}, and 3'-dAMP^{32} would be contributed by the complementary segment in the product DNA after complete hydrolysis by 5'-nucleases?

. . pApTpCpTpTpCpGpCpApTpGpCpApTpGpTpCpT . .

17-8 Shown below is a hypothetical segment of a DNA molecule. What would be the maximum number of bases potentially susceptible to modification by treatment with nitrous acid? What would be the maximum number of nitrogen base pairs potentially susceptible to a transitional mutation upon treatment with nitrous acid?

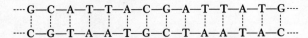

17-9 After a complete nearest-neighbor analysis of a DNA preparation, Kornberg and collaborators discovered that the relative frequencies of certain dinucleotide sequences were identical. For example, the frequency of ApG was identical to that of CpT; GpT was identical to ApC; TpC was identical to GpA; and CpA was identical to TpG. What characteristic of DNA structure was verified by this finding? What other pairs of dinucleotide sequences would exhibit the same pattern?

17-10 In discussing the *in vitro* synthesis of φX174 DNA, it was pointed out that bromouracil is a structural analog of thymine and can, as thymine does, pair with adenine via hydrogen bonding. This is true, however, only for the keto form of bromouracil. In the enol form, which exists only rarely, bromouracil prefers to bind with guanine. The latter property is the basis for the mutagenicity of bromouracil. Thus, if DNA biosynthesis occurs in the presence of the stable keto form, bromouracil will replace a few thymine residues. If then, after the replacement, the keto form of bromouracil undergoes a tautomerization to the enol form—particularly during the replication of DNA—what type of mutation will result?

18

Protein Biosynthesis and Regulation of Gene Function

Only a brief introduction is required for this chapter. Throughout previous chapters we have emphasized the primary importance of proteins in all living organisms. Particular emphasis was given to the crucial role of those proteins that function as catalysts, the enzymes. For obvious reasons then, the mechanism whereby proteins are produced in the cell is also of prime significance. In Chapter 6 and again in the preceding chapter, we have described the general features of this process, called *translation*. With an appreciation of these points, we can now turn our attention to examining some of the details of this complex and remarkable process. How do the ribosomes serve as the site of protein biosynthesis? How do the transfer-RNA molecules function in transporting amino acids to the ribosomal site? What is the nature of the genetic code contained in messenger-RNA? How is this genetic code utilized in the positioning of amino acids into a specific sequence? How is the overall process regulated by the cell? These are the questions we will consider.

So that our discussion can be coherent and hence your understanding can be clear, we will first examine the structures of ribosomes, transfer-RNA, and messenger-RNA. To further your appreciation and gradually introduce some of the principles that apply to various aspects of the translation process, these discussions will be presented in a historical perspective. We will then proceed to examine the general features of how the ribosomes, messenger-RNA, and transfer-RNA collectively participate in protein biosynthesis. After this the nature of the genetic code and the regulation of protein biosynthesis will be analyzed. Although our current knowledge of these subjects is not complete, it is quite extensive, with several early hypotheses having been confirmed, others refuted, and new important discoveries made since 1965. Consequently, be aware of this in reading other sources since they may be somewhat out of date. This advice also applies to the subjects of gene replication and gene transcription. In fact, one of the unfortunate features of this textbook—indeed, of any recent book that treats these subjects—is that it too will be partially obsolete by the time it is being used.

RIBOSOMES

DISCOVERY

The involvement of RNA in the biosynthesis of proteins was first detected by J. Brachet and T. Caspersson, who in the late 1930s and early 1940s (more than a decade before the discovery of DNA structure and two decades before the discovery of messenger-RNA) independently demonstrated that the cytoplasm of active, protein-producing cells possessed a large number of minute, RNA-containing particles. Brachet actually accomplished the isolation of these particles from a cell-free extract and demonstrated that they were also rich in protein. These early studies were later confirmed in 1952 by H. Schachman, A. Pardee, and R. Stanier, who obtained pictures of these particles under the electron microscope. The particles were termed *ribosomes* ("ribose-containing bodies"). Although the suggestion was made by Brachet in the early 1940s, nearly fifteen years elapsed before the precise role of the ribosomes in protein biosynthesis was elucidated, namely, that they *constitute the site within the cell where protein synthesis occurs, by providing a surface for the localized interaction of all the participating molecules*. This role has since been proven by extensive study, and is now an accepted fact. Although this is the primary biological role of ribosomes, it may not, however, be their only role. Because the reported evidence at present is largely circumstantial and conflicting, we will not comment further on additional ribosomal functions.

STRUCTURE

What does it mean that ribosomes are particles? This is a relatively basic question with a relatively basic answer, which—if understood correctly—can serve as the foundation for understanding the entire translation process. The fact is that a ribosome is a particle in the sense that it is a *multi-molecular aggregate*. Specifically, it is a ribonucleoprotein particle, an aggregate of individual RNA molecules and individual protein molecules. Until the late 1950s, however, the primary known characteristic of the structure of ribosomes was their sedimentation in a density gradient. In this regard, an intact ribosome is generally referred to as a "70S" particle or an "80S" particle, depending on the cellular source. Procaryotic cells (bacteria) contain the smaller 70S ribosomes, whereas eucaryotic cells (animals and higher plants) contain the larger 80S ribosomes. Although other differences besides size do exist, both types of ribosomes have a similar basic structure and function. Because the 70S species has been studied more, our discussion will be largely confined to it.

As shown first in the late 1950s by Watson and A. Tissieres, the basic composition of the 70S ribosome is approximately two-thirds RNA (64%) and one-third protein (36%). (80S ribosomes differ in this regard, containing a greater percentage of protein—about 45–50%, to be specific.) These workers, concurrently with others, also demonstrated that a 70S ribosome was in fact an aggregate of two *subunit* particles, each of which was itself composed of RNA and protein in nearly the same 2/1 ratio as the 70S particle. These subunits were characterized by unique sedimentation constants of "30S" (the lighter subunit) and "50S" (the heavy subunit). The discovery of this subunit composition was the result of studying the effect of ionic strength, notably the concentration of Mg^{++}, on the structure of isolated ribosomes. That is to say, it was a phenomenon observed *in vitro*. With low concentrations of Mg^{++} (10^{-4} M), only 30S and 50S particles were detected. With high concentrations of Mg^{++} (10^{-2} M), only 70S particles were detected. Most important was the fact that the process was reversible. Although originally an *in vitro* observation, recent studies have shown that the dissociation of 70S ribosomes to subunits and their reassociation to yield the intact 70S unit are key factors in the way in which ribosomes participate in protein biosynthesis *in vivo*. We will consider this further in a later section (see page 504).

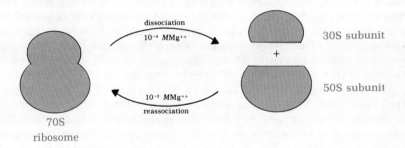

dissociation
10^{-4} M Mg^{++}

30S subunit

+

50S subunit

10^{-2} M Mg^{++}
reassociation

70S
ribosome

RIBOSOMAL-RNA AND RIBOSOMAL PROTEIN

Given the overall structural features of a ribosome and its subunit construction, the next logical questions are: What is the nature of the ribosomal-RNA component and of the ribosomal protein component? Recall that we have already dealt with these questions in Chapter 6 (page 165) when we first introduced the subject of ribosomes. At that time we pointed out that the study of each component is possible because with suitable laboratory methods, such as treatment with urea, with phenol, or with ammonium sulfate, one can dissociate the ribosomal-RNA from the ribosomal protein. When this is done on each isolated subunit, as is generally the case, it is possible to isolate and study the RNA and protein components of each subunit. A typical flow diagram summarizing how this is done and indicating the general ribosomal composition is given in Figure 18–1.

As shown in Figure 18–1, ribosomal-RNA consists of three different species, each characterized by a unique sedimentation constant— 23S, 16S, and 5S. The 23S and 5S RNA's are found exclusively in the heavy (50S) subunit, whereas the 16S RNA is found exclusively in the light (30S) subunit. Each RNA is believed to be a single-stranded molecule, with 23S RNA composed of about 3000 nucleotides, 16S RNA of about 1500 nucleotides, and 5S RNA of about 125 nucleotides. Finally, there appears to be only one molecule of each RNA in a single ribosome.

Although RNA is absolutely required for complete ribosomal activity, very little is currently known about the precise role played by each RNA molecule. Of course, each most probably has a share in imparting the overall structure to each subunit, and hence to the intact ribosome. Other more active roles undoubtedly exist and will likely be discovered in the near future. One aspect of current investigations is directed at elucidating the structure of the ribosomal-RNA's. Because it is the smallest, 5S RNA is the most clearly understood in this regard. In fact, as we mentioned in Chapter 6 (page 163), the entire nucleotide sequence of this component has been determined. This has been done with three different 5S RNA's obtained from both bacterial (two) and mammalian sources (one). Although the individual sequences show few similarities, each 5S RNA does contain an overall sequence capable of imparting to the whole molecule a folded conformation stabilized by complementary hydrogen bonding between different segments of the polynucleotide chain. In fact, all three of the 5S RNA's display several similarities in those segments which are complementary. One can argue then that an ordered native conformation probably exists for 5S RNA that is related

Figure 18–1 A diagrammatic representation of ribosomal structure and composition.

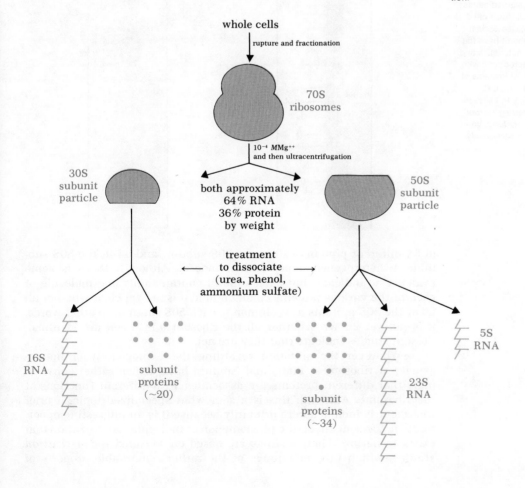

whole cells

rupture and fractionation

70S
ribosomes

10⁻⁴ MMg⁺⁺
and then ultracentrifugation

30S
subunit
particle

both approximately
64% RNA
36% protein
by weight

50S
subunit
particle

treatment
to dissociate
(urea, phenol,
ammonium sulfate)

16S
RNA

subunit
proteins
(~20)

subunit
proteins
(~34)

23S
RNA

5S
RNA

to whatever function it serves in the heavy subunit, and that the same is probably true of 23S RNA and 16S RNA.

As was also mentioned in Chapter 6, the ribosomal protein component is extremely complex, consisting of several different proteins (see Figure 18–1). Nevertheless, because of research by R. Traut, P. Traub, M. Nomura, and others, a considerable amount of information is available concerning them. In these studies, the technique of polyacrylamide gel electrophoresis (see page 21, Chapter 2) with its high resolving power has proved to be an extremely valuable analytical tool. This is clearly depicted in the stained gel patterns of the 30S and 50S proteins shown in Figure 18–2. On the basis of comparisons between the resolution achieved by gel electrophoresis and chromatographic methods, Traut has shown that the gel patterns in Figure 18–2 represent a total

Figure 18–2 Ribosomal proteins of *Escherichia coli* as analyzed by polyacrylamide gel electrophoresis. *Left:* Photograph of a stained gel after electrophoresis of the 30S subunit proteins. *Right:* Photograph of a stained gel after electrophoresis of the 50S subunit proteins. The numbers of stained bands in the gels are smaller than those cited in the text discussion, because certain of the proteins in each subunit have the same electrophoretic characteristics and thus are not resolved. (Reproduced with permission from "Ribosomal Proteins of *Escherichia coli,*" by R. R. Traut, C. Ahmed-Zadeh, T. A. Bickles, P. Pearson, and A. Tissieres, in *Cold Spring Harbor Symposia on Quantitative Biology,* Volume 34, 1969. Photographs generously supplied by R. Traut.)

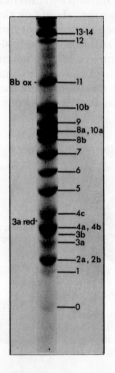
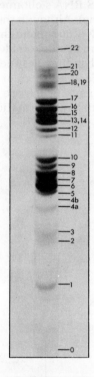

of 54 different proteins—20 in the 30S subunit and 34 in the 50S subunit. A heterogeneous population, indeed. Although there is some evidence to indicate that each subunit contains only one molecule of each of the various proteins common to it, it is not yet clear whether all 20 of the 30S proteins are common to each 50S subunit. In other words, it is not yet known whether all the ribosomes in a cell are identical. Present studies indicate that they are not.

Whatever the situation regarding the homogeneity or heterogeneity of ribosomes, Traub and Nomura have shown rather convincingly that different proteins are associated with different functions of the ribosome. Although this is a somewhat specialized topic, a brief treatment is included here primarily because it is an interesting opportunity to focus again on the phenomenon of molecular organization that exists in nature. Their findings are based on so-called *reconstitution studies,* which take advantage of the rather remarkable property of

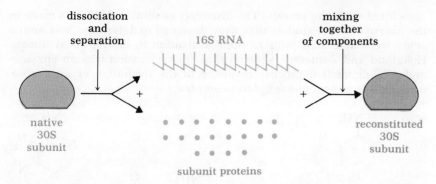

isolated ribosomal components to reassociate with each other, on mixing, to yield intact subunits. This is remarkable in that it occurs *in vitro*. If you think about it for a moment, you will realize, however, that the same event must occur *in vivo* as part of the formation of ribosomes from their constituent parts. The nifty feature about *in vitro* reconstitution is that one can determine whether all of the ribosomal proteins, or only certain ones, are required for assembly, and whether they are also required for various functions of the subunits. This is done by simply omitting a specific protein or group of proteins from the system. Because it is a simpler system with fewer parts, investigations have so far been limited to the 30S subunit. You may recall that in Chapter 6 we referred to one success, namely, that one particular protein of the 30S subunit was shown to be responsible for the binding of the antibiotic, streptomycin, to the ribosome (see page 165, Chapter 6 and page 510 in this chapter). Although several other correlations have been made, it is doubtful that reconstitution studies will ever yield a complete understanding of the essentiality or nonessentiality of all the ribosomal proteins. The difficulty is due to the fact that both ribosomal assembly and ribosomal function are probably dependent on both the concerted interaction of different proteins with each other and their interactions with ribosomal-RNA. This brings us then to a summary of the key features of ribosomal structure and function. *A ribosome is a highly organized multi-component particle whose functions are mediated cooperatively by the interaction of ribosomal-RNA and ribosomal protein.* This is basically what your understanding of a ribosome should be before we proceed to examine how it participates in the events of the translation process. A brief description of this participation is as follows: *each of the ribosome subunits provides a nucleoprotein surface composed of several sites for the binding of transfer-RNA, messenger-RNA, and other necessary factors all in one location.*

TRANSFER-RNA

DISCOVERY AND THE ADAPTOR HYPOTHESIS

Transfer-RNA was first discovered in 1956 by M. Hoagland and P. Zamecnik in eucaryotic cells and later in bacteria. At the time, this low-molecular-weight RNA was termed *soluble-RNA* because it was present as dissolved material in the cytoplasm of the cell and was not associated with any protein. The discovery of soluble-RNA was made in the course of other studies that were designed to determine how amino acids were activated prior to their utilization in protein biosynthesis. Hoagland and Zamecnik showed that this activation was an enzyme- and ATP-dependent process resulting in the formation of an *amino-acyl-AMP (aminoacyl-adenylate) complex.*

amino acid   ATP

activating enzyme
PP$_i$

aminoacyl-AMP
(*aminoacyl-adenylate*)

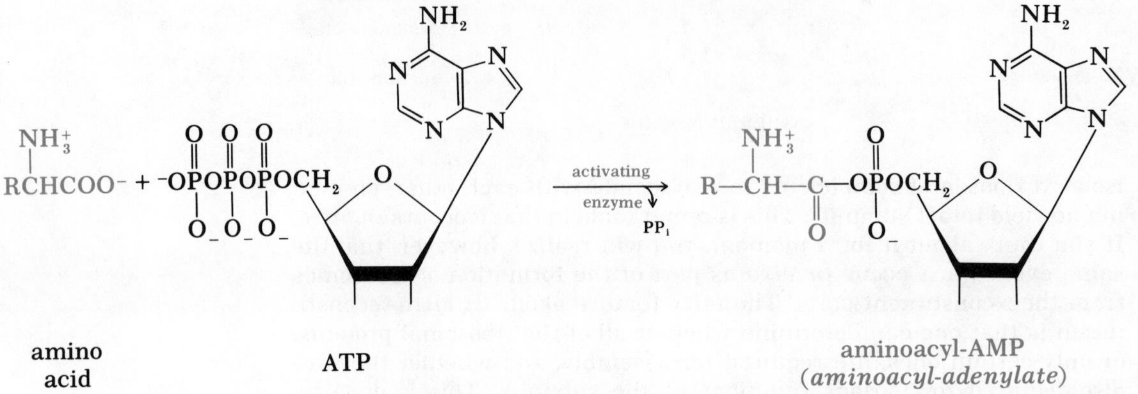

The significance of the relation of amino acid activation to soluble-RNA was not recognized, however, until Crick proposed in 1958 that the ordering of individual amino acids during the formation of a specific polypeptide might involve what he termed *adaptor molecules.* According to Crick, specific adaptors would bind with specific amino acids and then position the amino acids in proper order by recognizing (that is, adapting to) the genetic message contained in the nucleotide sequence of ribosomal-RNA. (In the late 1950s the existence of messenger-RNA was unknown and it was believed that the carrier of the genetic message from DNA was ribosomal-RNA.) Although he had no experimental evidence, Crick logically suggested that the adaptor molecule was a polynucleotide, since this would provide the basis for recognition of nucleotide sequences in the genetic message of ribosomal-RNA via complementary base pairing. A few months later, Hoagland and Zamecnik gave strong support to the adaptor hypothesis with the finding that the high-energy aminoacyl-adenylate complex could react in the presence of an enzyme, resulting in the transfer of the aminoacyl moiety to the soluble-RNA (hence, transfer-RNA) to yield an *amino-acyl-soluble-RNA* complex and AMP. This obviously fit nicely with

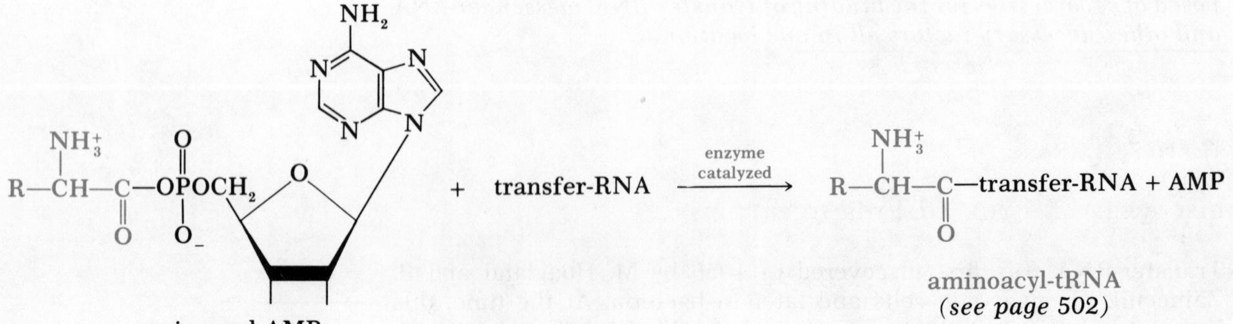

+   transfer-RNA

enzyme catalyzed

+ AMP

aminoacyl-AMP

aminoacyl-tRNA
(*see page* 502)

Crick's adaptor hypothesis. Further confirmations came shortly there-after, and the role of transfer-RNA molecules in the biosynthesis of proteins is now a well-proven fact. The use of the plural—transfer-RNA molecules—in the preceding sentence indicates that individual cells contain many different tRNA's rather than several copies of only one, and so they do. In fact, the number of different tRNA's per cell is esti-mated to be as high as 60. The significance of this will be examined in a later section when we discuss the various stages of protein biosynthesis. Before that, let us first examine the structure of transfer-RNA.

STRUCTURE

Although transfer-RNA molecules are single-stranded polynucleotide chains, it is certain that they possess an ordered conformation in the native state. The earliest indication of this was that pure preparations of transfer-RNA exhibited a significant hyperchromic effect when sub-jected to such treatments as heating, known to cause the disordering of double-stranded polynucleotides (see page 161, Chapter 6). The key de-velopment, however, that advanced our understanding of transfer-RNA structure was the determination by R. Holley and coworkers in 1965 of the entire nucleotide sequence (77 nucleotides) of alanine transfer-RNA from yeast. The sequence immediately revealed that the poly-nucleotide strand could be arranged in several different possible patterns, each displaying varying degrees of *intrastrand complemen-tary base pairing* that would stabilize double-stranded segments created by one or more folds along the chain. Of the various possibil-ities, the arrangement most widely accepted as representative of the native conformation is the so-called *cloverleaf* conformation, briefly described in Chapter 6 (page 163). A diagrammatic illustration of this—more detailed than that given in Chapter 6—is shown in Figure 18–3. Also depicted are the exact sequences of alanine transfer-RNA (yeast) and aspartate transfer-RNA (yeast). The sequence of the latter, reported in 1971 by Gangloff, is one of the most recent successes. These are not, however, the only sequences known. In fact, during the years from 1965 to mid-1972, the complete sequences of approximately twenty other transfer-RNA's from different sources, and partial sequences of several others, have been reported. The fact that each one has a unique se-quence but can still be arranged in the cloverleaf model gives strong cir-cumstantial evidence supporting this type of conformation. Despite the unique sequences of all transfer-RNA's so far determined, they all contain the same trinucleotide sequence at the 3'-terminus, namely, $\cdots$ pCpCpA(3'-OH).

A second conspicuous feature of tRNA structure is the presence of many unusual purine and pyrimidine nucleosides in addition to the usual four (U, C, G, and A) normally found in RNA. For example, in the alanine transfer-RNA shown in Figure 18–3, note the indication of T (thymidine), I (inosine), U^h (dihydrouridine), U^s (thiouridine), I^m (methyl inosine), G^m (methyl guanosine), G^{m_2} (dimethyl guanosine), and ψ (pseu-douridine). About 15 other unusual nucleosides have been isolated from various transfer-RNA preparations (see Appendix IV). Although the precise reason for their presence is still a mystery, several studies are in progress to determine whether they bear any relationship to the

Figure 18–3 A diagrammatic representation of the cloverleaf conformation of transfer-RNA molecules. *Above:* Symbolic depiction of the sequences for two different transfer-RNA's. Note the double-stranded regions stabilized by base pair hydrogen bonding between complementary segments. Also note the presence of unusual ribonucleosides (ψ, T, U^h, I^m, I, G^m, G^{m_2}, U^s). *Bottom:* Identification of the characteristic features of the fully extended cloverleaf model. This model is only an idealized representation of the native conformation, which is proposed to be considerably more distorted (see drawing on page 163, Chapter 6).

various functions of transfer-RNA molecules. Sequence studies indicate that undoubtedly there are such relationships. For example, only one copy of the dinucleotide sequence, ...$Tp\psi$..., is found in each of the transfer-RNA's so far studied, and in each case it is localized in the first loop from the 3'-terminus (loop I; see Figure 18–3). With a small number of exceptions, another repeating pattern is the presence of at least one dihydrouridine moiety in the first loop from the 5'-terminus (loop IV). While these unusual bases may be associated with the functions of transfer-RNA, it is also possible that their role is primarily structural in nature. To be more specific, it may be that their presence in strategic positions along the polynucleotide chain stabilizes the ordered conformation of the molecule in a negative or indirect fashion by not

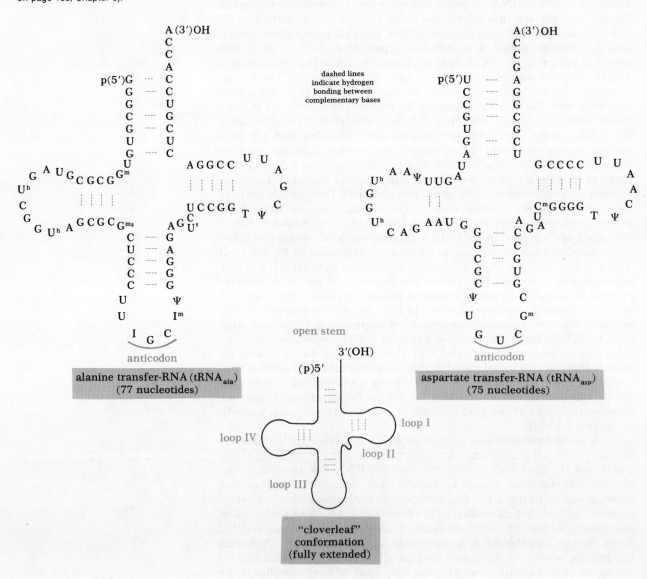

dashed lines
indicate hydrogen
bonding between
complementary bases

alanine transfer-RNA (tRNA$_{ala}$)
(77 nucleotides)

aspartate transfer-RNA (tRNA$_{asp}$)
(75 nucleotides)

open stem

3'(OH)

(p)5'

loop IV

loop I

loop II

loop III

"cloverleaf" conformation (fully extended)

pairing with complementary bases themselves and thus favoring the interactions between those segments of the chain that are complementary.

On the assumption that the cloverleaf model does represent the conformation of native transfer-RNA—even if it does so idealistically—assignments have been made correlating the characteristic features of the structure to several of the functions of transfer-RNA. One certain assignment is that the aminoacyl moiety is covalently attached to the ... pCpCpA(3'-OH) terminus of the open stem via the 3'-OH of the adenosine moiety (see page 502 for structure). Other less certain assignments are as follows: (a) loop I, containing ... Tpψ ..., may be responsible for the binding of transfer-RNA and an aminoacyl-AMP complex to the enzyme which catalyzes the transfer of the aminoacyl grouping to transfer-RNA; (b) loop III is proposed to contain a specific sequence of bases, called an *anticodon,* that recognizes a complementary sequence, called the *codon,* in messenger-RNA; and (c) loop IV, frequently containing dihydrouridine, is proposed to be involved in the binding of the aminoacyl-tRNA to the surface of the ribosome. A role of the minor loop, loop II, has not been suggested.

To summarize: a transfer-RNA molecule is a relatively small polynucleotide chain existing in a highly folded and partially double-stranded conformation which is stabilized by intrachain hydrogen bonding. It functions in the transport of activated aminoacyl groupings to the surface of the ribosome and positions them in a proper sequence by adapting to the information in messenger-RNA.

MESSENGER-RNA

Until 1961 the accepted theory concerning the flow of genetic information from DNA through RNA to protein was that the primary product of DNA transcription was ribosomal-RNA. That is to say, the base sequence of the protein-specifying genes in DNA was transcribed into RNA molecules that were then incorporated into the ribosomes. As part of the ribosome, the RNA then relayed the genetic information by serving as the template for the assembly of amino acids into specific proteins. This meant that most if not all of the ribosomes in the cell were genetically distinct. Each ribosome would contain a specific type of RNA with a specific nucleotide sequence that contained the information for the assembly of one or more specific proteins. In other words, specific proteins would be assembled on specific ribosomes. Furthermore, since ribosomes were known to be relatively stable particles that were not rapidly degraded by the cell, the RNA template for protein biosynthesis was likewise interpreted as being stable, existing for prolonged periods of time during the life of a cell.

The results of several different kinds of experiments by various workers in the late 1950s, however, cast a heavy shadow on this ribosomal theory. Without discussing the nature of these experiments, suffice it to say that it became apparent that molecules carrying the genetic information from DNA were *not* stable, but rather quite *unstable.* The situation prompted F. Jacob and J. Monod in 1961 to postulate the existence of a metabolically short-lived RNA molecule which they termed *messenger-RNA*. In effect, they were simply suggesting that the protein-determining information of DNA was transcribed into an RNA different from either ribosomal-RNA or transfer-RNA, both of which are metabolically long-lived molecules. Although this brief synopsis may indicate otherwise, Jacob and Monod were not simply making an obvious stab in the dark. From the results of their own work and that of others, they were convinced that such an RNA species existed. So confident were they that they published their messenger hypothesis before they had any real solid evidence that it was correct. Shortly thereafter, however, Jacob in collaboration with S. Brenner and M. Meselson proved that protein biosynthesis in bacteria was not directed by ribosomal-RNA but rather by a soluble-RNA molecule that became bound to the ribosomes. This was quickly confirmed by F. Gros, Watson, and coworkers and most convincingly by M. Nirenberg and J. Matthaei. The latter workers demonstrated that cell-free systems, capable of protein biosynthesis but deficient in natural messenger-RNA, exhibited a considerable increase in activity when a soluble-RNA (not transfer-RNA) was added. Conclusive proof was obtained when they added *polyuridylic acid,* a completely homogeneous, synthetic polynucleotide consisting only of uridylic acid, that is, . . .UpUpUpUpUpUpUp. . . . This resulted in the formation of *polyphenylalanine,* a homogeneous polypeptide containing only phenylalanine (. . . phe-phe-phe . . .), proving beyond a doubt that preformed soluble-RNA molecules, and not ribosomal-RNA, function as the messengers.

As for the structure of native messenger-RNA, it is believed to be simply a single-stranded polynucleotide chain with a basically linear conformation. The size of a messenger-RNA molecule is quite variable, containing anywhere from 300 to several thousand nucleotides. The smaller messengers generally represent complementary copies of single genes, whereas the larger ones are usually copies of a few adjacent genes. A final but important point to note is that the population of messenger-RNA in a cell at any one time is quite heterogeneous and constantly changing.

Having completed an analysis of ribosomes, transfer-RNA, and messenger-RNA, we are now in a position to consider their cooperative participation in the assembly of amino acids into proteins. This process is one of the most remarkable phenomena in nature.

ASSEMBLY OF AMINO ACIDS INTO PROTEINS: GENE TRANSLATION

How are the amino acids assembled into the polypeptide chains that comprise proteins? With our discussions in the preceding pages as a solid foundation, it is now possible to consider this question in some detail. However, because the overall mechanism is extremely complex, and because certain gaps still exist in our understanding of various aspects, our treatment will be generally descriptive and brief.

A proper beginning would be to identify the participants of the process. But, you ask, have we not already done this in the first part of this chapter? Well, yes we have, and then again, we have not. While it appears that this is begging the question, the fact of the matter is that the roster of participants is not limited to ribosomes, messenger-RNA, transfer-RNA, amino acids, ATP, and the enzymes responsible for the activation of the amino acids. Conclusive evidence now exists that other substances are involved and that they fulfill important roles. Significant in this group are GTP and a host of proteins. GTP we are familiar with. As for the proteins, some are freely dissolved in the cytoplasm while others are loosely associated with ribosomes. In recent years it has become customary to refer to these various proteins as *factors* that stimulate different operations of polypeptide biosynthesis. Thus, we have *initiation factors, elongation factors,* and *release factors*—factors for everything.

In order for our discussion of the translation process to be reasonably complete and meaningful, the known participation of all of the substances mentioned above should be included. To minimize confusion then, it is useful to consider the process as occurring in four stages, each involving certain operations. These stages are as follows, occurring in the order listed.

Stage 1: activation and selection of amino acids

Stage 2: initiation of polypeptide chain formation

Stage 3: elongation of the polypeptide chain

Stage 4: termination of polypeptide chain formation coupled with its release to the cytoplasm

STAGE 1

Activation and Selection of Amino Acids. The formation of covalent peptide bonds between amino acids is an endergonic process and thus requires an expenditure of metabolic energy. In the cell the energy is derived from the hydrolysis of ATP and GTP, the former occurring in the activation stage and the latter during both initiation and elongation. The ATP-dependent activation of amino acids is what concerns us here. Activation means simply that the amino acids are converted to a high-energy, chemically reactive state prior to their utilization in polypeptide assembly. Specifically, they are converted to *aminoacyl-tRNA complexes.* In discussing how this occurs, however, we will not be introducing any new material. This is so because this process involves the enzymatic transfer to transfer-RNA of an aminoacyl grouping from an aminoacyl-AMP complex, which in turn is formed by the enzyme discovered by Hoagland and Zamecnik to which we have already referred in an earlier section (see page 496). In fact, both reactions are catalyzed by the same enzyme, termed *aminoacyl-tRNA synthetase.* In other words, here we have a classic and important example of a single-enzyme, ATP-dependent process involving two coupled reactions. The first three equations given below summarize this. By then considering the eventual hydrolysis of the inorganic pyrophosphate by *pyrophosphatase* (see page 486, Chapter 17), it is clear that the overall formation of aminoacyl-tRNA is energetically favored by *two* exergonic reactions—ATP $\rightarrow$ AMP and $PP_i \rightarrow 2P_i$. Once again this represents an example of the efficient use of chemical energy in ATP.

Step 1:   amino acid + ATP $\xrightarrow[\text{synthetase (Mg}^{++})]{\text{aminoacyl-tRNA}}$ aminoacyl-AMP + PP_i

Step 2:   aminoacyl-AMP + tRNA $\xrightarrow[\text{synthetase (Mg}^{++})]{\text{aminoacyl-tRNA}}$ aminoacyl-tRNA + AMP

---

1 + 2:   amino acid + ATP + tRNA $\xrightarrow{\text{synthetase}}$ aminoacyl-tRNA + AMP + PP_i

Then: $PP_i \xrightarrow{\text{pyrophosphatase}} 2P_i$

Overall: amino acid + ATP + tRNA $\xrightarrow[\text{pyrophosphatase}]{\text{synthetase}}$ aminoacyl-tRNA + AMP + $2P_i$

As indicated earlier, the aminoacyl unit in the aminoacyl-tRNA complex is attached to the ribose moiety of the adenylate residue at the 3'-terminus of transfer-RNA. This yields an oxy ester linkage which is susceptible to attack by a suitable nucleophilic (electron-donating) group such as $-\dot{N}H_2$. We will examine this interaction further when we consider the elongation stage.

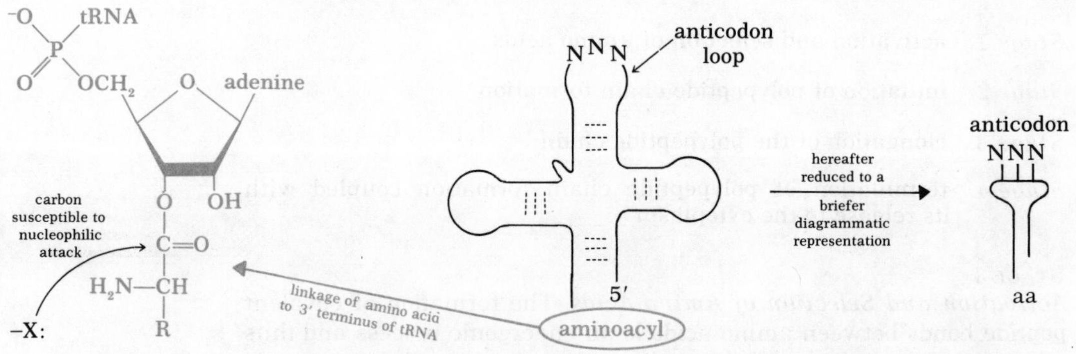

An equally important feature of the formation of aminoacyl-tRNA complexes is that the synthetase catalyzing the reaction is specific for both the amino acid and the transfer-RNA. In fact, it is proposed that a cell may contain at least 20 different synthetases, each having an optimum specificity for binding with one of the 20 amino acids and a corresponding tRNA. The biological significance of this specificity is that the enzyme *selects* a particular amino acid and *matches* it with an appropriate tRNA from the nearly 60 different ones that are believed present in each cell. Recall from our previous discussion that it is the transfer-RNA that adapts to the genetic code in messenger-RNA, and hence the matchup of amino acid and tRNA is quite crucial. The fact that cells contain nearly 60 different tRNA molecules, when ideally only 20 would be required, is explained by the fact that most amino acids are selected by at least two different tRNA molecules and some by three. By thinking about this for a moment, you can appreciate the significance of this relationship. In effect, it means that cells possess a certain degree of flexibility in the activation-selection process which, coupled with the specificity of the synthetase, will significantly reduce the chances for wrong matches to occur.

STAGE 2

Initiation of Polypeptide Chain Formation. Polypeptide chains are assembled in stepwise fashion, that is, one amino acid at a time. Obviously then, the overall process has a beginning, a middle, and an end. It is the beginning that concerns us here. As you will shortly discover, this is a rather remarkable process.

The first important advances in understanding how polypeptide biosynthesis starts occurred in 1964 with the efforts of K. Marcker and F. Sanger. Working with bacteria, they discovered that polypeptide chains in the process of being synthesized and presumably ones just completed had a characteristic distinguishing them from previously completed polypeptides. Specifically, it was observed that the N-terminal residue in the former group was *N-formylmethionine* (see below). Since it was already known from earlier studies that polypeptide chains were formed from the N-terminus to the C-terminus, it was proposed that the positioning first of an N-formylmethionine-tRNA complex (fmet-tRNA) on the messenger-RNA–ribosome apparatus represented the starting point.

The subsequent demonstrations that *E. coli* contains two transfer-RNAs for methionine although the genetic code predicts that only one is really necessary (see page 515), and also contains an enzyme that will catalyze the formylation of only one of the corresponding methionine-tRNA complexes, gave conclusive proof of this proposal. Symbolically, the two tRNA's are designated as $tRNA^{fmet}$ and $tRNA^{met}$ and the corresponding aminoacyl-tRNA complexes as $fmet\text{-}tRNA^{fmet}$ and $met\text{-}tRNA^{met}$. Although the nucleotide sequences of $tRNA^{fmet}$ and $tRNA^{met}$ are different, it is significant to note that they both contain the same

$$met \;+\; tRNA^{fmet} \longrightarrow met\text{-}tRNA^{fmet} \xrightarrow[\substack{FH_4}]{\substack{N^{10}\text{-}formyl\text{-}FH_4 \\ E}} N\text{-}formyl\text{-}met\text{-}tRNA^{fmet}$$

$$met \;+\; tRNA^{met} \longrightarrow met\text{-}tRNA^{met} \xrightarrow[]{\substack{N^{10}\text{-}formyl\text{-}FH_4 \\ E}} \text{no reaction}$$

$$\underset{\text{acyl grouping of N-formylmethionine-transfer-RNA}}{H_3CSCH_2CH_2\overset{\displaystyle NH}{\underset{}{CH}}\!-\!\overset{\displaystyle O}{\underset{}{C}}\!-\!\text{transfer-RNA}^{fmet}}$$

acyl grouping of N-formylmethionine-transfer-RNA

anticodon, namely, UAC. Hence, they both should have the ability to recognize the same mRNA codon, namely, AUG, and so they do. While it seems that this would tend to create some confusion for the translation process, there is clear evidence that such is not the case at all. Rather, the UAC anticodon of $fmet\text{-}tRNA^{fmet}$ recognizes the AUG codon only when the latter is at the beginning of the genetic message in mRNA. When AUG is localized within the message, it is recognized by non-formylated $met\text{-}tRNA^{met}$. Accordingly, the mRNA codon, AUG, is termed the genetic *initiation signal*, and the $fmet\text{-}tRNA^{fmet}$ complex is termed the *initiator*. Amazing!

After the fact, the significance of this to the translation process is logically interpreted, that is, it guarantees that the readout of the genetic message begins in an ordered and not a haphazard fashion. In other words, the UAC(fmet-tRNA)-AUG(mRNA) recognition, by occurring at the start of the message, ensures that the assembly of the polypeptide will commence in sequence from one end of the chain rather than at any random point along the chain. Specifically, the amino group of methionine, blocked as it is by the formyl unit, cannot be involved in peptide bond formation. Thus, one end of the growing chain (the N-terminus) is inert, so to speak, and elongation proceeds only in one direction, that is, toward the C-terminus. While this role of fmet-tRNA in lower procaryotic cells, particularly in bacteria, is now undisputed, there is evidence that it may not operate in higher eucaryotic cells. In view of recent studies, however, this generalization must be qualified. The qualification is that, although fmet-tRNA does not operate in protein biosynthesis occurring in the cytoplasm of eucaryotic cells, there is now evidence that it does serve as initiator in the biosynthesis of proteins occurring in the mitochondria of eucaryotic cells. This is a further indication of the suggested bacterial origin of the mitochondrion (see page 225, Chapter 9).

The basis for the preferential recognition of AUG at the start of the genetic message by fmet-tRNA was unknown until other aspects of the initiation process had been discovered. One such discovery, made by several workers in 1966, was that *in vitro* protein biosynthesis by cell-free systems of *E. coli* could be significantly stimulated by the addition of soluble protein extracts obtained from *E. coli*. Subsequently, it was shown that at least three different proteins are involved that *in vivo* are normally associated with ribosomes. They have been called *initiation factors* and are designated F_1, F_2, and F_3. In recent years all three have beeen highly purified and their biological properties determined. F_1 and F_3 are believed to mediate the binding of messenger-RNA to 30S ribosome subunits, a binding that is also *GTP-dependent*. F_2 has been implicated in the preferential binding of the fmet-tRNA initiator (rather than met-tRNA) to the mRNA-30S subunit complex.

Another related characteristic of initiation was uncovered in 1968 by Meselson and coworkers. They discovered that the process definitely involves the *dissociation of 70S ribosomes* into the 30S and 50S subunits. Known to occur *in vitro* at low Mg^{++} (see earlier discussion of ribosomes), there had been no previous evidence that ribosomal dissociation had any physiological significance. The primary stimulant to dissociation in the cell, however, is not a changing ionic concentration but rather a protein *dissociation* factor which turns out to be F_3.

A diagrammatic summary of these many features of the initiation process is given in Figure 18–4. First, promoted by the F_3 dissociation factor, the 70S ribosome dissociates to yield 30S and 50S subunits. Then, promoted by F_1, bound F_3, and GTP hydrolysis, messenger-RNA binds to the surface of the 30S subunit. This in turn is followed by the F_2-stimulated binding of the fmet-tRNA initiator to the mRNA-30S-F_3 complex. Finally, the 50S subunit reassociates with the 30S subunit accompanied by the release of F_3. (Is another factor, not yet discovered, required here?) The resultant 70S-mRNA-fmet-tRNA complex is then ready for elongation. In Figure 18–4, also note that the initiating codon in mRNA (AUG) is shown at the 5' end of messenger. This implies a feature of translation that we have not yet specifically mentioned, namely, that the translation of the genetic code occurs in the $5' \rightarrow 3'$ direction rather than in the $3' \rightarrow 5'$ direction. Can you ascertain why it would make a difference in which direction the code is translated?

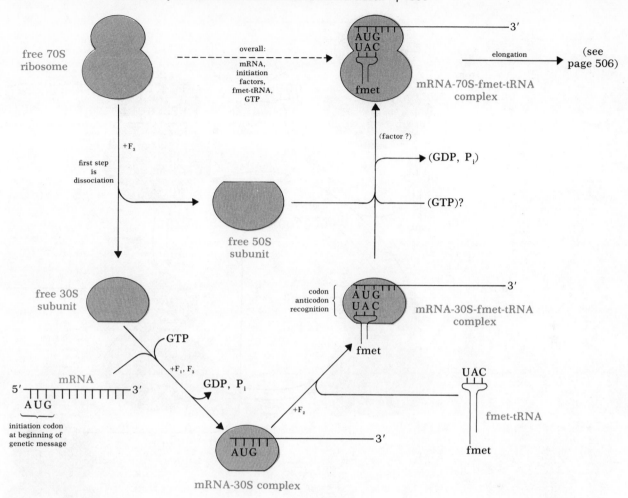

(see page 506)

Figure 18–4 A diagrammatic representation summarizing the major phases of the initiation of polypeptide biosynthesis.

STAGE 3

Elongation of the Polypeptide Chain The subsequent stepwise growth of the polypeptide is merely a succession of cyclic steps. Using, as an example, the first elongation step from the 70S-mRNA-fmet-tRNA initiating complex to form a dipeptide and its subsequent elongation, one such cycle would involve the following distinct phases, all of which are diagrammatically summarized in Figure 18–5. (a) The binding of a second aminoacyl-tRNA complex (aa_2-tRNA^{aa_2}) as governed by the next codon in messenger-RNA. The incoming aminoacyl-tRNA is also proposed to attach to the 50S subunit but at a second-binding site distinct from the first-binding site already occupied by fmet-tRNA. (b) An enzyme-catalyzed peptide bond formation between the two acyl groupings. The pertinent chemistry involves nucleophilic attack by the free amino group of the aminoacyl-tRNA just positioned at the carbonyl carbon of the N-formylmethionine grouping (see page 507). Note that the resultant peptide is attached to the transfer-RNA that was positioned in (a), that is, tRNA^{aa_2}. (c) The release of free tRNA^{fmet} from its initial site, accompanied by a displacement of fmet-aa_2-tRNA^{aa_2} to the 50S binding site

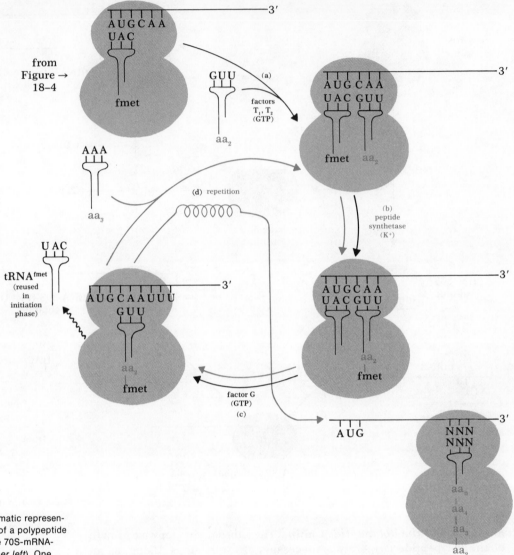

Figure 18–5 A diagrammatic representation of the elongation of a polypeptide chain beginning with the 70S-mRNA-fmet-tRNA complex (*upper left*). One complete cycle is depicted, giving an indication of the successive cycles resulting in the eventual assembly of the entire polypeptide, which is still attached to the ribosome via a tRNA (*lower right*).

vacated by tRNA[fmet]. Note that this process would effect a relative surface movement of messenger-RNA with respect to the ribosome. (d) A repetition of (a) through (c). In this case the next cycle would begin with the ordered positioning at the site previously vacated by fmet-aa₂-tRNA[aa₂] of aa₃-tRNA[aa₃], the aminoacyl-tRNA specified by the third codon in the messenger-RNA molecule. The cycle would be repeated many times until the polypeptide chain was completed, that is, until the C-terminal residue was inserted.

As indicated in Figure 18–5, the individual steps of one cycle also involve the participation of essential protein factors. Two such factors, designated T and G, have been detected and isolated from *E. coli*, other

tRNA^{fmet} O adenine   tRNA^{aa_2} O adenine $\xrightarrow[\text{(b)}]{\text{step}}$ tRNA^{fmet} O adenine   tRNA^{aa_2} O adenine

O   OH   O   OH   HO   OH   O   OH

O=C ⟵·········   O=C   O=C

CHR   CHR^2 CHR^2

N—CHO ··················· :NH$_2$ N—H
H   H

                                                         O=C

                                                         CHR

                                                         N—CHO
                                                         H

bacteria, yeasts, and mammalian cells. *Factor T* (for *transfer factor*) is actually composed of two components, T_1 and T_2. As for their function, both T_1 and T_2 promote the binding of the incoming aminoacyl-tRNA to the proper site on 50S subunit (step a). This binding is also known to be *GTP-dependent*. After formation of the peptide bond (step b), an event requiring K^+ and catalyzed by the enzyme *peptide synthetase* (also called peptidyl transferase and known to be associated with the 50S subunit), *factor G* promotes the displacement of the newly extended peptidyl-tRNA (step c) to the other site on the 50S subunit. Factor G is so designated because its activity is mediated by its binding to GTP.

STAGE 4

Termination of Polypeptide Chain Formation and Release of Completed Chain. Given the fact that specific proteins have a specific number of amino acids which are in a specific sequence, it should occur to you that the genetic message in mRNA ought to contain a signal indicating "stop elongation," just as it contains a signal indicating "start elongation." Indeed, such is the case, but the mechanisms are different. In the first place, it appears (at least in bacteria) that there are three separate mRNA codons representing *termination signals,* namely, UAA, UAG, and UGA. Recall that only one mRNA codon (AUG) signals initiation. The second difference involves the basis of signal recognition. Whereas the initiation signal is recognized by a specific formylamino-acyl-tRNA^{fmet} complex, the termination signals are recognized by soluble proteins, called *release factors.* In bacteria and yeasts there are at least two such release factors, designated R_1 and R_2. Presumably, the R_1 and R_2 proteins are capable of recognizing the mRNA termination signals, binding with them at the surface of the 30S subunit, and thus preventing the positioning of additional aminoacyl-tRNA's to the 50S subunit. They are called release factors because, in addition to the function just described, they also promote the release of the completed polypeptide chain from the tRNA to which the polypeptide is attached, and then of the free tRNA itself. Accompanying the release of polypeptide is the dissociation of the mRNA-70S ribosome complex. Thus, the mRNA and 70S ribosome are available for use over again. Recall, however, that the reuse of mRNA is limited because of its metabolic instability, that is, its susceptibility to hydrolysis by ribonucleases. Also note that the re-entry of the 70S ribosome would first require its dissociation (factor F_3 again) into 30S and 50S subunits.

Another feature of Figure 18–6 deserving comment is the indication that the completed polypeptide chain possesses an ordered conformation while it is still attached to the ribosome. Implied then is the suggestion that the three-dimensional conformation is gradually assumed during elongation rather than being formed only after release and requiring other factors. Although this is the most widely held belief, we are not really certain whether it is true. Finally, note that the last step of polypeptide biosynthesis, occurring after release, is the removal of the formylmethionine residue from the N-terminus.

SIMULTANEOUS SYNTHESIS OF POLYPEPTIDES ON POLYSOMES

In order to focus attention on the different steps of translation, our preceding discussions and the accompanying diagrams were limited to the growth of a single polypeptide on a single ribosome attached to a single mRNA. The *in vivo* process is more efficient, however, with a single messenger-RNA generally being translated *simultaneously by more than one ribosome*. In other words, a single mRNA is attached to a clus-

Figure 18–6 A diagrammatic representation summarizing the termination and release of a fully assembled polypeptide chain from the mRNA-70S complex.

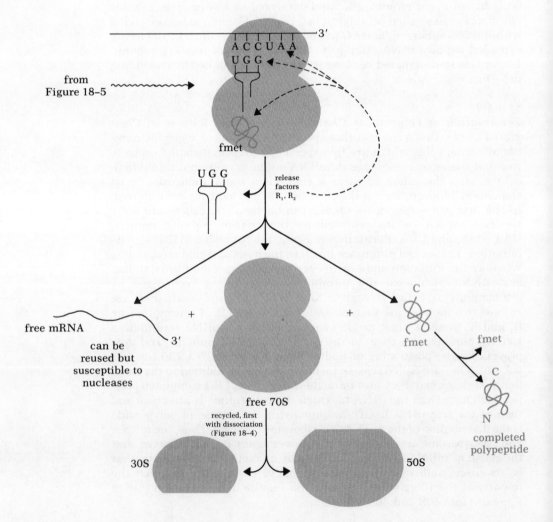

ter of ribosomes, termed a *polysomal complex,* with each individual ribosome involved in the assembly of a polypeptide chain. Of course, each of the ribosomal-associated stages of translation (initiation, elongation, and termination) would apply to each ribosome and to its growing polypeptide.

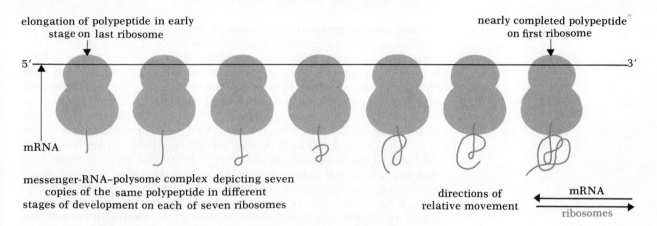

elongation of polypeptide in early
stage on last ribosome

nearly completed polypeptide
on first ribosome

5′

3′

mRNA

messenger-RNA–polysome complex depicting seven
copies of the same polypeptide in different
stages of development on each of seven ribosomes

directions of
relative movement

mRNA

ribosomes

The advantage conferred on the cell by this arrangement is that several copies of the polypeptide can be made before the mRNA undergoes degradation. The evidence for the polysomal apparatus is quite conclusive, being obtained in various ways including electron microscopy as shown in Figure 18–7. The size of polysomal complexes varies widely, but is generally a function of the length of the mRNA molecule.

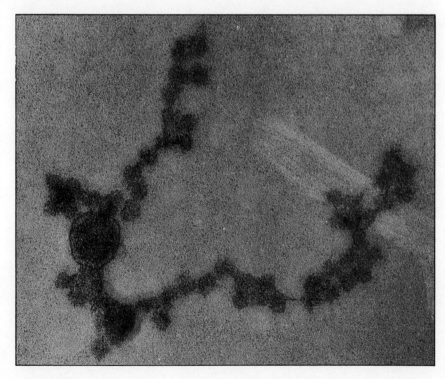

Figure 18–7 An electron micrograph of bacterial ribosomes arranged on messenger-RNA in a polysomal assembly. The thin thread most visible at the bottom and lower right and connecting the ribosomes is messenger-RNA. The large spherical object at center left is a piece of bacterial membrane. Magnification: 270,000×. (Reproduced with permission from "The Life Cycle of Bacterial Ribosomes," in *Advances in Microbial Physiology,* Volume 2, Academic Press, New York, 1968. Photograph generously supplied by Henry Slayter.)

Extremely large mRNA's consisting of a few thousand nucleotides may be complexed to as many as 50–100 ribosomes. Generally, however, polysomal clusters are comprised of 3–20 ribosomes.

ANTIBIOTICS AND PROTEIN BIOSYNTHESIS

Several antibiotics exert their effect by inhibiting protein biosynthesis. Depending on the antibiotic, however, the mode of action is quite variable, with different antibiotics inhibiting different steps in the overall translation process and in different ways. One of the most potent is *chloramphenicol,* which acts by binding to the aminoacyl-tRNA binding site of the 50S subunit and preventing further binding of aminoacyl-tRNA's. *Streptomycin,* as stated earlier, can bind to ribosomal proteins of the 30S subunit. Presumably this changes the conformation of the ribosome, causing a less favorable recognition between the codons of mRNA and the anticodons of aminoacyl-tRNA's. In addition to the fact that the translation process becomes sluggish, this also results in many errors in the positioning of aminoacyl-tRNA's, giving defective polypeptides. That is to say, the genetic instructions in mRNA are not read correctly. *Puromycin* inhibits translation by interrupting the elongation stage, yielding incomplete polypeptides. In terms of its structure, you may recall (page 147, Chapter 6) that puromycin is classified as a nucleoside. The special thing about the nucleoside structure of puromycin is that it is capable of being recognized by the aminoacyl-tRNA binding site of the 50S subunit as resembling the 3′-terminus of an aminoacyl-tRNA (see below). In other words, puromycin functions as a competitive inhibitor. When it becomes attached to the 50S subunit (an event that occurs at any time), the elongation of the growing polypeptide proceeds

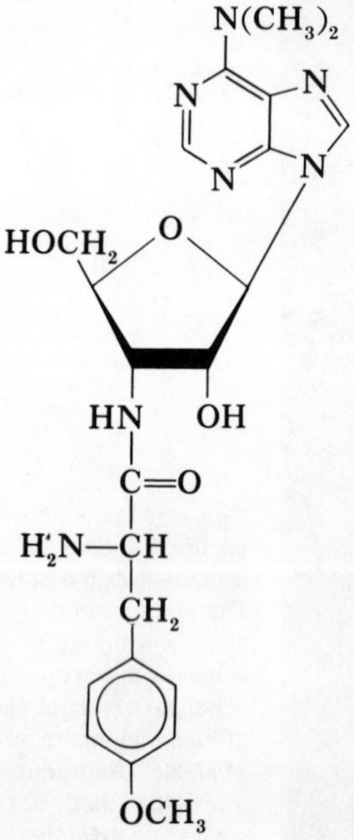

puromycin

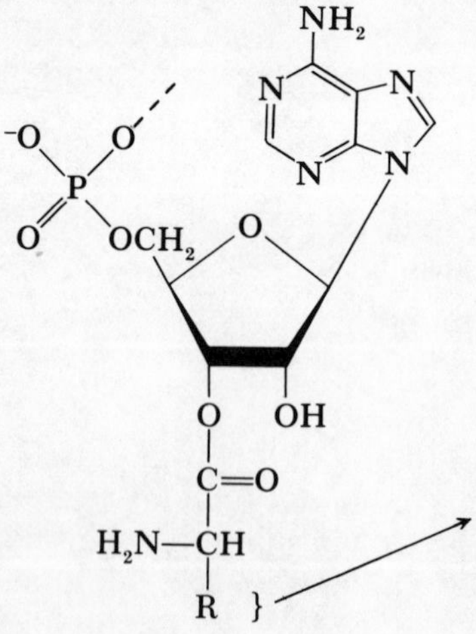

3′-terminus of
aminoacyl-tRNA

there would be a particularly close resemblance to puromycin when the R grouping corresponds to one of the aromatic amino acids (phe, tyr, trp)

no further. The partially completed polypeptide chain then links with puromycin to form a puromycin-peptide species which is then displaced from the ribosome. It is without function.

A detailed analysis of the mode of action of these and other antibiotics that inhibit protein biosynthesis is beyond the scope of this book. However, it should be noted that research in this area is quite extensive and a considerable amount of information is available. At the clinical level this research has definite applied implications, since the knowledge of the precise mechanism of action of antibiotics offers a basis for the development of modified ones with even better clinical properties, such as quicker action and fewer undesirable side effects. These latter occur for the most part because protein biosynthesis takes place in all organisms. The desirable situation then is to preferentially inhibit the process in the infectious cells with little or no effect in the host cells. In this regard, it is interesting to note that, although the general mechanism of the translation process that we have just described appears to operate universally in procaryotic and eucaryotic cells alike, specific variations are known. We have already mentioned the difference in ribosome structure and initiation signals. In terms of our current discussion, other differences are evidenced by the fact that certain of the antibiotics differ in their ability to inhibit protein synthesis in either procaryotic or eucaryotic cells. Chloramphenicol, for example, inhibits the assembly by 70S ribosomes in procaryotic cells, but is without appreciable effect on the process mediated by 80S ribosomes in eucaryotic cells.

THE GENETIC CODE

Twenty years ago the nature of the processes involved in the expression of chromosomal information was unknown, particularly at the molecular level. Beginning with the discovery of DNA structure by Watson and Crick in 1953, the mystery has been solved. It is now a well-proven fact that genetic information is encoded in the nucleotide sequence of DNA and is ultimately decoded into the amino acid sequence of polypeptide chains. In Chapter 17 and in the first half of this chapter, we have examined some of what is known about how this overall process occurs through the combined operations of transcription and translation. In this section we will now briefly examine the nature of the genetic code.

The discovery of DNA structure permitted the suggestion that the most likely and most efficient coding system would be one in which a small group of successive bases, arranged in a particular sequence, codes for a particular amino acid residue of a polypeptide chain. The simplest case would be if each small coding group contained two bases. Given the fact that there are only 4 different major bases in DNA (A, G, C, T), this type of code, called a *doublet code,* would permit 16 different base combinations (4×4). Were it a *triplet code* (3 successive bases), 64 different base combinations would be possible ($4 \times 4 \times 4$); and were it a quartet code (4 successive bases), 256 different base combinations would be possible; and so on. (*Note:* Hereafter, as is customarily done, the nature of the genetic code will be discussed in terms of its existence in messenger-RNA, having been transcribed from DNA. In this context, the DNA-complementary sequence of bases in mRNA that specify a particular amino acid are called *codons*. Although we have already utilized the term, its meaning was never clearly defined, but only inferred from the context in which it was used. The term will now be used routinely.) Since only 20 amino acids were known to occur in proteins, only the smaller coding systems were given any serious consideration. Assuming, however, that each amino acid is coded for by one codon, a doublet code is insufficient and a triplet code is excessive. This means then that the coding system is such that either certain amino acids have the same codon (if a doublet), or in many cases certain individual amino acids have more than one corresponding codon (if a triplet). For several years each possibility had its proponents. However, as indicated in this and the preceding chapter, the issue is now essentially resolved and the coding system is held to be triplet in nature, that is, 1 codon = three successive bases (nucleotides). Let us now examine how this came about.

The elucidation of the genetic code is largely due to the efforts of Marshall Nirenberg, H. Gobind Khorana, and Robert Holley. For their separate contributions, each of which had a key role in this area, the three were joint recipients of the Nobel Prize in 1968—Nirenberg for developing techniques that proved the messenger concept, established the triplet nature of the genetic code, and permitted the definition of the base composition and eventually the sequence of all 64 codons; Khorana for developing techniques for the chemical synthesis of polyribonucleotides; and Holley for developing techniques for the sequence determination of natural polyribonucleotides, notably, transfer-RNA.

The studies by Nirenberg (early 1960s) were based on the use of cell-free systems, deficient in messenger-RNA, but capable of polypeptide synthesis when cell extracts containing native mRNA or solutions containing unnatural, synthetically-prepared polyribonucleotides were added. It was the latter property that was exploited by Nirenberg in probing the nature of the genetic code. Recall that we have already mentioned (page 500) that synthetic homopolyribonucleotides resulted in the production of a homopolypeptide, such as poly-U yielding polyphenylalanine. Similarly, poly-A (polyadenylic acid) resulted in the production of polylysine; poly-C (polycytidylic acid) gave polyproline; and poly-G (polyguanylic acid) gave polyglycine. Although these observations conclusively proved the messenger hypothesis, they did not convincingly solve the problem of whether the nature of the genetic code was doublet or triplet. However, the fact that the number of phenylalanine residues in the polyphenylalanine chains more closely approximated the number of uridylic acid residues in the synthetic poly-U messenger divided by three strongly suggested that the code had a triplet nature.

Further evidence for the triplet code came from studies (performed independently by Nirenberg and S. Ochoa and their colleagues) with the same type of cell-free system, but with the use of *hetero*polyribonucleotides containing two bases rather than one. These hetero messengers were initially prepared by incubating a mixture of two diphosphonucleotides with *polynucleotide phosphorylase,* the first nucleotide-polymerizing enzyme to be discovered (Ochoa, 1955; see page 485). Thus, from mixtures of UDP and CDP, a UC-polyribonucleotide (poly-UC) could be prepared; from UDP and ADP, a poly-UA could be prepared; and so on. Unfortunately, one disadvantage was that the nucleotide sequences of these polymers were not known, because the

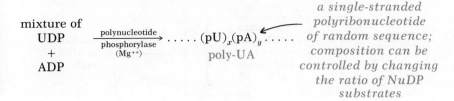

mixture of **UDP + ADP** $\xrightarrow[\substack{\text{phosphorylase} \\ (\text{Mg}^{++})}]{\text{polynucleotide}}$ ..... $(pU)_x(pA)_y$ ..... *a single-stranded polyribonucleotide of random sequence; composition can be controlled by changing the ratio of NuDP substrates*

poly-UA

polymerization catalyzed by polynucleotide phosphorylase was totally random. This means then that this type of polynucleotide could theoretically contain anywhere from 1 to 8 different codons with each present in different amounts. The maximum of 8 assumes a triplet code. For example, a poly-UA material could have any combination of UUU, UUA, UAU, AUU, AAU, AUA, UAA, and AAA. Although the sequence is unknown, it is possible from the base composition (% U and % A) of the polynucleotide to calculate the probable frequency of occurrence of codons having the following composition: U_3, U_2A, UA_2, and A_3. This then provided the basis for using this type of artificial messenger. Basically, what they did was to measure the identity and relative amount of each amino acid that was incorporated into polypeptide when the cell-free system was incubated in the presence of such a messenger. They then compared the data on the percent incorporation of the amino acids with the calculated probable frequency of occurrence for each of the four possible codon compositions. Without analyzing their complex data, suffice it to say that the results with several different heteropolynucleotides in separate experiments showed without question that correlations existed. Since the probable frequency of occurrence of codons with 1 of 4 compositions was based on the assumption that the code had a triplet nature, the data supported the validity of that assumption. In addition, it was possible to establish amino acid coding assignments to many triplet compositions and in some cases to triplet sequences. For example, UUU = phe; and many others. The nature of the genetic code was well on its way to being solved. (Note that it was possible to assign triplet sequences only to those codons that contained a single base.)

Conclusive proof of the triplet code was eventually achieved by Khorana and coworkers in 1964. These workers also utilized the approach of cell-free synthesis of polypeptides in the presence of unnatural heteropolyribonucleotide messengers, but they employed chemically prepared RNA's of *known sequence*. The unique contribution of the Khorana group was the development of the procedures to prepare such RNA's. As an example of their findings, consider the following. One of the RNA's they successfully prepared was a poly-UG with 50% U and 50% G and with a sequence of UGUGUGUGUGUGUGUG .... Now, if the genetic code were read in groups of three successive bases, one would predict that when this type of synthetic RNA was used as messenger, it should be read as UGU-GUG-UGU-GUG-UGU-GUG ..., and the resultant polypeptide should consist of only two amino acids in *alternating* sequence. This is exactly what was found. Specifically, the polypeptide consisted of cysteine and valine (cys-val-cys-val-cys-val ...). Thus, codons had to be translated as triplets. If they were translated as doublets, the polypeptide would have been homogeneous, containing only one amino acid. Why?

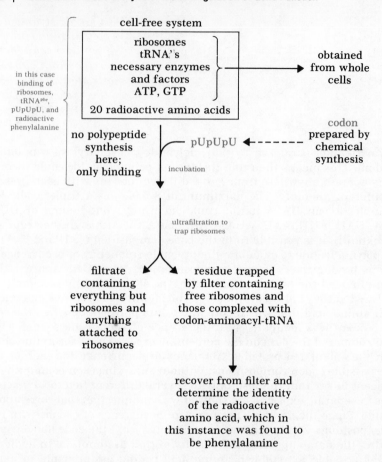

Figure 18-8 A summary of Nirenberg's binding assay of synthetic codons. The description of the cell-free system basically applies to all other experiments mentioned in the text where it was used.

In addition to proving the triplet nature of the code, the Khorana group also determined the sequences for several codons. The yeoman work of elucidating codon sequence, however, was done in the most direct way possible by Nirenberg, who chemically synthesized all 64 possible codons and then assayed for the ability of each one to direct the *binding* of specific aminoacyl-tRNA's to ribosomes, again in a cell-free system (see Figure 18–8). The basis of this assay was that each synthetic codon would be recognized by its complementary anticodon in a specific tRNA to which was attached a specific amino acid. No peptide synthesis occurred. What did occur was the formation of a ribosome-codon-aminoacyl-tRNA complex. By determining which amino acid was present in the complex when a particular codon was used, a coding assignment could be made directly. With this technique, nearly 50 codon sequences were unequivocally assigned to code for certain amino acids. Ambiguities in the assays of the others prevented complete success, although probable assignments were made in several cases.

Eventually, with improvements in the binding assay and with the work of other investigators using different approaches—including *in vivo* studies with mutant organisms—the entire genetic code has been defined. Figure 18–9 summarizes this knowledge in a tabular form made popular by Crick. Two distinctive features of the genetic code are repre-

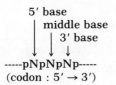

5′ base
| middle base
| | 3′ base
↓ ↓ ↓
-----pNpNpNp-----
(codon : 5′ → 3′)

base at 5′ end of codon ↓	middle base of codon →				base at 3′ end of codon ↓
	U	C	A	G	
U	phe-UUU	ser-UCU	tyr-UAU	cys-UGU	U
	phe-UUC	ser-UCC	tyr-UAC	cys-UGC	C
	leu-UUA	ser-UCA	termination UAA	termination UGA	A
	leu-UUG	ser-UCG	termination UAG	trp-UGG	G
C	leu-CUU	pro-CCU	his-CAU	arg-CGU	U
	leu-CUC	pro-CCC	his-CAC	arg-CGC	C
	leu-CUA	pro-CCA	gln-CAA	arg-CGA	A
	leu-CUG	pro-CCG	gln-CAG	arg-CGG	G
A	ileu-AUU	thr-ACU	asn-AAU	ser-AGU	U
	ileu-AUC	thr-ACC	asn-AAC	ser-AGC	C
	ileu-AUA	thr-ACA	lys-AAA	arg-AGA	A
	met-AUG	thr-ACG	lys-AAG	arg-AGG	G
G	val-GUU	ala-GCU	asp-GAU	gly-GGU	U
	val-GUC	ala-GCC	asp-GAC	gly-GGC	C
	val-GUA	ala-GCA	glu-GAA	gly-GGA	A
	val-GUG	ala-GCG	glu-GAG	gly-GGG	G

Figure 18–9 A summary of the 64 triplet codons of the genetic code and their known coding assignments.

sented in Figure 18–9. First, all possible triplets have a known function, with 61 coding for amino acids and the other 3 coding for termination of polypeptide chain formation. Secondly, the code is grossly *degenerate,* meaning that several amino acids are coded for by more than one codon. Indeed, with the notable exceptions of methionine and tryptophan, which have only one codon, the phenomenon of degeneracy applies to all of the amino acids. In fact, three amino acids (arg, ser, and leu) show sixfold degeneracy (6 codons). It is customarily argued, and rightly so, that the degeneracy of the code confers definite selective advantages on living organisms. The advantages are that certain errors in DNA replication, DNA transcription, and RNA translation can occur without a necessary change in the genetic information or in its expression. Consider the codon, GCU, for example, arising from the transcription of CGA in DNA and coding for alanine. If this were the only code for alanine, then any alteration during replication or transcription of the CGA sequence would change the information. However, because of the four-fold degeneracy that exists in the third position, only an error involving the first two bases would change the information.

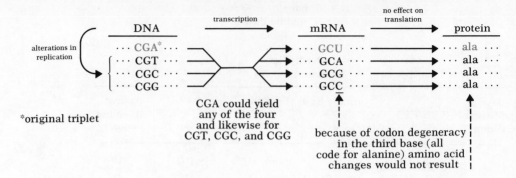

*original triplet

CGA could yield
any of the four
and likewise for
CGT, CGC, and CGG

because of codon degeneracy
in the third base (all
code for alanine) amino acid
changes would not result

Close inspection of Figure 18–9 reveals that in all cases the degeneracy of the code involves the *third* base of the triplets. On still closer inspection, note that where only twofold degeneracy exists, the pattern of the third base change always involves a purine for a purine or a pyrimidine for a pyrimidine: $NNPu_a$ and $NNPu_b$ or $NNPy_a$ and $NNPy_b$. Both characteristics indicate then that the genetic code may originally have been a doublet one that eventually evolved into a triplet code. Precisely when the transition may have occurred is not certain, but it would have had to occur before the emergence of bacteria, which themselves have the triplet code.

Other important features of the genetic code in terms of its existence in DNA (mRNA) and its relationship to amino acid sequences are: (a) it is *commaless;* (b) it is *non-overlapping;* (c) it is partially *ambiguous;* (d) it is *colinear* with amino acid sequence; and finally, (e) it is *universal.* To say that the code is commaless means simply that every nucleotide in mRNA (DNA) is part of a codon that specifies some instruction, be it initiation, amino acid insertion, or termination. In other words, there are no non-information gaps. Related to this is the non-overlapping nature of the code. This means that each nucleotide is an integral part of only one triplet codon and no other. That is to say, nucleotides are *not shared* by adjacent codons.

To say that the code is partially ambiguous refers to evidence that under certain conditions misreadings of the code during translation may occur. A misreading means that a codon, coding for amino acid A, is translated instead as coding for amino acid B. Although coding ambiguity would also confer selective advantage on living organisms—for example, base change mutations giving rise to new codons could occur without a corresponding change in translation if the new codon were ambiguously translated according to the initial codon—the extent to which this may operate in nature is not known. Since this is a complex phenomenon, we will not discuss it further.

The colinearity of the genetic message means simply that a precise sequence of nucleotides in a gene segment of DNA corresponds to a precise sequence of amino acid residues in the polypeptide chain for which the gene is programmed. Although this is basically implicit in the DNA → RNA → protein relationship for the flow of genetic information, it was conclusively proved only recently (in 1967) by C. Yanofsky and coworkers. What they did was to first determine the complete amino acid sequence (267 residues) of one (chain A) of the two polypeptide chains that comprise *tryptophan synthetase,* a dimeric protein catalyzing the last reaction in tryptophan biosynthesis. Working with bacteria, this was done for the normal A chain produced by normal, wild-type cells and for several abnormal A chains produced by mutant cells. (The mutant bacteria were initially selected on the basis of an inability to produce tryptophan because of the formation of a defective tryptophan synthetase. These tryptophan-requiring mutants were further screened with respect to that one of the two polypeptide chains comprising tryptophan synthetase that was defective.) The goal was to catalogue the positions of amino acid replacements in the mutant A chain, and then to correlate them with the positions of the corresponding mutated sites in the gene that is programmed for this polypeptide. The correlations were based on measuring the frequency of recombination between any two mutant strains to give a normal recombinant that would produce a normal synthetase. Although the precise nucleotide sequence of the A gene cannot be directly determined, it is possible with this technique to *map the gene* in terms of the relative positions of the mutated sites. The results of their monumental undertaking proved beyond doubt that the amino acid sequence of the A chain and the map of the A gene were colinear. The implication of the DNA → RNA → protein relationship was correct. For further information on the strategy and results of these experiments, refer to the article by Yanofsky cited at the end of this chapter.

The universality of the code, supported recently with experiments by Nirenberg, means simply but profoundly that all living organisms use the same codons with much the same coding assignments in effecting the translation of genetic information. Indeed, as we have stated earlier, with the exception of known variations regarding specific steps, the basic mechanism of the entire translation process appears to apply to all cells. This means then that the general operation of the molecular apparatus responsible for gene expression (protein biosynthesis) was probably already perfected with the evolution of photosynthetic bacteria some 3,000,000,000 years ago, and that it has since remained essentially unchanged. I submit this to you as the single most illustrative index of the theme of biochemical unity in our biosphere.

CODON-ANTICODON RECOGNITION

A key factor in the translation of the genetic code is the recognition of individual codons in messenger-RNA by the anticodons of aminoacyl-tRNA based on formation of complementary purine-pyrimidine base pairs. As we have seen in previous sections, this "reading" of a messenger-RNA molecule results in the stepwise growth of a polypeptide chain in a highly ordered fashion. At one time it was thought that each codon was probably recognized by a specific tRNA. Although seemingly a logical relationship, it proved to be otherwise. With the increase in the study of both the structure and the function of transfer-RNA molecules, prompted mostly by the success of Holley in 1965, it is now known that this one-to-one relationship is not completely true. While some tRNA's do indeed recognize and bind with only one specific codon, it is known that certain others have the ability to do so with two or three different codons. Since these latter observations were originally made *in vitro* on the basis of measuring the ability of purified transfer-RNA molecules to bind with artificial codons prepared chemically, an immediate question arose as to whether this multiple-codon recognition had any biological significance in the reading of the genetic code. Crick believed that it did and, furthermore, that it was related to the degeneracy of the code. In 1966 he expressed his thoughts in what he termed the *"wobble hypothesis."* The treatment we are about to give this subject is certainly more extensive than is called for in an introductory course. Yet it can be worth while because, in explaining the nature of the wobble hypothesis, we will focus attention on the nature of the crucial codon-anticodon recognition and briefly review some previous material.

WOBBLE HYPOTHESIS

In effect, the wobble hypothesis proposes that all of the bases in the anticodon are not localized in a rigid spatial orientation. In particular, Crick suggested that the base at the 5' end of the anticodon is capable of undergoing slight fluctuations in its orientation, that is, it can "wobble." In itself, of course, this means nothing. Crick, however, proposed that this freedom to assume slightly different spatial orientations allows the base at the 5' end of the anticodon to form hydrogen bonds with two or three different bases at the 3' end of two or three different codons. In other words, he proposed that the wobble permits the 5' anticodon base to form hydrogen bonds with bases other than its optimal complement, yielding *novel base pairs*. The base pairs are novel in the sense that they do not follow the well-characterized classical pairings of A-T, G-C, and A-U already known to exist in DNA and RNA.

There are basically two reasons for specifying the base at the 5' end of the anticodon as the wobble base, and its pairing with the base at the 3' end of the codon. First, there was evidence that the different codons recognized by the same transfer-RNA were those coding for the same amino acid. Recall that these are the degenerate codons which,

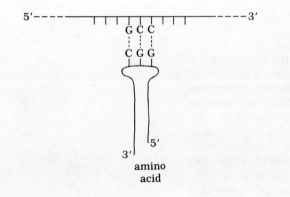

thus:

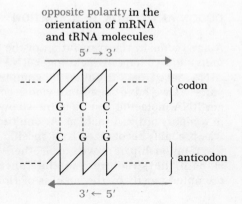

we pointed out, are different from each other primarily in the identity of the base at the 3' end. The second reason was based on the demonstration that the code in messenger-RNA was read in the 5' → 3' direction. This being the case, it means then that the optimum condition for hydrogen bonding between the anticodon in tRNA and the codon in mRNA would be for the anticodon to be oriented in an anti-parallel fashion with opposite strand polarity. In other words, in recognizing the codons of mRNA in the 5' → 3' direction, the anticodons are oriented in the 3' → 5' direction. There is nothing new, novel, or confusing about this type of orientation. Indeed, it is the same type of arrangement that exists in a double-stranded DNA.

A final feature of Crick's wobble hypothesis is that novel base pairing would be *restricted* to certain combinations. The restrictions were based on model building and the then well-documented structural requirements for optimal complementary hydrogen bonding between purines and pyrimidines. In other words, because of structural limitations, certain combinations would not be possible regardless of the spatial orientation of the wobble base. The possible pairings predicted by Crick are summarized in Table 18-1. The reason for including hypoxanthine (designated I for corresponding nucleoside) along with

Base at the 5' End of Anticodon	Base at the 3' End of Codon
I	A, C, or U
G	C or U
U	A or G
A*	U
C*	G

*Wobble does not permit any novel combinations with these bases when they are in the anticodon.

Table 18–1 Base pair combinations predicted by Crick according to the wobble hypothesis.

the four major bases of tRNA was that the available sequence data on tRNA's indicated that I was a component of some anticodons. In fact, it was found by Holley in the presumed anticodon loop of the first tRNA sequence to be determined (see Figure 18–3, loop III). In Table 18–1, also note that novel pairing is predicted only if the anticodon wobble base is I, G, or U. Because the codon and anticodon are oriented in opposite directions, Crick predicted that the other two bases, A and C, regardless of wobble must still obey the conventional pairing with their respective partners, U and G. Finally, note that the number of predicted novel pairings with any one anticodon base is such that it does not allow any tRNA to recognize four different codons. The limit is three, and this only with tRNA's having I as the anticodon wobble base.

Having described its basic meaning, let us now briefly examine how the wobble concept would work. As a specific example, consider the sequence of yeast alanine-tRNA (Figure 18–3), having the anticodon sequence of IGC, or more specifically, (5')IGC(3') or (3')CGI(5'). Since it is called alanine-tRNA, obviously this means that it recognizes an alanine codon. It is known (Figure 18–8), however, that alanine displays a fourfold degeneracy, with the four codons being GCU, GCC, GCA, and GCG (all 5' → 3'). To account for this degeneracy, it is possible that four different alanine-tRNA's exist in the cell. If, however, the wobble con-

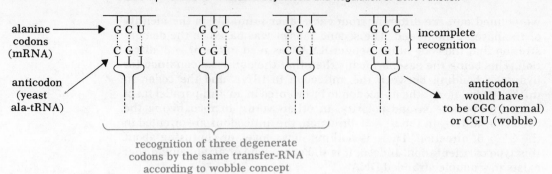

alanine ⟶ codons (mRNA)

anticodon (yeast ala-tRNA)

incomplete recognition

anticodon would have to be CGC (normal) or CGU (wobble)

recognition of three degenerate codons by the same transfer-RNA according to wobble concept

cept applies, then it is possible that all four codons could be recognized by only two different tRNA's (see above). Furthermore, the one isolated by Holley could recognize three of the four. Why? Well, the 5′ base of the anticodon is I, which means that the CGI anticodon could recognize GCU, GCC, and GCA, but not GCG. It so happens that this is precisely the pattern observed in binding studies with purified alanine-tRNA and synthetic preparations of these four codons. Although a second alanine-tRNA in yeast containing an anticodon sequence complementary to the GCG codon has not yet been found, this does not negate the agreement of the properties of the known alanine-tRNA with the wobble concept. This agreement, by the way, has been observed with other tRNA's and is not confined to alanine-tRNA. There are several other consistencies of the wobble hypothesis with data on the structure and codon-binding properties of different transfer-RNA molecules. One such agreement, but at the other end of the spectrum, so to speak, is exhibited by a bacterial leucine-tRNA shown to have the anticodon sequence, (3′)GAA(5′). In this case, despite the fact that the genetic code exhibits a sixfold degeneracy for leucine (see Figure 18–8 again), this leucine-tRNA recognizes only one of the six codons, namely, (5′)CUU(3′). Since the 5′ base in the anticodon is A, which can pair only with its normal complementary base, U (see Table 18–1), this is what you would expect on the basis of the wobble hypothesis. Once again it appears that Crick has correctly clarified the nature of the flow of genetic information.

CELLULAR CONTROL OF GENE EXPRESSION

Rapid progress in the understanding of the nature of life processes is currently being made by thousands of investigators throughout the world. Of course, both the significance of the work and the talent of the workers cover a broad spectrum. Periodically, however, the zeal and genius of a few result in outstanding discoveries or theories that have a profound and sometimes revolutionary effect. Several examples of this have been cited throughout this book and many, many more exist. In the area of gene expression, one of the most brilliant theories was proposed in 1961 by F. Jacob and J. Monod (the same Jacob and Monod who proposed the messenger-RNA hypothesis, and the same Monod who proposed the theory of allosterism explaining the regulation of enzyme activity). Their proposal is termed the *induction-repression theory* and deals with the regulation of gene expression, particularly the *regulation of protein biosynthesis*. For their outstanding contributions, especially in the area of molecular genetics, Jacob, Monod and Andre Lwoff—the latter particularly for his pioneering studies of the genetics of viral infection of bacteria—were jointly awarded the Nobel Prize in 1965.

To introduce the theory, let us begin by briefly considering the experimental background which led to its formulation. In the early 1950s, Lwoff, Jacob, and coworkers were investigating the effect of ultraviolet (UV) radiation on *lysogenic* bacteria. This obviously needs a little explanation (Figure 18–10). The term "lysogenic" refers to bacterial cells which have been infected by the chromosome of a bacterial virus but in which the viral chromosome is dormant. That is to say, the host cell

Figure 18–10   Left: A diagrammatic summary of viral infection of bacteria. When the viral chromosome is incorporated into the bacterial chromosome, the former is inactivated and the resultant cell is said to be lysogenic. This means that the chromosome of the cell now contains the genetic information that can result in its lytic destruction (dashed lines), which can occur spontaneously at any time. Top right: A diagrammatic summary of two separate induction phenomena. Although not shown, the induction of loss of lysogenicity by UV radiation would proceed through the detachment of the viral chromosome.

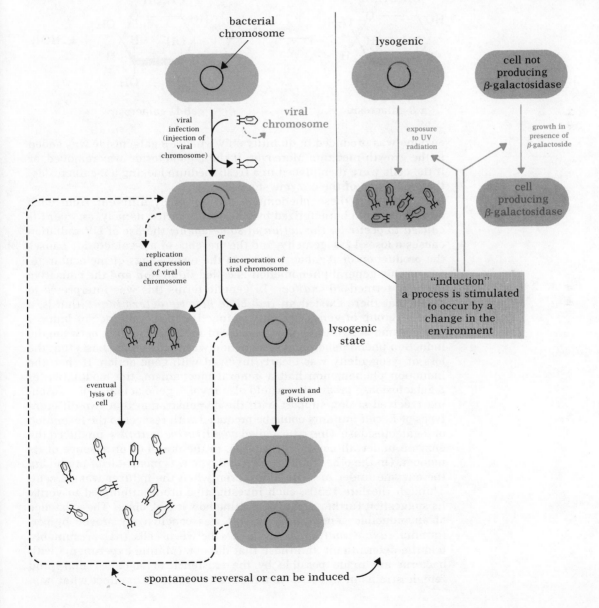

is not destroyed. Indeed, it can grow and divide for several generations much like a non-infected cell. At any time, however, the inactive viral chromosome can become activated, resulting in the intracellular production of several viral particles and the lysis of the host cell. In other words, the lysogenic state is not permanent. If lysogenic cells are exposed to UV radiation, one observes a rapid and essentially complete loss of the lysogenic state with an accompanying production of viruses and cell lysis. At the same time (and literally down the hall), Monod and coworkers were studying the production of *β-galactosidase* in *E. coli* (also Figure 18–10). This is an enzyme that catalyzes the hydrolysis of a *β*-galactoside such as lactose, for example, as the first step in its metabolism. The feature that interested the Monod group was that the

a *β*-galactoside   *β*-D-galactose

enzyme was produced in quantity only when a *β*-galactoside was added to the growth medium. Moreover, if the *β*-galactoside was removed, or if the cells were then placed in a fresh medium lacking a *β*-galactoside, the production of the enzyme stopped.

Although these phenomena are obviously different from each other, they are characterized by a basic similarity, namely, *an event is caused to occur by the action of some agent;* the use of UV radiation causes a loss of lysogenicity, and the presence of a *β*-galactoside causes the production of *β*-galactosidase. In the terminology of molecular genetics, this general phenomenon is called *induction* and the causative agent is termed an *inducer.* In genetic terms this was interpreted to mean that there existed an *inducible genetic determinant,* that is, a gene or group of genes, which was inactive in the absence of inducer and became activated in the presence of inducer. The link between the induction phenomenon and gene action was made on the basis that the loss of lysogenicity was clearly involved with gene action. If then the induction phenomenon had a general mechanism, the modulation of *β*-galactosidase production would also involve gene action. This reasoning received strong support with the demonstration that two different types of *E. coli* mutants could be produced with respect to the formation of *β*-galactosidase. One type, called *constitutive mutants,* produced the enzyme under all conditions, that is, in the presence or absence of its inducer. On the other hand, the second type was incapable of producing the enzyme under any condition, even when the inducer was present. Through the late 1950s, each investigative group attempted to verify its suggestion further and to determine how it took place. The existence of an inducible genetic determinant was conclusively proven by performing *sexual mating experiments* between cells that presumably had the determinant and those that did not. (Mating experiments with bacteria are made possible by the existence of so-called male and female strains of *E. coli.* When incubated together, in effect what happens is that male and female cells attach to each other and during this conjugation there occurs a transfer of the DNA chromosome from one cell, called the donor, to the other, called the host. If the conjugation is not disturbed, a complete chromosome will be transferred. If it is disrupted, only a segment of the chromosome is transferred. Whatever the case, after transfer the two DNA's can undergo an interchange of genes via a process called *genetic recombination,* producing a new species that now contains genetic information—that is, genetic determinants—from both the host and the donor. The phenomenon was discovered and brilliantly studied by J. Lederberg—Nobel Prize, 1958.) The basic rationale was that if the inducible determinant were indeed genetic —that is, chromosomal in nature—then it should be possible for it to be transferred to a cell that lacks it. Although highly oversimplified, the following diagram summarizes the two types of matings that were done. As indicated, the results were positive in each case. In one instance the determinant of lysogenicity was transferred to non-lysogenic cells, and in the other the determinant for β-galactosidase inducibility was transferred to constitutive mutant cells.

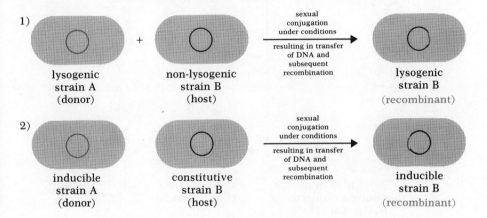

1)

lysogenic strain A (donor) + non-lysogenic strain B (host)

sexual conjugation under conditions resulting in transfer of DNA and subsequent recombination →

lysogenic strain B (recombinant)

2)

inducible strain A (donor) constitutive strain B (host)

sexual conjugation under conditions resulting in transfer of DNA and subsequent recombination →

inducible strain B (recombinant)

For reasons which we will not go into, further investigations by Jacob and Monod into the nature of induction centered primarily on the β-galactosidase system. The experiments that provided a key insight into the genetic characteristics of induction were performed in 1959 by Jacob, Monod, and A. Pardee. By using special mating techniques, they were able to produce what are termed *heterozygous diploids* of *E. coli* from constitutive mutant cells (host) and normal, inducible cells (donor cells). "Diploid" means that the cell contains twice as many chromosomes as it normally does, and "heterozygous" means that the newly acquired chromosomes are different from those originally present. The special techniques referred to included procedures that prevented genetic recombination from taking place after chromosomal transfer. (If recombination were not prevented, then a diploid cell would not result.) In terms of *E. coli,* this simply means that a diploid cell would contain two different chromosomes since *E. coli* normally contains only one. Actually, the diploid cells they produced were characterized not by the presence of two intact chromosomes, but rather of one intact chromosome (from the host) and a segment of a second chromosome transferred to the host cell by the donor cell during mating (see below). More specifically, they were able to isolate diploid cells containing a chromosomal segment possessing the genetic determinant of the constitutive donor. That is, the diploids contained the normal inducible determinant and a constitutive determinant. Presumably, the latter was basically a mutated inducible determinant. When these diploids were examined for their ability to produce β-galactosidase, it was observed that the *inducible determinant was dominant* over the constitutive determinant. In other words, the diploid behaved as the original inducible host cell, producing β-galactosidase only when it was grown in the presence of the inducer. In still other words, despite the fact that the diploid state was characterized by the presence of a constitutive determinant, the cells did not produce the enzyme in the absence of inducer. Somehow the constitutive determinant was being regulated by the inducible determinant.

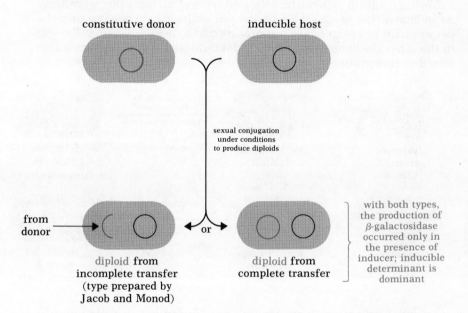

constitutive donor   inducible host

sexual conjugation under conditions to produce diploids

from donor

diploid **from incomplete transfer** (type prepared by Jacob and Monod)

or

diploid **from complete transfer**

with both types, the production of β-galactosidase occurred only in the presence of inducer; inducible determinant is dominant

On the basis of results such as these from many other mating experiments, Jacob and Monod proposed that the regulation of genetic expression is under a *double genetic determinism within the same chromosome segment* governing the production of β-galactosidase. By this they meant that two different types of genes were involved in gene expression. One type, termed a *structural gene,* was responsible for specifying the configuration (amino acid sequence) of the protein. Furthermore, it is the structural gene whose function is induced. The second, termed a *regulatory gene,* was responsible for controlling the expression of the structural genes. They further proposed that the natural effect of the regulatory gene was to inhibit the expression of the structural gene. This inhibition was explained as resulting from the fact that the regulatory gene first directed the formation of a product, which they called a *repressor,* that somehow blocked polypeptide biosynthesis. Finally, they proposed that the inducer short-circuits this repression, possibly by rendering the repressor inactive by binding to it. According to these descriptions, a constitutive mutant would then be a cell that contains a damaged (malfunctional) regulatory gene but an

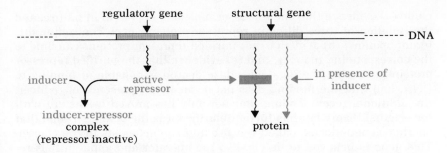

undamaged (functional) structural gene.

The further suggestions of Jacob and Monod as to how these events occurred at the molecular level were based on three developments. The first came from additional mating experiments which conclusively proved that the *repressor substance was a product released to the cytoplasm*. The second was their proposal of the *messenger-RNA hypothesis*. Given the proposed sequence of

$$\text{DNA-genes} \xrightarrow{\text{transcription}} \text{mRNA} \xrightarrow{\text{translation}} \text{protein}$$

as the route of gene expression and their proof that the repressor was a soluble product of the regulatory gene, they theorized that the repressor was either an RNA or protein material which could then exert its action either during the transcription of the structural gene or during the translation of the corresponding mRNA, or both. Their third and perhaps most important discovery (again from mating experiments) was that certain constitutive mutants could not contain a malfunctional regulatory gene. Indeed, the regulatory gene was not damaged at all. To explain this anomaly, Jacob and Monod argued that these mutants must have contained another damaged locus, which they termed *the operator gene*. They further proposed (again on the basis of additional mating experiments) that the function of the operator gene was to serve as a receptor binding site for the repressor. The operator gene was hypothesized to be adjacent to the structural gene (genes), and the combined region was termed an *operon*.

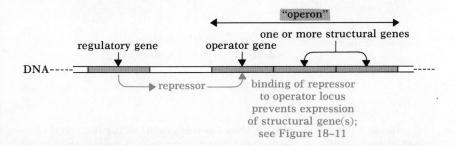

By now you should have become conditioned to appreciating that what may first appear more like fiction is actually fact. So it is with the Jacob-Monod theory for gene control by induction, with recent discoveries providing rather convincing proof of the mechanism. These include (a) evidence that the repressor molecule is protein in nature, and the isolation of three different repressor proteins, each controlling different operons; (b) evidence that purified repressor proteins can bind to the corresponding inducer; and (c) evidence that the purified repressor protein governing the β-galactosidase operon is capable of binding to DNA, and that the binding does not occur in the presence of inducer. An additional recent finding that not only has proved consistent with the original theory but has further clarified it is the demonstration that another genetic locus, called the *promoter gene*, exists in the operon. This gene is believed to lie close to the operator and apparently is responsible for binding RNA polymerase. The combined participation of all these factors in the control of the β-galactosidase operon by induction is diagrammatically summarized in Figure 18–11.

Figure 18–11 A diagrammatic summary of gene control by induction. *Upper half:* In the absence of inducer, protein biosynthesis is inhibited by the action of the repressor. *Lower half:* In the presence of inducer, the repressor is deactivated and the inhibition of protein biosynthesis is removed. As indicated, it is proposed that the transcription product of the operon is one massive messenger-RNA molecule which is then translated in segments. The positioning of the various genetic loci is based on chromosome mapping studies. The regulatory gene is not known to be adjacent to the operon.

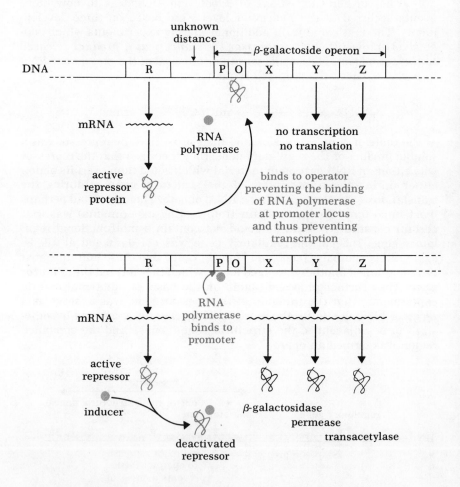

In each section of Figure 18–11 is a segment of the bacterial chromosome that contains all of the known genetic loci necessary for the metabolism of β-galactosides; these loci are mapped according to their known relative positions. The genetic loci represented are the regulatory gene (I), the promoter gene (P), the operator gene (O), and three structural genes (X, Y, and Z). The X gene codes for β-galactosidase;

the Y gene for *β-galactoside permease,* functioning in the transport of β-galactosides across the cell membrane; and the Z gene for *transacetylase,* whose exact function is unknown. Although we have mentioned only β-galactosidase, actually all three enzymes are under coordinate control by the regulatory gene and all are induced by a β-galactoside. The top half of Figure 18–11 summarizes the positive action of the repressor in the absence of inducer. The active repressor protein binds to the operator gene, preventing the binding of RNA polymerase to the promoter locus, and thus transcription does not occur. The bottom half summarizes the action of the inducer, which binds to the repressor protein, rendering it inactive for binding to the operator locus. The absence of repressor binding to the operator then permits the binding of RNA polymerase to the promoter locus, which allows transcription and then translation to occur. The basic feature to note here is that the regulation of protein biosynthesis is not mediated directly in the process of translation, but indirectly by control at the level of transcription. In other words, *transcription is controlled directly and translation is controlled consequentially.*

In the introduction to this section, it was stated that the subject of our discussion was to be the theory of induction-repression for the regulation of protein biosynthesis. Although it may seem that our discussion is now complete, it is actually only half-complete, because we have not yet considered the *repression* of protein biosynthesis. The confusion here is because of the term "repressor" used to refer to the product of the regulatory gene. As used above, the repression of protein biosynthesis refers to a mode of gene control essentially operating in *reverse of induction.* That is to say, in this case the *presence* of a low-molecular-weight substance, frequently a normal metabolite within the cell, causes the *inhibition* of the biosynthesis of certain proteins. The most remarkable example of this is the inhibition (that is, the repression) in bacteria by histidine of the production of ten different enzymes all responsible for the biosynthesis of histidine. Yes, ten genes are coordinately inhibited. Knowing of this type of phenomenon, Jacob and Monod explained that the mechanism proposed for gene control by induction could also apply to the gene control by repression. To distinguish the repressing metabolite from the repressor protein, the former was called a *corepressor.* As summarized in Figure 18–12, the corepressor is proposed to bind the *inactive* repressor protein, resulting in a corepressor-repressor protein complex which is now active in the sense that the complex binds to the operator locus and prevents transcription as described earlier.

To summarize: (1) an operon controlled by induction is subject to a regulatory gene that produces an active repressor protein normally having the ability to bind to the operator locus, preventing transcription of the operon; induction of protein biosynthesis then occurs as a result of the inducer's binding to and deactivating the repressor; (2) an operon controlled by repression is subject to a regulatory gene that produces an inactive repressor protein that does not normally have the ability to bind at the operator locus, and transcription of the operon is not prevented; repression of protein biosynthesis then occurs as a result of the corepressor's binding with and activating the repressor protein. Figures 18–11 and 18–12 essentially summarize these relationships. On close analysis, you will see they are simply the reverse of each other.

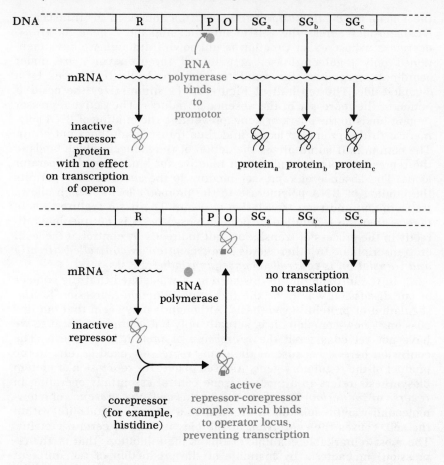

Figure 18–12 A diagrammatic summary of gene control by repression. *Upper half:* The repressor product of the regulatory gene is normally inactive, and thus there is no inhibition of protein biosynthesis. *Lower half:* In the presence of corepressor, the repressor protein is activated and, by then binding to the operator locus, represses the expression of the operon. The diagram refers to no specific operon, and the SG notations represent hypothetical structural genes. As mentioned in the text, the histidine operon would contain ten structural genes.

BIOLOGICAL SIGNIFICANCE OF INDUCTION-REPRESSION

It is important to understand not only the nature of a biological phenomenon but also its consequences for the living state. As for the related phenomena of induction and repression, it is not difficult to appreciate that their significance as control systems is that they allow an organism *to adapt to a changing environment.* The ability to adapt leads, of course, to metabolic economy. Why should a cell produce the enzymes necessary for the entry and hydrolysis of a β-galactoside if the latter is not present in the external growth medium? Why should a cell produce the ten enzymes for the biosynthesis of histidine if the intracellular concentration of histidine is sufficient to sustain normal metabolism? To put it simply, there is no reason why it should and every reason why it should not. Although it is logical, it is, nevertheless, a truly remarkable characteristic of living cells that they have evolved on the basis that it is more efficient to conserve energy and resources than to use them wastefully. We have now completed an analysis of the two major molecular mechanisms common to all living cells that permit them to act accordingly. One is the regulation of protein biosynthesis by induction and repression, the other the regulation of protein (enzyme) activity by allosteric effects.

The overall significance of controlling protein biosynthesis in any type of organism is difficult to evaluate. Lest you interpret otherwise, however, this control is not confined solely to the enzymes associated with the metabolism of β-galactosides and histidine. Consider, for example, certain numbers concerning *E. coli*. Estimates on the size of the *E. coli* chromosome indicate that there is enough information to code for anywhere from 2000–4000 polypeptides. Whatever the actual number, it is estimated that perhaps only one-half are produced when *E. coli* is growing normally on an adequate glucose-containing medium. The point is that the *proteins present in a cell at any time may be only a portion of the total number that potentially could be produced.* The production of the rest is apparently under control. Finally, it should be noted that this control mechanism is not confined to bacteria, but is common to higher organisms including man. Here again, however, the extent to which it may operate is largely unknown. To what extent is it related to natural defense mechanisms? To what extent is it related to cellular differentiation? Is it related to infectious diseases? Is it related to cancer? Is it related to genetic diseases? In future years it is likely that we will have answers to such questions and to many others. To increase the probability of these successes, however, basic research must continue in order to determine more of the details of how this control mechanism operates. In this regard, recent studies have shown, for example, that the control by induction is also under a strict complementary control by cyclic-AMP.

This effect of cyclic-AMP in bacteria is interesting, but it is only one of several functions that have been ascribed to cyclic-AMP since it was first isolated in 1957 by Earl Sutherland. For the isolation-identification and his subsequent proposal of the "secondary messenger" role of cyclic-AMP in mediating the action of various hormones, Sutherland was awarded the Nobel Prize for Medicine in 1971. He is the first lone-recipient of the award in ten years. There are many who suspect that future findings about the biochemistry of this wonder molecule may provide major breakthroughs in understanding the operations of living cells and their ability for self-regulation, particularly the eucaryotic cells of mammalian organisms.

3',5'-cyclic-AMP

LITERATURE

ANFINSEN, C. B. (ed.), *Protein Biosynthesis*. New York: Academic Press, 1970. Contains articles by different authors on various aspects of transcription and translation, including an excellent paper by Marshall Nirenberg on the flow of information from gene to protein.

CLARK, R. F. C., and K. A. MARCKER, "How Proteins Start," *Scientific American,* 218, 36–42 (1968). Discussion of the discovery of formyl-methionine.

CRICK, F. H. C., "The Genetic Code: II," *Scientific American,* 215, 55–62 (1966). An updated description of the nature of the genetic code and of how it works.

DAVIS, B. D., R. DULBECCO, H. N. EISEN, H. S. GINSBERG, and W. B. WOOD. *Principles of Microbiology and Immunology.* New York: Harper & Row, Publishers, 1967. Chapters 8 and 9 of this textbook treat the subjects of translation, the nature of the genetic code, and genetic regulatory mechanisms.

DE CROMBRUGGHE, B., B. CHEN, M. GOTTESMAN, J. PASTAN, H. E. VARMUS, M. EMMER, and R. L. PERLMAN, "Regulation of mRNA Synthesis in a Soluble Cell-free System," *Nature New Biology,* 230, 37–40 (1971). Experimental evidence for a requirement of cyclic-AMP in the transcription of the β-galactoside operon.

HOUSMAN, D., M. JACOBS-LORENA, U. L. RAJBHANDRY, H. F. LODISH, "Initiation of Hemoglobin Synthesis by Methionyl-tRNA", *Nature,* 227, 913–918 (1970). Experimental evidence for a different initiator in eucaryotic organisms.

JACOB, F., and J. MONOD, "Genetic Regulatory Mechanisms in the Synthesis of Proteins", *J. Mol. Biol.,* 3, 318–356 (1961). The original paper proposing the messenger-RNA hypothesis and the nature of gene control by induction and repression of operons by regulatory genes.

JOST, J. P. and H. V. RICKENBURG, "Cyclic AMP," in *Annual Review of Biochemistry,"* Volume 40, 741–774 (1971). An excellent review article on the progress of recent research into the metabolism of cyclic-AMP and its effects on various biochemical and physiological processes.

LEVITT, M., "Detailed Molecular Model for Transfer Ribonucleic Acid," *Nature,* 224, 759–763 (1969). An evaluation of various models proposed for the three-dimensional conformation of tRNA molecules.

LUCAS-LENARD, J. and F. LIPMANN, "Protein Biosynthesis," in *Annual Review of Biochemistry,* Volume 40, 409–448 (1971). A review article of the initiation, elongation, and termination stages of the translation process as they are currently understood in both prokaryotic and eukaryotic organisms.

MARSHALL, R. E., C. T. CASKEY, and M. NIRENBERG, "Fine Structure of RNA Codewords Recognized by Bacterial, Amphibian, and Mammalian Transfer-RNA," *Science,* 155, 820–825 (1967). Conclusive evidence for the universality of the basic language of the genetic code on the basis of *in vitro* binding studies with 50 synthetic codons, with a discussion of specific variations in terms of their phylogenetic and evolutionary significance.

The Mechanism of Protein Synthesis, Volume 34 of *Cold Spring Harbor Symposia on Quantitative Biology.* New York: Cold Spring Harbor Laboratory, 1969. A collection of papers delivered by primary researchers in investigations of mRNA translation. Volume 31 (1966) is devoted to the nature of the genetic code.

NIRENBERG, M. W., "The Genetic Code: II," *Scientific American,* 208, 80–94 (1963). A description of (a) classical experiments with synthetic oligo- and polyribo-nucleotides proving that the sequence of bases in an RNA molecule specifies the order of insertion of amino acids during the assembly of a polypeptide chain; (b) the nature of the genetic code; and (c) how many of the triplet codes were determined by laboratory studies.

NOMURA, M., "Ribosomes," *Scientific American,* 221, 28–35 (1969). An account of the anatomy of a ribosome with particular attention given to the ribosomal proteins.

PASTAN, I., and R. L. PERLMAN, "Cyclic-AMP in Metabolism", *Nature New Biology,* 229, 5–7 (1971). A current review article on the relationship of cyclic-AMP in the hormonal regulation of metabolism in the animal kingdom.

PTHASHNE, M., and W. GILBERT, "Genetic Repressors," *Scientific American*, **222**, 36–44 (1970). Description of the experiments proving that the repressor is a protein, and discussion of repressor action.

RICH, A., "Polyribosomes," *Scientific American*, **209**, 44–53 (1963). A description of experiments and electron microscopic investigations proving that clusters of ribosomes serve as the active sites of protein biosynthesis.

RICH, A., "The Structural Basis of Protein Synthesis," in *Molecular Organization and Biological Function*, J. M. Allen, Editor, 20–36. New York: Harper & Row, Publishers, 1967. An excellent discussion of the participation of ribosomal and polysomal structures in protein biosynthesis.

RICHMOND, M. H., "Enzymic Adaptation in Bacteria: Its Biochemical and Genetic Basis," in Volume 4 of *Essays in Biochemistry*, P. N. Campbell and G. D. Greville (eds.), 105–154. New York: Academic Press, 1968. A good review article.

STENT, G. S., *Molecular Genetics: An Introductory Narrative*. San Francisco: W. H. Freeman and Company, 1971. A new and excellent textbook. Authoritative treatment of RNA translation (Chapter 17), the genetic code (Chapter 18), the regulation of gene function (Chapter 20), and the ramifications of molecular genetics as they apply to further study into the nature of life, particularly in higher organisms (Chapter 21).

WATSON, J. D., "Involvement of RNA in the Synthesis of Proteins, *Science*, **140**, 17–26 (1963). The author's Nobel address.

WATSON, J. D., *Molecular Biology of the Gene*, Second Edition. New York: W. A. Benjamin, Inc., 1970. Chapters 12, 13, and 14 are devoted to mRNA translation, the genetic code, and gene regulation.

YANOFSKY, C., "Gene Structure and Protein Structure," *Scientific American*, **216**, 80–94 (1967). Discussion of the proof for the colinearity of base sequence in DNA and of amino acid sequence in proteins.

EXERCISES

18-1 Without resorting to elaborate diagrams such as those in Figures 18–4, 18–5, and 18–6 summarize your understanding of the role of ribosomes in polypeptide biosynthesis.

18-2 As stated on more than one occasion in previous chapters, the sulfa drugs are potent chemotherapeutic agents used in the treatment of infection (see pages 117 and 441). In part, the action of sulfa drugs is related to their ability to interfere with protein biosynthesis in the infectious organism. The inhibition of what stage of polypeptide biosynthesis would account for this interference? Explain. (Review the proposed mode of action of the sulfa drugs; see pages cited above.)

18-3 On the basis of sensitive *in vitro* binding assays, recent studies have shown that fmet-tRNA[fmet] can recognize the GUG codon nearly as efficiently as it does the AUG codon. Although considerably weaker, binding with UUG and CUG was also observed. Comment on the possible biological significance of these observations.

18-4 What general characteristic of the genetic code is typified by the information given in problem 18–3? More specifically, what is so unusual about the data? That is, in the context that they represent a general characteristic of the genetic code, is there anything unique or atypical about these data to distinguish them from other data representing the same general phenomenon?

18–5 The polypeptide chain of myoglobin contains 153 amino acid residues. Theoretically then, how many nucleotides would be present in the gene that specifies the configuration of this polypeptide?

18–6 The amino acid sequence of the polypeptide chain of whale myoglobin is given on page 86. In symbolic fashion, write a nucleotide sequence in the gene of whale DNA that would correspond to residues 30 through 37 of the myoglobin chain. Then determine the number of base substitution mutations that could occur in this gene segment without a resultant change in the amino acid sequence. Finally, indicate how base substitutions in the first position of one codon and in the middle position of another codon would account for the differences that could exist in the myoglobin polypeptide gene in the horse.

18–7 On page 520 it was stated that a leucine-tRNA molecule (yeast) having the anticodon, (3′)GAA, is capable of binding only with one of the six degenerate codons assigned to leucine (see Figure 18–9). Given the fact that a second leucine-tRNA (yeast) having the anticodon, (3′)AAC, has been isolated, predict (a) what codon or codons it would bind with, and (b) the *minimum* and the *maximum* number of additional leucine-tRNA's that would be required to recognize the codons that still remain unaccounted for.

18–8 On page 522 it was stated that Jacob and Monod had isolated two types of *E. coli* mutants with respect to β-galactosidase production, namely, constitutive mutants, producing the enzyme in both the absence and the presence of inducer, and other mutants that could not produce the enzyme under any circumstances. In the latter group, would the sites of mutation in the β-galactosidase segment of the chromosome exist in (a) the regulatory gene; (b) the promoter gene; (c) the operator gene; and/or (d) the structural gene? Explain.

18–9 The biosynthesis of tryptophan from anthranilic acid (see page 428) involves four steps, each catalyzed by a different enzyme. From the graph given below, what conclusions can you draw regarding the regulation of this anabolic pathway? (The graph represents the variation in the total cellular concentrations of the four enzymes involved as changes were made in the composition of the growth medium. The growth medium at time zero consisted of glucose and inorganic ions.)

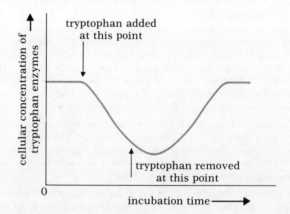

18–10 Given below are descriptions of the genetic characteristics of four different donor and host strains of *E. coli*. Assuming these were mated under conditions to produce partial diploids, predict whether the diploid obtained from each combination would produce increased amounts of β-galactosidase when a β-galactoside was added to the growth medium.

Description of the State of Genetic Determinants

	Donor		Host		
	functional genes	malfunctional gene	functional genes	malfunctional gene	
1	regulatory structural	operator	operator regulatory structural	none	1
2	operator structural	regulatory	operator regulatory structural	none	2
3	operator structural	regulatory	operator regulatory	structural	3
4	regulatory structural	operator	operator structural	regulatory	4

Appendixes

I

Literature Sources in Biochemistry and Related Sciences

Research Journals

Acta Chemica Scandinavica (Acta Chem. Scand.)

Analytical Biochemistry (Anal. Biochem.)

Archives of Biochemistry and Biophysics (Arch. Biochem. Biophys.)

Biochemical and Biophysical Research Communications (Biochem. Biophys. Res. Commun.)

Biochemical Genetics (Biochem. Genet.)

Biochemical Journal (Biochem. J.)

Biochemische Zeitschrift (currently European Journal of Biochemistry) (Biochem. Z.; Eur. J. Biochem.)

Biochemistry (Biochemistry)

Biochimica et Biophysica Acta (Biochim. Biophys. Acta)

Biokhimiya (Russian) (Biokhimiya)

Bioorganic Chemistry (Bioorg. Chem.)

Biopolymers (Biopolymers)

Bioscience (Bioscience)

Canadian Journal of Biochemistry (Can. J. Biochem.)

Canadian Journal of Microbiology (Can. J. Microbiol.)

Cancer Research (Cancer Res.)

Chemistry and Physics of Lipids (Chem. Phys. Lipids)

Clinical Chemistry (Clin. Chem.)

Comparative Biochemistry and Physiology (Comp. Biochem. Physiol.)

Comptes Rendus

European Journal of Biochemistry (formerly Biochemische Zeitschrift)

Experimental Cell Research (Exp. Cell Res.)

Federation Proceedings (Fed. Proc.)

Immunology (Immunology)

Indian Journal of Biochemistry (Indian J. Biochem.)

Journal of the American Chemical Society (J. Am. Chem. Soc.)

Journal of Bacteriology (J. Bacteriol.)

Journal of Biochemistry (Japan) (J. Biochem. (Tokyo))

Journal of Bioenergetics (J. Bioenerg.)

Journal of Biological Chemistry (J. Biol. Chem.)

Journal of Cell Biology (J. Cell Biol.)

Journal of Cellular Physiology (J. Cell. Physiol.)

Journal of Chromatography (J. Chromatogr.)

Journal of Electron Microscopy (J. Electron Microsc.)

Journal of Experimental Biology (J. Exp. Biol.)

Journal of General Microbiology (J. Gen. Microbiol.)

Journal of General Physiology (J. Gen. Physiol.)

Journal of Histochemistry and Cytochemistry (J. Histochem. Cytochem.)
Journal of Immunology (J. Immunol.)
Journal of Lipid Research (J. Lipid Res.)
Journal of Medicinal Chemistry (J. Med. Chem.)
Journal of Membrane Biology (J. Membrane Biol.)
Journal of Molecular Biology (J. Mol. Biol.)
Journal of Neurochemistry (J. Neurochem.)
Journal of Nutrition (J. Nutr.)
Journal of Pharmacology (J. Pharmacol.)
Journal of Physiology (J. Physiol.)
Journal of Theoretical Biology (J. Theor. Biol.)
Journal of Ultrastructure Research (J. Ultrastruct. Res.)
Journal of Virology (J. Virol.)
Lipids (Lipids)

Molecular Pharmacology (Mol. Pharmacol.)
Mycologia (Mycologia)
Nature (Nature)
Nature New Biology (Nat. New Biol.)
Naturwissenschaften (Naturwissenschaften)
Plant Physiology (Plant Physiol.)
Proceedings of the National Academy of Sciences (U.S.) (Proc. Natl. Acad. Sci. USA)
Proceedings of the Royal Society (Proc. R. Soc.)
Proceedings of the Society for Experimental Biology and Medicine (Proc. Soc. Exp. Biol. Med.)
Science (Science)
Steroids (Steroids)
Tetrahedron (Tetrahedron)

Review Journals and Annual Publications

Advances in Carbohydrate Chemistry (Adv. Carbohydr. Chem.)
Advances in Cell and Molecular Biology (Adv. Cell Mol. Biol.)
Advances in Comparative Physiology and Biochemistry (Adv. Comp. Physiol. Biochem.)
Advances in Enzyme Regulation (Adv. Enzyme Regul.)
Advances in Enzymology (Adv. Enzymol.)
Advances in Experimental Medicine and Biology (Adv. Exp. Med. Biol.)
Advances in Genetics (Adv. Genet.)
Advances in Immunology (Adv. Immunol.)
Advances in Lipid Research (Adv. Lipid Res.)
Advances in Microbial Physiology (Adv. Microb. Physiol.)
Advances in Protein Chemistry (Adv. Protein Chem.)
Annual Review of Biochemistry (Annu. Rev. Biochem.)
Annual Review of Entomology (Annu. Rev. Entomol.)
Annual Review of Genetics (Annu. Rev. Genet.)
Annual Review of Medicine (Annu. Rev. Med.)
Annual Review of Microbiology (Annu. Rev. Microbiol.)

Annual Review of Pharmacology (Annu. Rev. Pharmacol.)
Annual Review of Physiology (Annu. Rev. Physiol.)
Annual Review of Plant Physiology (Annu. Rev. Plant Physiol.)
Bacteriological Reviews (Bacteriol. Rev.)
Biochemical Society Symposia (Biochem. Soc. Symp.)
Biological Reviews (Biol. Rev.)
Chemical Reviews (Chem. Rev.)
Cold Spring Harbor Symposia on Quantitative Biology (Cold Spring Harbor Symp. Quant. Biol.)
Essays in Biochemistry (Essays Biochem.)
Physiological Reviews (Physiol. Rev.)
Progress in Biophysics and Molecular Biology (Prog. Biophys. Mol. Biol.)
Progress in the Chemistry of Fats and Other Lipids (Prog. Chem. Fats Other Lipids)
Progress in Nucleic Acid Research and Molecular Biology (Prog. Nucleic Acid Res. Mol. Biol.)
Subcellular Biochemistry (Subcell. Biochem.)
Vitamins and Hormones (Vitam. Horm.)

II

Some Naturally Occurring Peptides

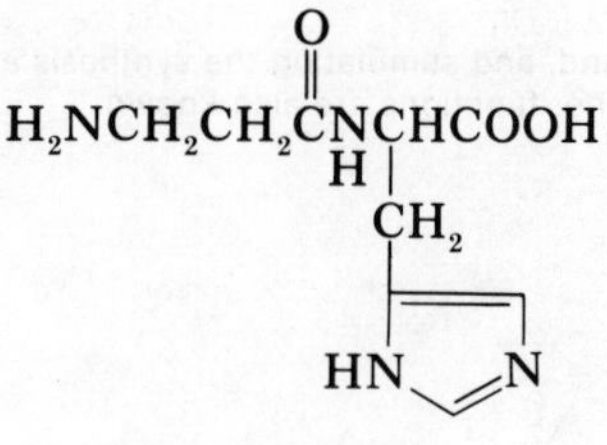

carnosine
(β-alanyl-L-histidine)

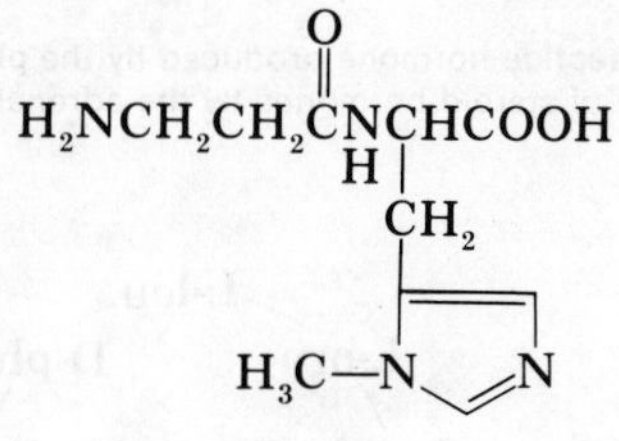

anserine
(β-alanyl-2-methyl histidine)

Both dipeptides are present in muscle tissue of vertebrates; their precise function is unknown.

asp-arg-val-tyr-val-his-pro-phe-his-leu

angiotensin I

asp-arg-val-tyr-val-his-pro-phe

angiotensin II

Both peptides are present in blood, with angiotensin II (formed from angiotensin I) producing a marked increase in blood pressure; angiotensin I is produced from a blood protein by the action of an enzyme, termed renin, which is produced in the kidney.

arg-pro-pro-gly-phe-ser-pro-phe-arg

bradykinin

A peptide produced from a plasma protein by the action of proteolytic enzymes in snake venom; in animals it is a potent antagonist of smooth-muscle contraction.

asp-glu-gly-pro-tyr-lys-met-glu-his-phe[10]-arg-trp-gly-ser-pro-pro-lys-asp[18]

β-melanocyte-stimulating hormone

An oligopeptide hormone produced by the pituitary gland, and capable of stimulating pigment production in the melanocyte cells of skin.

his-ser-gln-gly-thr-phe-thr-ser-asp-tyr[10]-ser-lys-tyr-leu-asp-ser-arg-arg-ala-
gln-asp[20]-phe-val-gln-trp-leu-met-asn-thr[29]

glucagon

An oligopeptide hormone produced by the pancreas, and capable of stimulating the catabolism of glycogen (see page 276).

ser-tyr-ser-met-glu-his-phe-arg-trp-gly[10]-lys-pro-val-gly-lys-lys-arg-arg-pro-
val-lys[20]-val-tyr-pro-asp-ala-gly-glu-asp-gln[30]-ser-ala-glu-ala-phe-pro-
leu-glu-phe[39]

corticotropin
(adrenocorticotropic hormone—ACTH)

An oligopeptide hormone produced by the pituitary gland, and stimulating the synthesis and secretion of steroid hormones by the adrenal gland; other functions are also known.

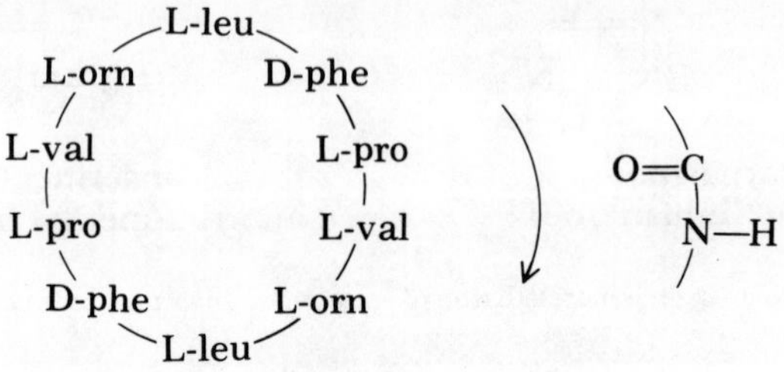

Gramicidin S (antibiotic)

A cyclic oligopeptide containing D- and L- amino acids; L-orn = L-ornithine (see page 424).

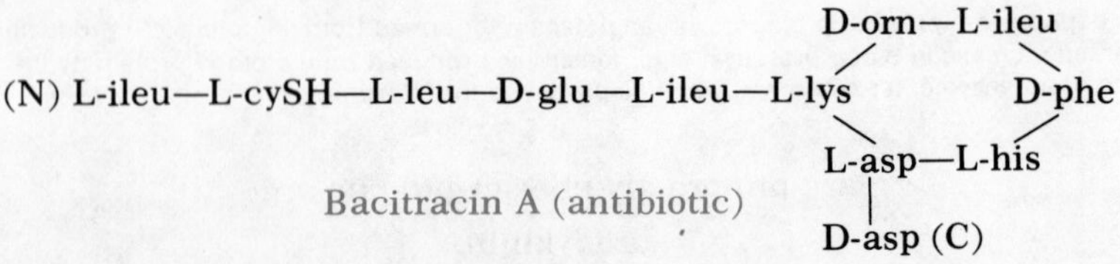

(N) L-ileu—L-cySH—L-leu—D-glu—L-ileu—L-lys

Bacitracin A (antibiotic)

A partially cyclic oligopeptide containing D- and L-amino acids; note the presence of both D- and L-aspartic acid; produced by *Bacillus subtilis*.

III

A Partial Listing of Genetic Disorders in Man and the Malfunctional or Deficient Protein or Enzyme*

Disease	Protein or Enzyme
Acatalasia	catalase (red blood cells)
Albinism	tyrosinase
Alkaptonuria	homogentisic acid oxidase
Cystathioninuria	cystathionase
Fabry's disease	ganglioside-hydrolyzing enzyme
Galactosemia	galactose-1-phosphate uridyl transferase
Gaucher's disease	glucocerebroside-hydrolyzing enzyme
Glycogen storage disease	different types:
	α-amylase
	debranching enzyme
	glucose-1-phosphatase
	liver phosphorylase
	muscle phosphofructokinase
	muscle phosphorylase
Goiter	iodotyrosine dehalogenase
Gout and Lesch-Nyhan syndrome	hypoxanthine-guanine phosphoribosyl transferase
Hemolytic anemias	different types:
	glucose-6-phosphate dehydrogenase
	glutathione reductase
	phosphoglucoisomerase
	pyruvate kinase
	triose phosphate isomerase
Hemophilia	clotting protein (anti-hemophilic factor) in blood
Histidinemia	histidase
Homocystinuria	cystathionine synthetase

Hyperammonemia	ornithine transcarbamylase
Hypophosphatasia	alkaline phosphatase
Isovalericacidemia	isovaleryl-SCoA dehydrogenase
Maple syrup urine disease	α-keto acid decarboxylase
McArdle's syndrome	muscle phosphorylase
Metachromatic leukodystrophy	sphingolipid sulfatase
Methemoglobinemia	NADPH-methemoglobin reductase and NADH-methemoglobin reductase
Niemann-Pick disease	sphingomyelin-hydrolyzing enzyme
Phenylketonuria	phenylalanine hydroxylase
Pulmonary emphysema	α-globulin of blood
Sickle cell anemia	hemoglobin
Tay Sachs disease	ganglioside-degrading enzyme
Tyrosinemia	hydroxyphenylpyruvate oxidase
Von Gierke's disease	glucose-6-phosphatase
Wilson's disease	ceruloplasmin (blood protein)

* Detailed descriptions of the clinical symptoms, biochemical characteristics, and treatments of these diseases are available in the following sources, particularly in the book edited by Stanbury et al.

AMPOLA, M. G., "Errors of Amino Acid Metabolism" in *Handbook of Biochemistry and Selected Data for Molecular Biology,* ed. H. A. Sober. Cleveland: The Chemical Rubber Co., 1970. B105–B111.

DAVIE, E. W., and O. D. RATNOFF, "The Proteins of Blood Coagulation," in *The Proteins,* vol. 3, ed. Hans Neurath. New York: Academic Press, 1965.

STANBURY, J., J. WYNGAARDEN, and D. FREDRICKSON, eds., *Metabolic Basis of Inherited Disease,* 2d ed. New York: McGraw-Hill Book Company, 1966.

IV

The Structure of Some Unusual Nucleosides Occurring in Transfer-RNA

Derivatives of adenosine:

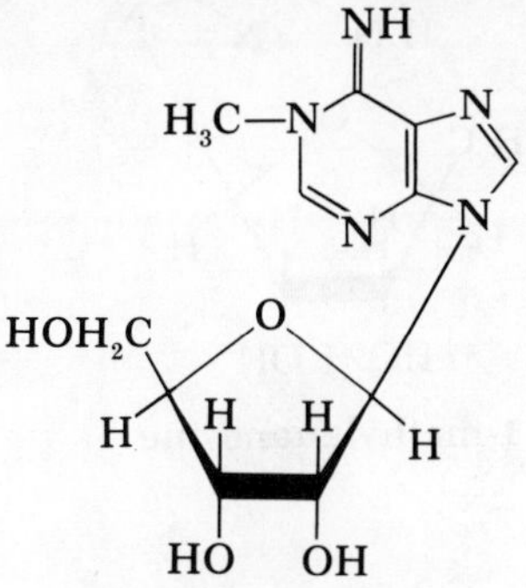

1-methyladenosine

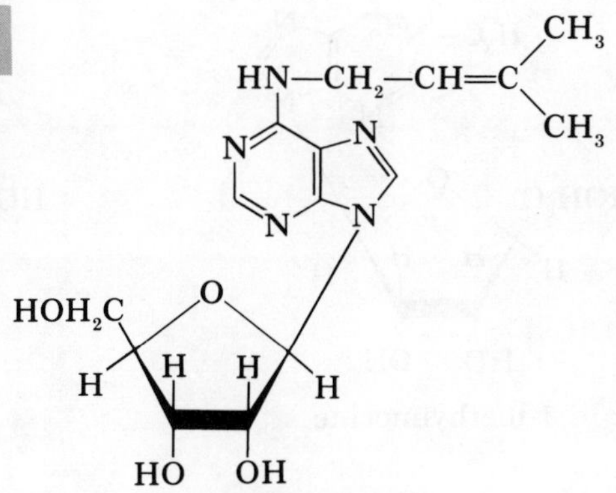

N⁶-(Δ²-isopentenyl)-adenosine

N^6-(Δ^2-isopentenyl)-adenosine

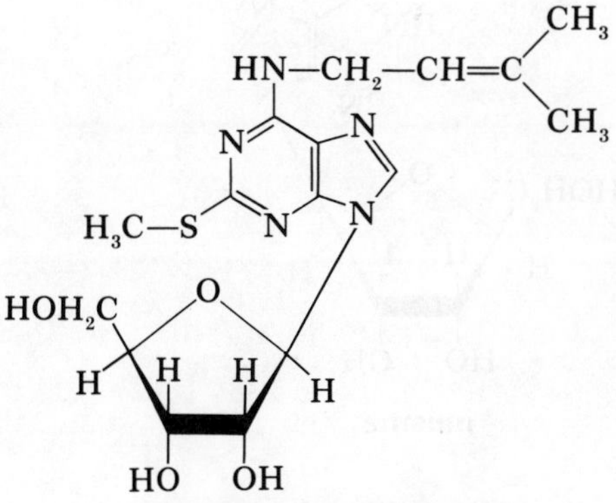

2-methylthio-(Δ^2-iso-pentenyl)-adenosine

Derivatives of uridine:

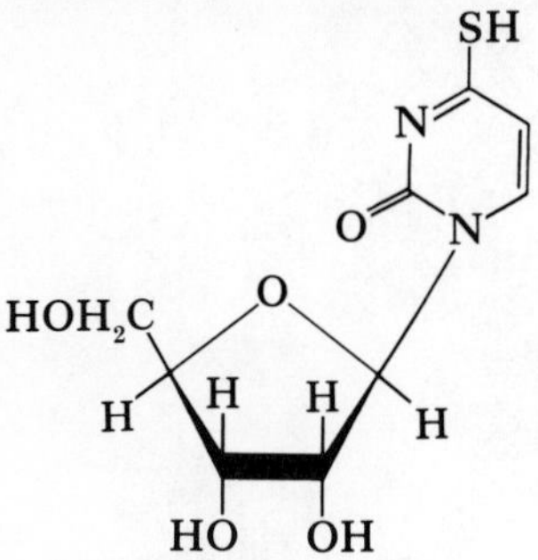

4-thiouridine

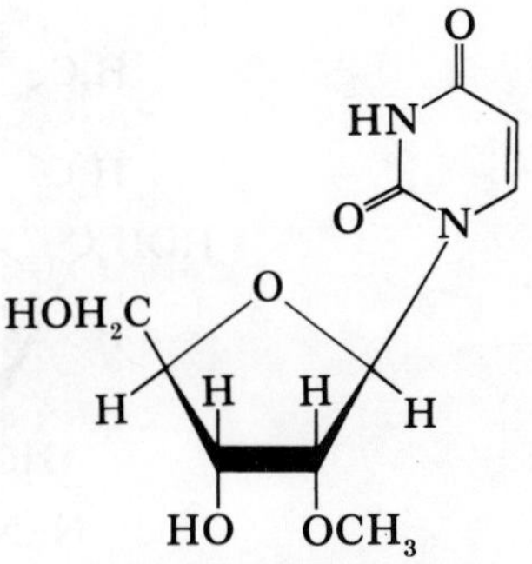

2'-O-methyluridine

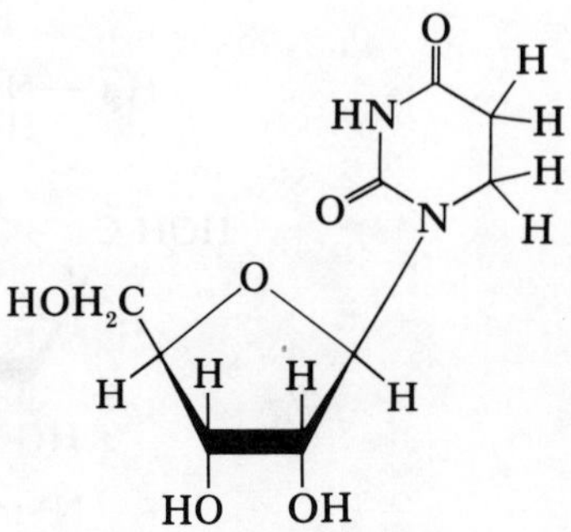

5,6-dihydrouridine

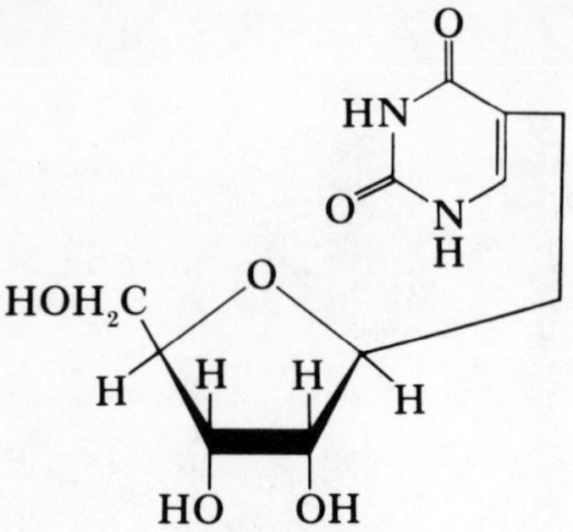

pseudouridine

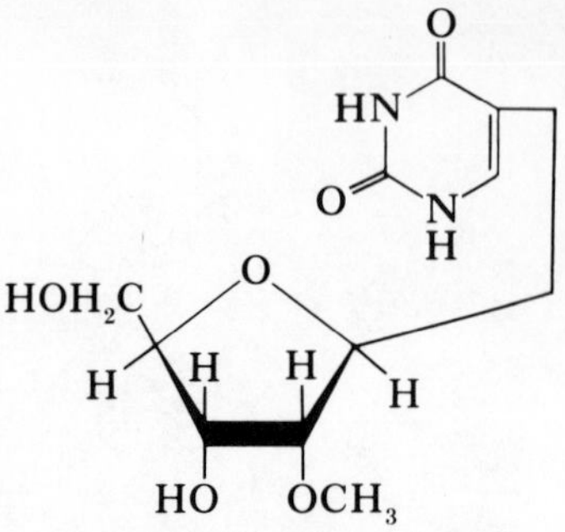

2'-O-methylpseudouridine

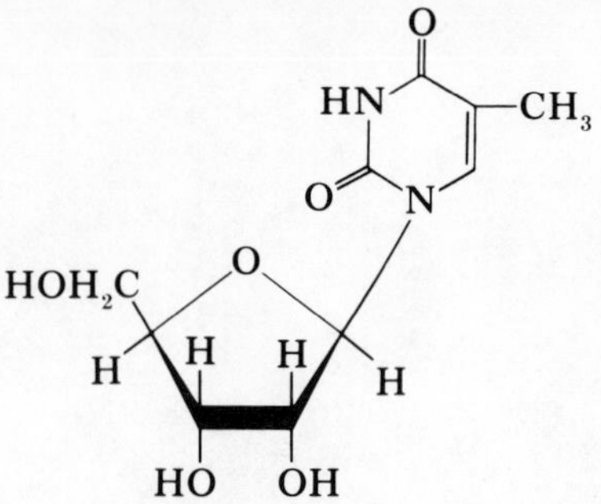

ribosylthymidine
(5-methyluridine)

Derivatives of guanosine:

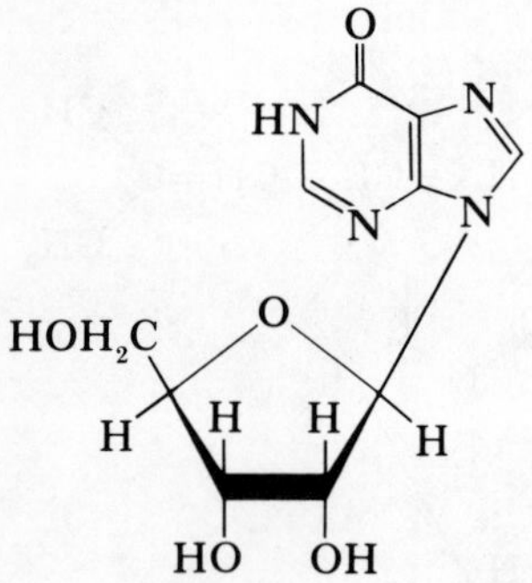

inosine

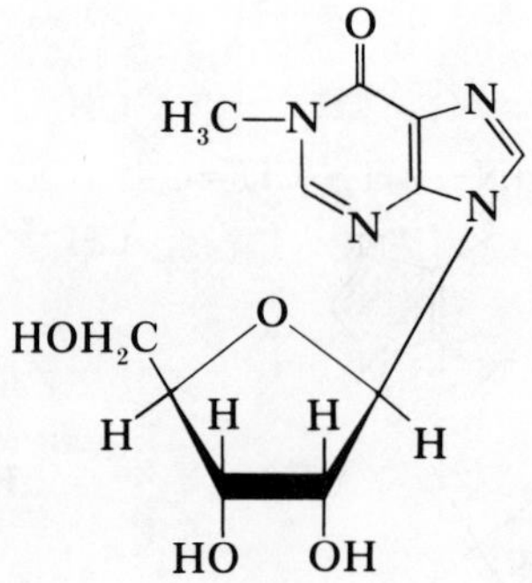

1-methylinosine

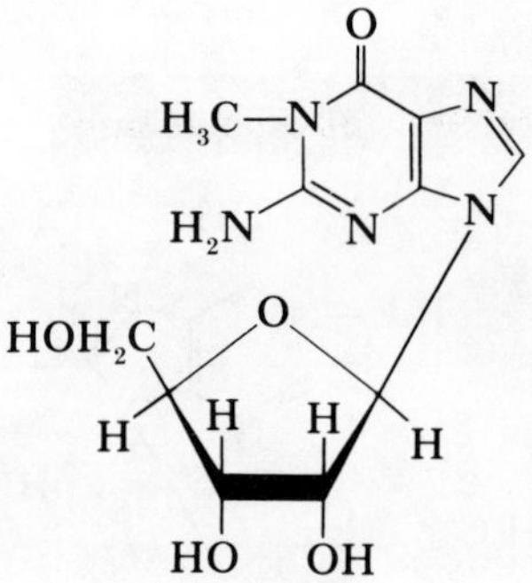

1-methylguanosine

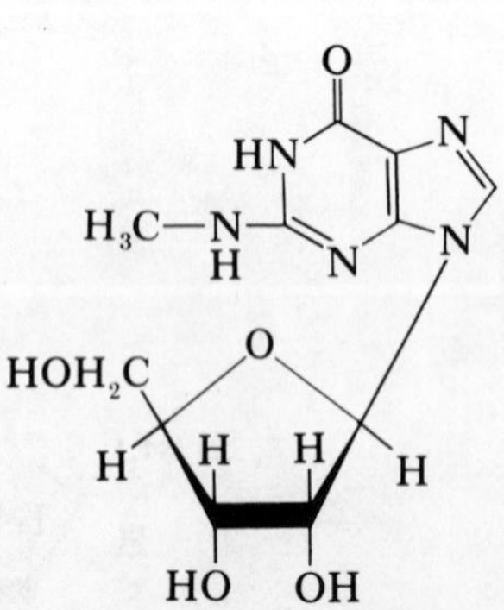

N²-methyl
guanosine

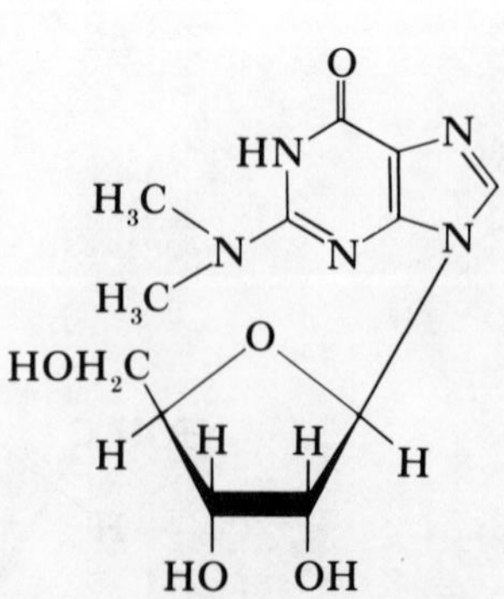

N²,N²-dimethyl
guanosine

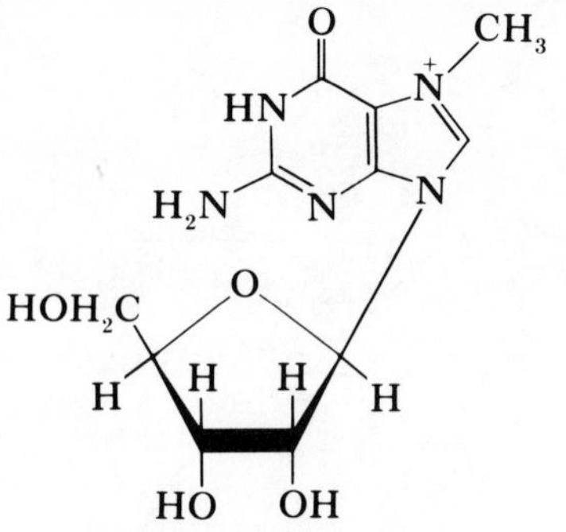

7-methyl
guanosine

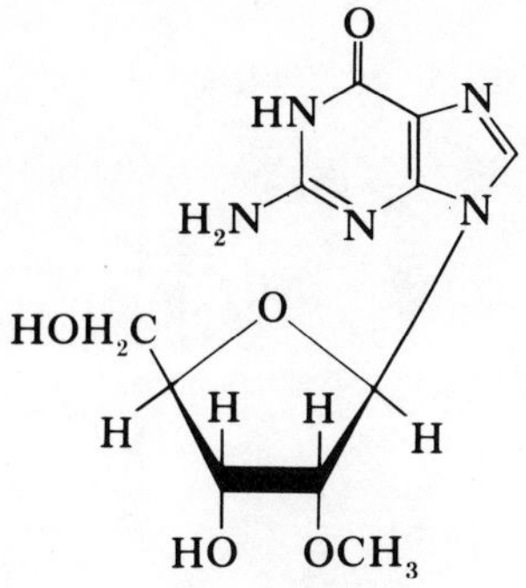

2'-O-methyl
guanosine

Derivatives of cytidine:

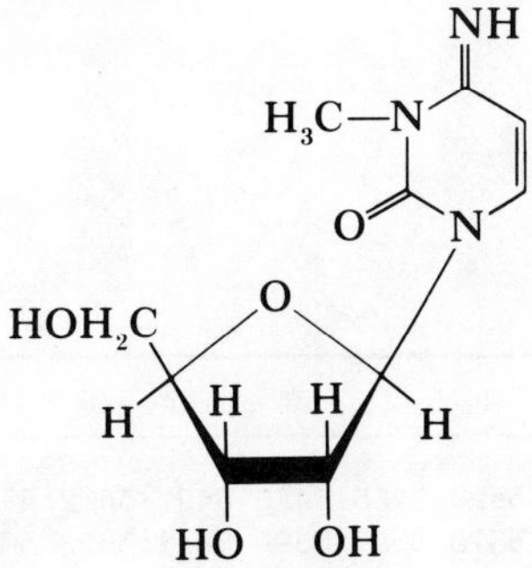

3-methyl
cytidine

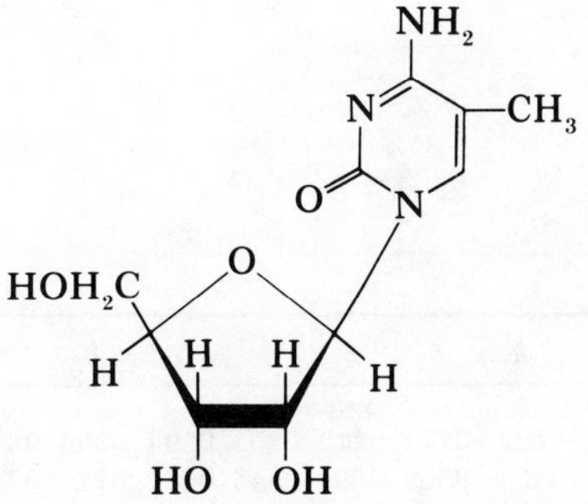

5-methyl
cytidine

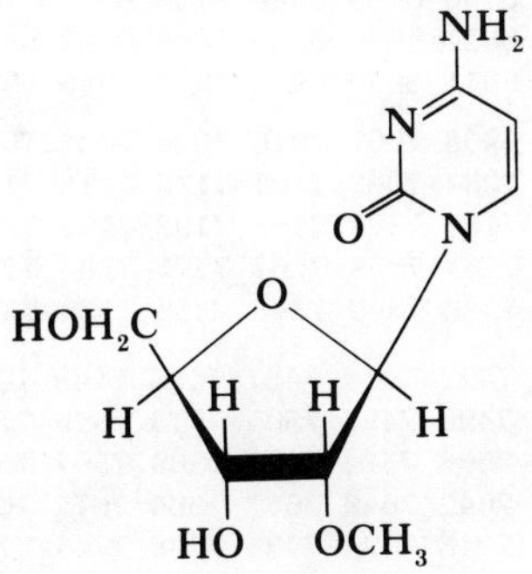

2'-O-methyl
cytidine

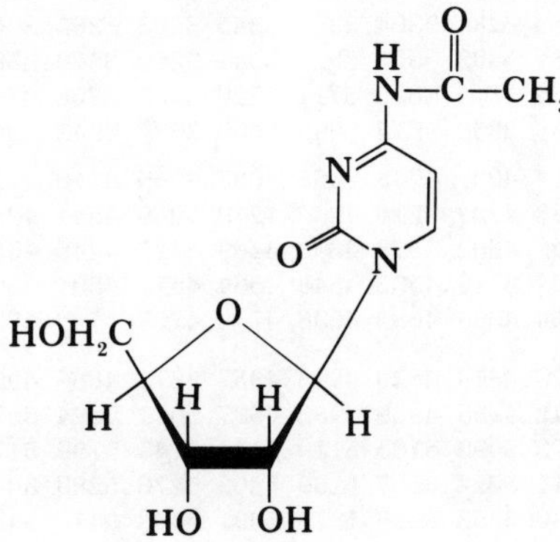

N^4-acetyl
cytidine

V

Table of Logarithms

N	0	1	2	3	4	5	6	7	8	9	N	0	1	2	3	4	5	6	7	8	9
10	0000	0043	0086	0128	0170	0212	0253	0294	0334	0374	35	5441	5453	5465	5478	5490	5502	5514	5527	5539	5551
11	0414	0453	0492	0531	0569	0607	0645	0682	0719	0755	36	5563	5575	5587	5599	5611	5623	5635	5647	5658	5670
12	0792	0828	0864	0899	0934	0969	1004	1038	1072	1106	37	5682	5694	5705	5717	5729	5740	5752	5763	5775	5786
13	1139	1173	1206	1239	1271	1303	1335	1367	1399	1430	38	5798	5809	5821	5832	5843	5855	5866	5877	5888	5899
14	1461	1492	1523	1553	1584	1614	1644	1673	1703	1732	39	5911	5922	5933	5944	5955	5966	5977	5988	5999	6010
15	1761	1790	1818	1847	1875	1903	1931	1959	1987	2014	40	6021	6031	6042	6053	6064	6075	6085	6096	6107	6117
16	2041	2068	2095	2122	2148	2175	2201	2227	2253	2279	41	6128	6138	6149	6160	6170	6180	6191	6201	6212	6222
17	2304	2330	2355	2380	2405	2430	2455	2480	2504	2529	42	6232	6243	6253	6263	6274	6284	6294	6304	6314	6325
18	2533	2577	2601	2625	2648	2672	2695	2718	2742	2765	43	6335	6345	6355	6365	6375	6385	6395	6405	6415	6425
19	2788	2810	2833	2856	2878	2900	2923	2945	2967	2989	44	6435	6444	6454	6464	6474	6484	6493	6503	6513	6522
20	3010	3032	3054	3075	3096	3118	3139	3160	3181	3201	45	6532	6542	6551	6561	6571	6580	6590	6599	6609	6618
21	3222	3243	3263	3284	3304	3324	3345	3365	3385	3404	46	6628	6637	6646	6656	6665	6675	6684	6693	6702	6712
22	3424	3444	3464	3483	3502	3522	3541	3560	3579	3598	47	6721	6730	6739	6749	6758	6767	6776	6785	6794	6803
23	3617	3636	3655	3674	3692	3711	3729	3747	3766	3784	48	6812	6821	6830	6839	6848	6857	6866	6875	6884	6893
24	3802	3820	3838	3856	3874	3892	3909	3927	3945	3962	49	6902	6911	6920	6928	6937	6946	6955	6964	6972	6981
25	3979	3997	4014	4031	4048	4065	4085	4099	4116	4133	50	6990	6998	7007	7016	7024	7033	7042	7050	7059	7067
26	4150	4166	4183	4200	4216	4232	4249	4265	4281	4298	51	7076	7084	7093	7101	7110	7118	7126	7135	7143	7152
27	4314	4330	4346	4362	4378	4393	4409	4425	4440	4456	52	7160	7168	7177	7185	7193	7202	7210	7218	7226	7235
28	4472	4487	4502	4518	4533	4548	4564	4579	4594	4609	53	7243	7251	7259	7267	7275	7284	7292	7300	7308	7316
29	4624	4639	4654	4669	4683	4698	4713	4728	4742	4757	54	7324	7332	7340	7348	7356	7364	7372	7380	7388	7396
30	4771	4786	4800	4814	4829	4843	4857	4871	4886	4900	55	7404	7412	7419	7427	7435	7443	7451	7459	7466	7474
31	4914	4928	4942	4955	4969	4983	4997	5011	5024	5038	56	7482	7490	7497	7505	7513	7520	7528	7536	7543	7551
32	5051	5065	5079	5092	5105	5119	5132	5145	5159	5172	57	7559	7566	7574	7582	7589	7597	7604	7612	7619	7627
33	5185	5198	5211	5224	5237	5250	5263	5276	5289	5302	58	7634	7642	7649	7657	7664	7672	7679	7686	7694	7701
34	5315	5328	5340	5353	5366	5378	5391	5403	5416	5428	59	7709	7716	7723	7731	7738	7745	7752	7760	7767	7774

N	0	1	2	3	4	5	6	7	8	9	N	0	1	2	3	4	5	6	7	8	9

N	0	1	2	3	4	5	6	7	8	9	N	0	1	2	3	4	5	6	7	8	9
60	7782	7789	7796	7803	7810	7818	7825	7832	7839	7846	80	9031	9036	9042	9047	9053	9058	9063	9069	9074	9079
61	7853	7860	7868	7875	7882	7889	7896	7903	7910	7917	81	9085	9090	9096	9101	9106	9112	9117	9122	9128	9133
62	7924	7931	7938	7945	7952	7959	7966	7973	7980	7987	82	9138	9143	9149	9154	9159	9165	9170	9175	9180	9186
63	7993	8000	8007	8014	8021	8028	8035	8041	8048	8055	83	9191	9196	9201	9206	9212	9217	9222	9227	9232	9238
64	8062	8069	8075	8082	8089	8096	8102	8109	8116	8122	84	9243	9248	9253	9258	9263	9269	9274	9279	9284	9289
65	8129	8136	8142	8149	8156	8162	8169	8176	8182	8189	85	9294	9299	9304	9309	9315	9320	9325	9330	9335	9340
66	8195	8202	8209	8215	8222	8228	8235	8241	8248	8254	86	9345	9350	9355	9360	9365	9370	9375	9380	9385	9390
67	8261	8267	8274	8280	8287	8293	8299	8306	8312	8319	87	9395	9400	9405	9410	9415	9420	9425	9430	9435	9440
68	8325	8331	8338	8344	8351	8357	8363	8370	8376	8382	88	9445	9450	9455	9460	9465	9469	9474	9479	9484	9489
69	8388	8395	8401	8407	8414	8420	8426	8432	8439	8445	89	9494	9499	9504	9509	9513	9518	9523	9528	9533	9538
70	8451	8457	8463	8470	8476	8482	8488	8494	8500	8506	90	9542	9547	9552	9557	9562	9566	9571	9576	9581	9586
71	8513	8519	8525	8531	8537	8543	8549	8555	8561	8567	91	9590	9595	9600	9605	9609	9614	9619	9624	9628	9633
72	8573	8579	8585	8591	8597	8603	8609	8615	8621	8627	92	9638	9643	9647	9652	9657	9661	9666	9671	9675	9680
73	8633	8639	8645	8651	8657	8663	8669	8675	8681	8686	93	9685	9689	9694	9699	9703	9708	9713	9717	9722	9727
74	8692	8698	8704	8710	8716	8722	8727	8733	8739	8745	94	9731	9736	9741	9745	9750	9754	9759	9763	9768	9773
75	8751	8756	8762	8768	8774	8779	8785	8791	8797	8802	95	9777	9782	9786	9791	9795	9800	9805	9809	9814	9818
76	8808	8814	8820	8825	8831	8837	8842	8848	8854	8859	96	9823	9827	9832	9836	9841	9845	9850	9854	9859	9863
77	8865	8871	8876	8882	8887	8893	8899	8904	8910	8915	97	9868	9872	9877	9881	9886	9890	9894	9899	9903	9908
78	8921	8927	8932	8938	8943	8949	8954	8960	8965	8971	98	9912	9917	9921	9926	9930	9934	9939	9943	9948	9952
79	8976	8982	8987	8993	8998	9004	9009	9015	9020	9025	99	9956	9961	9965	9969	9974	9978	9983	9987	9991	9996

N	0	1	2	3	4	5	6	7	8	9	N	0	1	2	3	4	5	6	7	8	9

Index

Ammonia (*cont.*)
  as nitrogen source, 418, 425
  use by microbes, 335
Ammonium sulfate fractionation, 97–98
Ampholytes, 35
Amylase
  pancreatic, 187
  salivary, 187
α-Amylase, 186–87
β-Amylase, 186–87
Amylopectin, 185–87
Amylose, 185–87
Amytal, 350
Anabolism, 243–44, 260–61
  amino acid, 326
  carbohydrate, 323–24
  fatty acid, 397–404
  lipid, 325
  nucleotide, 449–59
  protein, 326
  relation to β-oxidation, 397
  soluble pathway, 398–404
Analytical procedures, development, 6–7
Anaplerotic reactions, 324, 326, 394, 395
Androgens, 411
Androsterone, 411
Anemia
  and hexose-monophosphate shunt, 293
  pernicious, 442
  sickle cell, mutations and, 476
Anion exchangers, 15, 17
Anions, 35
Antibiotics, 11, 76, 80
  and protein biosynthesis, 510–11
Anticodons, 499, 503
Antigens, 11
Antimycin A, as respiratory inhibitor, 350, 351, 353
Apoenzyme, 108
D-Arabinose, 172
Arachidic acid, 197
Arginase, 424
Arginine
  degeneracy, 515
  and glycogenesis, 417
  ionization, 65, 66
  in protamines, 80
  structure, 61, 62
  in urea cycle, 424
Argininosuccinate, in urea cycle, 424
Arnon, D. I., 366, 377
Arrhenius, S., 36, 54
Asparagine, 66, 419
  and glycogenesis, 417
  structure, 62
Aspartate
  and glycogenesis, 417
  in photosynthesis, 384–85
  in protein anabolism, 326
  in purine pathway, 452

Aspartate (*cont.*)
  in purine and pyrimidine synthesis, 326
  transamination, 321, 419
  in urea cycle, 424, 425
L-Aspartate, and ATCase, 129
Aspartate transcarbamylase
  dissociation, 136–37
  feedback control, 124–25
  inhibition, 127–28, 457
  stimulation of ATP, 458
Aspartic acid
  ionization, 64, 66
  structure, 62
Aspirin, and prostaglandins, 200
Atmungsferment, 343
ATP (*see* Adenosine triphosphate)
ATP/ADP ratio, 330–31
ATP: citrate lyase, 325
Atractyloside, 356
Autocatalysis
  in glycolysis, 272
  in pyrimidine pathway, 452
  in respiratory chain, 349–50
  in soluble anabolic pathway, 401
Avidin, 398
Azides, respiratory inhibition, 350

B

Bacitracin, 76
Bacteria
  amino acid synthesis, 415
  cell walls, 188–90
  cyclic-AMP in, 529
  enzymes, 395–96
  lysogenic, 521–22
  mating experiments with, 522–23
  mutant, 479–80, 517
  and ribosomes, 491
  unicellular, 216
  urea use, 423
Bacteriochlorophyll, 371
Barbiturates, 350
Base pair additions, 476, 478
Base pair deletions, 476, 478
Base pair substitutions, 476–78
Base pairs, novel, 518–19
Bases, 36–41
  Bronsted, 37
  definition, 36
  nitrogen (*see* Nitrogen bases)
Bassham, J. A., 380, 381
Bautz, E., 482
Beer-Lambert Law, 26
Beer-Lambert relationship, 70
Benson, A. A., 380, 381
Benzer, Seymour, 476
Benzoate, in fatty acid catabolism, 389–90
Beta rays, 27
Bicarbonate, pK_a, 48
Biocatalysis, natural regulation, 124–38

Biochemical analysis, objectives, 10–12
Biochemistry
  definition, 1–3
  as experimental science, 2
  history, 2–3
  and living cell, 3
  main research areas, 4–7
  methods, 9–30
  scope, 1–8
Bioenergetics, 4
Biological phenomena, molecular basis, 6
Biology
  molecular, 155–56
  and physical sciences, 2, 3
Biomolecules, high-energy, 243–55
Biopolymers, chemical structure, 5
  (*see also* Polymers)
Biotin, 109, 398–99
  in pyruvate carboxylation, 284
Birth control, 208–9
Blood clotting, and vitamin K, 443
Bones, development, and vitamin D, 443
Brachet, J., 491
Brain
  catecholamines in, 431
  enzymes in, 420
  phosphorylase in, 276
  and serotonin, 430
Brenner, S., 480, 500
Bromouracil, 472
  as mutagenic agent, 478
5-Bromouracil, 146
Bronsted proposal, 37
Buchner brothers, 264
Buffers, 36, 41–53
  biological, requirements, 46–50
  definition, 41
  effectiveness and concentration, 46
  factors in selecting, 47
  mechanism of action, 45–46
  phosphate, 45–46
    preparation, 50–51
  preparation, 50–52
  in protein studies, 96
  tris, 50
    preparation, 52
  zwitterionic, 48–49
Buffering capacity, 43
γ-Butyrobetaine, from transmethylation, 438
Butyryl-S-ACP, 402

C

Calorie, 55
Calvin, M., 380, 381
Calvin-Benson-Bassham cycle, 380–85
  overall chemical effect, 384